CHILD HEALTH AND HUMAN DEVELOPMENT YEARBOOK 2013

PEDIATRICS, CHILD AND ADOLESCENT HEALTH

JOAV MERRICK – SERIES EDITOR –

NATIONAL INSTITUTE OF CHILD HEALTH AND HUMAN DEVELOPMENT, MINISTRY OF SOCIAL AFFAIRS, JERUSALEM

Child and Adolescent Health Yearbook 2012
Joav Merrick (Editor)
2012. ISBN: 978-1-61942-788-4 (Hardcover)
2012. ISBN: 978-1-61942-789-1 (e-book)

Child Health and Human Development Yearbook 2011
Joav Merrick (Editor)
2012. ISBN: 978-1-61942-969-7 (Hardcover)
2012. ISBN: 978-1-61942-970-3 (e-book)

Child and Adolescent Health Yearbook 2011
Joav Merrick (Editor)
2012. ISBN: 978-1-61942-782-2 (Hardcover)
2012. ISBN: 978-1-61942-783-9 (e-book)

Tropical Pediatrics: A Public Health Concern of International Proportions
Richard R Roach, Donald E Greydanus, Dilip R Patel, Douglas N Homnick and Joav Merrick (Editors)
2012. ISBN: 978-1-61942-831-7 (Hardcover)
2012. ISBN: 978-1-61942-840-9 (e-book)

Child Health and Human Development Yearbook 2012
Joav Merrick (Editor)
2012. ISBN: 978-1-61942-978-9 (Hardcover)
2012. ISBN: 978-1-61942-979-6 (e-book)

Developmental Issues in Chinese Adolescents
Daniel TL Shek, Rachel CF Sun and Joav Merrick (Editors)
2012. ISBN: 978-1-62081-262-4 (Hardcover)
2012. ISBN: 978-1-62081-270-9 (e-book)

Positive Youth Development: Theory, Research and Application
Daniel TL Shek, Rachel CF Sun and Joav Merrick (Editors)
2012. ISBN: 978-1-62081-305-8 (Hardcover)
2012. ISBN: 978-1-62081-347-8 (e-book)

Understanding Autism Spectrum Disorder: Current Research Aspects
Ditza A Zachor and Joav Merrick (Editors)
2012. ISBN: 978-1-62081-353-9 (Hardcover)
2012. ISBN: 978-1-62081-390-4 (e-book)

Positive Youth Development: A New School Curriculum to Tackle Adolescent Developmental Issues
Hing Keung Ma, Daniel TL Shek and Joav Merrick (Editors)
2012. ISBN: 978-1-62081-384-3 (Hardcover)
2012. ISBN: 978-1-62081-385-0 (e-book)

Transition from Pediatric to Adult Medical Care
David Wood, John G Reiss, Maria E Ferris, Linda R Edwards and Joav Merrick (Editors)
2012. ISBN: 978-1-62081-409-3 (Hardcover)
2012. ISBN: 978-1-62081-412-3 (e-book)

Adolescence and Behavior Issues in a Chinese Context
Daniel TL Shek, Rachel CF Sun, and Joav Merrick (Editors)
2013. ISBN: 978-1-62618-614-9 (Hardcover)
2013. ISBN: 978-1-62618-692-7 (e-book)

PEDIATRICS, CHILD AND ADOLESCENT HEALTH

CHILD HEALTH AND HUMAN DEVELOPMENT YEARBOOK 2013

JOAV MERRICK
EDITOR

New York

Additional color graphics may be available in the e-book version of this book.

Library of Congress Cataloging-in-Publication Data

ISBN: 978-1-63117-939-6

ISSN: 2152-3770

Published by Nova Science Publishers, Inc. † New York

Contents

Introduction   **xi**

    Joav Merrick

Section one – Development and Chinese teens   **1**

Chapter 1   Reflective journals of students taking a positive youth
development course in a university context in Hong Kong   **3**
    Daniel TL Shek and Florence KY Wu

Chapter 2   Psychometric properties of the existence subscale of the Purpose
in Life Questionnaire for Chinese adolescents in Hong Kong   **15**
    Ben MF Law

Chapter 3   Subjective outcome evaluation of the project P.A.T.H.S.
(extension phase) based on the perspective of program implementer   **25**
    Daniel TL Shek and Lu Yu

Chapter 4   Subjective outcome evaluation of the Project P.A.T.H.S.
in different cohorts of students   **39**
    Daniel TL Shek and Cecilia MS Ma

Chapter 5   Student classroom misbehavior: An exploratory study
based on teachers' perceptions   **55**
    Rachel CF Sun and Daniel TL Shek

Chapter 6   Family and personal adjustment of economically
disadvantaged Chinese adolescents in Hong Kong   **69**
    Daniel TL Shek and Pik Fong Tsui

Chapter 7   Post-lecture evaluation of a positive youth development
subject for university students in Hong Kong   **83**
    Daniel TL Shek

Chapter 8   Evaluation of the effectiveness of a positive youth
development program for secondary students in Macau   **95**
    Andrew L Luk, Ka Man Leong and Annah ML Au

Chapter 9   Measurement of prosocial reasoning among Chinese adolescents   **107**
*Frank HY Lai, Andrew MH Siu, Chewtyn CH Chan
and Daniel TL Shek*

Chapter 10   Predictors of prosocial behavior among Chinese high
school students in Hong Kong   **119**
Andrew MH Siu, Daniel TL Shek and Frank HY Lai

Chapter 11   Classroom misbehavior in the eyes of students: A qualitative study   **131**
Rachel CF Sun and Daniel TL Shek

Chapter 12   Associations between pathological gambling and psychiatric
comorbidity among help-seeking populations in Hong Kong   **145**
Daniel TL Shek, Elda ML Chan and Ryan HY Wong

Chapter 13   Internet addiction phenomenon in early adolescents in Hong Kong   **169**
Daniel TL Shek and Lu Yu

Chapter 14   Consumption of pornographic materials among
Hong Kong early adolescents: A replication   **185**
Daniel TL Shek and Cecilia MS Ma

Section two – Child and adolescent health   **197**

Chapter 15   Multi-level determinants of regional variations in infant
mortality in India: A state level analysis   **199**
Shamindra Nath Roy

Chapter 16   Assessment of energy and nutrient intakes among
Saharawi children hosted in Spain   **221**
*Gloria Domènech, Sabina Escortell, Rosa Gilabert,
Manuel Lucena, Ma C Martínez, Jordi Mañes
and Jose M Soriano*

Chapter 17   Family size transition and its implication over child care in
Andhra Pradesh, India   **229**
Ritwika Mukherjee

Chapter 18   Schoolchildren's familiarization with the meaning
of loss and death: The role of theatrical games   **251**
*Angeliki Nikolakopoulou, Fotini Garagouni–Areou,
Christina Roussi-Vergou and Maria Zafiropoulou*

Chapter 19   Teaching young mothers to identify developmental milestones   **259**
*Katelyn M Guastaferro, John R Lutzker, Julie J Jabaley,
Jenelle R Shanley and Daniel B Crimmins*

Chapter 20   Reproductive wastage in carrier couples of hemoglobinopathies:
Experiences from a retrospective study in Madhya Pradesh, India   **273**
Ranbir S Balgir

Chapter 21   Don't tag me as mentally retarded, as I am normal:
A case study to understand the emotional development,
dreams and insecurities of mentally challenged people   **285**
Munir Moosa Sadruddin and Zaira Wahab

Chapter 22   Using VML (Verbal Motor Learning) method techniques
in treatment of prosody disorder due to childhood
apraxia of speech: A case study   **297**
Elad Vashdi

Section three – International health   **305**

Chapter 23   DIR®/Floortime™: Evidence-based practice towards
the treatment of autism and sensory processing
disorder in children and adolescents   **307**
Esther B Hess

Chapter 24   Do inequalities in child health get wider as countries develop?   **319**
Nayan Chakravarty and Sanghamitra Pati

Chapter 25   Low-fat, no-fat and sugar free: An examination of children's
knowledge of nutrition, food preferences and television use   **327**
Kim Bissell

Chapter 26   Memorable stories: A qualitative study of mothers'
experiences with breastfeeding   **337**
Cecilia S Obeng and Adrienne Shivers

Chapter 27   Factors associated with accidental burn injuries in children
twelve years and below admitted at Chitungwiza and Harare
Central Hospitals in Zimbabwe   **343**
*Theodora M Chikwanha, Tamisayi Chinhengo
and Addmore Chadambuka*

Chapter 28   Patterns and determinants of gender bias in child health in India   **353**
Nilanjan Patra

Chapter 29   The effect of bibliotherapy on anxiety in children with cancer   **411**
*Nicole M Schneider, Mary Peterson, Kathleen A Gathercoal
and Elizabeth Hamilton*

Chapter 30   Association of parental involvement and the delay
of sexual initiation in Grenadian adolescents   **423**
*Cecilia Hegamin-Younger, Rohan Jeremiah,
Christine Richards, Aaron Buzzard, Lynn Fakeye
and Cherise Adjodha*

Chapter 31   Categorization activities performed by children with
intellectual disability and typically developing children   **433**
Olga Megalakaki and Hanan Yazbek

Section four – Acknowledgments   **449**

Chapter 32   About the editor   **451**

Chapter 33   About the National Institute of Child Health and Human Development in Israel   **453**

Chapter 34   About the book series "Pediatrics, child and adolescent health"   **457**

Index   **459**

Introduction

Joav Merrick[*], *MD, MMedSc, DMSc*[1,2,3,4]

[1]National Institute of Child Health and Human Development, Jerusalem,
[2]Office of the Medical Director, Health Services, Division for Intellectual and
Developmental Disabilities, Ministry of Social Affairs and Social Services, Jerusalem,
[3]Division of Pediatrics, Hadassah Hebrew University Medical Center, Mt Scopus
Campus, Jerusalem, Israel and [4]Kentucky Children's Hospital, University of Kentucky,
Lexington, United States of America

In many places, young people are regarded as future assets of the society. Hence, adolescent prevention programs are commonly developed to tackle adolescent risk behavior and positive youth development programs are designed to promote holistic development in adolescents. However, a survey of the literature shows that research on adolescents is mainly confined to the Western societies. For Chinese psychologists, pediatricians, psychiatrists, and allied human service workers, knowledge about adolescent development is largely developed in the Western culture. To what extent Western knowledge on adolescent development is applicable to Chinese young people? Are Chinese adolescent risk behaviors similar to those in Western societies? To what extent intervention programs, such as adolescent prevention programs, are applicable to Chinese people? These are important questions to be addressed by human service professionals working with Chinese adolescents and their families.

In the first section of this Yearbook we look at cross-cultural variations in adolescent risk behavior, assessment, and intervention programs with attention to the Chinse context especially in Hong Kong with the Project P.A.T.H.S on positive youth development. This project has now also been implemented in other parts of China, including Shanghai and Macau. Furthermore, the positive youth development constructs adopted in the Project P.A.T.H.S. are also used in a "university version" of the Project P.A.T.H.S. entitled "Tomorrow's Leaders" at The Hong Kong Polytechnic University. The preliminary evaluation result of this subject is very encouraging and in the long run, it is suggested that

[*] Correspondence: Professor Joav Merrick, MD, MMedSci, DMSc, Medical Director, Health Services, Division for Intellectual and Developmental Disabilities, Ministry of Social Affairs and Social Services, POBox 1260, IL-91012 Jerusalem, Israel. E-mail: jmerrick@zahav.net.il.

more adolescent prevention and positive youth development programs should be developed in different Chinese communities.

In this context alcohol related problems are a major public health concern in the western world. Alcohol use disorders (AUD) are also an important social and medical problem (1-3), as well as less severe alcohol-related problems, associated with significant social costs (4). For example, in 1998 the social costs of AUD in the United States (US) were estimated at $184.6 billion.

Although alcohol-abusing drinkers and their families bear some of these costs (e.g., medical and legal costs), the non-abusing population also bears costs related to the adverse social consequences of problems, such as alcohol-related motor vehicle crashes, crime, violence and increased health care costs. AUD as well as other alcohol-related problems are of major concern to clinicians, researchers, and policymakers due to the enormous social costs they impose. For example, as of 2004 in the US, 45 states, the District of Columbia, and Puerto Rico had enacted laws making it illegal to drive with a blood alcohol concentration of .08 grams per deciliter or higher.

The CDC (Center for Disease Control and Prevention) analyzed data from the 1991-2011 National Youth Risk Behavior Surveys (YRBS) to describe the trend in prevalence of drinking and driving (defined as driving one or more times when they had been drinking alcohol during the 30 days before the survey) among US high school students aged over 16 years (5). During this period the national prevalence of self-reported drinking and driving among high school students declined by 54%, from 22.3% to 10.3% (5). In 2011, 84.6% of students who drove after drinking also binge drank. Drinking and driving prevalence varied across states, from 4.6% in Utah to 14.5% in North Dakota with higher prevalences clustered among states in the upper Midwest and along the Gulf Coast.

Motor vehicle crashes are the leading cause of death among teens in the United States and for example in 2010, a total of 2,211 passenger vehicle occupants aged 16-19 years died in crashes on public roadways; 1,280 (58%) were drivers (5). One in five drivers aged 16-19 years involved in fatal crashes had a positive blood alcohol concentration (5).

In 2011, the overall prevalence of drinking and driving was 10.3% representing about 950,000 high school students aged 16-19 years in the United States and approximately 2.4 million episodes of drinking and driving during the past 30 days (5). Male students (11.7%) were significantly more likely than female students (8.8%) to drink and drive. Drinking and driving was significantly more prevalent among white (10.6%) and Hispanic (11.5%) students than black (6.6%) students and drinking and driving increased significantly by age with drinking and driving more than three times higher among those who binge drank.

This report (5) shows that interventions have had an impact, but there is still more work to do to reduce teen access to alcohol and reduce opportunities to drink and drive.

References

[1]   Kandel I, Merrick J, Sher L, eds. Adolescence and alcohol: An international perspective. London: Freund, 2006.

[2]   Winokur G, Clayton PJ, eds. Medical basis of psychiatry, 2nd ed. Philadelphia: WB Saunders, 1994.

[3]   Sher L, Kandel I, Merrick J, eds. Alcohol-related cognitive disaorders. Research and clinical perspectives. New York: Nova Science, 2009.

[4] Bray JW, Zarkin GA. Economic evaluation of alcoholism treatment. Alcohol Res Health 2006;29(1):27-33.
[5] Shults RA, O'Malley Olsen E. Vital signs: Drinking and driving among high school students aged ≥ 16 years. United States, 1991–2011. MMWR
[6] 2012;61(39):796-800.

Section one –
Development and chinese teens

In: Child Health and Human Development Yearbook 2013   ISBN: 978-1-63117-939-6
Editor: Joav Merrick   © 2014 Nova Science Publishers, Inc.

Chapter 1

Reflective journals of students taking a positive youth development course in a university context in Hong Kong

Daniel TL Shek, PhD, FHKPS, BBS, SBS, JP[*1,2,3,4],
and Florence KY Wu, EdD[1]

[1]Department of Applied Social Sciences, The Hong Kong Polytechnic University,
Hong Kong, PRC
[2]Centre for Innovative Programmes for Adolescents and Families,
The Hong Kong Polytechnic University, Hong Kong, PRC
[3]Department of Social Work, East China Normal University, Shanghai, PRC
[4]Kiang Wu Nursing College of Macau, Macau, PRC

Abstract

To promote the holistic development of university students, a course entitled "Tomorrow's Leaders" was developed and offered at The Hong Kong Polytechnic University. Based on a case study approach, reflective journals of five outstanding students of the course are presented and analyzed (i.e., thick description), with several themes emerging from the reflection. First, the students liked the course and they identified many positive attributes. Second, the students appreciated the instructors. Third, the students viewed that the course contributed to different aspects of their development. Fourth, some areas of improvements were proposed. In conjunction with other evaluation mechanisms, the present findings strongly suggest that the course is able to promote psychosocial competencies in university students taking this course.

* Correspondence: Professor Daniel TL Shek, PhD, FHKPS, BBS, SBS, JP, Associate Vice President (Undergraduate Programme), Chair Professor of Applied Social Sciences, Department of Applied Social Sciencies, Faculty of Health and Social Sciences, The Hong Kong Polytechnic University, Room HJ407, Core H, Hunghom, Hong Kong, PRC. E-mail: daniel.shek@polyu.edu.hk.

Keywords: Qualitative evaluation, thick description, positive youth development, Chinese university students, Hong Kong

Introduction

The education system in Hong Kong is undergoing a huge reform. Beginning from 2012/13 academic year, university education in Hong Kong will be changed from a three-year curriculum to a four-year curriculum. How should we nurture university students under the new curriculum? While universities in Hong Kong normally claim to promote "holistic development" in university students, this is rarely reflected in the credit-bearing courses, where intellectual abilities alone are usually emphasized (1). Against this background, a course entitled "Tomorrow's Leaders" was developed at The Hong Kong Polytechnic University (2). The course was piloted in the 2010/11 school year and different evaluation mechanisms were used to evaluate the course, including objective outcome evaluation, subjective outcome evaluation, process evaluation and qualitative evaluation based on reflective notes of the students.

With the generous support and donation of the Wofoo Foundation, scholarships were awarded to five outstanding students in this course. It is argued that by focusing on these "extreme" cases, we can get an additional perspective on the implementation and outcomes of the course. Therefore, these five students were invited to write a personal reflection about the course. After obtaining the consent of the students to disclose their names and with minor language editing, sharing of the five students are included in this paper. Consistent with the spirit of "thick description" in qualitative research, sharing by these five students are included in this paper.

The qualitative data were analyzed based on the case study approach. Yin (3) pointed out that a case study "investigates a contemporary phenomenon within its real-life context, especially when the boundaries between phenomenon and context are not clearly evident' (page 13). There are also findings showing that the case study approach is a flexible strategy to understand the reality using different types of data (4, 5).

Reflective journal 1 (CHOW Tsz Ho, George)

'The first time I heard of the subject "Tomorrow's Leaders" was probably at the end of August, 2011 on the Common Orientation Day for freshmen. It is now almost one year. The reason why I chose this as my general education subject is not that I want to be a leader but that I want to understand more about leadership.

Leaders are important persons who lead a group of people to finish a job. The group of people can range from a few teammates to several billion people. Leaders are decision makers whose decisions are affecting the development of a team or even a country. It is interesting to know more about the successful traits of these people. Therefore, I enrolled in the subject.

In fact, the subject met my expectation. In the first lecture, the teacher told us that this course was not designed to transform us to brilliant leaders. They were there to provide materials and guide us to have reflection. In the very same lecture, there were many class activities which made the class very interactive and the activities could be articulated into the theories. For instance, there were self-assessments which allowed us to reflect on ourselves in different aspects so that we understood ourselves more and knew how to perform better. The helpful lecturer usually came over to each group to see if we could follow properly.

Incorporated with many meaningful class activities, the lectures were very well-organised and the learning materials were very well-prepared. There was a lecture outline for each lecture, providing an overview of the lecture. The outlines are good materials for preview and review. The lecture content was on Power Point slides which were also well-structured and informative. It included concise explanation for various aspects and vivid examples for the explanation. Through attending the lectures and reading the lecture notes, our understanding towards each leadership competence was deepened.

In order to complete the course, we had to prepare a group project presentation and write an individual term paper. Both assignments provided valuable learning experiences to us. For the group project presentation, we tried our best to introduce one of the leadership competencies – emotional competence. This job was not easy because we had to plan what content to include, what format to use and how much time for each section. After deciding the rough frame of the presentation, we divided it into several parts and made everyone have a role in the construction of the project. I was responsible to think of a way to strengthen the chosen attribute and then told my fellow classmates. During the process, it gave me a feeling of being a teacher. The fact is that preparing a class activity which can articulate your theory is not that easy. There are books written specifically for class activities but they were found to be not suitable because of difficulty in implementation. At that time, I suddenly realized how mighty our lecturer was. On the day of presentation, our group wore full suites to present. In my opinion, we looked very smart and united. During the presentation, we used many different formats to facilitate classmates' understanding and promoted their level of participation. For example, we had dramas, hypothetical situations and questions. We made the presentation both informative and interactive. Every member did a good job.

The individual term paper was a great challenge to all of us. It required us to critically discuss the concept of leadership quality covered in the group presentation on the conceptual level and to evaluate the extent to which we possess this leadership quality. We think that was difficult because we are science students. It is unusual for us to discuss conceptual stuff, not to mention to discuss the concept critically. The last resort was, of course, to go to the library to borrow a stack of books related to the topic. Extracting useful information from that stack of books is not an easy job. In the process, I had to look for various definitions of emotional intelligences and emotional competence, look for their virtues and drawbacks, and evaluate myself and cite references. In fact, it was very time-consuming and exhausting, especially at the time of having many deadlines and the final examination was approaching. However, writing the individual term paper gave me a valuable opportunity to have a very deep understanding towards the specific competence chosen. Happily, I got distinction out of for my work. This gives me great encouragement and fulfilment.

After finishing the course, I found that it provided a good introduction to various leadership traits and allowed us to reflect on ourselves. I think this is paramount for our personal development. There is a Chinese proverb: "Seeing a virtuous person makes you think of being as good as him". How true? If we do not know what the successful traits of good leaders are, how can we be one of them in the future? Therefore, it is good that we have this course in university as a general education subject.

From my point of view, a good leader must possess his/her own belief and work it out unflinchingly. His/her belief and action work together make him/her a leader with integrity. Only in that way, a leader can get trust from supporters who are willing to follow him/her. Being a good leader is not merely by possessing those leadership traits: self understanding, emotional competence, cognitive competence, resilience, social competence, positive personal identity, assertiveness etc. Leaders must be passionate, honest and devoted. Without these qualities, leaders are no different from manipulators.

In conclusion, I would like to thank every teacher who has devoted his/her effort in developing the course. They have made this course very enjoyable and enriching. Moreover, I would also like to thank the donor of Wofoo Foundation Scholarship. The generosity of the Foundation has made the learning atmosphere very active and I am very honoured that the scholarship was granted to me. In the future, I hope more and more junior schoolmates will enroll in this course and learn to be tomorrow's leaders.'

Reflective journal 2 (Leung Wai Chun)

'As a recipient of Wofoo Foundation Scholarship, it is my pleasure to have this opportunity to write a few words expressing how the subject inspired me and helped my personal development. Furthermore, I would like to share some personal feelings after finishing the subject as well.

The subject facilitates me to be more confident in taking up a leader's role in my social work profession. The course introduced thirteen elements that a successful leader should possess. I have heard some of them before but some of them were new to me. One new element has inspired me a lot and provided me insight to be a leader is "spirituality". A spiritual leadership style should include spiritual values such as integrity, honesty, and humility. By showing us a movie called "Invictus", the teacher used Nelson Mandela as an example to demonstrate these elements. During the movie, I was impressed by the decision made by Mandela. He provided meaning (i.e., unity of one nation) for every political decision even though such decision would be at the expense of his political capital. He could create ethical influence and climate that would influence the others. His belief of unity and caring for his original enemies guided him to be the president. This element inspired me that as a social worker, despite facing difficulties and structural constraints, there are some human values that I have to uphold – that is honest communication with self and others and at the same time be respectful and caring to every human, even the one you hate or originally is your enemy. Of course, this type of leadership quality sounds hard to achieve. It is difficult to love the one you hate. However, such leadership practice is attractive to me and I think I am willing to learn to be a spiritual leader in order to make ethical influence to my followers.

Another element that inspired me is resilience. Resilience as a capacity refers to the capacity of an individual for adapting to changes and stressful events in a healthy way and it results in positive and beneficial outcomes after going through stressful event. In an agency, challenges are always present and it is the team leader's duty and responsibility to lead the whole team to overcome the difficulties. These challenges may become a driving force to team growth if the challenges are finally settled. As being stressful may be a good time for oneself or the whole group to grow, I took action to do something during the class. I am relatively weak in English, especially for oral English. I feel stressful when speaking English.

However, as realizing my limitation and being encouraged by the teacher, I decided to take the initiative to express my opinion in English in class. This course gave me a chance to train up my attitude towards challenges and I think it would be very useful in my future career.

Here comes my personal feeling about the subject. It is good for the subject to use a lot of activities to facilitate our learning. This is a unique element of the subject as it uses an experiential learning approach. We could learn the qualities of a leader through participating in the activities. As a social work student, I am very familiar with such practice and joined the activities happily with my fellow classmates. The study mode is not familiar with those students who came from other departments but I thought they were interested in this study mode as it would make the learning more interesting and relaxing.

Another feeling is that there may be some room for course improvement. Before choosing this subject, I thought the course could include some outdoor activities such as adventure based training for us to train up our leadership. However, although the theoretical bases of the qualities of a leader were taught during the course, there was a lack of real practice time. The small games for classmates were not practical enough for us to better know such qualities. Although the worksheets provided could help us reflect our qualities of leadership, they did not give us enough practical experiences to reflect myself.

It is only the first trial of this subject in the university and it is inevitable for the course to have such minor limitations. I believe with improvement, the course could help more students know how to be a tomorrow's leader!'

Reflective journal 3 (Lai Cho Ching)

'Each year, there are many graduates from the universities. Do you ever think of how to become an outstanding one? In order to be well-prepared, we need to raise our competitiveness as contemporary society sets an increasingly high standard for talents. Various qualities, such as analytic skills, communication skills and leadership, become more essential and significant. Among these qualities, leadership is an indispensable factor.

Leadership is about the communication among team members. It helps to achieve successful businesses and championship teams since it is believed that teamwork can bring a synergy effect to both work efficiency and productivity. Everyone wants to be a leader. How to be a good leader? Here is a chance for us to learn how to lead people.

This year, an innovative general education program, which is called "Tomorrow's Leaders", was launched. "Tomorrow's Leaders" gave me a precious opportunity to reinforce my personal development, especially for the leadership aspect. The subject really inspired me a lot, not only in terms of theories and knowledge, but it also provided a valuable learning experience to me. It gave a comprehensive inspiration to my holistic personal development.

"Tomorrow's Leaders" was a relatively "unique" general education subject. Instead of holding lectures in a boring and dull manner—sitting in the lecture hall and simply listening to what the lecturer says, "Tomorrow's Leaders" gave us interesting and unforgettable learning experience. Well-organised lectures were given to enable our understanding of various useful leadership theories. The leadership theories of basic personal qualities of effective leaders were integrated with different in-class activities. Various in-class activities were held to generate practical experiences. With in-class interactions, the frame of classroom disappeared. Besides learning from the professor, learning from our peers also benefited us a lot. Thus, we could learn in an interactive way. Not just for fun, the activities could effectively reflect our intra-personal and interpersonal qualities. They gave us a better understanding of the theories. With those practical exercises, our self-awareness was developed. We could understand ourselves better by interacting with each other. Peers could point out the weaknesses of each other. Realizing our weaknesses, our specific leadership qualities were reinforced and improved during the fruitful in-class activities. Our learning efficiency was therefore greatly enhanced in the course.

"Tomorrow's Leaders" was also useful to our daily lives. We could apply leadership qualities that we have learnt during the course in different aspects. Undoubtedly, the knowledge helped us to be a leader during teamwork. It also taught us how to be a leader in our own life – coping with life stresses instead of being overwhelmed by the stress. University students faced a lot of pressure from study, part-time job, etc. The course definitely helped us to have better management in our lives. Emotional intelligence referred to the recognition of our own emotional state and the emotional states of others. It helped us to keep an optimistic attitude towards life. Negative situations need not be accompanied by negative emotions if we have a healthy perception. So, we can maintain our mental health and our lives will become easier. This quality is especially important nowadays. Under high work pressure, we have to control impulsive feelings and behaviors so that we can manage our emotions healthily. Time management was another important topic. It helped us control over the amount of time spent on specific activities wisely. We have to do lots of things everyday. So, we need to learn how to manage the task but not to be managed by the task. Not just doing things cautiously, it was also important to do things in an efficient and productive way.

In addition to in-class continuous assessment, group project gave us a good chance to practice what we have learned. Based on the topics we discussed during the lessons, each group needed to investigate the topics more deeply. It strengthened our knowledge in different leadership qualities. At the same time, our interpersonal skills were polished during the discussion. It let us practice the theories in daily life experience. Since there were many members in one group, we learned to listen and accept different opinions. Members with different types of thinking could train us how to tolerate different opinions. It was certainly an important quality to become a wise leader—listening to different opinions. On the other hand, presentation was an effective learning process. Presenters could practice public speaking and have self-reflection, while audience could learn from others' good work. To have further improvement, professors gave comments based on our performance regarding the content and presentation skills. Thus, students could learn from mistakes and avoid them.

Ethical issue was another topic covered in "Tomorrow's Leaders". This topic was an important topic but it was frequently ignored by people. Ethics determined the proper way of action for an individual. It was the framework for us to categorize our values and pursue them. It was also a controversial topic as different people might have different ethical standards. However, ethics played an important role in establishing reliability and reputation of ourselves. When we considered ethics in making decisions, we could build up our integrity and honesty. These were the best ways to let others trust and follow a leader. During the lessons, in-class activities about ethical struggling were launched. The "real" examples gave us a chance to understand our bottom line—what will we do if we really face this situation in the future? Peers may act differently under the same situation. Students could discuss and exchange their opinions. Although we might hold opposite opinions, it could act as a reminder in our future.

Undoubtedly, leadership is an irreplaceable quality in today's society. A good and responsible leader can promote communication among team members. He/she can help to achieve successful businesses and championship teams since well-cooperated teamwork can bring a synergy effect to both work efficiency and productivity. "Tomorrow's Leaders" certainly gave me a precious opportunity to reinforce my different aspects of personal development, especially for the leadership aspect. Besides theories and knowledge, the valuable learning experience also inspired me a lot. It gave students a platform to explore their full potential and become a true leader.'

Reflective journal 4 (Yuen Chi Kin)

'This is Calvin, a recipient of the Wofoo Foundation Scholarship 2010/2011 in the subject of "Tomorrow's Leaders", which was offered by the Department of Applied Social Sciences. I am also a Year 2 student of the BSc (Hons) in Hotel Management program. I was graduated from the Hong Kong Institute of Vocational Education with the Higher Diploma in International Hospitality Management. With outstanding results, I applied for the Bachelor programme through the Non-JUPAS system and I am now a Year 2 student at the School of Hotel and Tourism Management of The Hong Kong Polytechnic University. "Tomorrow's Leaders" was a general education subject which attempted to broaden students' knowledge in other disciplines. This subject was brand new in the past semester, but I was attracted by the dynamic syllabus and the interactive teaching styles.

As a student who majored in hotel management, the study of leadership became particularly important. This subject covers most of the important topics that are required for a successful leader, or a manager. It covered knowledge from self-understanding to interpersonal communication and from ethics and morality to team building, with many topics that factually strengthen my knowledge to be a good and effective leader.

This is my second time to study a subject offered by the Department of Applied Social Sciences in this year. The first one was about psychology, and my second time here was also wonderful. You may have an idea that learning leadership is boring. However, the creative and interactive learning approaches broke this preconception. I can say this is the best subject that I have ever taken. The teaching team used different media and designed different games for every single topic, and student interaction and participation got at least one-third of the lecture time. It was not only about the knowledge from textbook. The lecturer always shared with us on the practical side, and we did have time to practice for each topic in a relaxing environment.

No matter for my study or personal development, the subject is definitely beneficial to me. Getting familiar with myself serves as the basis of getting well with others, which further helps every student's growth in leadership in a great deal. For me, completion of this subject gave me a fresh and altered my mind on my sense of being, everyday life and my future career plan. For example, my mode of thinking and my approaches for processing data have been changed, I know how to control my emotions when I am under pressure and I got a better approach to please others and form effective teamwork. All these will be valuable for correcting my mind, rewarding my study, strengthening my leadership skills, and probably shaping my future life.

The subject also required students to complete a group presentation and an individual assignment. It brought us a chance to interact with others and motivated us to seek for in-depth knowledge in a particular topic through self-learning. For instance, my chosen topic was "Ethics and Morality", which required us to associate it with the managerial and leadership styles. Diverse theories, models, cases studies and discussions were included in the presentation. We also presented recommendations on the organizational, personal and educational levels. By preparing the presentation and the individual assignment, we could all possess in-depth knowledge of this subject, and the presentation did provide valuable information to our classmates. At the same time, we also gained from the presentations conducted by other students, which included the topics of self-understanding, emotional competence, cognitive competence, resilience, spirituality, social competence, positive personal identity and interpersonal communication. These topics are required for being a successful and great leader. The teaching approach gave us a perfect and relaxing atmosphere to absorb the knowledge that we need. I would definitely recommend this subject to everyone that I know.

All in all, I am really glad that I had selected this subject during the subject registration and successfully completed it. The gladness is not only about getting a good grade of A+ but also receiving a scholarship that reduces my financial burden on the study. The truth is that I did enjoy studying this subject and I did enjoy it in every single lesson. I paid attention to every topic and kept thinking about that after the lecture. I strongly believe that it is beneficial to my personal development and my future career.

On the other hand, the scholarship serves as an acknowledgment of my hard work throughout the semester. It also becomes the driving force for my internship. By receiving the scholarship, the financial burden of my family was also relieved, and I can simply concentrate on my study and work for the best. The scholarship also supports me financially for my personal development. I have just completed a three months overseas internship in this summer at the Walt Disney World, Orlando, Florida. I am also going to represent the school to attend a four-day industrial convention in Haikou and Sanya in late September.

Frankly speaking, the subject and the scholarship reinforced my faith to be a good leader in the future. It is not only about the one in the workplace, but also a good leader in the society. Lastly, I would like to take this opportunity to express my specific thanks to Wofoo Foundation for donating the scholarship that recognizes my hard work and motivates me to further excel in my academic performance. I would also like to thank the School of Hotel and Tourism Management and the Department of Applied Social Sciences of The Hong Kong Polytechnic University for offering me such an amazing and professional subject. Finally, I must thank Dr. Lit (my lecturer) and the teaching team for providing me the incredible knowledge and enjoyable learning atmosphere, and nominating me for the scholarship.'

Reflective journal 5 (Tong Chun Wai)

'After three months, I still remembered what I have learnt in "Tomorrow's Leaders". This module is really good for me because I did reflect my life experience and what I have learnt in this module. Also, I was very lucky that my teammates and I built up a good relationship during the class. They helped me find out my strengths and weaknesses. I am really thankful of this. This article is a good chance for me to share my feelings towards this subject. In the following parts, I will mainly share my feeling about the class schedule and how this subject has inspired me. At the same time, I will share my life experience and share about what I will do in order to be tomorrow's leader.

After I attended this subject, I found that this subject was not just a leadership training course but it also a personal development training course for the young people. When I looked at the class schedule, many topics were about personal development such as self-understanding, emotional competence, resilience, social competence, team building and interpersonal communication, etc. These topics were about adolescent personal development and mainly focused on improving the weaknesses of contemporary young people.

When we read the newspapers or magazines today, we can find some articles criticizing the behavior of the post-80s, such as bad communication skills, bad emotional intelligence, weak social competence and weak adversity quotient. In fact, I am one of the post-80s and I cannot deny that these are not lies because I know that there are some common weaknesses of our generation. The reasons for our weaknesses may be due to the fact that we are too lucky to born in a wealthy society and always be protected by our families. For me, I am more concerned about how to improve these weaknesses instead of analyzing why I had these weaknesses. Therefore, I appreciate that the content of this course is trying to improve our weaknesses. In other words, this subject is well-designed for the youths nowadays.

For university education, I agree the education should mainly focus on our professional skills training and help us prepare for our future career. However, when we get into the university, most of us are adult already. So, it may be one of the best moments for us to think of our lives and ourselves. For example, we may need to think about our life goals. What can we do for the society? How do others people think of us? I really think that as a university student, we really need to think of these questions because we are not kids anymore and we will get into the society very soon.

This subject I took really inspires me to critically think of these questions and to prepare myself to get into the society. One of the lessons I liked the most is the first lesson which is about self understanding. People may think that self understanding is not for improving the weaknesses of young people or enhancing youth leadership skills. However, it does not make sense if we can enhance our leadership skills and improve our weaknesses but we do not understand ourselves at the same time. Personally, I think the fastest way to find out our weaknesses and our talents is trying to understand ourselves first. Many people think that they really understand themselves but it is not true because some of their weaknesses and talents may be hard to be found out by themselves. They need their friends, families and teachers to find out for them. After knowing our personality, it is easier to find out our weaknesses and talents. So, I consider self understanding as the first step of being a successful leader.

Personally, this subject is very useful and is inspiring me in my life experience. I know that being a successful leader or improving my weaknesses is a life-long process but I will try my best to do this. The easiest way and most efficient way for me to step forward to become a leader is to enhance my communication skills. The reason behind is that good communication may be the only way for me and my future teammates to get familiar with each other. It is the only way for me to know how my teammates feel about me and to know what I have done may not be good enough. I cannot imagine if there is no communication between the leader and team members but the team can still be effective and efficient.

For my whole life, especially being a leader, I would try to communicate with people around me like my family, friends and teammates in order to know about their feelings and opinions. I remembered when I was studying at Secondary 5, I was a school basketball team member. My teammates and I lost the first game in a match and everyone was quite depressed about it because we were the champion one year ago. We really doubted our ability to win the championship again in that year. However, my teammate and I decided to have a meeting after that match. We spent nearly 2 hours to discuss why we lost that game and we shared our opinions on team or teammates one by one. We figured out that we lacked communication in that match. Many mistakes caused the failure and some teammates even blamed others in that match. After listening to all views of the teammates, we came up with some suggestions in order to win the next match. Finally, we beat the same team which won us in the first game in the final round and we won the championship again. I really think that the meeting was a turning point because after that meeting, we knew that we still wanted to be the champion again and we improved ourselves.

Therefore, up till now, I have been trying to enhance my communication skills. I used different methods to communicate and I found that communication skills might not work every time but it works very often.

As a result, in my near future, I will try my best to find out some communication skills which are good for me to communicate with my teammates and others. I know that only communication skills are not enough for being a successful leader. Therefore, I would like to open my eyes to learn how to be a good and successful leader so that I can use those skills in my future career and in my whole life.'

Discussion

Four major observations could be highlighted. First, the students appreciated the course, including its content and design. Second, the students had very favourable perceptions of the instructors, including their knowledge, attitudes and skills. Third, they perceived that the course was able to promote their holistic development – the course promoted their self-understanding as well as reflections and provided many opportunities for practice of skills. Finally, there are suggestions for refinement in the course which are also revealed by other evaluation strategies such as the post-lecture subjective outcome method. Of course, we should bear in mind the present findings are based on the Wofoo Foundation Scholarship recipients which may show the positive aspects of the course. While this possibility may exist, it is noteworthy that the present findings are generally in line with the evaluation findings based on objective outcome evaluation, subjective outcome evaluation, process evaluation and qualitative evaluation strategies that the course was well-received by the students and it promoted the holistic development of students. Consistent with the evaluation findings based on the Project P.A.T.H.S. based on junior secondary school students (6-12), the present study suggests that positive youth development approach is a promising strategy to promote psychosocial competencies in university students.

Acknowledgments

The development of the course titled "Tomorrow's Leaders" and the evaluation study were financially supported by The Hong Kong Polytechnic University via the Teaching Development Grant and the funding for the 3-3-4 new curriculum. We would also like to thank the Wofoo Foundation for the establishment of several scholarships for those outstanding students taking the course. Members of the Curriculum Development Team include Daniel TL Shek, Rachel CF Sun, Yat Hung Chui, Siu Wai Lit, Yida YH Chung, Sowa Ngai, Yammy LY Chak, Pik Fong Tsui, Cecilia MS Ma, Lu Yu, and Moon YM Law. This paper was originally published in The Scientific World Journal, Volume 2012, Article ID 131560, 8 pages. doi:10.1100/2012/131560.

References

[1]   Shek DTL. Nurturing holistic development of university students in Hong Kong: where are we and where should we go? ScientificWorldJournal 2010;10:563-75.

[2]   Shek DTL. Development of a positive youth development subject in a university context in Hong Kong. Int J Disabil Hum Dev 2012;11(3):173-79.

[3]   Yin RK. Case study research: design and methods. Thousand Oaks, CA: Sage, 2003.

[4]   Yin RK. Discovering the future of the case study method in evaluation research. Evaluat Pract 1994;15(3):283-90.

[5]   Yin RK. The case study method as a tool for doing evaluation. Curr Sociol 1992;40(1):121-37.

[6]   Shek DTL, Sun RCF. Development, implementation and evaluation of a holistic positive youth development program: Project P.A.T.H.S. in Hong Kong. Int J Disabil Hum Dev 2009;8(2):107-18.

[7]   Shek DTL, Ng CSM, Tsui PF. Qualitative evaluation of the Project P.A.T.H.S.: findings based on focus groups. Int J Disabil Hum Dev 2010;9(4):307-13.

[8]   Shek DTL. Using students' weekly diaries to evaluate positive youth development programs: are findings based on multiple studies consistent? Soc Indic Res 2010;95(3):475-87.

[9]   Shek DTL, Sun RCF. Subjective outcome evaluation based on secondary data analyses: the Project P.A.T.H.S. in Hong Kong. ScientificWorldJournal 2010;10:224-37.

[10]   Shek DTL. Quantitative evaluation of the training program of the Project P.A.T.H.S. in Hong Kong. Int J Adolesc Med Health 2010;22(3):425-36.

[11]   Shek DTL, Sun RCF. Secondary data analyses of subjective outcome evaluation findings of the Project P.A.T.H.S. in Hong Kong. ScientificWorldJournal 2010;10:2101-11.

[12]   Sun RCF, Shek DTL. Life satisfaction, positive youth development and problem behaviour among Chinese adolescents in Hong Kong. Soc Indic Res 2010;95(3):455-74.

Submitted: November 01, 2011. Revised: December 15, 2011. Accepted: December 20, 2011.

In: Child Health and Human Development Yearbook 2013   ISBN: 978-1-63117-939-6
Editor: Joav Merrick   © 2014 Nova Science Publishers, Inc.

Chapter 2

Psychometric properties of the existence subscale of the Purpose in Life Questionnaire for Chinese adolescents in Hong Kong

Ben MF Law, PhD [*]

Department of Social Work and Social Administration, The University of Hong Kong,
Hong Kong, PRC

Abstract

The current study aims to test the psychometric properties of the Existence Subscale of the Purpose in Life Questionnaire (EPIL) for early adolescence. The Purpose in Life Questionnaire (PIL), originally created by Craumbaugh and Maholick, is a 20-item scale measuring different dimensions of life purposes. The current study selected seven items representative of the existence dimension to form another scale, the EPIL. The analysis was based on 2,842 early adolescents, ranging from 11 to 14 years old. Principal axis factoring found one factor, with 60% variance explained. Cronbach's alpha for the EPIL was 0.89, which was high. The factor structure was stable across genders. Criterion-related validity was determined when the scale was used to differentiate volunteers and non-volunteers. Construct validity was found when the scale was associated with life satisfaction. The results give support to the fact that the EPIL could be used alone to measure the psychological well-being of early adolescents and the appropriateness of the EPIL in adolescent research.

Keywords: Purpose in Life, scale development, early adolescence

[*] Correspondence: Ben MF Law, PhD, RSW, Department of Social Work and Social Administration, The University of Hong Kong, Hong Kong, PRC. E-mail: blaw@hku.hk.

Introduction

The Prime Minister of the United Kingdom, David Cameron, attributed the August 2011 social unrest in London to one fundamental reason, the lack of morality. The drive provided by the life purpose (or life meaning) is one avenue toward human morality and meaningful existence (1). Human existence has to tackle his or her own being and the relations among people, materials and transcendental quests. One key factor maintaining human existence is the will to meaning. According to Frankl (2), human nature is subject to the "will to meaning." Thus, life purposes are important to human motivation. Damon, Menon, and Bronk (3) emphasized the distinctiveness of purpose: (a) it is a goal which is more stable and far-reaching; (b) it is a personal search but intended for a desire to make a different world or matters larger than self; and (c) it is always directed toward a finished end (p. 121). Life purposes can be derived from three sources (2), namely, (a) creative work or art or scholarly endeavor; (b) deep experiences and inter-personal relationships; and (c) one's attitudes toward human suffering that cannot be avoided. Yalom (4) contended that the problem of life meaning is that a human being seems to be predestined to instill a meaning to life. However, every individual has to decide and commit one's own meaning to his or her own life. Without life purposes, an individual will experience "existential frustration," characterized by meaninglessness, boredom, and a hollow personal existence. This is the dilemma of each individual.

The concept of purpose in life has been researched extensively. Ryff (5) has delineated that the purpose in life is a distinctive domain of psychological well-being. People with high life purposes tend to have life goals and a sense of directedness. They feel there is a meaning to present and past lives. They hold beliefs, aims, and objectives for living. People with high life purposes also demonstrate greater self-confidence, self-acceptance, and life satisfaction (6). Greater religiosity exists (7). Positive mental adjustment, such as stability, maturity, responsibility, and good health also characterize these people (8). They cope with life stresses more effectively (9). On the other hand, people with low life purposes tend to have suicidal ideation (10), hopelessness (11), psychopathology (12), and depression (13).

Most of the studies were conducted in the West and utilized adults as subjects (10,14). Few studies focused on adolescents and were implemented in non-Western contexts (15). Worse, no studies related to purpose in life and early adolescents (ages 11 to 14 years) exist. Majority of early adolescents are studying in junior or high schools. Life purposes may be linked to academic achievement and interpersonal issues, which could be the sources of life meaning according to Frankl's formulation (2). During this early transition period, adolescents are exposed to changes in educational, interpersonal, health, and identity issues (16). Their life purposes may change accordingly (17). Life purposes during adolescence can facilitate the development of prosocial behavior, moral commitment, achievement, and high self-esteem (18). Life purposes can facilitate the formation of moral identity (19). Thus, healthy adolescent psychosocial development should include the dimension of life purposes (20). Based on this, an investigation of life purposes among early adolescents is needed.

One problem related to the studies of life purposes and early adolescents is the measurement issue. Generally, the most common scale used is the Purpose in Life Questionnaire (PIL) (21). The PIL is a 20-item self-report and 7-point attitude scale which measures the extent to which respondents perceive their lives as meaningful and purposeful.

Each item presents two antagonistic ends (e.g., exciting versus dull life) from which respondents have to determine their conditions. Their perception is an ontological significance of life.

The scale is relatively reliable, in terms of Cronbach's alpha (0.84) (15) and split-half reliability (0.92) (22). One area of concern is the factor structure of PIL. Yalom (4) suggested that PIL should consist of six areas, namely, life meaning, life satisfaction, freedom, fear of death, suicide, and personal perception of life. Shek (15) obtained a five-factor solution (quality of life, goal, death, choice, and retirement) with two general factors (existence and death). Other studies have found within the PIL one general factor (23, 24) with different primary factors.

Direct use of the PIL on early adolescents may be problematic. Some items, such as the clarity of life goals, are too abstract for early adolescents. Several items, such as a reason for existence and whether the respondent has a sense of meaning in the world, may be beyond the lived experience of early adolescents. One dimension proposed by Shek (15), death, is not a topic adolescents normally think about, unless they are directly faced with it (25). Selection of related items and formation of another scale with sound psychometric properties is more practical, especially when we want to examine the purposes in life among early adolescents.

In view of the issues arising from item relevance to early adolescents and the categories of sub-scales, studies related to PIL and early adolescents practically do not exist. Thus, if we want to adopt the PIL for early adolescents, the constraints cited above should be addressed. One solution is to select relevant domains and choose the items with reference to those domains. Subscales have been used independently in personality research, such as the Big Five (26). When part of the scale is used, the psychometric properties, such as reliability and validity of the scale, are affected.

The current study explores the psychometric properties of the Existence Subscale of the PIL (EPIL). As suggested by Shek (15), there are two general factors. Compared with the "death" factor, the "existence" factor is more relevant to adolescents and, thus, selected. Existence includes one's enthusiasm and excitement about life, a belief that one's daily activities are worthwhile, as well as a sense that one's life has meaning. One dimension of life meaning and purposes in life is the manifestation of prosocial behavior such as volunteerism (5): People with high life purposes tend to involve more in prosocial activities. The use of volunteers and non-volunteers can differentiate whether the instrument is sensitive to measure the existence dimension of purposes in life. Purposes in life and life satisfaction are closely connected as they share the same construct, psychological well-being (5). The relationship between purposes in life and life satisfaction suggests construct validity.

Methods

The current paper focused on the validation of the EPIL. Based on a large-scale survey in Hong Kong, the reliability, validity (criterion-related validity and construct validity), and factor structure of the scale were examined. The analyses were performed with IBM SPSS Statistics version 19.0

Study participants and procedure

A total of 2,842 high school students from Grades 7 to 9 in Hong Kong (ages range from 11 to 14) participated in the convenience sampling study. Among the participants, 1,747 (61.5%) were girls, whereas 1,095 (38.5%) were boys. The mean age of the participants was 13.33 (SD = 0.73).

Both parental and participant consents were obtained. All respondents completed the scales and demographic characteristics in a self-administration format, with adequate time provided.

Instruments

Existential scale of the purpose in life questionnaire (EPIL)

Craumbaugh and Maholick (21) designed the PIL, whereas Shek (15) validated the scale in the Chinese context. For the original PIL, Craumbaugh and Maholick did not evaluate the factorial structure of the PIL. They designed items mainly to quantify the existential concept of purposes in life in relation to existential frustration. The internal factors were not their concerns. Shek' study categorized items into two general concepts, namely existence and death.

The current EPIL selected items related to the existence domain from Shek's study (PIL 1, 2,5,6, 8,9,11,12,16,19). A group of adolescents in a secondary school was asked to evaluate the content of the EPIL during a pilot study. PIL 5 and PIL19 were suggested to be removed because they thought that the meaning was very similar to PIL 2. Both statements are about the excitement of everyday life. The meaning of PIL 2 was direct and easy to grasp. Item 11 was selected because some adolescents did not get the meaning very well, i.e. I often wonder why I exist. Seven items were used as the foundation of EPIL (PIL 1, 2, 6, 8, 9, 12, 16). The original numbering of the items is adopted for sake of clarity.

Satisfaction with life scale (LS)

Diener, Emmons, Larsen, and Griffin (27) designed the Satisfaction with Life Scale (LS) which was validated by Shek (28) in the Chinese context. The scale is a 5-item, 6-point Likert scale. In the current study, the reliability of the Satisfaction with Life Scale (LS) was 0.85, in terms of Cronbach's a.

Results

The principal axis factoring with varimax rotation resulted in a one-factor solution which explained a 60.09% variance (Table 1). The eigen value of the first factor was 4.21, whereas the second factor was less than the unity, that is, 0.74.

Table 1. Total variance explained and eigenvalues

Factor	Eigen values	Variance explained
1	4.21	60.09%
2	0.74	10.54%
3	0.61	8.71%
4	0.43	6.16%
5	0.42	5.92%
6	0.32	4.50%
7	0.29	4.08%

The original one-factor framework could be demonstrated by this principal axis factoring. To test the stability of the factor structure, two independent principal axes factoring with varimax rotations were performed for boys and girls respectively. One identical factor with an eigenvalue greater than the unity was obtained for both genders. The variances explained for boys and girls were 58.66% and 61.19%, respectively. Factor loadings range from .52 to .84 (Table 2). The coefficient of congruence was 0.998. The factor structure was stable across genders.

Based on Cronbach's alpha, the reliability of EPIL was 0.89, which is very high. The reliabilities for boys' and girls' samples are 0.88 and 0.89 respectively. The Squared Multiple Correlations (SMC) range from .35 to .62. The item-total correlations range from .49 to .74, which are in general high. The scale showed good internal consistency. The Cronbach's alpha if one item is deleted range from .85 to .87. Table 2 shows the item statistics of the EPIL. Table 3 shows the inter-item correlation matrix, the relationships between items are significant.

Purpose in life is associated with prosocial behavior; hence, criterion-related validity was determined along this line of thinking. Two groups of respondents were identified. The first group included those who have volunteered in the past 12 months (volunteers), and the second comprised those who have not volunteered in the past 12 months (non-volunteers). The mean of the EPIL for volunteers was 4.99 (SD = 1.14), whereas that for non-volunteers was 4.75 (SD = 1.28). The univariate analysis showed that the mean EPIL of volunteers is significantly higher than that of the non-volunteers ($t = 5.14$, $p < 0.001$). The effect size, Cohen's d, was 0.12, which is a small value. The criterion-related validity was attained.

Psychological well-being is associated with life satisfaction (5). The EPIL is a component of psychological well-being; hence, such association with LS is hypothesized. Construct validity was performed along this dimension. The result showed a correlation between EPIL and LS of 0.56. This correlation is moderately high. All individual items are associated with LS (Table 3). The construct validity was attained.

Table 2. Items statistics of Existence Subscale of Purpose in life Scale (n = 2,842)

Items equivalent to PIL	mean	SD	median	mode	SE	Corrected item-total correlation	Squared multiple correlation	Cronbach's alpha if item deleted	Factor loading
1. I am usually completed bored – enthusiastic	5.02	1.38	5.00	5	0.03	0.74	0.60	0.85	0.80
2. Life to me seems always exciting – completely routine	4.97	1.41	5.00	5	0.03	0.70	0.58	0.86	0.77
6. If I could choose, I would prefer never to have been – embrace my current life	5.14	1.74	5.00	7	0.03	0.71	0.51	0.85	0.76
8. I achieving life goals, I made no progress – progressed to complete fulfillment	4.47	1.29	5.00	5	0.02	0.59	0.40	0.87	0.64
9. My life is empty, filled with despair, running over with good things	4.99	1.54	5.00	5	0.03	0.78	0.62	0.85	0.84
12. As I view the world in relation to my life, the world completely confuses me – fits meaningfully with my life	4.62	1.55	5.00	5	0.03	0.71	0.52	0.85	0.77
16. With regard to suicide, I have thought of it seriously as a way out – never given it a second thought	5.15	1.97	6.00	7	0.04	0.49	0.35	0.88	0.52

Table 3. Inter-item correlation matrix

	PIL1	PIL2	PIL6	PIL8	PIL9	PIL12	PIL16
PIL2	.71***						
PIL6	.59***	.58***					
PIL8	.48***	.46***	.48***				
PIL9	.66***	.64***	.63***	.57***			
PIL12	.58***	.56***	.58***	.53***	.65***		
PIL16	.40***	.35***	.45***	.32**	.44***	.42***	
LS	.47***	.45***	.42***	.45***	.50***	.46***	.31**

PIL = purpose in life items; LS = satisfaction with life scale.
*** $p < .001$.
** $p < .01$.

Discussion

The current study selected seven conceptually linked items from Shek's original Chinese version of the PIL (15) to form the EPIL. The psychometric properties were explored. The EPIL attained high internal consistency (0.89) and high item-total correlation (0.53). The reliability of the EPIL was very high, compared with those of recent studies (14). The principal axial factoring showed that one factor could be extracted from the scale. The coefficients of congruence analysis showed that the factor can be replicated across boys and girls. The variance explained was greater than 60%, considerably higher than that of a similar study conducted with adolescents aged 11 to 20 with the 20-item full scale (15). Thus, the EPIL is powerful in explaining the variance. The factor structure was stable across genders. The criterion-related validity was derived when the EPIL scores between volunteers and non-volunteers were compared. The construct validity was attained when the EPIL score was highly associated with the LS score.

The major difference between EPIL and PIL is that EPIL is a subset of the PIL. The EPIL consists of seven items from the existence domain of PIL. The psychometric properties are empirically validated in this study.

The existence dimension refers to an individual perception of his or her life. Life has meaning under all circumstances. Frankl contended that our main motivation for living is the will to find a life meaning. We have the freedom to find meaning in what we do and in what we experience. The existence dimension of the purpose in life includes whether life is perceived to be enthusiastic versus boring, exciting versus monotonous, or new versus unchanged. Youth researchers can use the scale to examine the concept of life meaning among early adolescents. A norm table can be designed to examine the trend of the purpose in life among early adolescents, as well as for cross-cultural comparison. The EPIL provides an avenue for unique and down-to-earth application of measuring life purposes. The "existence" domain of PIL is more relevant to adolescents. Other domains such as death and retirement are not entirely relevant to early adolescents (15,24). The EPIL provides a practical approach to measure early adolescents' purposes in life.

The current study has several limitations. First, the research findings are based on the perceptions of early adolescents in Hong Kong. There is a need to replicate the current study in adolescents with different ethnicities and contexts. Second, the respondents are from convenience sampling and not from sampling, although the sample size is large. The application of the findings to other adolescent populations should be interpreted with caution because of questionable generalizability. Third, items specifically related to early adolescents' purposes in life are not included. One example is the inclusion of the importance of the academic achievement, which is demonstrated to be one of the utmost concerns among adolescents (30). Fourth, most existing studies adopt the PIL, which differs from the EPIL. Thus, EPIL scores cannot be compared with past PIL scores directly. Despite these limitations, the current study is the first to validate the EPIL for early adolescents. The measure can be used as outcome indicators in positive youth development programs in Chinese contexts. In fact, in the Project P.A.T.H.S., measures derived from the PIL were used to assess the existential well-being of Chinese adolescents in Hong Kong (31-35).

NOTE

This article is a reprint of another published journal article:

Law, BMF. Psychometric properties of the existence subscale of the purpose in life questionnaire for Chinese adolescents in Hong Kong. [Int J Child Health Human Dev] 2013:6(1):19-26.

References

[1]   China Post. David Cameron struggles to restore, inspire morality. Accessed 2011 Sept 01. URL: http://www.chinapost.com.tw/ editorial/world-issues/2011/08/22/314081/ p2/David-Cameron.htm

[2]   Frankl VE. Logotherapy and existential analysis – a review. [Am J Psychother] 1966;20:252-60.

[3]   Damon W, Menon J, Bronk KC. The development of purpose during adolescence. [Appl Dev Sci] 2003;7(3):119-28.

[4]   Yalom ID. Existential Psychotherapy. New York: Basic Books, 1980.

[5]   Ryff CD. Happiness is everything, or is it? Explorations on the meaning of psychological well-being. [J Pers Soc Psychol] 1989;57(6):1069-81

[6]   Molcar CC. Stuempfig DW. Effects of world view on purpose in life. [J Psychol] 2001;122:365-71.

[7]   Paloutzian RF. Purpose in life and value changes following conversion. [J Pers Soc Psychol] 1981;41:1153- 60.

[8]   Burgess-Wells J, Bush H, Marshall D. Purpose in life and breast health behavior in Hispanic and Anglo women. [J Holistic Nurs] 2002;20:232-49.

[9]   Debats D, Drost J, Hansen P. Experiences of meaning in life: A combined qualitative and quantitative approach. [Br J Psychol] 1995;86:359-75.

[10]   Marsh A, Smith L, Piek J, Saunders B. The Purpose in Life: Psychometric properties for social drinkers and drinkers in alcohol treatment. [Edu Psychol Meas] 2003;63(5):859 -71.

[11]   Plahuta JM, McCulloch JD, Kasarskis EJ, Ross MA, Walter RC, McDonald ER. Amyotrophic lateral sclerosis and hopelessness: psychosocial factors. [Soc Sci Med] 2002;55:2131-40.

[12]   Kish G, Moody D. Psychopathology and life purpose. [Int J Logo] 1989; 12(1):40-5.

[13]   Kinnier R et al. Depression, meaninglessness, and substance abuse in 'normal' and hospitalized adolescents. [J Alcohol Drug Educ] 1994;30(2):101-11.

[14]   Jonsen E, Fagerstrom L, Lundman B, Nygren B, Vahakangas M, Strandberg G. Psychometric properties of the Swedish version of the Purpose in Life scale. [Scand J Caring Sci] 2101;24:41-8.

[15]   Shek DTL. Reliability and factorial structure of the Chinese version of the Purpose in Life Questionnaire. [J Clin Psychol] 1988;44(3):383-92.

[16]   Dryfoos J. Adolescents at risk: Prevalence and prevention. New York: Oxford University Press, 1990.

[17]   Debats, DL. Sources of meaning: An investigation of significant commitments in life. [J Humanist Psychol] 1999;39(4):30-57.

[18]   Damon W, Gregory A. The youth charter: Towards the formation of adolescent moral identity. [J Moral Educ] 1997;26:117-31.

[19]   Hart D, Damon W. Self-understanding and social-cognitive development. [Early Child Dev Care] 1988;40:5-23.

[20]   Lerner RM et al. Positive youth development, participation in community youth development programs, and community contributions of fifth-grade adolescents: findings from the first wave of the 4-H study of positive youth development. [J Early Adolescence] 2005; 25(1):17-71.

[21]   Craumbaugh JC, Maholick LT. An experimental study in existentialism: The psychometric approach to Frankl's concept of noogenic neurosis. [J Clin Psychol] 1964;20:200-07.

[22]   Craumbaugh JC. Cross-validation of purpose in life test based on Frankl's concepts. [J Individ Psychol] 1968;24:74-81.

[23]   Chamberlain K, Zika S. Measuring meaning in life: An examination of three scales. [Pers Individ Dif] 1988;9:589- 96.

[24]   Newcomb M, Bentler P, Fahey B. Cocaine use and psychopathology: Associations among young adults. [Int J Addict] 1987;22:1167-88.

[25]   Bering JM, Bjorklund DF. The natural emergence of reasoning ability about the afterlife as a developmental regularity. [Dev Psychol] 2004;50:217-33.

[26]   McCrae RR, Costa PT. Personality in adulthood: A five-factor theory perspective. New York: Guilford, 2003.

[27]   Diener E, Emmons RA, Larsen RJ, Griffin S. The Satisfaction with Life Scale. [J Pers Assess] 1985;49:71-75.

[28]   Shek DTL. Meaning in life and psychological well-being: An empirical study using the Chinese version of the Purpose in Life Questionnaire. [J Genet Psychol] 1992;153(2);185-200.

[29]   Law BMF, Shek DTL. Beliefs about volunteerism, volunteering intention, volunteering behavior and purpose in life among Chinese adolescents in Hong Kong. [Scientific World Journal] 2009;9:856- 65.

[30]   Huan VS, See YL , Ang RP, Har CH. The impact of adolescent concerns on their academic stress. [Educ Rev] 2008;60(2):169-78.

[31]   Shek DTL. Using students' weekly diaries to evaluate positive youth development programs: are findings based on multiple studies consistent? [Soc Indic Res] 2010;95(3):475-87.

[32]   Shek DTL. Quantitative evaluation of the training program of the Project P.A.T.H.S. in Hong Kong. [Int J Adolesc Med Health] 2010;21(3):425-35.

[33]   Shek DTL, Ng CSM, Tsui PF. Qualitative evaluation of the Project P.A.T.H.S.: findings based on focus groups. [Int J Disabil Hum Dev] 2010;9: 307-13.

[34]   Shek DTL, Sun RCF. Effectiveness of the Tier 1 Program of Project P.A.T.H.S.: findings Based on Three Years of Program Implementation" [Scientific World Journal] 2010;10:1509–19.

[35]   Shek DTL, Sun RCF. Development, implementation and evaluation of a holistic positive youth development program: Project P.A.T.H.S. in Hong Kong. [Int J Disabl Hum Dev] 2009;8(2):107-17.

Submitted: November 01, 2011. Revised: December 15, 2011. Accepted: December 20, 2011.

In: Child Health and Human Development Yearbook 2013   ISBN: 978-1-63117-939-6
Editor: Joav Merrick   © 2014 Nova Science Publishers, Inc.

Chapter 3

Subjective outcome evaluation of the project P.A.T.H.S. (extension phase) based on the perspective of program implementer

Daniel TL Shek, PhD, FHKPS, BBS, SBS, JP[*,1,2,3,4], *and Lu Yu*[1]
[1]Department of Applied Social Sciences,
The Hong Kong Polytechnic University, Hong Kong, PRC
[2]Centre for Innovative Programmes for Adolescents and Families,
The Hong Kong Polytechnic University, Hong Kong, PRC
[3]Department of Social Work, East China Normal University, Shanghai, PRC
[4]Kiang Wu Nursing College of Macau, Macau, PRC

Abstract

A total of 231 schools participated in the Project P.A.T.H.S. in 2009/2010 school year. After completion of the Tier 1 Program, subjective outcome evaluation data were collected from 3,259 program implementers. Based on the consolidated data with schools as units, results showed that participants had positive perceptions of the program, implementers and benefits of the program. More than four-fifth of the implementers regarded the program as helpful to the program participants. Multiple regression analyses revealed that perceived qualities of the program and the program implementers predicted perceived effectiveness of the program. Similar to previous studies, compared to implementers' perception about their performance, the perceived program content appeared to be a stronger predictor of program success. The present study provides additional support for the effectiveness of the Tier 1 Program of the Project P.A.T.H.S. in Hong Kong.

* Correspondence: Professor Daniel TL Shek, PhD, FHKPS, BBS, SBS, JP, Associate Vice President (Undergraduate Programme), Chair Professor of Applied Social Sciences, Department of Applied Social Sciences, The Hong Kong Polytechnic University, Room HJ407, Core H, Hunghom, Hong Kong, PRC. E-mail: daniel.shek@polyu.edu.hk.

Keywords: Chinese adolescents, positive youth development, program implementers, subjective outcome evaluation

Introduction

How to prevent adolescent risk behaviors, such as delinquency, drug abuse, unprotected sexual behavior, and school failure, has been a challenging issue for psychologists, educators, policy makers, and other helping professionals (1-3). In recent years, the research paradigm that different adolescent risk behaviors are treated as separate and independent problems is changing. Instead, emphasis has been put on the interconnections among various risk behaviors and their shared risk, protective, and facilitative factors. Both theoretical models and empirical studies have supported one common predictor of a wide range of risk behaviors in youth-positive youth development or youth developmental assets (4). Accordingly, numerous youth programs have been developed with a focus on promoting the development of core competences and adaptive features of adolescents, which can be generally subsumed under the category of positive youth development approach (5-7).

The approach of positive youth development has been widely adopted in designing programs for adolescents in the West (8). However, such programs are rarely developed and carried out in Asian countries, especially different Chinese communities (9). In view of this situation, Shek and researchers from five universities in Hong Kong developed a large-scale positive youth development program entitled the Project P.A.T.H.S. (Positive Adolescent Training through Holistic Social Programmes) to promote healthy development in Hong Kong adolescents and to prevent various youth risk behaviors (10,11). Funded by the Hong Kong Jockey Club Trust Charities since 2005 (with funding of HK$400 million in the initial phase and HK$350 million in the extension phase), the project has been implemented in about half of the secondary schools in Hong Kong for consecutively seven years. There are two tiers of program in the project. Tier 1 Program is a universal positive youth development program provided for secondary 1 to 3 students in Hong Kong. Tier 2 Program takes a selective approach which aims at around one-fifth of the Tier 1 Program participants who have greater psychosocial needs.

As the Project P.A.T.H.S. has been implemented in a large scale in Hong Kong adolescents, one important question that must be asked is how effective the project is. To answer this question, systematic evaluation of the program is necessary. Since the launch of the program, numerous evaluation studies have been carried out, with the use of a variety of evaluative strategies, including objective outcome evaluation, subjective outcome evaluation, focus group interview, case studies, direct observation, and a longitudinal randomized group controlled trial (12,13). Findings based on these evaluation studies in the past seven years have generally shown positive program effects of the Project P.A.T.H.S. in promoting different competences and developmental assets and preventing various risk behaviors in the program participants (14-17). For example, based on eight waves of data collected in five consecutive years, Shek and colleagues reported that students who had participated in the Project P.A.T.H.S. showed better developmental outcomes than did students in a randomized controlled group, in terms of both positive youth development indicators (e.g., resilience, moral competence, and prosocial involvement) and different risk behaviors such as substance abuse and delinquent behaviors (18, 19).

While objective outcome evaluation, particularly randomized controlled trial, is considered the "gold" standard for the assessment of program effectiveness, subjective outcome evaluation has several unique advantages in program evaluation (20-22). First, as compared to objective outcome evaluation, subjective outcome evaluation provides a way to find out different stakeholders' opinions and subjective experiences of the program. Second, subjective outcome evaluation offers immediate and important information about the implementation of a program before its effects on objective indicators can be observed. Third, subjective outcome evaluation is a more cost-effective evaluative method than objective outcome evaluation. Fourth, subjective outcome evaluation by program implementers contains valuable message about problems and difficulties encountered in program implementation which contribute to the improvement of the program in the future. In evaluating the Project P.A.T.H.S., subjective outcome evaluation was conducted in both program participants and program implementers to obtain a comprehensive picture about different stakeholder's views towards the project (23).

Although very encouraging evaluation findings have been reported for the initial phase of the project, it is important to know whether similar positive findings could be found for the extension phase. Against this background, subjective outcome evaluation findings based on the perspectives of program workers who implemented the Tier 1 Program in the 2009/2010 school year were reported in this paper. In addition, instructors' perceptions about the program, their own performance, and the effectiveness of the project were contrasted among different grade levels to learn about whether program workers at different grades have different views about the program. Previous findings suggested that instructors who taught the curriculum in the lower forms had more positive perceptions than did instructors teaching the program in the higher forms. As such, it was hypothesized that similar pattern regarding the grade effect on program implementers' subjective evaluation would also be observed in the present sample. Besides, the relationships among program implementers' views towards the program, perceptions about the instructor, and the overall effectiveness of the program were examined to gain a further understanding of critical factors that influence perceived program effectiveness by program workers. Based on prior findings, it was hypothesized that program implementers' perceived program quality and their own performance would significantly predict their subjective evaluation on program effectiveness.

Methods

Participants and procedures

A total of 231 schools joined the Project P.A.T.H.S. in the fourth year of the full implementation phase in the 2009/2010 school year (i.e., the first year in the extension phase), with 219,185 and 173 schools in secondary 1, secondary 2 and secondary 3 levels, respectively. The mean number of students per school was 154.36 (ranged from 6 to 240 students), with an average of 4.50 classes per school (ranged from 1 to 12 classes). Among them, 32.24% of the respondent schools adopted the full program (i.e., 20-hour program involving 40 units) whereas 67.76% of the respondent schools adopted the core program (i.e., 10-hour program involving 20 units). The mean number of sessions used to implement the program was 28.54 (ranged from 2 to 48 sessions). While 47.31% of the respondent schools incorporated the program into the formal curriculum (e.g., Liberal Studies, Life Education), 52.69% used other modes (e.g., using form teacher's periods and other combinations) to implement the program. The mean numbers of social workers and teachers implementing the program per school per form were 1.71 (ranged from 0 to 7) and 5.11 (ranged from 0 to 27), respectively.

After the Tier 1 Program was completed, the implementers were invited to respond to a Subjective Outcome Evaluation Form (Form B) developed by the first author (24). In the school year 2009-2010, a total of 3,259 questionnaires were completed. The data collection was conducted after the completion of the program. To facilitate the program evaluation, the Research Team developed an evaluation manual with standardized instructions for collecting the subjective outcome evaluation data (24). In addition, adequate training was provided to the implementers during the 20-hour training workshops on how to collect and analyze the data collected by Form B.

Instruments

The Subjective Outcome Evaluation Form (Form B) was used in the present study, including the following parts:

- Program implementers' perceptions of the program, such as program objectives, design, classroom atmosphere, interaction among the students, and the respondents' participation during class (10 items).
- Program implementers' perceptions of their own practice, including their understanding of the course, teaching skills, professional attitude, involvement, and interaction with the students (10 items).
- Implementers' perceptions of the effectiveness of the program on students, such as promotion of different psychosocial competencies, resilience, and overall personal development (16 items).
- The extent to which the implementers would recommend the program to other students with similar needs (1 item).
- The extent to which the implementers would teach similar programs in future (1 item).
- The extent to which the program implementation has helped the implementers' professional growth (1 item).
- Things that the implementers obtained from the program (open-ended question).
- Things that the implementers appreciated most (open-ended question).
- Difficulties encountered (open-ended question).
- Areas that require improvement (open-ended question).

For the quantitative data, the program workers who collected the data were requested to input the data in an EXCEL file developed by the Research Team which would automatically compute the frequencies and percentages associated with the different ratings for an item. When the schools submitted the hard copy of the reports, they were also requested to submit the soft copy of the consolidated data sheets. After receiving the consolidated data by the funding body, the research team aggregated the data to "re-construct" the overall profile based on the subjective outcome evaluation data. It should be noted that although both qualitative and quantitative data were collected, the present paper only focused on the quantitative reports. Qualitative findings are to be reported elsewhere.

Data analysis

Percentage data were examined using descriptive statistics. A composite measure of each factor (i.e., perceived qualities of program content, perceived qualities of program implementers, and perceived program effectiveness) was created based on the total scores of each scale divided by the number of items. Pearson correlation analysis was used to examine if the program content and program implementers were related to the program effectiveness. To compare program implementers' evaluation across different grades, several one-way ANOVAs were conducted with the three subscale scores as the dependent variables and grade as the independent variable. Hierarchical linear regression analyses were further performed to examine the relationship between different aspects of implementers' evaluation about the project and the program effectiveness. All analyses were performed by using the Statistical Package for Social Sciences Version 17.0.

Results

The quantitative findings based on the closed-ended questions are presented in this paper. Several observations can be highlighted from the findings. First, the participants generally had positive perceptions of the program (Table 1), including clear objectives of the curriculum (94.80%), well-planned teaching activities (90.51%), and very pleasant classroom atmosphere (87.88%). Second, a high proportion of the implementers had positive evaluation of their performance (Table 2). For example, 98.18% of the implementers perceived that they were ready to help their students; 97.43% of the implementers expressed that they cared for the students; 96.35% believed that they had good professional attitudes. Third, as shown in Table 3, many implementers perceived that the program promoted the development of students, including their resilience (91.84%), social competence (93.73%), life reflections (91.61%), and overall development (93.16%). Fourth, 89.73% of the implementers would recommend the program to students with similar needs. Fifth, 83.36% of the implementers expressed that they would teach similar courses again in the future. Finally, 84.37% of the respondents indicated that the program had contributed to their professional development.

Reliability analysis with the schools as the unit of analyses showed that Form B was internally consistent (Table 4): 10 items related to the program ($\alpha = .95$), 10 items related to the implementer ($\alpha = .94$), 16 items related to the benefits ($\alpha = .98$), and the overall 36 items measuring program effectiveness ($\alpha = .98$). Results of correlation analyses showed that both

Daniel TL Shek and Lu Yu

program content (r = .79, p < .01) and program implementers (r = .65, p < .01) were strongly associated with program effectiveness.

To examine differences in the perceived variables (i.e., program content, program implementers, and program effectiveness) across grade levels, several one-way ANOVAs were performed with the perceived variables as dependent variables and grade level (i.e., secondary 1 to 3) as independent variable. Significant results were only found in program content, $F_{(2,574)} = 3.77$, p = .02. Post hoc analysis using Tukey's procedure with Bonferroni adjustment (i.e., p = .02) revealed that significant difference was found between secondary 1 (M = 4.47) and secondary 3 (M = 4.36) participants (p = .03), with the secondary 1 Program perceived to be relatively more favorable than the secondary 3 Program.

Multiple regression analyses were performed on both the whole sample and the responses of students in different grades separately. Table 5 presents the findings. Overall, higher positive views towards the program and program implementers predicted higher perceived program effectiveness (p < .01). The prediction of program effectiveness was stronger for perceptions of program (β = .70) than for views towards implementers (β = .13).

The model explained 63% of the variance toward the prediction of program effectiveness. For participants in different grades, the pattern of relationships and the amount of variance in program effectiveness explained by the two predictors were very similar. While views towards program content consistently predicted program effectiveness across grades, the relationship between views towards implementers and program effectiveness was only significant for the analyses based on the secondary 2 participants.

Table 1. Summary of the program implementers' perception towards the program

	Respondents with positive responses (options 4-6)							
	S1		S2		S3		Overall	
	n	%	n	%	n	%	N	%
1. The objectives of the curriculum are very clear.	1214	95.37	979	94.86	887	93.96	3080	94.80
2. The design of the curriculum is very good.	1125	88.37	873	84.68	803	85.06	2801	86.24
3. The activities were carefully planned.	1160	91.19	924	89.71	854	90.47	2938	90.51
4. The classroom atmosphere was very pleasant.	1156	90.95	897	87.17	796	84.50	2849	87.88
5. There was much peer interaction amongst the students.	1127	88.74	875	84.87	776	82.73	2778	85.77
6. Students participated actively during lessons (including discussions, sharing, games, etc.).	1121	88.06	866	84.00	755	80.15	2742	84.47
7. The program has a strong and sound theoretical support.	1090	85.69	889	86.06	812	86.11	2791	85.93
8. The teaching experience I encountered enhanced my interest in the course.	1051	82.76	826	80.19	751	79.64	2628	81.04
9. Overall speaking, I have very positive evaluation of the program.	1071	84.26	839	81.30	756	80.08	2666	82.11
10. On the whole, students like this curriculum very much.	1086	85.38	816	79.15	729	77.31	2631	81.05

Note: all items are on a 6-point Likert scale with 1 = strongly disagree, 2 = disagree, 3 = slightly disagree, 4 = slightly agree, 5 = agree, 6 = strongly agree. Only respondents with positive responses (options 4-6) are shown in the table. S1: Secondary 1 level; S2: Secondary 2 level; S3: Secondary 3 level.

Table 2. Summary of the program implementers' perception towards their own performance

	Respondents with positive responses (options 4-6)							
	S1		S2		S3		Overall	
	n	%	n	%	n	%	N	%
1. I have a good mastery of the curriculum.	1142	90.21	897	87.34	825	87.77	2864	88.59
2. I prepared well for the lessons.	1143	90.71	919	89.57	835	89.11	2897	89.89
3. My teaching skills were good.	1153	91.51	921	89.59	832	88.79	2906	90.11
4. I have good professional attitudes.	1220	96.60	993	96.69	898	95.63	3111	96.35
5. I was very involved.	1194	94.46	965	93.87	863	91.81	3022	93.50
6. I gained a lot during the course of instruction.	1083	86.02	859	83.72	786	83.71	2728	84.62
7. I cared for the students.	1237	97.63	1002	97.47	913	97.13	3152	97.43
8. I was ready to offer help to students when needed.	1247	98.42	1010	98.25	919	97.77	3176	98.18
9. I had much interaction with the students.	1200	94.79	964	93.87	875	93.09	3039	94.00
10. Overall speaking, I have very positive evaluation of myself as an instructor.	1228	96.92	981	95.43	899	95.64	3108	96.07

Note: all items are on a 6-point Likert scale with 1 = strongly disagree, 2 = disagree, 3 = slightly disagree, 4 = slightly agree, 5 = agree, 6 = strongly agree. Only respondents with positive responses (options 4-6) are shown in the table. S1: Secondary 1 level; S2: Secondary 2 level; S3: Secondary 3 level.

Table 3. Summary of the program implementers' perception towards the program effectiveness

The extent to which the Tier 1 Program (i.e., the program in which all students have joined) has helped your students:	Respondents with positive responses (options 3-5)							
	S1		S2		S3		Overall	
	n	%	n	%	n	%	N	%
1. It has strengthened students' bonding with teachers, classmates, and their families.	1163	91.79	932	90.57	846	90.00	2941	90.88
2. It has strengthened students' resilience in adverse conditions.	1127	89.02	905	87.78	829	88.19	2936	91.84
3. It has enhanced students' social competence.	1185	93.53	941	91.63	854	90.95	2541	93.73
4. It has improved students' ability in handling	1164	91.94	934	90.77	842	89.77	2108	88.83

Table 3. (Continued)

The extent to which the Tier 1 Program (i.e., the program in which all students have joined) has helped your students:	Respondents with positive responses (options 3-5)							
	S1		S2		S3		Overall	
	n	%	n	%	n	%	N	%
5. It has enhanced students' cognitive competence.	1118	88.38	887	86.03	831	88.50	1964	72.74
6. Students' ability to resist harmful influences has been improved.	1126	89.08	899	87.37	814	86.69	2004	64.79
7. It has strengthened students' ability to distinguish between the good and the bad.	1181	93.21	948	91.95	856	91.36	2463	76.37
8. It has increased students' competence in making sensible and wise choices.	1152	91.07	915	88.92	838	89.15	2938	90.79
9. It has helped students to have life reflections.	1104	87.48	909	88.34	839	89.26	2917	91.61
10. It has reinforced students' self-confidence.	1063	83.97	835	81.07	769	81.81	2389	86.31
11. It has increased students' self-awareness.	1179	93.87	937	90.97	864	91.91	2243	90.52
12. It has helped students to face the future with a positive attitude.	1091	86.72	884	85.91	818	87.11	1916	74.35
13. It has helped students to cultivate compassion and care about others.	1109	88.23	903	87.84	823	87.55	1995	63.58
14. It has encouraged students to care about the community.	1032	82.23	846	82.14	765	81.30	2205	68.46
15. It has promoted students' sense of responsibility in serving the society.	1030	81.94	843	81.77	779	82.78	2712	84.07
16. It has enriched the overall development of the students.	1189	94.67	953	92.43	877	93.20	3044	95.27

Note: all items are on a 5-point Likert scale with 1 = unhelpful, 2 = not very helpful, 3 = slightly helpful, 4 = helpful, 5 = very helpful. Only respondents with positive responses (options 3-5) are shown in the table. S1: Secondary 1 level; S2: Secondary 2 level; S3: Secondary 3 level.

Table 4. Means, standard deviations, Cronbach's alphas, and means of inter-item correlations among the variables by grade

	S1		S2		S3		Overall	
	M (SD)	α (Mean[#])	M (SD)	α (Mean[#])	M (SD)	α (Mean[#])	M (SD)	α (Mean[#])
Program content (10 items)	4.47 (.42)	.95 (.65)	4.39 (.47)	.95 (.66)	4.36 (.53)	.95 (.67)	4.41 (.48)	.95 (.66)
Program implementers (10 items)	4.68 (.31)	.93 (.59)	4.62 (.36)	.94 (.63)	4.63 (.40)	.96 (.69)	4.65 (.36)	.94 (.64)
Program effectiveness (16 items)	3.44 (.40)	.97 (.71)	3.41 (.43)	.98 (.71)	3.41 (.44)	.98 (.73)	3.42 (.42)	.98 (.71)
Total effectiveness (36 items)	4.07 (.34)	.98 (.52)	4.02 (.39)	.98 (.57)	4.01 (.42)	.98 (.60)	4.04 (.38)	.98 (.56)

[#] Mean interitem correlations.

Table 5. Multiple regression analyses predicting program effectiveness

	Predictors		Model	
	Program content	Program implementers		
	β[a]	β[a]	R	R^2
S1	.71**	.09	.77	.59
S2	.65**	.20**	.80	.64
S3	.74**	.09	.82	.67
Overall	.70**	.13**	.79	.63

[a] Standardized coefficients.
*$p < .05$, **$p < .01$.

Discussion

The present study investigated the subjective outcome evaluation by program workers who implemented the Tier 1 Program of the Project P.A.T.H.S. in the 2009/2010 academic year. The findings showed that program implementers generally held positive views towards the program, the instructors and perceived the program as effective to promote healthy development of the participants. Program implementers' perceptions about the program and instructor significantly predicted their subjective evaluation about the program effectiveness, with views towards program content being a stronger predictor than views towards instructors. Moreover, these findings held true for participants from different grade levels. There are three unique features of this study. First, the sample size was quite large. Actually, it is very rare to see such a large number of program implementers participated in outcome evaluation in the literature. Second, a validated measure of subjective outcome evaluation was used. Third, as there are few studies on the evaluation of positive youth development programs in general, particularly in Chinese people, the present study is an important addition to the literature.

Overall, more than 80% of the participated program implementers had positive evaluation about different aspects of the program content, including the good curriculum design, strong theoretical support, pleasant classroom atmosphere, and active participation of the students. In particular, more than 90% of the instructors agreed that the objectives of the curriculum were very clear and the activities were carefully planned. Explicit learning objectives with respect to the required skills and a variety of instructional activities to facilitate learning are two critical components in outcome-based education which embraces the notion that the learner is accountable for his or her own achievements and represents the most updated approach to nowadays education (25-28). The present findings that these two items received the highest subjective evaluation from teachers suggest that the outcome-based approach has been well incorporated in the implementation of the Project P.A.T.H.S. Other opinions from teachers such as "there was much peer interaction amongst the students" and "on the whole students like this curriculum very much" provide further support for the successfulness of using this approach to deliver the Project P.A.T.H.S. in Hong Kong students.

Program implementers also viewed their own performance in teaching the program favorably, in terms of mastery and preparedness of the curriculum, teaching skills and attitudes towards the course and students, personal gains, interaction with students, and general evaluation of oneself as an instructor of the program. While self-fulfilling prophecy may explain the findings, it is noteworthy that this observation is consistent with the previous findings that the students also perceived that the instructors in a favorable light (12, 29), hence supporting the validity of the present finding.

With respect to the perceived effectiveness of the program, program implementers regarded the program as having promoted positive development in the participated students in multiple areas. For example, more than 90% of the instructors agreed that the project had enhanced students' bonding with others, resilience in adverse conditions, social competence, ability to make sensible and wise choices, and overall development. Students who attended the program were evaluated as having more life-reflections and self-awareness. These findings are consistent with previous results based on other evaluation methods regarding the effectiveness of the Project P.A.T.H.S., such as the objective outcome evaluation and the subjective evaluation by students (29,30).

Program implementers' subjective outcome evaluation was also compared among different grades. No significant grade differences were detected in program implementers' views about their own performance and perceived effectiveness of the program, which suggests that program implementers from different grade levels had similar favorable views towards the instructor and the program effectiveness. However, it was found that program content was evaluated more positively by secondary 1 implementers than secondary 3 implementers. Similar findings were also noted in previous studies. While the curriculum designed for different grades have different content including various activities and topics for discussion, the basic framework of the course that consists of eight core positive youth development constructs is the same across grade. Therefore, the secondary 1 program may be perceived more fresh and attractive to teachers than secondary 3 program. Besides, students in junior grade may also show more interests and better involvement in the course than senior students who attended the program since they entered the secondary school. This finding provides some insights for the curriculum design in the future. Perhaps more novel units and topics especially suitable for senior secondary students could be developed and incorporated into the curriculum. Despite the grade difference, program implementers in the secondary 3 grade still reported favorable views towards the curriculum, with more than three fourths of the participants having positive evaluation about different aspects of the program content, which suggests that the curriculum is generally well received by the instructors.

Results of regression analyses suggest that for the whole sample of students both perceived program and instructors significantly predicted the perceived effectiveness of the program, supporting the critical roles of program quality and implementers in program success. However, when data in different grades were analyzed separately, while program workers' subjective evaluation of the program quality consistently predicted perceived effectiveness of the program across grade, the effect of views about instructors' performance was only significant for secondary 2 participants. Apparently, program worker's evaluation about the program content appeared to be a stronger predictor than did their evaluation about instructors' performance. Similar findings were reported in Shek et al.'s paper (31). While a variety of factors at different ecological levels were found to affect the implementation of a program, high program quality has always been considered the first requisite to the success of the program (32, 33). Without a good design of the curriculum in the very beginning, it is impossible that the program will produce desirable outcomes in its participants, even with excellent program staff, highly-motived students, and supportive administrative environment. In fact, it is likely that quality of program and quality of implementers interactively affect the effectiveness of a program. For example, good curriculum content often increases the interests and motivation of instructors to teach the course (34), and thus the instructors may spend more time in preparation, show more passion in their teaching, and deliver the content in a more effective way. Therefore, when the effects of program content were controlled, the prediction of program instructors' performance on program effectiveness decreased. Another possibility is that this may be a statistical artifact as the range of scores for the evaluation of instructors was not wide. Future studies may focus on examining the interactive effects between program content and program implementers to identify more fundamental factors that determine program success. In addition, it is unclear why in the present study the evaluation of instructors only predicted program effectiveness for secondary 2 participants, but not for secondary 1 and 3 participants. This finding is inconsistent with previous report (31) and the literature in which the critical role of program implementers to program success is constantly highlighted (13, 21). Obviously, replication study is needed. In particular, grade difference in the effect of program implementers' performance on program effectiveness should be further explored.

There are several limitations of the present study that should be acknowledged. First, the data were collected in a self-reported manner, which may be biased by the implementers' personal attitudes and perceptions towards the program. To reduce the potential bias, several measures were taken. First, program implementers responded to the questionnaire anonymously and the confidentiality was repeatedly assured. Second, in the questionnaire, no threatening questions were asked that might elicit the respondents' feelings of role conflict and social desirability. Third, participants were encouraged to candidly report their negative views or feelings in the survey and open-ended questions were provided for the teachers to record their suggestions on how to improve the program. Despite of these measures, the present findings should be interpreted with cautions and evaluative studies that use other approaches, such as objective outcome evaluation based on developmental indicators, program participants' subjective evaluation, and process evaluation must be conducted for the purpose of triangulation. The second limitation of the present study is that only two general indicators of program quality and program implementers' performance were used to predict overall effectiveness of the project, which makes it impossible to identify specific aspects that are particularly important for program success. Besides, different factors may increase/decrease the program effects in different areas. For example, good performance of the teacher may have particular effects in strengthening students' bonding with teachers. Future studies may include different indicators of program content and implementers as well as program effectiveness in the prediction model. Thirdly, previous studies have revealed that school and organization characteristics influence program effectiveness and implementation quality (34-36). These contextual factors should be considered in further research. Finally, as the present findings were "reconstructed" from the evaluation reports submitted by the agencies, the unit of analyses was schools, instead of individuals. Therefore, individual variations were lost in the process which may lower the power of statistical analyses. Despite of these limitations, the present study constitutes an important addition to the current literature about the effectiveness of the Project P.A.T.H.S. in promoting positive youth development in Hong Kong adolescents.

Acknowledgments

The preparation for this paper and the Project P.A.T.H.S. were financially supported by The Hong Kong Jockey Club Charities Trust. "This paper was originally published in The Scientific World Journal, Volume 2012, Article ID 589257, 8 pages doi:10.1100/2012/589257."

References

[1]   Substance Abuse and Mental Health Services Administration. Results from the 2009 National Survey on Drug Use and Health: Volume I. Summary of national findings. Rockville, MD: Office Applied Studies; 2010.

[2]   Arteaga I, Chen CC, Reynolds AJ. Childhood predictors of adult substance abuse. Children Youth Serv Rev 2010;32(8):1108-20.

[3]   Adesola A. Time to act. Drug Salvation Force 1998;2:49.

[4]   Pittman KJ, Irby M, Tolman J, Yohalem, N, Ferber T. Preventing problems, promoting development, encouraging engagement: competing priorities or inseparable goals? Washington, DC: Forum for Youth Investment, Impact Strategies. 2003. Accessed 2014 April 10. URL: http://test.forumfyi.org/files/Preventing%20Problems,%20Promoting%20Development,%20Encouraging%20Engagement.pdf

[5]   Wilson SJ, Lipsey M. The effects of school-based social information processing interventions on aggressive behavior, part I: universal Programs. Campbell Collaboration Syst Rev 2006;5:1-42.

[6]   Tremblay RE, Pagani-Kurtz L, Masse LC, Vitaro F, Pihl RO. A bi-modal preventive intervention for disruptive kindergarten boys: its impact through mid-adolescence. J Consult Clin Psychol 1995;63:560-68.

[7]   Hawkins JD, Brown EC, Oesterle S, Arthur MW, Abbott RD, Catalano RF. Early effects of communities that care on targeted risks and initiation of delinquent behavior and substance use. J Adolesc Health 2008;43:15-22.

[8] Catalano RF, Berglund ML, Ryan JAM, Lonczak HS, Hawkins JD. Positive youth development in the United States: research findings on evaluations of positive youth development programs. Ann Am Acad Pol Soc Sci 2004;591:98-124.

[9] Shek DTL, Yu L. A review of validated youth prevention and positive youth development programmes in Asia. Int J Adolesc Med Health 2011;23(4):317-24.

[10] Shek DTL, Ma HK, Merrick J, editors. Positive youth development: development of a pioneering program in a Chinese context. London and Tel Aviv: Freund Publishing Company; 2007.

[11] Shek DTL. Conceptual framework underlying the development of a positive youth development program in Hong Kong. Int J Adolesc Med Health 2006;18(3):303-14.

[12] Shek DTL. Objective and subjective outcome evaluation of Project P.A.T.H.S.: first year evaluation findings. Int Public Health J 2009;1: 245-54.

[13] Shek DTL, Yu L, Ho VYT. Implementation of the secondary 2 program of the project P.A.T.H.S.: observations based on the co-walker scheme. Int J Adolesc Med Health 2012;24(3):253-60.

[14] Shek DTL. Effectiveness of the tier 1 program of project P.A.T.H.S.: findings based on the first 2 years of program implementation. ScientificWorldJournal 2009;9:539-47.

[15] Shek DTL, Sun RCF. Effectiveness of the tier 1 program of project P.A.T.H.S.: findings based on three years of program implementation. ScientificWorldJournal 2010;10:1509-19.

[16] Shek DTL, Ma CMS. Impact of the project P.A.T.H.S. in the junior secondary school years: individual growth curve analyses. ScientificWorldJournal 2011;11:253-66.

[17] Shek DTL, Yu L. Prevention of adolescent problem behavior: longitudinal impact of the project P.A.T.H.S. in Hong Kong. ScientificWorldJournal 2011;11:546-67.

[18] Shek DTL, Yu L. Longitudinal impact of the project P.A.T.H.S. on adolescent risk behavior: what happened after five years? ScientificWorldJournal 2012 Jan 29;316029. doi: 10.1100/2012/316029.

[19] Shek DTL, Ma CMS. Impact of the project P.A.T.H.S. in the junior secondary school years: objective outcome evaluation based on eight waves of longitudinal data. ScientificWorldJournal 2012 April 24: 170345. doi: 10.1100/2012/170345. .

[20] Winefield HR, Barlow JA. Client and worker satisfaction in a child protection agency. Child Abuse Neglect 1995;19(8):897-905.

[21] Peterson D, Esbensen FA. The outlook is G.R.E.A.T. What educators say about school-based prevention and the Gang Resistance Education and Training (G.R.E.A.T.) program? Eval Rev 2004;28(3):218-45.

[22] Najavits LM, Ghinassi F, van Horn A, et al. Therapist satisfaction with four manual-based treatments on a national multisite trial: an exploratory study. Psychother Theory Res Pract Train 2004;41(1):26-37.

[23] Shek, DTL, Siu AMH, Lee TY. Subjective outcome evaluation of the project P.A.T.H.S.: findings based on the perspective of the program implementers. ScientificWorldJournal 2007;7:195-203.

[24] Shek DTL, Siu AMH, Lui J, Lung WMD. P.A.T.H.S. to adulthood: a jockey club youth enhancement scheme (evaluation manual). Hong Kong: The Social Welfare Practice and Research Centre, Chinese University of Hong Kong; 2006.

[25] Van der Horst H, McDonald R. OBE. Outcomes-based education: a teacher's manual. Pretoria: Kagiso; 1997.

[26] Capper CA, Jamison MTJ. Outcome-based education re-examined: from structural functionalism to post structuralism. Educ Pol 1993;7(4):427-46.

[27] Conradie D. Outcome-based education (OBE). What is it? EE Bulletin 1997;13:8-11.

[28] Olivier C. Outcome-based education and training programmes: processes, knowledge, skills, OBET production. Ifafi; 1997.

[29] Shek DTL, Ng CSM. Subjective outcome evaluation of the project P.A.T.H.S. (secondary 2 program): views of the program participants. ScientificWorldJournal 2009;9:1012-22.

[30] Shek DTL. Objective outcome evaluation of the project P.A.T.H.S. in Hong Kong: findings based on individual growth curve models. ScientificWorldJournal 2010;10:182-91.

[31] Shek DTL, Ma CMS, Tang CYP. Subjective outcome evaluation of the project P.A.T.H.S.: findings based on different datasets. Int J Adolesc Med Health 2011;23(3):237-43.

[32]   Riley BL, Taylor SM, Eillott SJ. Determinants of implementing heart healthy promotion activities in Ontario public health units: a social ecological perspective. Health Educ Res 2001;16(4):425-41.

[33]   Shediac-Rizkallah MC, Bone LR. Planning for the sustainability of community-based health programs: conceptual frameworks and future directions for research, practice and policy. Health Educ Res 1998;13(1):87-108.

[34]   Weissberg RP, O'Brien MU. What works in school-based social and emotional learning programs for positive youth development. Ann Am Acad Pol Soc Sci 2004;591:86-97.

[35]   Payne AA, Gottfredson DC, Gottfredson GD. School predictors of the intensity of implementation of school-based prevention programs: results from a national study. Prev Sci 2006;7(2):225-37.

[36]   Elliot DS, Mihalic S. Issues in disseminating and replicating effective prevention programs. Prev Sci 2004;5(1):47-53.

Submitted: November 01, 2011. Revised: December 15, 2011. Accepted: December 20, 2011.

In: Child Health and Human Development Yearbook 2013   ISBN: 978-1-63117-939-6
Editor: Joav Merrick   © 2014 Nova Science Publishers, Inc.

Chapter 4

Subjective outcome evaluation of the Project P.A.T.H.S. in different cohorts of students

Daniel TL Shek, PhD, FHKPS, BBS, SBS, JP[*1,2,3,4],
and Cecilia MS Ma, PhD[1]

[1]Department of Applied Social Sciences, The Hong Kong Polytechnic University, Hong Kong, PRC
[2]Centre for Innovative Programmes for Adolescents and Families, The Hong Kong Polytechnic University, Hong Kong, PRC
[3]Department of Social Work, East China Normal University, Shanghai, PRC
[4]Kiang Wu Nursing College of Macau, Macau, PRC

Abstract

The Project P.A.T.H.S. is an indigenously developed positive youth development program in Hong Kong. In the extension phase (2009/10 school year), subjective outcome evaluation data were collected from 231 schools involving 89,068 participants after completion of the curricula-based Tier 1 Program. With schools as the units of analysis, results showed that participants generally had positive perceptions of the program content and implementers, with over four-fifth of the participants regarded the program as helpful to them. There were some significant grade differences in the subjective outcome evaluation findings, although the related effect size was not strong. Multiple regression analyses revealed that program content and program implementers predicted perceived effectiveness of the program. The present study suggests that irrespective of cohorts, students in the junior secondary years perceived the program to be beneficial to them.

* Correspondence: Professor Daniel TL Shek, PhD, FHKPS, BBS, SBS, JP, Associate Vice President (Undergraduate Programme), Chair Professor of Applied Social Sciences, Department of Applied Social Sciences, Faculty of Health and Social Sciences, The Hong Kong Polytechnic University, Room HJ407, Core H, Hunghom, Hong Kong, PRC. E-mail: daniel.shek@polyu.edu.hk.

Keywords: Adolescence, positive youth development, Project P.A.T.H.S., subjective outcome evaluation, Hong Kong

Introduction

The increasing popularity of implementing effective adolescent prevention programs in recent decades has been a key initiative to tackle adolescent developmental problems (1-4). Researchers (5-7) identified eight factors that are essential for the implementation of adolescent prevention programs. These include fidelity (i.e., the extent to which the program is implemented as originally designed), dosage (i.e., the number of sessions offered during implementation), quality of delivery (i.e., the extent to which the program is delivered in an authentic manner), participant responsiveness (i.e., participants' involvement and satisfaction), program differentiation (i.e., the extent to which a program's theory and practices can be distinguished from other available programs), monitoring (i.e., documenting the nature and amount of services received by the service recipients), program reach (i.e., the proportion of the intended audience who participated in the intervention), and adaptation (i.e., the extent to which the program is different from the original designed during implementation).

Research findings showed that positive attitudes toward the program content and program implementers were associated with program outcomes (8-13). However, little is known about the relative influence of these factors on program effectiveness as prior studies mainly focused on one component only (6, 14-16). For example, Rohrbach et al. (13) noted the inter-relationships of these factors and suggested to explore their relative influences on program effectiveness in the future evaluation research. Berkel et al. (17, p. 24) highlighted that "program evaluations have rarely examined more than one dimension in a single study and thus have not untangled possible relations between them". To fill this gap, the present study explored the relative influence of two program implementation factors on perceived program outcomes.

Prevention researchers noted the importance of providing culturally competent interventions for a given population (18-20). However, as adolescent prevention programs were predominantly conducted in the Western countries, it is not clear whether the previous findings would vary by different subgroups of participants, such as adolescents in non-Western contexts. This question makes sense because assuming the application of concepts and behaviors is universal to every individual in a population is debatable which may lead to problematic results (21). Catalano, Gavin and Markham (22) argued that more effort is needed "to understand how well they can be implemented in real-world settings and what effects they are likely to have…and examine differences of effects on relevant subgroups (e.g., culture, gender, age, etc.)" (p. S93). It appears that findings from non-Western cultural contexts would certainly expand the scope of program evaluation literature.

The Project "P.A.T.H.S. to Adulthood: A Jockey Club Youth Enhancement Scheme" is a large-scale positive youth development program designed for junior secondary school students (Secondary 1 to 3, i.e., Grades 7 to 9) in Hong Kong (23). The word "P.A.T.H.S." denotes Positive Adolescent Training through Holistic Social Programmes. It consists of two tiers of program. The Tier 1 Program targets all students joining the program in a particular form (i.e., universal prevention initiative). Through the use of structured curriculum, students learn competencies with reference to the 15 positive youth development construct (23). The Tier 2 Program is specially designed for students with greater psychosocial needs in different psychosocial domains (i.e., selective prevention). After completion of the Tier 1 Program, program participants were required to complete a subjective outcome evaluation form (Form A).

Qualitative and quantitative data collected based on the original phase of the project generally suggested that participants (students and program implementers) perceived the program positively (24-35). However, little is known whether the impact of program implementation factors on program effectiveness would be sustained in the extension phase. Also, it is not clear whether these relationships would vary by students' grade level. In particular, the relative influence of these factors on program outcomes is relatively unexplored. Against the above background, the purpose of the study was to examine the effectiveness of the Tier 1 Program of the Project P.A.T.H.S. and to test the relative influence of two aspects of program implementation, namely perceptions of the program (content as well as implementation) and program implementers on perceived program effectiveness. It also attempted to investigate whether the predictive effects of these factors would differ across grade levels.

Methods

Participants and procedures

A total of 231 schools with 89,068 students joined the Project P.A.T.H.S. in the extension phase of the Full Implementation Phase in the school year 2009/10 (The initial phase of the project was started from the academic year 2005/06 to 2008/09). A total of 577 aggregated data sets from the participating schools were collected across three grade levels (i.e., Secondary 1 level: 219 schools, Secondary 2 level: 185 schools and Secondary 3 level: 173 schools). The mean number of students per school was 154.36 (ranged from 6 to 240 students), with an average of 4.50 classes per school (ranged from 1 to 12 classes). Among them, 32.24% of the respondent schools adopted the full program (i.e., 20-hour program involving 40 units) whereas 67.76% of the respondent schools adopted the core program (i.e., 10-hour program involving 20 units). The mean number of sessions used to implement the program was 28.54 (ranged from 2 to 48 sessions). While 47.31% of the participating schools incorporated the program into the formal curriculum (e.g., Liberal Studies, Life Education), 52.69% used other modes (e.g., classes and events that differed from normal class schedule) to implement the program. The mean number of social workers and teachers implementing the program per school were 1.71 (ranged from 0 to 7) and 5.11 (ranged from 0 to 27), respectively.

After completion of the Tier 1 Program, the participants were invited to respond to a Subjective Outcome Evaluation Form (Form A) developed by the first author (36). The data collection was carried out at the last session of the program. On the day of data collection, the purpose of the evaluation was mentioned, and confidentiality of the data was repeatedly emphasized to all students. The students were asked to indicate their wish if they did not want to participate in the study (i.e., "passive" informed consent was obtained from the students). All participants responded to all scales in the evaluation form in a self-administration format. Adequate time was provided for the participants to complete the questionnaire.

Instruments

The Subjective Outcome Evaluation Form (Form A) was used. Broadly speaking, there are several parts in this evaluation form as follows:

- Participants' perceptions of the program, such as program objectives, design, classroom atmosphere, interaction among the students, and the respondents' participation during class (10 items).
- Participants' perceptions of the program implementers, such as the preparation of the instructor, professional attitude, involvement, and interaction with the students (10 items).
- Participants' perceptions of the effectiveness of the program, such as promotion of different psychosocial competencies, resilience and overall personal development (16 items).
- The extent to which the participants would recommend the program to other people with similar needs (1 item).
- The extent to which the participants would join similar programs in the future (1 item).
- Overall satisfaction with the program (1 item).
- Things that the participants learned from the program (open-ended question).
- Things that the participants appreciated most (open-ended question).
- Opinion about the instructor(s) (open-ended question).
- Areas that require improvement (open-ended question).

For the quantitative data, the implementers collecting the data in each school were requested to input the data in an EXCEL file developed by the Research Team which would automatically compute the frequencies and percentages associated with the different ratings for an item. When the schools submitted the reports, they were also requested to submit the soft copy of the consolidated data sheets. In the reports prepared by the schools, the workers were also required to estimate the degree of adherence to the program manuals (i.e., the extent to which the program is implemented in accordance with the program manuals).

To facilitate the program evaluation, the Research Team developed an evaluation manual with standardized instructions for collecting the subjective outcome evaluation data (36). In addition, adequate training was provided to the implementers during the 20-hour training workshops on how to collect and analyze the data collected by Form A.

After receiving the consolidated data by the funding body, the data were aggregated to "re-construct" the overall profile based on the subjective outcome evaluation data by the Research Team.

Data analyses

Percentage findings were examined using descriptive statistics. A composite measure of each domain (i.e., perceived qualities of program, perceived qualities of program implementers, and perceived program effectiveness) was created based on the total scores of each factor divided by the number of items in that domain. Pearson correlation analysis was used to examine if the program content and program implementers were related to the program effectiveness. One-way analysis of variance (ANOVA) was used to assess the differences in the mean of each factor across grade levels. Multiple regression analysis was performed to compare which factor would predict the program effectiveness. All analyses were performed by using the Statistical Package for Social Sciences Version 19.0.

Results

Quantitative findings based on the closed-ended questions are presented in this paper. Several observations can be highlighted from the findings. In the first place, roughly four-fifth of the participants generally had positive perceptions of the program (Table 1), including clear objectives of the curriculum (85.32%), well-planned teaching activities (83.59%), and adequate peer interaction amongst the students (82.90%). In addition, a high proportion of the students had positive evaluation of the instructors (Table 2). For example, 89.44% of the participants perceived that the program implementers were very involved; 89% of the participants agreed that implementers encouraged them to participate in the activities; 88.86% perceived that the implementers were ready to offer help when they are in needs.

As shown in Table 3, more than four-fifth of the respondents perceived that the program promoted their development, including the ability to distinguish between the good and the bad (86.04%), competence in making sensible and wise choices (85.15%), ability to resist harmful influences (85.04%), and overall development (85.33%). Interestingly, while roughly three-quarter (78.55%) of the participants would recommend the program to their friends who have similar needs, only 67.79% of them would join similar programs in the future. Finally, more than four-fifth (85.65%) of the participants indicated that they were satisfied with the program (Table 4). Regarding the degree of program adherence estimated by the program implementers, the mean level of adherence was 83.50%, with a range from 14.5% to 100%.

Results of reliability analysis showed that Form A was internally consistent (Table 5): 10 items related to the program content ($\alpha = .98$), 10 items related to the program implementers ($\alpha = .99$), 16 items related to the benefits ($\alpha = 1.00$), and the overall 36 items measuring program effectiveness ($\alpha = .99$). Results of correlation analysis showed that both program content ($r = .84$, $p < .01$) and program implementers ($r = .76$, $p < .01$) were strongly associated with program effectiveness. These positive relationships were consistent across all grade levels (Table 6).

To examine differences in the subjective outcome measures (i.e., program content, program implementers, and program effectiveness) across levels, a series of one-way ANOVAs were performed with different subjective outcome indicators as dependent variables and grade level (i.e., Secondary 1 to 3 levels) as an independent variable. Significant results were found for program content ($F_{(2,574)} = 6.07$, $p < .01$), program implementers ($F_{(2,}$

$_{574)} = 8.62, p < .01$), program effectiveness ($F_{(2, 574)} = 11.51, p < .01$) and the total scale ($F_{(2, 574)} = 9.85, p < .01$) (Table 5).

Post-hoc analysis using the Bonferroni adjustment ($p = .02$) revealed that significant differences were found between Secondary 1 ($M = 4.37$) and Secondary 2 ($M = 4.26$) students towards their perceptions on program content ($p < .01$) and their perceptions on program implementers (Secondary 1: $M = 4.68$, Secondary 2: $M = 4.55$, $p < .01$). Significant grade differences were also shown when comparing students' perceptions toward the program effectiveness (Secondary 1: $M = 3.50$, Secondary 2: $M = 3.37$, Secondary 3: $M = 3.41$, $p < .01$). Similar results were revealed in the overall program effectiveness (Secondary 1: $M = 4.07$, Secondary 2: $M = 3.95$, $p < .01$; Secondary 3: $M = 4.00$, $p < .05$). It is noteworthy that the above differences were not significant between Secondary 2 and 3 classes ($p > .05$).

Table 1. Summary of the program participants' perceptions toward the program content

| | Respondents with positive responses (Options 4-6) | | | | | | | |
| | S1 | | S2 | | S3 | | Overall | |
	n	%	n	%	n	%	N	%
1. The objectives of the curriculum are very clear.	26,181	85.98	22,387	84.33	21,933	85.66	70,501	85.32
2. The design of the curriculum is very good.	25,224	82.88	21,351	80.49	21,176	82.72	67,751	82.03
3. The activities were carefully planned.	25,664	84.47	21,779	82.21	21,504	84.10	68,947	83.59
4. The classroom atmosphere was very pleasant.	24,977	82.29	21,568	81.56	21,410	83.81	67,955	82.55
5. There was much peer interaction amongst the students.	25,078	82.86	21,612	81.95	21,380	83.90	68,070	82.90
6. I participated actively during lessons (including discussions, sharing, games, etc.).	25,110	82.60	21,246	80.26	21,048	82.36	67,404	81.74
7. I was encouraged to do my best.	24,085	79.24	20,425	77.08	20,358	79.63	64,868	78.65
8. The learning experience I encountered enhanced my interest towards the lessons.	24,168	79.70	20,425	77.24	20,398	79.96	64,991	78.97
9. Overall speaking, I have very positive evaluation of the program.	24,092	79.33	20,592	77.76	20,489	80.16	65,173	79.08
10. On the whole, I like this curriculum very much.	24,305	80.25	20,672	78.22	20,530	80.49	65,507	79.65

Note: All items are on a 6-point Likert scale with 1 = strongly disagree, 2 = disagree, 3 = slightly disagree, 4 = slightly agree, 5 = agree, 6 = strongly agree. Only respondents with positive responses (Options 4-6) are shown in the table. S1: Secondary 1 level; S2: Secondary 2 level; S3: Secondary 3 level.

Table 2. Summary of the program participants' perceptions toward the program implementers

| | Respondents with positive responses (Options 4-6) | | | | | | | |
| | S1 | | S2 | | S3 | | Overall | |
	n	%	n	%	n	%	N	%
1. The instructor(s) had a good mastery of the curriculum.	26,689	87.72	22,957	86.62	22,661	88.66	72,307	87.67
2. The instructor(s) was well prepared for the lessons.	27,119	89.15	23,263	87.75	22,822	89.29	73,204	88.73
3. The instructor(s)' teaching skills were good.	26,688	87.87	22,676	85.62	22,421	87.83	71,785	87.11
4. The instructor(s) showed good professional attitudes.	27,077	89.10	23,204	87.56	22,805	89.31	73,086	88.66
5. The instructor(s) was very involved.	27,283	89.76	23,400	88.38	23,007	90.17	73,690	89.44
6. The instructor(s) encouraged students to participate in the activities.	27,255	89.73	23,265	87.80	22,842	89.46	73,362	89.00
7. The instructor(s) cared for the students.	26,602	87.60	22,726	85.79	22,384	87.66	71,712	87.02
8. The instructor(s) was ready to offer help to students when needed.	27,101	89.24	23,235	87.74	22,882	89.61	73,218	88.86
9. The instructor(s) had much interaction with the students.	26,127	85.99	22,429	84.68	22,205	86.99	70,761	85.89
10. Overall speaking, I have very positive evaluation of the instructors.	27,016	88.83	23,326	87.97	22,915	89.67	73,257	88.82

Note: All items are on a 6-point Likert scale with 1 = strongly disagree, 2 = disagree, 3 = slightly disagree, 4 = slightly agree, 5 = agree, 6 = strongly agree. Only respondents with positive responses (Options 4-6) are shown in the table. S1: Secondary 1 level; S2: Secondary 2 level; S3: Secondary 3 level.

Table 3. Summary of the program participants' perceptions toward the program effectiveness

| The extent to which the Tier 1 Program (i.e., the program in which all students have joined) has helped your students: | Respondents with positive responses (Options 3-5) | | | | | | | |
| | S1 | | S2 | | S3 | | Overall | |
	n	%	n	%	n	%	N	%
1. It has strengthened my bonding with teachers, classmates and my family.	24,664	81.03	20,825	78.78	20,605	80.71	66,094	80.17
2. It has strengthened my resilience in adverse conditions.	25,200	82.87	21,329	80.69	20,963	82.13	67,492	81.90

Table 3. (Continued)

The extent to which the Tier 1 Program (i.e., the program in which all students have joined) has helped your students:	Respondents with positive responses (Options 3-5)							
	S1		S2		S3		Overall	
	n	%	n	%	n	%	N	%
3. It has enhanced my social competence.	25,833	85.00	21,681	82.15	21,390	83.86	68,904	83.67
4. It has improved my ability in handling and expressing my emotions.	25,569	84.14	21,567	81.69	21,260	83.37	68,396	83.07
5. It has enhanced my cognitive competence.	25,592	84.28	21,538	81.69	21,139	82.87	68,269	82.95
6. My ability to resist harmful influences has been improved.	26,187	86.22	22,190	84.03	21,647	84.88	70,024	85.04
7. It has strengthened my ability to distinguish between the good and the bad.	26,472	87.15	22,442	85.02	21,909	85.94	70,823	86.04
8. It has increased my competence in making sensible and wise choices.	26,289	86.54	22,137	83.86	21,685	85.04	70,111	85.15
9. It has helped me to have life reflections.	25,328	83.42	21,678	82.14	21,442	84.13	68,448	83.23
10. It has reinforced my self-confidence.	25,057	82.50	20,920	79.25	20,552	80.64	66,529	80.80
11. It has increased students' self-awareness.	25465	83.87	21,382	81.08	21,051	82.60	67,898	82.52
12. It has helped students to face the future with a positive attitude.	25,749	84.82	21,675	82.16	21,423	84.14	68,847	83.71
13. It has helped students to cultivate compassion and care about others.	25,591	84.29	21,775	82.56	21,420	84.01	68,786	83.62
14. It has encouraged students to care about the community.	24,984	82.28	21,128	80.10	20,830	81.70	66,942	81.36
15. It has promoted students' sense of responsibility in serving the society.	25,309	83.34	21,336	80.85	20,962	82.19	67,607	82.13
16. It has enriched the overall development of the students.	26,189	86.21	22,189	84.10	21,829	85.67	70,207	85.33

Note: All items are on a 5-point Likert scale with 1 = unhelpful, 2 = not very helpful, 3 = slightly helpful, 4 = helpful, 5 = very helpful. Only respondents with positive responses (Options 3-5) are shown in the table. S1: Secondary 1 level; S2: Secondary 2 level; S3: Secondary 3 level.

Table 4. Other aspects of subjective outcome evaluation based on the program participants' perception

If your friends have needs and conditions similar to yours, will you suggest him/her to join this course?

Respondents with positive responses (Options 3-4)								
S1		S2		S3		Overall	
n	%	n	%	n	%	N	%
24,324	81.92	19,886	76.41	19,326	77.32	63,536	78.55

Note: The item is on a 4-point Likert scale with 1 = definitely will not suggest, 2 = will not suggest, 3 = will suggest, 4 = definitely will suggest. Only respondents with positive responses (Options 3-4) are shown in the table. S1: Secondary 1 level; S2: Secondary 2 level; S3: Secondary 3 level.

Will you participate in similar courses again in the future?

Respondents with positive responses (Options 3-4)								
S1		S2		S3		Overall	
n	%	n	%	n	%	N	%
21,242	71.50	17,003	65.30	16,647	66.57	54,892	67.79

Note: The item is on a 4-point Likert scale with 1 = definitely will not participate, 2 = will not participate, 3 = will participate, 4 = definitely will participate. Only respondents with positive responses (Options 3-4) are shown in the table. S1: Secondary 1 level; S2: Secondary 2 level; S3: Secondary 3 level.

On the whole, are you satisfied with this course?

Respondents with positive responses (Options 4-6)								
S1		S2		S3		Overall	
n	%	n	%	n	%	N	%
25,978	87.05	22,005	84.23	21,452	85.66	69,435	85.65

Note: All items are on a 6-point Likert scale with 1 = very dissatisfied, 2 = moderately dissatisfied, 3 = slightly dissatisfied, 4 = slightly satisfied, 5 = moderately satisfied, 6 = very satisfied. Only respondents with positive responses (Options 4-6) are shown in the table. S1: Secondary 1 level; S2: Secondary 2 level; S3: Secondary 3 level.

Table 5. Mean, standard deviations, Cronbach's alphas, and mean of inter-item correlations among the variables by grade

	S1		S2		S3		Overall	
	M (SD)	α (Mean[#])	M (SD)	α (Mean[#])	M (SD)	α (Mean[#])	M (SD)	α (Mean[#])
Program content (10 items)	4.37** (.29)	.98 (.84)	4.26** (.31)	.99 (.89)	4.33 (.32)	.99 (.90)	4.32 (.31)	.98 (.87)
Program implementers (10 items)	4.68** (.30)	.99 (.89)	4.55** (.31)	1.00 (.95)	4.61 (.31)	1.00 (.95)	4.61 (.31)	.99 (.93)
Program effectiveness (16 items)	3.50** (.25)	.99 (.91)	3.37** (.29)	1.00 (.95)	3.41** (.30)	1.00 (.96)	3.43 (.28)	1.00 (.94)
Total effectiveness (36 items)	4.07** (.25)	.99 (.76)	3.95** (.29)	1.00 (.85)	4.00* (.29)	.99 (.84)	4.01 (.28)	.99 (.82)

[#] Mean inter-item correlations. *$p < .05$, ** $p < .01$; Bonferroni adjustment ($p = .02$). S1: Secondary 1 level; S2: Secondary 2 level; S3: Secondary 3 level.

Table 6. Correlation coefficients on the relationship between program components and program effectiveness

Variable	S1	S2	S3	Overall
Program content (10 items)	.78**	.88**	.87**	.84**
Program implementers (10 items)	.73**	.78**	.76**	.76**

$**p < .01$. S1: Secondary 1 level; S2: Secondary 2 level; S3: Secondary 3 level.

Table 7. Multiple regression analyses predicting program effectiveness

	Predictors			
	Program content	Program implementers	Model	
	$ß^a$	$ß^a$	R	R^2
S1	.62**	.18	.78	.61
S2	1.14**	-.28**	.89	.78
S3	.94**	-.08	.87	.76
Overall	.85**	-.01	.84	.71

[a] Standardized coefficients. $**p < .01$. S1: Secondary 1 level; S2: Secondary 2 level; S3: Secondary 3 level.

Overall speaking, junior students perceived the program more effective than their senior counterparts. However, it is noteworthy that the effect size of grade differences was not strong.

Table 7 presents multiple regression analysis results. Program content was positively associated with perceived program effectiveness ($p < .01$). On the other hand, program implementer was not associated with program effectiveness ($p > .05$). However, the result based on the Secondary 2 students showed that perception towards the program implementer was negatively associated with perceived program effectiveness ($ß = -.28$, $p < .01$). Further analyses showed that program content ($ß = .85$, $p < .01$) had a significant predictive effect on program effectiveness while this relationship was not significant in program implementer ($ß = -.01$, $p > .05$). This model explained 71% of the variance toward the prediction of program effectiveness.

Discussion

The present findings revealed that the program participants generally rated their participation in the program positively. In line with the previous findings using various methods and collected from different sources (24-30), the majority of the participants reported that they were satisfied with the program content had an enjoyable experience, and perceived the program as beneficial to develop their personal and social competencies. The present study provided support for the hypothesis that perceptions of the program content and program implementers were positively associated with program effectiveness. Findings suggested that participants' needs and interests were satisfied as they would participate again or recommend similar programs to their peers in the future. Taken as a whole, evaluation findings in the extension phase are highly similar to those reported in the original phase. From a triangulation point of view, data collected from different sources based on different methods generally suggest that the program is well-received by different stakeholders.

The second aim of the study was to examine the relative influence of two program implementation factors (i.e., perceived program attributes and program implementers) on program effectiveness. Results of the regression analyses indicated that program content but not program implementers had a significant predictive effect on program effectiveness outcome. In line with previous studies (8, 9, 37-39), clear objectives of the curriculum, provision of well-designed teaching activities, participants' active participation and perception of a motivated learning environment were associated with program outcomes. The findings indicated the importance of a well-planned program and the success of eliciting participants' engagement for program effectiveness.

Another purpose of the study was to examine whether the relationships between program implementation factors and program evaluation outcomes would vary by the students' grade levels. Consistent with the previous study (34), Secondary 1 students perceived the program more favorably as compared to their higher grade level counterparts (i.e., Secondary 2 and 3 students). This observation might be related to the characteristics of the students. Compared to Secondary 3 students, Secondary 1 students were new to the project, they were more interested and motivated to learn and participate in the program activities. Also, senior students were likely to act critically and engage in rebellious behaviors during this period of stress. Nevertheless, the differences observed were not great, further studies to examine the related phenomena are needed.

It is interesting to note the negative predictive effect of program implementers on perceived program effectiveness. Some might question whether this result was related to the program implementers' teaching background. It is noteworthy that all program implementers of the Tier 1 Program were all experienced teachers and frontline social workers who had at least 3 years of experience in working with youths and received relevant formalized training workshops for more than 20 hours. Second, previous study (34) showed that program participants generally perceived program implementers positively (e.g., using effective and interactive teaching methods and skills, eliciting participants' learning motivation in the learning process, displaying enthusiasm in teaching). One possible explanation of this unexpected result might be related to the unit of analysis of the data. In the current study, data was aggregated at the school-level and the school means for each scale were computed and used for analysis. Clearly, it is important to examine this issue again using individual data rather than aggregate data. In addition, it would be helpful to test the associations between various dimensions of program implementation and program outcomes using advanced statistical technique. To increase the precision of measuring the effects of different program implementation factors on each level (e.g., students, classroom and schools), future research should use multilevel statistical modeling to analyze the nested data (i.e., students nested within classrooms/schools).

While the present study focused on the influence of two program implementation factors, it is possible that other facilitators (e.g., fidelity, adaptation, dosage, reach) will also influence program effectiveness. For example, high levels of fidelity and increased cultural relevance of the program have been associated with program outcomes (6, 40, 41). Program evaluation researchers noted the need of developing a theoretical model that identifies how different implementation factors exert their influence on program outcomes, and thus untangle their conjointly effects on program effectiveness outcomes. Future research should include other factors in order to depict a comprehensive picture about the complex process of effective program implementation.

Providing a positive developmental experience in early adolescence would promote individuals' different competencies and reduce negative outcomes (42). Consistent with Western literature, a positive youth development program appears to be a promising approach to promote individuals' personal, emotional, social, and spiritual competencies and to deter a range of problem and risky behavior among Hong Kong adolescents (43, 44). Understanding the factors underlying the complex program implementation process is critical in achieving their intended outcomes. The findings in the present study underscore the impact of program content and program implementers on perceived program effectiveness.

There are several limitations of this study. First, the use of self-report measure from a single perspective is limited to give a full picture concerning subjective outcome evaluation. However, this approach is commonly used in program evaluation research (6, 7, 9, 12). In addition, reliability of the scales is very promising. Therefore, we could argue that the findings in the study are reliable and valid. Another limitation is the cross-sectional nature of the data.

Future research should collect data at several points in time and also include predictors from various contexts, such as school and community. In particular, in seeking to monitor the rate of change of the perceived program effectiveness over time, growth curve modeling could be used to examine whether the predictive effects of the program implementation components on the shape of growth and the variability in individual trajectories would vary by the number of waves. However, in doing this, we must collect anonymous personal identifiers from the students. Third, aggregated data with schools with units of analyses rather than individual data were used in this study. Theoretically speaking, it would be interesting to look at the differences in the findings based on these two methods.

Finally, ordinary least square analyses were used. As structural equation modeling may give a better estimation of the suppressors in the predictors, such techniques could be considered in future studies.

Despite the above limitations, the current study contributes to the positive youth development literature. It sheds light on what program components are associated with perceived program effectiveness. Shek, Ma and Merrick (45) argued that more research work is needed on subjective outcome evaluation, especially in social work education. To promote the dissemination of efficacious programs, it is important to consider characteristics of the participants.

As supported by Catalano et al. (22), "if we are to discern why these (positive youth development) programs are effective, it is clear that it will be important in the future for programs to define and assess implementation methods and change strategies, and that they also evaluate the impact on youth development constructs .... and how these effects varied by subgroups" (p. S94). The findings of the study attempt to address this gap in the program evaluation research. It provides insights to practitioners when designing and implementing effective positive youth development programs for Chinese adolescents.

Most importantly, in conjunction with the previous findings, the present findings show that the influence of program attributes and program implementers on program effectiveness is relatively stable in different cohorts of students in Hong Kong (46-50).

ACKNOWLEDGMENTS

The preparation for this paper and the Project P.A.T.H.S. were financially supported by The Hong Kong Jockey Club Charities Trust. This paper was originally published in The Scientific World Journal, Volumn 2012, Article ID 493957, 9 pages doi: 10.1100/2012/493957

References

[1] Catalano RF, Arthur MW, Hawkins JD, Berglund ML, Olson JJ. Comprehensive community and school-based interventions to prevent antisocial behavior. In: Loeber R, Farringto DF, editors. Serious and violent juvenile offenders. CA: Sage, 1998. p. 248-83.

[2] Gottfredson DC. Delinquency and schools. New York: Cambridge University Press, 2001.

[3] Payne AA, Eckert R. The relative importance of provider, program, school, and community predictors of the implementation quality of school-based prevention programs. Prev Sci 2010;11(2):126-41.

[4] Wilson SJ, Lipsey MW, Derzon JH. The effects of school-based intervention programs on aggressive behavior: a meta-analysis. J Consult Clin Psychol 2003;71(1):136-49.

[5] Dane AV, Schneider BH. Program integrity in primary and early secondary prevention: are implementation effects out of control? Clin Psychol Rev 1998;18(1):23-45.

[6] Durlak JA, DuPre EP. Implementation matters: a review of research on the influence of implementation on program outcomes and the factors affecting implementation. Am J Commun Psychol 2008;41(3-4):327-50.

[7] Dusenbury L, Brannigan R, Falco M, Hansen WB. A review of research on fidelity of implementation: implications for drug abuse prevention in school setting. Health Educ Res 2003;18(2):237-56.

[8] Blake SM, Simkin L, Ledsky R, Perkins C, Calabrese JM. Effects of a parent-child communications intervention on young adolescents' risk for early onset of sexual intercourse. Fam Plan Percept 2001;33(2):52-61.

[9] Garvey C, Julion W, Fogg L, Kratovil A, Gross D. Measuring participation in a prevention trial with parents of young children. Res Nurs Health 2006;29(3):212-22.

[10] Eames C, Daley D, Hutchings J, Whitaker CJ, Jones K, Hughes JC, Bywater T. Treatment fidelity as a predictor of behavior change in parents attending group-based parent training. Child Care Health Dev 2009;35(5):603-12.

[11] Forgatch MS, Patterson GR, DeGarmo DS. Evaluating fidelity: predictive validity for a measure of competent adherence to the Oregon model of parent management training. Behav Ther 2005;36(1):3-13.

[12] Prado G, Pantin H, Schwartz SJ, Lupei NS, Szapocznik J. Predictors of engagement and retention into a parent-centered, eco-developmental HIV preventive intervention for Hispanic adolescents and their families. J Pediatr Psychol 2006;31(9):874-90.

[13] Rohrbach LA, Gunning M, Sun P, Sussman S. The Project Towards No Drug Abuse (TND) dissemination trail: implementation fidelity and immediate outcomes. Prev Sci 2010;11(1):77-88.

[14] Elliott DS, Mihalic S. Issues in disseminating and replicating effective prevention programs. Prev Sci 2004;5(1):47-53.

[15] Lillehoj CJ, Griffin KW, Spoth R. Program provider and observer ratings of school-based preventive intervention implementation: agreement and relation to youth outcomes. Health Educ Res 2004;31(2):242-57.

[16] Shelef K, Diamond GM, Diamond GS, Liddle HA. Adolescent and parent alliance and treatment outcome in multidimensional family therapy. J Consult Clin Psychol 2005;73(4):689-98.

[17] Berkel C, Mauricio AM, Schoenfelder E, Sandler IN. Putting the pieces together: an integrated model of program implementation. Prev Sci 2011;12(1):23-33.

[18]   Botvin GJ. Advancing prevention science and practice: challenges, critical issues, and future directions. Prev Sci 2004;5(1):69-72.

[19]   Castro FG, Barrera M, Martinez CR. The cultural adaptation of prevention interventions: resolving tensions between fidelity and fit. Prev Sci 2004;5(1):41-5.

[20]   Dusenbury LA, Brannigan R, Hansen WB, Walsh J, Falco M. Quality of implementation: developing measures crucial to understanding the diffusion of preventive interventions. Health Educ Res 2005;20(3):308-13.

[21]   von Eye A. Developing the person-oriented approach: theory and methods of analysis. Dev Psychopathol 2010;22(2):277-85.

[22]   Catalano RF, Gavin LE, Markham CM. Future directions for positive youth development as a strategy to promote adolescent sexual and reproductive health. J Adolesc Health 2010;46(3):S92-6.

[23]   Shek DTL. Construction of a positive youth development program in Hong Kong. Int J Adolesc Med Health 2006;18(3):299-302.

[24]   Shek DTL. Using students' weekly diaries to evaluate positive youth development programs: are findings based on multiple studies consistent? Soc Indic Res 2010;95(3):457-87.

[25]   Shek DTL, Sun RCF. Interim evaluation of the Secondary 3 Program of Project P.A.T.H.S.: insights based on the Experimental Implementation Phase. Int J Pub Health 2009;1:289-300.

[26]   Shek DTL, Ma CMS, Sun RCF. Evaluation of a positive youth development program for adolescents with greater psychosocial needs: integrated views of program implementers. ScientificWorldJournal 2010;10:1890-900.

[27]   Shek DTL, Ng CSM. Subjective outcome evaluation of the Project P.A.T.H.S. (Secondary 2 Program): views of the program participants. ScientificWorldJournal 2009;9:1012-22.

[28]   Shek DTL, Sun RCF. Evaluation of Project P.A.T.H.S. (Secondary 1 Program) by the program participants: findings based on the full implementation phase. J Adolesc 2008;43(172):807-22.

[29]   Shek DTL, Sun RCF, Chan CW. Evaluation of Project P.A.T.H.S. (Secondary 2 Program) by the program participants: findings based on the experimental implementation phase. ScientificWorldJournal 2008;8:526-35.

[30]   Shek DTL, Ng CSM, Tsui PF. Qualitative evaluation of the Project P.A.T.H.S.: findings based on focus groups. Int J Disabil Hum Dev 2010;307(9):303-13.

[31]   Shek DTL, Sun RCF. Subjective outcome evaluation based on secondary data analyses: the Project P.A.T.H.S. in Hong Kong. ScientificWorldJournal 2010;10:224-37.

[32]   Shek DTL. Quantitative evaluation of the training program of the Project P.A.T.H.S. in Hong Kong. Int J Adolesc Med Health 2010;22(3):425-35.

[33]   Shek DTL, Ma CMS. Subjective outcome evaluation findings: factors related to the perceived effectiveness of the Tier 2 Program of the Project P.A.T.H.S. ScientificWorldJournal 2010;10:250-60.

[34]   Shek DTL, Ma CMS, Tang CYP. Subjective outcome evaluation of the Project P.A.T.H.S.: findings based on different datasets. Int J Disabil Hum Dev 2011;10:249-55.

[35]   Shek DTL, Sun RCF, Tang CYP. Experimental Implementation of the Secondary 3 Program of Project P.A.T.H.S.: observations based on the co-walker scheme. ScientificWorldJournal 2009;9:1003-11.

[36]   Shek DTL, Siu AMH, Lui JHY, Lung DWM. P.A.T.H.S. to adulthood: A Jockey Club Youth Enhancement Scheme evaluation manual. Hong Kong: Social Welfare Practice Research Centre, The Chinese University of Hong Kong, 2006.

[37]   Rapee RM, Wignall A, Sheffield J, Kowalenko N, Davis A, McLoone J, Spence SH. Adolescents' reactions to universal and indicated prevention programs for depression: perceived stigma and consumer satisfaction. Prev Sci 2006;7(2):167-77.

[38]   Tolan PH, Hanish LD, McKay MM, Dickey MH. Evaluating process in child and family interventions: aggression prevention as an example. J Fam Psychol 2002;16(2):220-36.

[39]   Baydar N, Reid MJ, Webster-Stratton C. The role of mental health factors and program engagement in the effectiveness of a preventive parenting program for head start mothers. Child Dev 2003;74(5):1433-53.

[40]   McGraw SA, Sellers DE, Johnson CC, Stone EJ, Bachman KJ, Bebchuk J,...Edmundson EW. Using process data to explain outcomes: an illustration from the Child and Adolescent Trail for Cardiovascular Health (CATCH). Evaluat Rev 1996;20(3):291-312.

[41]   Ialongo NS, Werthamer L, Kellam SG, Brown CH, Wang S, Lin Y. Proximal impact of two first-grade preventive interventions on the early risk behaviors for later substance abuse, depression, and antisocial behavior. Am J Commun Psychol 1999;27(5):599-641.

[42]   Durlak JA, Taylor RD, Kawashima K, Pachan MK, DuPre EP, Celio CI,...Weissberg RP. Effects of positive youth development programs on school, family, and community systems. Am J Commun Psychol 2007;39(3-4):269-86.

[43]   Shek DTL, Yu L. Prevention of adolescent problem behavior: longitudinal impact of the Project P.A.T.H.S. in Hong Kong. ScientificWorldJournal 2011;11:546-67.

[44]   Shek DTL, Ma CMS. Impact of the Project P.A.T.H.S. on adolescent developmental outcomes in Hong Kong: findings based on seven waves of data. Int J Adolesc Med Health 2012;24(3):231-44.

[45]   Shek DTL, Ma HK, Merrick J. Positive youth development: development of a pioneering program in a Chinese context. London: Freund Publishing House, 2007.

[46]   Shek DTL, Sun RCF. Effectiveness of the tier 1 program of Project P.A.T.H.S.: findings based on three years of program implementation. ScientificWorldJournal 2010;10:1509-19.

[47]   Shek DTL, Ng CSM, Tsui PF. Qualitative evaluation of the Project P.A.T.H.S.: findings based on focus groups. Int J Disabil Hum Dev 2010;9(4):307-313.

[48]   Shek DTL. Using students' weekly diaries to evaluate positive youth development programs: are findings based on multiple studies consistent? Soc Indic Res 2010;95(3):475-87.

[49]   Shek DTL. Quantitative evaluation of the training program of the Project P.A.T.H.S. in Hong Kong. Int J Adolesc Med Health 2010;22(3):425-35.

[50]   Shek DTL, Sun RCF. Development, implementation and evaluation of a holistic positive youth development program: Project P.A.T.H.S. in Hong Kong. Int J Disabil Hum Dev 2009;8(2):107-17.

Submitted: November 01, 2011. Revised: December 15, 2011. Accepted: December 20, 2011.

In: Child Health and Human Development Yearbook 2013   ISBN: 978-1-63117-939-6
Editor: Joav Merrick   © 2014 Nova Science Publishers, Inc.

Chapter 5

Student classroom misbehavior: An exploratory study based on teachers' perceptions

Rachel CF Sun, PhD[*1],
and Daniel TL Shek, PhD, FHKPS, BBS, JP[2,3,4,5,6]

[1]Faculty of Education, The University of Hong Kong, Hong Kong, PRC
[2]Department of Applied Social Sciences, The Hong Kong Polytechnic University, Hong Kong, PRC
[3]Public Policy Research Institute, The Hong Kong Polytechnic University, Hong Kong, PRC
[4]Department of Social Work, East China Normal University, Shanghai, PRC
[5]Kiang Wu Nursing College of Macau, Macau, PRC
[6]Division of Adolescent Medicine, Department of Pediatrics, Kentucky Children's Hospital, University of Kentucky College of Medicine, Lexington, Kentucky, United States of America

Abstract

This study aimed to examine the conceptions of junior secondary school student misbehaviors in classroom, and to identify the most common, disruptive and unacceptable student problem behaviors from teachers' perspective. Twelve individual interviews with teachers were conducted. A list of 17 student problem behaviors was generated. Results showed that the most common and disruptive problem behavior was talking out of turn, followed by non-attentiveness, daydreaming and idleness. The most unacceptable problem behavior was disrespecting teachers in terms of disobedience and rudeness, followed by talking out of turn and verbal aggression. The findings revealed that teachers perceived student problem behaviors as those behaviors involving rule-

* Correspondence: Assistant Professor Rachel CF Sun, PhD, Faculty of Education, The University of Hong Kong, Pokfulam Road, Hong Kong, PRC. E-mail: rachels@hku.hk.

breaking, violating the implicit norms or expectations, being inappropriate in the classroom settings and upsetting teaching and learning, which mainly required intervention from teachers.

Keywords: Student problem behavior, classroom misbehavior, teachers' perception, Chinese classroom, Hong Kong

Introduction

Student misbehaviors such as disruptive talking, chronic avoidance of work, clowning, interfering with teaching activities, harassing classmates, verbal insults, rudeness to teacher, defiance and hostility (1), ranging from infrequent to frequent, mild to severe, is a thorny issue in everyday classroom. Teachers usually reported that these disturbing behaviors in the classroom are intolerable (2) and stress-provoking (3), and they had to spend a great deal of time and energy to manage the classroom (4, 5). Obviously, student misbehaviors retard the smoothness and effectiveness of teaching, and also impede the learning of the student and his / her classmates. Moreover, research findings have shown that school misbehavior not only escalated with time, but also lowered academic achievement and increased delinquent behavior (6, 7). To lessen these immediate and gradual adverse effects of student misbehaviors, it is of primary importance to identify what exactly are these behaviors inside classroom.

In the literature, different terms have been used to describe problematic behaviors of students. For instance, Stewart et al. (8) referred student misconduct to disciplinary violations in school, for instance, tardiness, vandalism, fighting, stealing, and drinking on campus. When there are explicit rules and regulations in school and classroom, violation of these is apparently a "misbehavior or misconduct or discipline problem". Nevertheless, a particular behavior is viewed as problematic may not necessarily be rule-breaking, but inappropriate or disturbing in the classroom setting. For instance, daydreaming in class, not completing homework, talking in class, lesson disruption, bullying and rudeness to the teacher are named as "problem behaviors" (9), "behavior problems" (10, 11) or "disruptive behaviors" (4, 12). These behaviors referred to "an activity that causes distress for teachers, interrupts the learning process and that leads teachers to make continual comments to the student" (13, page 60), or "the myriad activities which disrupt and impede the teaching-learning process" (14, page 43). Noting that school misconduct is one of the manifests of the problem behavior syndrome (15-17), the term "problem behavior" was used to refer to all externalizing behaviors that violate explicit rules or implicit norms, disturb the classroom order, and irritate the process of teaching and learning in this study.

Several scales have been developed to measure teachers' perceptions of classroom problem behaviors. For instance, in the United Kingdom, Wheldall and Merrett (10) used ten items, including eating, non-verbal noise, disobedience, talking out of turn, idleness / slowness, unpunctuality, hindering others, physical aggression, untidiness, and out of seat, to measure behavior problems among primary school students. Houghton, Wheldall and Merrett (11) also used these behaviors to measure secondary school students' behavior problems, with a replacement of eating with verbal abuse because they found that teachers did not perceive eating as a problem behavior among secondary school students whereas verbal abuse was a more relevant behavior problem.

However, the cultural relevance of these scales to describe and measure disruptive behavior among primary and secondary school students in Hong Kong Chinese classroom is a concern that should be addressed. For example, Ho and Leung (12) and Leung and Ho (4) modified Wheldall and Merrett's scale (10) by dropping disobedience, and adding six student behaviors commonly reported by local teachers in Chinese school settings. These included verbal abuse, forgetfulness, non-attentiveness, gambling, reading other materials and doing other things. However, as these descriptors of students' disruptive behaviors were formed almost a decade ago, their validity and applicability to Chinese classrooms nowadays may be questioned. Some student behaviors that have not be mentioned in the previous studies, such as daydreaming, sleeping, looking out of window, playing with personal stuff in private, bullying, disrespecting, talking back, arguing, quarrelling or fighting with teachers, complaining, and lack of independent initiative were found by a recent study in exploring Chinese teachers' perceptions of students' classroom misbehavior (18). On top of this, uncooperativeness, emotional disturbance, over-activity and withdrawal were also reported as student classroom behavior problems by Chinese elementary school teachers (5). Although these two studies were recent, both were conducted in mainland China. It is thus argued that the scales developed in these studies as well as the findings may be limited to describing student problem behaviors in mainland China classroom, which is different from the pluralistic classroom in which Confucian and Western teaching and learning approaches are used in Hong Kong. As such, direct employment of an existing scale is hardly sufficient to tap all the classroom problem behaviors exhibited by students. It is therefore important to carry out a qualitative research study to unravel relevant and up-to-dated descriptions of the students' problem behaviors in Hong Kong classroom based on the views of teachers.

Apart from exploring different categories of student problem behaviors inside classroom, it is also valuable to identify the common ones and the disruptive ones from the teachers' perspectives. Existing research findings showed that, among various types of student problem behaviors, "talking out of turn", "hindering others" and "idleness" were commonly reported by secondary school teachers as the most frequent and troublesome misbehaviors in the United Kingdom (11) and Australia (19). Similar to these findings in the West, "talking out of turn" was rated by both primary and secondary school teachers as the most frequent and troublesome misbehavior, followed by "non-attentiveness" and "forgetfulness" – another two typical students' disruptive behaviors in Hong Kong classroom (4, 12). In mainland China, "non-attentiveness", "talking out of turn" and "over-active" were reported as the most frequent and troublesome classroom behavior problems by the elementary school teachers in three provinces (5). On the other hand, "daydreaming", "talking out of turn" and "playing with personal stuff" were rated as the most frequent classroom misbehaviors by a group of elementary, middle and high school teachers in another two provinces, while "daydreaming", "slowness" and "talking out of turn" were the most troublesome classroom misbehaviors (18). Apparently, "talking out of turn" is usually ranked as highly popular and disturbing student misbehavior across time and cultures and in different grade levels of students. With a specific focus on studying the problem behaviors of junior secondary students in Hong Kong classroom, this study attempted to replicate the previous studies in examining the problem behaviors perceived by teachers as the most common and disruptive. In addition, this study further attempted to investigate the most unacceptable problem behaviors in the eyes of teachers and the underlying reasons behind.

The primary goal of this study was to examine classroom problem behaviors among junior secondary school students in Hong Kong based on the views of teachers. The aims of this study were to (i) generate a list of categories of students' problem behaviors perceived by teachers in Hong Kong junior secondary school classroom, (ii) identify problem behaviors that were perceived as the most common, the most disruptive to teaching and learning in classroom, and the most unacceptable problem behavior and the reasons. Noting that the most frequent misbehavior can be somehow objectively observed, a particular behavior is regarded as the most disruptive or unacceptable depends on the teachers' subjective judgment and values, professional training and years of teaching experiences. Therefore, this study recruited teachers with different years of teaching experiences and training background, in order to get a comprehensive view of the issue. It is a descriptive and exploratory qualitative research study. Academically, the present findings would add to the local literature, as recent research studies on this topic are scanty in Hong Kong (8, 9). Even though there were some studies, they were conducted a decade ago (4, 12), and limited to focusing on the mainland China educational settings (5, 18). Practically, it was expected that the findings would have profound importance to counseling and guidance work in the school context.

Methods

Three schools, each admitting students having low, medium or high academic competencies, were invited to join this study. In each school, four teachers who had experiences of teaching junior secondary grades (Grade 7, 8, and/or 9) and/or were members of the school counseling team and/or discipline teams were invited to join an individual interview. In total, twelve teachers (5 males and 7 females) participated in this study. Four of them were members of the school counseling team and three were members of the discipline team. The average of their teaching experiences was 9.25 years (range = 1-22 years). Their participation was voluntary and written consent from the school principals and the interviewees were obtained prior to data collection. Issues of anonymity and confidentiality in handling the data were also clearly explained at the beginning of each interview.

Instrument

A self-constructed semi-structured interview guide was used for each individual interview. In the interview guide, questions and prompts used to explore the interviewees' perceptions of students' problem behaviors and their management strategies in the classroom and school contexts. The interviewees were asked to define "problem behaviors" based on their own understanding and interpretation. They were invited to use real-life examples to further illustrate their views. The average time for an interview was 49 minutes (range = 33-78 minutes). Each interview was conducted by two trained interviewers in Cantonese (the mother tongue of both the interviewers and interviewees). The interviews were audio-taped with informants' prior consent, and transcribed in verbatim after the interview.

As many questions were covered in the interview guide, only data related to the following questions were analyzed in this paper:

- In the classroom, what student problem behaviors are there? Please list out as many as possible and describe.
- Among these problem behaviors, which are the most common?
- Among these problem behaviors, which are the most disruptive to teaching and learning?
- Among these problem behaviors, which are the most unacceptable? Please illustrate.

Data analysis

Findings pertinent to teachers' perceptions of students' problem behavior inside classroom are reported in this paper. Data was analyzed by using general qualitative analyses techniques (20). First level of coding was conducted by a colleague who has a Bachelor degree of Psychology and teaching experiences. Semantically similar words, phrases, and/or sentences that formed meaningful units in each conclusion at the raw response level were grouped whereas semantically different data were divided. Further checking and second levels of coding and categorization were conducted by the first author, in which similar codes were grouped to reflect higher-order categories of theme. The coding and categorization were finalized with consensus among the coders, and further checked by a colleague with a Bachelor degree of Psychology and professional counseling training.

As the code and categorization were inductively derived from the data, both intra- and inter-rater reliability on the coding were calculated to ensure the credibility of the findings. In the reliability test, 20 raw responses were randomly selected for each rater to code without referring to the original codes. The intra-rater reliability tests were conducted by the two coders independently; whereas the inter-rater reliability tests were conducted by two colleagues (one has a Master degree and several years of teaching experiences and one has a Bachelor degree) independently. The reliability of the categorization was on the high side, because the intra-rater agreement percentages were both 100%; while the inter-rater agreement percentages were 80% and 95%.

Results

Categories of classroom problem behaviors

Table 1 summarizes 88 responses regarding students' problem behaviors inside classroom reported by 12 informants. The responses were classified into 17 main categories and 6 of them were further divided into subcategories. As shown in Table 1, the problem behaviors reported by the teachers were mostly "doing something in private", "talking out of turn", "verbal aggression", "disrespecting teachers", "non-attentiveness / daydreaming / idleness", "sleeping", "habitual failure in submitting assignments" and "out of seat".

Teachers reported that students would do something in private which was unrelated to the lesson, such as reading, drawing, and doing other homework. Some teachers pointed out that it was a rising phenomenon that students liked to use electronic devices, such as mobile phone for texting people inside or outside classroom, playing electronic games, surfing webpage or listening to music. In response to this phenomenon, there were regulations in some schools prohibiting students to switch on their mobile phones inside school.

"Talking out of turn" was another problem behavior which was mainly referred to students chatting among themselves on irrelevant topics that disrupt the lessons, calling out and making remarks on somebody or something without teachers' permission. It is distinguished from "verbal aggression" which was referred to more hostile verbal expression, such as teasing, attacking, quarrelling and speaking foul language.

"Disrespecting teachers" appeared to be an attitude, but the teachers could concretely describe some behaviors under this category. For instance, a teacher mentioned that refusing to follow instructions was a disobedient and disrespectful behavior. Teacher B02 commented that "…challenging your (teachers') authority, mainly like, if you ask them not to do something, they are rebellious and insist to behave the other way round. They won't listen to teacher's opinion. They will insist to do what they think…These behaviors are mainly perceived in lower competent classes at the moment".

Another teacher illustrated that disrespecting teachers meant rudeness, talking back and confronting teachers. As remarked by Teacher C04, "sometimes they will even dispute against their teacher…A student gave an irrelevant answer to teacher's question, i.e., the teacher asked a serious question but the student gave a casual answer. If the teacher commented on, the student would be enraged and hostile, and then disputed against the teacher. Scolding teacher was unusual, unless the student was agitated. At the school level, I think there were less than five cases of scolding teacher in an academic year. Quite rare. When arguing, students usually had poor attitudes, especially boys. Hence, teachers would scold at them, and the students would become hostile, temper-losing… more seriously, they would knock tables or throw books to express their anger. But this situation was very rare; say one to two cases a year".

"Non-attentiveness / daydreaming / idleness", "sleeping", and "out of seat" (including changing seats deliberately, wandering around the classroom, catching, running away from the classroom without permission) were commonly reported as problem behaviors inside classroom. Some teachers also regarded failure to submit assignments on time in a habitual manner as one of the problem behaviors, as reflected in the following narrative: "(failure in submitting homework on time) is one of the problems if you are talking about student's misbehavior at school…this is quite a big problem in fact…There are a large proportion of students who fail to submit their homework on time, especially among Form 1 (Grade 7) student…Only half class can submit the homework on time if you set the deadline once. You need to chase after them for the homework…I think Form 1 (Grade 7) students are more likely to fail to submit their homework. In Form 2 (Grade 8), some classes can do better" (Teacher C03).

Table 1. A Summary of the Teachers' Perceptions of Student Problem Behaviors inside Classroom

Category	Subcategory	No. of responses	No. of responses regarding on the most common problem behavior	No. of responses regarding on the most disruptive behavior	No. of responses regarding on the most unacceptable problem behavior
Doing something in private	Dealing with personal stuff	3	0	0	0
	Doing homework	2	0	0	0
	Using electronic device (for texting, playing games, surfing webpage, listening to music)	4	0	0	0
	Irrelevant reading	2	0	0	0
	Irrelevant drawing	2	0	0	0
	Subtotal	13	0	0	1
Talking out of turn	Calling out	1	0	0	1
	Making remarks	1	0	0	0
	Having disruptive conversation	9	5	2	2
	Subtotal	11	5	2	3
Verbal aggression	Teasing classmates	4	0	0	1
	Attacking classmates	3	1	1	0
	Quarrelling with classmates	1	0	0	0
	Speaking foul language	2	0	0	1
	Subtotal	10	1	1	2
Disrespecting teachers	Disobedience / Refusing to carry out instructions	4	0	0	2
	Rudeness / Talking back, arguing with teacher	4	1	1	3
	Subtotal	8	1	1	5
Non-attentiveness / Daydreaming / Idleness		7	2	2	1
Sleeping		6	0	1	0

Table 1. (Continued)

Category	Subcategory	No. of responses	No. of responses regarding on the most common problem behavior	No. of responses regarding on the most disruptive behavior	No. of responses regarding on the most unacceptable problem behavior
Out of seat	Changing seats	1	1	0	0
	Wandering around the classroom	2	0	1	1
	Catching	1	0	0	0
	Running away from the classroom	1	0	0	0
	Subtotal	5	1	1	1
Habitual failure in submitting assignments		5	0	0	1
Physical aggression	Striking classmates	2	0	0	0
	Pushing classmates	1	0	0	0
	Destroying things	1	0	0	0
	Subtotal	4	0	0	0
Copying homework		4	1	0	0
Non-verbal communication	Via body language, facial expressions, papers	4	0	0	0
Clowning		3	0	0	1
Playing		3	0	0	0
Lateness to class		2	0	0	0
Eating / Drinking		1	1	0	0
Have not yet prepared textbook well		1	0	0	0
Passive engagement in class		1	0	0	1
Total responses		88	12	8	15

Some teachers added that some of the aforementioned problem behaviors, such as "talking out of turn" and "disrespecting teachers", were commonly found among a specific group of students who had special education needs. A teacher mentioned, "once I taught a student with SEN (Special Educational Needs) who had attention deficit... He had problems in getting along with his classmates. When other classmates had wrong answers, he would immediately call out and point out their mistakes. This in fact slightly affected the class." (Teacher C01). Another teacher reported, "I know that there are one or two SEN student(s) in every grade in our school. These students are quite disruptive. For example, they often have emotional disturbance, run away from classroom and sometimes fight against with their teachers" (Teacher B01).

Problem behaviors that were most common and disruptive to teaching and learning

Among various classroom problem behaviors reported, comparatively more teachers pointed out that "having disruptive conversation" was a form of "talking out of turn", which was the most common and the most disruptive to teaching and learning (see Table 1). A teacher explained, "chatting during lesson affects teaching and learning most... Whereas other behaviors such as daydreaming only affect self-learning, chatting will alter the whole class atmosphere as well as class progress. I have to stop the chatting, otherwise I cannot teach and the students who chat will miss the content of the lesson. If I do nothing, other students will imitate and join the conversation...As the classroom is small, others can still hear even you talk in a low voice. Moreover, students are very attentive to the surroundings. So such chatting can be disruptive even you chat in a very low voice" (Teacher C04).

"Non-attentiveness / daydreaming / idleness" was the next common and disruptive problem behavior. A teacher explained, "daydreaming during lesson will affect learning. If they are not attentive to the teacher, they have already missed some knowledge" (Teacher B04).

The most unacceptable problem behaviors inside classroom

As indicated in Table 1, "disrespecting teachers" were rated by five teachers as the most unacceptable problem behavior. As revealed in the interviews, such behavior indicated that students lacked proper attitudes and values in interpersonal relationships as well as in their morality. As Teacher C04 remarked, "disputing against teachers is disrespecting teachers...Other misbehaviors are just behaviors. The underlying reasons of these behaviors are simple. For instance, chatting in the middle of lesson could take place because they feel bored; or they just pop up some ideas to share with their neighbors. However, if they argue back or disrespect their teachers, it is something related to their attitudes and values. So I think this is the biggest problem...Normally, they behave offensively against individual teachers, a certain kind of teachers including those who are too gentle or those who are rigid but not convincing". Another teacher added, "(in confrontation)...some students like to twist the fact and shout their fallacy out loud to amuse their classmates. This is something that I cannot accept…It is obvious that he does not hold a point but still insists he is correct. I think this kind of behavior is unacceptable" (Teacher C03)

"Talking out of turn" and "verbal aggression" were also mentioned by teachers as unacceptable, because these behaviors disrupted the classroom order, which required teachers to spend time in managing classroom discipline and thus would adversely affect teaching. Among these verbal aggressive behaviors, teachers revealed that they could not accept students speaking foul language and teasing others, particularly insult would hurt the bullied.

Furthermore, individual teachers mentioned that "non-attentiveness / daydreaming / idleness", "out of seat", "habitual failure in submitting assignments", "clowning", and "passive engagement in class" as unacceptable, mainly because these behaviors would affect student learning and classroom atmosphere. For instance, in a teacher's perception of "non-attentiveness", he expressed that "if all students are unwilling or not motivated to learn, it will be very disastrous" (Teacher A01). Another teacher explained why "out of seat" was unacceptable, "if they sit still on their chairs, it is settled and they are less likely to have distracting behaviors or more severe problem behaviors. If they are out of seat, they may act out. There is a greater chance that they will distract other students and so the whole class. Therefore I think this behavior is relatively unacceptable" (Teacher C01). Another teacher showed his view on "passive engagement in class" by stating that "… the most unacceptable behavior? I think it is inactive during lesson. To me, it is misbehavior although it is not obvious. If there are a number of passive students in my class, it is hard for me to teach them. No matter how and what I teach, they just don't want to learn. Compared with these inactive students, those who make noise in class are better. At least there is interaction even we argue" (Teacher A02).

Discussion

Based on the perspective of teachers, this study attempted to generate a list of categories of students' problem behaviors in Hong Kong junior secondary school classroom, and to identify the most common, disruptive and unacceptable student problem behaviors.

As shown in Table 1, a list of 17 student problem behaviors was reported by the teachers, including doing something in private, talking out of turn, verbal aggression, disrespecting teachers, non-attentiveness / daydreaming / idleness, sleeping, out of seat, habitual failure in submitting assignments, physical aggression, copying homework, non-verbal communication, clowning, playing, lateness to class, eating / drinking, have not yet prepared textbook well, and passive engagement in class. Among them, the most common and disruptive misbehavior was talking out of turn, particularly in the form of disruptive conversation. The next one was non-attentiveness / daydreaming / idleness. The most unacceptable problem behavior was disrespecting teachers in terms of disobedience and rudeness, followed by talking out of turn and verbal aggression. Teachers would consider these behaviors as intolerable when they disrupt teaching, affect student learning adversely, or suggest the fact that students do not have proper values and attitudes. These findings indicate that teachers are concerned about classroom learning and student development, and they expect that there are respect, obedience, order and discipline in the classroom.

There were some unique findings of this study, although most of the categories of problem behaviors identified are similar to those reported in the previous studies. First, "doing something in private" was regarded as a student problem behavior in secondary school classroom in Chinese cultural contexts (12,18), while it was not included in some studies conducted in the West (11, 19). In this category, on top of dealing with personal stuff, doing other homework, reading and drawing that are unrelated to the lesson, this study showed that using electronic devices (e.g., mobile phone) for texting, playing games, surfing webpage and listening to music were regarded as problematic nowadays. With particular focus to Hong Kong, mobile phones are popular among adolescents. As these electronic devices are multi-functional and audio-visual stimulating, some students would be tempted to use them for communication and fulfilling personal satisfaction even during lesson. Actually, doing something in private is an off-task behavior in which students are doing something irrelevant to classroom learning. Others, like non-attentiveness, idleness, and daydreaming were grouped together as a category of problem behaviors in this study because they were mentioned as related to the fact that students were tired, lazy, or lacking learning motivation. Sleeping was a single category, because it was an obvious off-task behavior and would be disruptive if students imitate each others.

Similar to most of the existing studies (10-12), "talking out of turn" included calling out, making remarks and having disruptive conversation. All these referred to verbal disturbance in the lesson without teacher's permission. This conception is much wider than the narrow definition in Ding et al.'s study (18) where "talking out of turn" was simply referred to calling out answers without raising hands and being called upon by teachers. As usual, "talking out of turn" was rated by teachers as the most common and disruptive to teaching and learning. It was due to the fact that the noises are disruptive and teachers need to spend time to manage, otherwise such behaviors would escalate in term of frequency and intensity and would be contagious. Another reason is that when compared to "non-attentiveness / daydreaming / idleness", irrelevant chatting is more than an off-task behavior that adversely affects students' own learning. It is also a distracting behavior hampering others' learning in the same classroom.

Following talking out of turn, "verbal aggression" appeared to be a distinct problem behavior which was disruptive as well as hostile, such as speaking foul language, making offensive or insulting remarks to tease and assault classmates, that further led to quarrelling or mutual attacking (11, 12). All these might escalate to "physical aggression", such as striking and pushing each others and destroying things in the classroom. The lack of sympathy or hostility involved in these aggressive behaviors was mentioned as intolerable as the teachers recognized the hurt involved. It reflected that caring was valued in the eyes of the teachers when they judged a behavior was problematic or not.

It is not surprising that "disrespecting teachers" was highlighted in this study as a kind of unacceptable problem behavior, because respect and obedience are the deeply rooted values in Chinese education. "Disrespecting teachers" embraced disobedience, i.e., refusing or failing to carry out instructions (10, 11, 12), and rudeness, i.e., talking back and arguing with teachers (18). Sometimes, these behaviors would also be perceived as offensive to authority. These findings further demonstrated that these values are still strongly held in teacher expectations, and thus behaviors that fail to comply were pinpointed as disrespectful and the students were judged as lacking proper values and attitudes. The findings suggest that problem behaviors include those breaking explicit rules as well as those infringing implicit norms or expectations.

Apart from respect and obedience, order and discipline are essential elements of the Chinese classroom. Therefore, "out of seat", "playing", "clowning", "lateness to class", "eating / drinking", "copying homework", and "habitual failure in submitting assignments" were some common student problem behaviors perceived as disruptive to classroom order. The interviews revealed that on one hand, the teachers would like to have more control on the classroom order and discipline for not only easy management but also facilitating student learning. On the other hand, they would like students to have more self-control or self-discipline which is an important ingredient in learning. Moreover, "have not yet prepared textbook well" and "passive engagement in class" were some unique problem behaviors reported by the teachers in this study. It also reflected that some teachers expected students to get ready for the lesson and take an active role to learn throughout the lesson. If students were passive and not engaged, similar to daydreaming and not paying attention, teachers tended to regard students as irresponsible for their learning and even lacking learning motivation. Again, perception or labeling of problem behaviors results from the mismatches between the student behaviors and the social expectations. In short, the present findings indicated that student problem behaviors are not necessarily rule-breaking, but violating the implicit norms (e.g., the cultural values of respect, obedience, order and discipline) or expectations (e.g., students can control their behaviors and be responsible for their own and others' learning). These problem behaviors are inappropriate in the classroom settings, as well as upsetting the classroom teaching and learning, which mainly require intervention from teachers.

Although some unique findings were observed in this study, there were some limitations involved. First, as only twelve teachers from three secondary schools were involved, representativeness of the findings should be viewed with caution. Second, as only teachers were interviewed, the findings may reveal the assumptions and biases of the teachers due to their social role as "teacher". Therefore, it would be more comprehensive if the views of the students can be also included. Apart from looking at the categorization and descriptions of student problem behaviors, it would be more insightful if the antecedents of these behaviors or effective classroom management strategies could be explored in future. In particular, it would be exciting to see how curricular-based programs can help to reduce classroom misbehavior. One example that should be considered is the Project P.A.T.H.S. (Positive Adolescent Training through Holistic Social Programmes) in Hong Kong (21). There are findings showing that the program could promote holistic youth development and reduce adolescent substance abuse and delinquent behavior (22-24). It would be interesting to see whether the program can lessen classroom misbehavior in the long run.

Acknowledgments

The authorship of this paper is equally shared by both authors. The research and preparation for this paper was financially supported by the Faculty Research Fund, Faculty of Education, The University of Hong Kong. Special thanks to Ms. Evana Lam and Ms. Katrina Cheung for their assistance in data collection and analysis.

References

[1]   Reed DF, Kirkpatrick C. Disruptive students in the classroom: a review of the literature. Richmond, VA: Metropolitan Educational Research Consortium, 1998.

[2]   Johnson HL, Fullwood HL. Disturbing behaviors in the secondary classroom: how do general educators perceive problem behaviors? [J Instruct Psychol] 2006;33(1):20-39.

[3]   Lewis R. Teachers coping with the stress of classroom discipline. [Soc Psychol Educ] 1999;3(3):155-71.

[4]   Leung J, Ho C. Disruptive classroom behavior perceived by Hong Kong primary school teachers. [J Educ Res] 2001;16(2):223-37.

[5]   Shen J, Zhang N, Zhang C, Caldarella P, Richardson MJ, Shatzer RH. Chinese elementary school teachers' perceptions of students' classroom behaviour problems. [Educ Psychol] 2009;29(2):187-201.

[6]   Bryant AL, Schulenberg J, Bachman JG, O'Malley PM, Johnston LD. Understanding the links among school misbehavior, academic achievement, and cigarette use: a national panel study of adolescents. [Prev Sci] 2000;1(2):71-87.

[7]   Weerman FM, Harland P, van der Laan PH. Misbehavior at school and delinquency elsewhere: a complex relationship. [Crim Justice Rev] 2007;32(4):358-79.

[8]   Stewart SM, Bond MH, McBride-Chang C, Fielding R, Deeds O, Westrick J. Parent and adolescent contributors to teenage misconduct in Western and Asian high school students in Hong Kong. [Int J Behav Dev] 1998;22(4):847-69.

[9]   Ho IT. A comparison of Australian and Chinese teachers' attributions for student problem behaviors. [Educ Psychol] 2004;24(3):375-91.

[10]   Wheldall K, Merrett F. Which classroom behaviors do primary school teachers say they find most troublesome. [Educ Rev] 1988;40(1):13-27.

[11]   Houghton S, Wheldall K, Merrett F. Classroom behavior problems which secondary school teachers say they find most troublesome. [J Br Educ Res] 1988;14(3):297-312.

[12]   Ho C, Leung J. Disruptive classroom behaviors of secondary and primary school students. [J Educ Res] 2002;17(2):219-33.

[13]   Arbuckle C, Little E. Teachers' perceptions and management of disruptive classroom behaviour during the middle years (years five to nine). [Aust J Educ Dev Psychol] 2004;4:59-70.

[14]   Thompson B. Disruptive behaviours in barbadian classrooms: implications for universal secondary education in the Caribbean. [J Eastern Caribbean Stud] 2009;34(3):39-58.

[15]   Jessor R, Jessor SL. Problem behavior and psychosocial development: a longitudinal study of youth. New York: Academic Press, 1977.

[16]   Jessor R, Turbin MS, Costa FM, Dong Q, Zhang H, Wang C. Adolescent problem behavior in China and the United States: a cross-national study of psychosocial protective factors. [J Res Adolesc] 2003;13(3):329-60.

[17]   Vazsonyi AT, Chen P, Jenkins DD, Burcu E, Torrente G, Sheu CJ. Jessor's problem behavior theory: cross-national evidence from Hungary, the Netherlands, Slovenia, Spain, Switzerland, Taiwan, Turkey and the United States. [Dev Psychol] 2010;46(6):1779-91.

[18]   Ding M, Li Y, Li X, Kulm G. Chinese teachers' perceptions of students' classroom misbehaviour. [Educ Psychol] 2008;28(3):305-24.

[19]   Little E. Secondary school teachers' perceptions of students' problem behaviours. [Educ Psychol] 2005;25(4):369-77.

[20]   Miles MB, Huberman AM. Qualitative data analysis: a sourcebook of new methods. USA, CA: Sage, 1994.

[21]   Shek DTL, Sun RCF. Development, implementation and evaluation of a holistic positive youth development program: project P.A.T.H.S. in Hong Kong. [Int J Disabil Hum Dev] 2009;8(2):107-17.

[22]   Shek DTL, Sun RCF. Effectiveness of the Tier 1 Program of project P.A.T.H.S.: findings based on three years of program implementation. [ScientificWorldJournal] 2010;10:1509–19.

[23]   Shek DTL, Ng CSM, Tsui PF. Qualitative evaluation of the project P.A.T.H.S.: Findings based on focus groups. [Int J Disabil Hum Dev] 2010;9(4):307-13.

[24]   Shek DTL. Using students' weekly diaries to evaluate positive youth development programs: are findings based on multiple studies consistent? [Soc Indic Res] 2010;95(3):475-87.

Submitted: November 01, 2011. Revised: December 15, 2011. Accepted: December 20, 2011.

In: Child Health and Human Development Yearbook 2013   ISBN: 978-1-63117-939-6
Editor: Joav Merrick   © 2014 Nova Science Publishers, Inc.

Chapter 6

Family and personal adjustment of economically disadvantaged Chinese adolescents in Hong Kong

Daniel TL Shek, PhD, FHKPS, BBS, SBS, JP[*1,2,3,4],
and Pik Fong Tsui, MA[1]

[1]Department of Applied Social Sciences, The Hong Kong Polytechnic University, Hong Kong, PRC
[2]Centre for Innovative Programmes for Adolescents and Families, The Hong Kong Polytechnic University, Hong Kong, PRC
[3]Department of Social Work, East China Normal University, Shanghai, PRC
[4]Kiang Wu Nursing College of Macau, Macau, PRC

Abstract

This study attempted to examine the relationship between poverty and adolescent developmental outcomes in the family and personal domains in 3,328 Chinese secondary school students in Hong Kong. Developmental outcomes included positive youth development constructs, problem behaviors, perceived family interaction, and parental parenting. Results showed that adolescents experiencing poverty did not differ from non-poor adolescents in terms of risk behavior, and in most indicators of positive youth development. On the other hand, adolescents with economic disadvantage displayed lower levels of positive identity, family interaction, and perceived paternal parenting than did those without economic disadvantage.

Keywords: Chinese adolescents, positive youth development, economic disadvantage, family functioning, poverty

---

[*] Correspondence: Professor Daniel TL Shek, PhD, FHKPS, BBS, SBS, JP, Associate Vice President (Undergraudate Programme), Chair Professor of Applied Social Sciences, Department of Applied Social Sciences, Faculty of Health and Social Sciences, The Hong Kong Polytechnic University, Hunghom, Room HJ 407, Core H, Hong Kong, PRC. E-mail: daniel.shek@polyu.edu.hk.

Introduction

In 2009, Hong Kong was ranked the first in wealth disparity in the world (1). The poorest 10% of people shared 2% of the territory's wealth while the richest 10% of the people possessed 34% of Hong Kong's wealth. The wealth gap between the poor and the rich is becoming severe. In the fourth quarter of 2009, the household median income in Hong Kong was HK$17,500 (roughly equivalent to US$2,244). Hong Kong has no "official" poverty line but there is a so-called "safety net" for the poor. The Comprehensive Social Security Assistance (CSSA) is a welfare scheme of the Hong Kong Government for people whose income is insufficient to satisfy their basic needs. According to the figures reported by the Hong Kong Census and Statistics Department, there were a total of 130,900 children and adolescents aged 6-14 living in households with income below CSSA in 2009 (2).

What is the effect of poverty? In the multi-dimensional perspective proposed by the United Nations (3), what matter most of poverty is "a focus on the opportunities - such as a set of endowments, access to markets, etc. - that are available to people. If an individual does not possess sufficient endowments or capabilities, such as a basic education, or does not have the opportunity to acquire them, he or she will have a limited ability to escape poverty" (p. 9). Opportunities are especially important to adolescents who are undergoing intensive development in different physical and psychosocial domains. A review of the literature reveals that a variety of mechanisms linked socioeconomic status to child development. In particular, poverty adversely affects children's cognitive, social, psychological, academic, behavioral, and emotional development (4-6). For example, Leung and Shek (7, 8) argued that economic disadvantage impaired family processes which in turns would negatively impact adolescent development.

Various studies have shown that adolescent mental health problems were associated with poverty. Eamon (9) studied a sample of 898 young adolescents and found that poverty predicted young adolescent depressive symptoms. Similar results were found in the longitudinal study conducted by Najman et al. (10). The research examined 2,609 adolescents aged 14-21 who provided self-report data on their level of anxiety and depression. Results indicated that family poverty led to higher rates of adolescent anxiety and depression. After examining 1,704 low-income adolescents, Hammack et al. (11) reported that poor adolescents were more likely to exhibit symptoms of depression, anxiety, hostility, and aggression.

Identity formation is a very important stage of adolescents. After reviewing the literature on identity and poverty, Phillips and Pittman (12) argued that poverty had a negative impact on identity processes of adolescents and pointed out that "stress, social stigma or marginalization, and the nature of the opportunity structures faced by many poor adolescents conspire to create a context that is not conducive to exploring identity issues" (p. 123). The study conducted by Crocker and Major (13) indicated that stigmatized groups generally had lower global self-esteem than did the non-stigma groups. Other studies also showed that poverty induced stigma on people (14). Based on such research findings, it can be conjectured that social stigma associated with poverty makes adolescents feeling inferior to their economically advantaged counterparts.

Limited opportunities brought forth by poverty also impair the future orientation of poor adolescents. McLoyd et al. (5) reviewed studies concerning the future orientations of adolescents and concluded that socioeconomic status and parenting style were important factors predicting future orientation. Poor adolescents were more aware of the limited life chances and they were reported to have lower occupational aspirations and expectations as well as future orientations compared to economically advantaged adolescents.

Apart from poorer mental health, adolescents in poverty were also found to have higher propensity to delinquent behaviors (15, 16), such as substance abuse, sex-related problems, school failure, and school dropout. Using structural equation models, Brook et al. (17) found that family poverty was associated with poor parent-child relationship which finally contributed to the risky sexual behavior in South African adolescents. Moreover, poor neighborhoods and feelings of hopelessness associated with economic disadvantage also increased the tendency of delinquent behaviors among poor adolescents (18). Research suggests that poverty has a significant direct effect on adolescent antisocial behavior, and that parent-child conflict, neighborhood problems, and deviant peer pressure are significant mediators (19).

According to the family stress model, it is proposed that "economic hardship adversely affects children's psychological adjustment indirectly through its impact on the parent's behavior toward the child" (5, p. 451). Research studies showed that dimensions of family functioning were correlated with adolescent psychological well-being (20, 21). Hammack et al.'s (11) study found that family stress was a mediator between poverty and depressed mood in low-income African-American adolescents. In the Chinese context, several studies examined the relationship between poverty and adolescent development outcomes. Shek (22) studied 3,017 Hong Kong secondary school students with and without economic disadvantage and found that perceived paternal behavioral control and father-child relational qualities were more negative in poor students than in non-poor students. Besides, students experiencing economic disadvantage also had poorer psychological well-being than their wealthier counterparts. In another study, Shek (23) investigated perceived family functioning and family adjustment in Chinese adolescents with economic disadvantage. Results showed that perceived family functioning was related to adolescent psychological well-being (existential well-being, life satisfaction, self-esteem, and general psychiatric morbidity) and problem behavior (substance abuse and delinquency). However, contrary to existing literature, Kwan (24) found that adolescents experiencing economic disadvantage in Hong Kong had better mental health than did economic advantaged respondents. Besides, he did not find any relationship between economic well-being and life satisfaction.

Although poverty is a hot issue in the territory in the past decade which can be reflected from the establishment of the Commission on Poverty and the Community Care Fund, Hong Kong lacks comprehensive studies on the influence of poverty on adolescent development. Focusing on adolescents' potentials instead of their deficits is a current trend in youth studies, and researchers have put efforts in evaluating the effects of positive youth development programs toward adolescent development (25). As indicated by McLoyd et al. (5), "despite strong scholarly interest in understanding positive youth development and finding ways to promote it, empirical work on these issues specifically in relation to youth who are poor or from low SES (socioeconomic status) backgrounds is very sparse" (p. 477). Against this background, this study tried to examine if adolescents with and without economic disadvantage differ in their different adjustment domains, including personal domain (such as different positive youth development constructs including bonding, resilience, social competence, emotional competence, cognitive competence, behavioral competence, moral competence, self-determination, self-efficacy, beliefs in the future, clear and positive identity, prosocial norms, prosocial involvements, and spirituality) and family process (including family functioning and parental control). The findings reported in this paper were derived from the first wave of a six-year longitudinal study that was designed to investigate different developmental domains of adolescents in Hong Kong. Because a large volume of data has been generated from this study, the primary focus of this paper is placed on the difference between adolescents with and without economic disadvantage on personal adjustment (positive youth development constructs and problematic behavior) and family processes (family functioning and parental control).

Methods

The present study is part of a large longitudinal study aiming at tracking the developmental trends based on different positive youth development indicators and risk behaviors among Hong Kong adolescents over time. A total of 28 secondary schools in Hong Kong were randomly selected to participate in the study. In this paper, data pertinent to the relationship between economic situation of the respondents and adolescent development in the first wave of a six-year longitudinal are presented.

Participants and procedures

All Secondary 1 students in the selected schools were invited to complete a questionnaire anonymously. A total of 3,328 students recruited from 28 secondary schools responded to the questionnaire (mean age = 12.59 years, SD = .74). These included 1,719 boys, 1,572 girls, and 37 students did not indicate their gender. Most students were born in Hong Kong (78.1%); 19.9% of the participants came from Mainland China, and 2.0% were from other places. The background demographic information of the participants is summarized in Table 1. Students were asked about their family financial conditions. As stated before, as Hong Kong has no poverty line, respondents whose families were receiving Comprehensive Social Security Assistance (CSSA) were categorized as the poor group (N = 225) while those who did not receive CSSA formed the non-poor group (N = 2,606). For the remaining 465 respondents, they did not indicate whether they were receiving CSSA and thus their data were excluded from the present study.

Data collection was conducted by a trained research assistant in classroom settings with standardized instructions. At each measurement occasion, the purposes of the study were introduced and confidentiality of the data collected was repeatedly ensured for all participants. School, parent, and student consent had been obtained prior to data collection. Participants responded to the questionnaires in a self-administered format with sufficient time given. The questionnaire took roughly 30 to 45 minutes to complete. The research assistant was present throughout the administration process to answer possible questions from the participants.

Table 1. Descriptive statistics about participants

Categorical variables	n	%	
Gender			
Male	1,719	52.2%	
Female	1,572	47.8%	
Place of birth			
Hong Kong	2,590	78.3%	
Mainland China	655	19.8%	
Others	64	1.9%	
Family economic status			
Receiving CSSA	225	6.8%	
Not receiving CSSA	2,606	78.3%	
Others	465	13.9%	
Receiving School Textbook Assistance Scheme			
Full grant	368	11.61%	
Half grant	771	24.32%	
Not receiving any grant	2,031	64.07%	
Continuous variables	Mean	SD	Range
Age	12.59	0.74	10-18
CBC	4.45	0.75	1-6
PA	4.50	0.89	1-6
GPYDQ	4.50	0.71	1-6
PIT	4.24	0.96	1-6

Notes:

CSSA = Comprehensive Social Security Assistance.

CBC = cognitive behavioral competence; PA = prosocial attributes; GPYDQ = general positive youth development; PIT = positive identity.

Instruments

In the school year of 2009-2010, the participants responded to a comprehensive youth development questionnaire including both existing instruments and scales developed by the first author. Participants were invited to respond to a composite questionnaire asking them about different aspects of their development. The following only highlights those measures related to the present study.

Participants' demographic information

Questions on gender, age, place of birth, number of family members, parents' marital status, parents' educational level, and family financial situation were asked.

Chinese Positive Youth Development Scale (CPYDS)

The CPYDS is an instrument assessing different positive youth development constructs. It consists of 15 subscales which include bonding (BO), resilience (RE), social competence (SC), recognition for positive behavior (PB), emotional competence (EC), cognitive competence (CC), behavioral competence (BC), moral competence (MC), self-determination (SD), self-efficacy (SE), clear and positive identity (SI), beliefs in the future (BF), prosocial involvement (PI), prosocial norms (PN), and spirituality (SP). Each construct has three items in the questionnaire. Except spirituality which is a measure of a 7-point scale, all other constructs assess the respondents in a 6-point Likert scale (1 = strongly disagree to 6 = strongly agree). The higher scores in the sale denote a higher level of psychosocial competence.

Details of the items can be seen in Shek et al. (26). Using multi-group confirmatory factor analyses, Shek and Ma (27) showed that the 15 basic dimensions of the CPYDS could be subsumed under four higher-order factors, including cognitive-behavioral competencies (CBC), prosocial attributes (PA), positive identity (PIT), and general positive youth development qualities (GPYDQ). Evidence of factorial invariance in terms of configuration, first-order factor loadings, second-order factor loadings, intercepts of measured variable, and intercepts of first-order latent factor, was found. In short, existing research findings showed that the CPYDS is a valid and reliable instrument.

These four composite indicators were used to assess the participants' positive youth development in the present study. The mean scores of the four indicators ranged from 1 to 6 with higher scores representing high competence in the constructs. Descriptive statistics about all variables under study are listed in Table 1.

Delinquent behavior

The respondents were asked if they had performed the following problem behaviors and the frequency they performed such behaviors in the past one year on a six-point Likert scale (0 = never; 1 = one to two times; 2 = three to four times; 3 = five to six times; 4 = seven to eight times; 5 = nine to ten times; 6 = more than ten times): stealing, cheating, truancy, running away from home, damaging others' properties, assault, having sexual intercourse with others, gang fighting, speaking foul language, staying outside the home overnight without parental consent, strong arming others, and trespasses (28).

Substance use

Eight items were used to assess the participants' frequency of using different types of substance in the past half a year, including alcohol, tobacco, ketamine, cannabis, cough mixture, organic solvent, pills (including ecstasy and methaqualone), and heroin. Participants rated the occurrence of these behaviors on a six-point Likert scale (0 = never; 1 = 1-2 times; 2 = 3-5 times; 3 = more than 5 times; 4 = several times a month; 5 = several times a week; 6 = everyday).

Family functioning

Family functioning domains including communication, conflict, and harmony of respondents were assessed by 9 items. This 9-item measure is a simplified version of the Chinese Family Assessment Instrument developed by the first author (29). In the present study, three subscales, including mutuality (mutual support, love, and concern among family members), communication (frequency and nature of interaction among family members), conflicts and harmony (presence of conflicts and harmonious behavior in the family) were examined. A higher total score on the subscales indicated a higher level of positive family functioning.

Paternal parenting

There were 17 items assessing paternal parenting, including paternal knowledge ("My father clearly knows my situation in my school"; "My father clearly understands who my friends are"), paternal expectation ("My father requires me to have good behavior in school"; "My father has explicit requirements about how I make friends with others"), paternal monitoring ("My father actively understands my situation in school"; "My father takes initiatives to understand who my friends are"; "My father actively understands what I do after school"), satisfaction with paternal control ("I feel that how my father disciplines me is reasonable"; "I am glad to fulfill my father's expectations about me"; "I believe how my father disciplines me is beneficial to me"), paternal psychological control ("My father always wants to change my thoughts"; "My father thinks that his thoughts are more important than my thoughts"; "My father wants to control everything in my life"; "My father always wants to change me to fit his standard"), and father-child relationship ("I'm very satisfied my relationship with my father"; "I actively share the things that happen in my life with my father"; "I actively share my feelings with my father"). Participants rated the paternal parenting in a 4-point Likert scale (1 = totally disagree; 2 = disagree; 3 = agree; 4 = totally agree). Reliability analysis of the 17 items showed that this scale was reliable (alpha = .88).

Maternal parenting

Identical items for paternal parenting were used to assess the maternal parenting, including maternal knowledge (2 items), maternal expectation (2 items), maternal monitoring (3 items), satisfaction with maternal control (3 items), maternal psychological control (4 items), and mother-child relationship (3 items). Participants rated their relationship with their mothers in a 4-point Likert-scale (1 = totally disagree; 2 = disagree; 3 = agree; 4 = totally agree). Reliability analysis of the 17 items showed that this scale was reliable (alpha = .87).

Results

An examination of the characteristics of the poverty and non-poverty groups showed that there was no difference between the two groups in terms of gender ratio. Yet, there were significant differences between the two groups in terms of age (M = 12.77, SD = .84 for the poor group and M = 12.55, SD = .70 for the non-poor group; t = 4.47, $p < .0001$). Because of the possible confounding effect of age, multivariate analysis of covariance was performed to examine the differences between the poor group and non-poor group on the developmental variables to control for the effect of age.

Tables 2 and 3 present the occurrence of problem behavior and substance abuse behavior in the poor and non-poor groups. For the differences between the two groups on different problem behaviors, a multivariate analysis of variance (MANCOVA) with poor and non-poor groups as the main factor and age as the covariate was performed. No significant difference was found between the two groups in terms of problem behavior and substance abuse behavior. Regarding positive youth development qualities, a MANCOVA was carried out with the poor group versus the non-poor group as the independent variable, the scores of CPYDS subscales (CBC, PA, PIT, GPYDQ) as dependent variables, and age as the covariate (see Table 4). There was a significant difference between poor and non-poor groups on the combined dependent variables: $F(4,2306) = 4.3$, $p < .01$, Wilks' Lambda = .99, partial eta squared = .007. When the dependent variables were examined separately with Bonferroni adjustment ($p = .013$), the only difference found was in the score of PIT (positive identity): $F(1,2310) = 13.18$, $p < .001$, partial eta squared = .006. PIT is the mean score of belief in the future (BF) and clear and positive identity (SI). The mean scores indicated that the poor group reported a lower level of PIT (M = 4.03, SD = 1.09) than did the non-poor group (M = 4.30, SD = .93).

Table 2. Past year exposure to substances

	Never (%)		Attempted (%)	
	Poor Group	Non-poor Group	Poor Group	Non-poor Group
Smoking	90.1	95.3	9.9	4.7
Drinking	70.7	71.3	29.3	28.7
Use Ketamine	99.6	99.8	0.4	0.2
Use Cannabis	99.6	99.8	0.4	0.2
Use cough medicine without coughing	99.6	99.3	0.4	0.7
Use organic solvent	99.1	97.7	0.9	2.3
Use pills (e.g., Ecstasy)	100.0	85.0	0	15.0
Use or inject Heroin	100.0	96.1	0	3.9

Table 3. Delinquent behaviors between poor and non-poor groups in the past year

	Never (%)		Attempted (%) (1-4 times)		Attempted (%) (5 times or above)	
	Poor Group	Non-poor Group	Poor Group	Non-poor Group	Poor Group	Non-poor Group
Stealing	86.5	90.3	12.7	9.0	1.0	0.7
Cheating	38.1	38.4	43.1	42.2	18.8	19.4
Truancy	95.9	97.2	3.2	2.1	0.9	0.7
Running away from home	94.1	96.7	5.4	3.0	0.5	0.3
Damaging others' properties	88.8	86.1	10.3	12.1	0.9	1.8
Assault	90.5	88.6	7.2	9.3	2.3	2.1
Having sexual intercourse with others	98.2	99.6	1.8	0.3	0	0.1
Group fighting	96.3	97.1	2.3	2.5	1.4	0.4
Speaking foul language	24.9	30.3	37.1	38.0	38.0	31.7
Staying outside overnight without parents' consent	97.2	97.2	2.3	2.1	0.5	0.7
Strong arming others	79.1	85.0	16.8	11.3	4.1	3.7
Trespasses	96.8	96.1	3.2	3.2	0	0.7

Table 4. Differences between poor group and non-poor group in positive youth development constructs

Measures	Poor Group		Non-poor Group		F value
	Mean	SD	Mean	SD	
CBC	4.37	0.83	4.45	0.74	2.50
PA	4.45	0.93	4.53	0.87	1.70
GPYDQ	4.51	0.75	4.59	0.71	2.36
PIT	4.04	1.08	4.27	0.94	11.82*
Problem behavior	0.41	0.42	0.39	0.46	0.03
Substance abuse	0.08	0.19	0.09	0.21	0.44
Family interaction	3.48	0.83	3.78	0.81	25.28*
Paternal parenting	2.29	0.72	2.63	0.52	64.35*
Maternal parenting	2.86	0.58	2.93	0.50	4.32

Note. An overall alpha level based on Bonferroni adjustment was carried out to adjust for inflated Type 1 error.
*$p < .01$.

Regarding differences between the two groups on family processes (family interaction, paternal parenting, and maternal parenting), a MANCOVA was performed with poor group versus non-poor group as the independent variable, the family interaction, paternal parenting, and maternal parenting as the dependent variables, and age as the covariate (see Table 4). Results showed that the effects for the three dependent variables together were significantly related to groups, $F(3,2172) = 20.65$, $p < .001$. When the results for the dependent variables were examined separately, significant group effects were found in both family interaction and paternal parenting. The mean scores indicated that the poor group had lower scores on family interaction (M = 3.56, SD = .84) than did the non-poor group (M = 3.78, SD = .84). The poor group also had worse perceived paternal parenting (M = 2.28, SD = .73) than did the Non-poor group (M = 2.63, SD = .52). The effect size of the differences ranged from low to moderate levels.

Discussion

The present study attempted to find out the relationship between poverty and adolescent developmental outcomes, parental control, and family communication. Compared to adolescents experiencing economic disadvantage, adolescents not experiencing economic disadvantage had higher scores in PIT (i.e., positive identity). This finding is consistent with the Western literature which suggests that adolescents in poverty are more likely to be pessimistic about their future lives (30). It can be argued that poverty leads adolescents fall into a spiraling circle regarding their hope for the future. As pointed out by Eamon (9), "lowered aspirations among poor youth may result from realistic appraisals of available opportunities and experiential recognition of the limited lives of the adults around them, but at the same time lowered aspirations may result in self-imposed limitations that further reduce opportunities. In addition to having low aspirations, poor youth also tend to have low occupational and educational expectations" (p. 117).

In line with other studies (13, 14) that poverty was found to be directly linked to social stigma, the findings in the present study also showed a similar phenomenon that adolescents in hardship had poorer identity. As existing studies mainly used negative indicators such as internalizing and externalizing behavior in understanding the impact of poverty on adolescent development, it is necessary to examine the influence of economic disadvantage on other aspects of positive youth development in future studies. In this study, no significant difference was found between the poor group and non-poor group in terms of problem behaviors. The result is echoing the findings from other studies using the same subjects (31-33) stating that socioeconomic status is not a predictor for problematic behaviors, consumption of pornography materials, and internet addiction.

Having reviewed the conceptual and methodological issues in studying the relationship between adolescent development and economic disadvantage, Leung and Shek (7, 8) proposed a number of future research directions which include the identification of protective factors among poor adolescents and the incorporation of the cultural dimension to capture the ideological ingredients. Moreover, many researchers try to find out the mediating factors between poverty and adolescent developmental outcomes (10, 15, 18). Thus, it would be interesting if we can test the mediating factors of adolescent developmental outcomes for this group of Chinese adolescents as well as to find out those protective factors of poor adolescents in Hong Kong in future studies. Besides, it is important to look at the moderating effect of poverty on adolescent developmental outcomes. Furthermore, some studies focus on the prolonged effect of poverty on children and adolescents (34). As the present study is the first wave of a six-year longitudinal study, it would be more promising if data analyzed can be done for different waves to evaluate the prolonged effect of poverty on Chinese adolescents over time.

Regarding the family factors, there were significant differences between the two groups in family interaction and paternal parenting and these results were in line with Shek's studies (22, 23). Fathers in the poor group were found to be perceived as poorer in parenting. It might be because fathers were viewed as the bread winners in traditional Chinese families and depending on CSSA for a living may cause stress between fathers and children. Moreover, as stated by Shek (22), poor fathers "might be blamed for causing poverty in the family, their children might perceive their parental control attributes and parent-child relational qualities negatively." (p. 185).

There are several strengths of this study. First, a large sample was involved which was randomly selected from schools in Hong Kong. Second, validated instruments were used to assess individual and family processes. Third, a wide range of personal and family adjustment measures were included in the study. Despite these strengths, several limitations of the study should be noted. First, caution must be made about the operational definition and classification of "poor" adolescents in the present study. As stated before, we simply categorized those respondents who had received CSSA as the poor group but this may not be the best classification. According to the statistics of the Hong Kong Council of Social Services (35), 25.8% of children aged 6 to 14 could be regarded as living in poverty when using the household income as an indicator. Nevertheless, the poor group in the present study only accounted for 7.9% of the total respondents. As suggested by Wadsworth et al. (16), "there is growing consensus that SES (Socio-economic status) is best computed from parental education, occupational status, and family income." (p. 160). We may get a clearer picture about the performance in different positive youth development constructs of adolescents in hardship if we can take into account other criteria for defining poverty. The authors have attempted to calculate the family household income in this study. However, due to too much missing data (because students may not be clear about their family financial situation), we could only use CSSA as a criterion for defining the poor group. Nevertheless, it is noteworthy that eligibility for CSSA is the "official" definition of poverty in Hong Kong. Second, only data reported by the students were collected in this study. It would be more comprehensive if we can get parents' views when analyzing parental control and family interaction. Third, as there is no conclusive finding on gender differences in the impact of poverty on adolescent development, gender was not included as a covariate in the present study. As such, this point should be taken into account in future studies.

Despite the above limitations, the present study gives us some ideas about the performance of poor adolescents in different positive youth development constructs. There is a need to find out some means to alleviate the adverse effects of poverty on adolescents.

School-based positive youth development programs such as the Project P.A.T.H.S. in Hong Kong may be a way out because there is evidence showing that universal positive youth development programs can help enhance different psychosocial competencies of participants (36-38) and at the same time not imposing any stigmatization effect on them. As stated before, research investigating the relationship between positive youth development and poverty is rare and the present study can be viewed as an addition to the existing literature, especially in the Chinese context.

Acknowledgments

The preparation for this paper and the Project P.A.T.H.S. were financially supported by The Hong Kong Jockey Club Charities Trust. This paper was originally published in The Scientific World Journal, Volume 2012, Article ID 142689, 8 pages doi:10.1100/2012/142689

References

[1]   Einhom B. Countries with the biggest rich and poor. Business Week October 16, 2009. Accessed 2011 Jun 30. URL: http://images.businessweek.com/ss/09/10/1013_biggest_rich_poor_ gap_globally /index.htm

[2]   Census and Statistics Department, Hong Kong. Indicators of Poverty – An update for 2009. Accessed 2011 Jun 30. URL: http://www.lwb.gov.hk/eng/other_info/2009 Poverty Indicators_eng.pdf

[3]   United Nations. Rethinking poverty. Report on the world situation 2010. New York: United Nations. Accessed 2011 Jul 8. URL: http://www.un.org/esa/socdev/rwss/docs/2010/fullreport.pdf

[4]   Bradley RH, Corwyn RF. Socioeconomic status and child development. Annu Rev Psychol 2002;53:371-99.

[5]   McLoyd VC, Kaplan R, Purtell KM, Bagley E, Hardaway CR, Smalls C. Poverty and socioeconomic disadvantage in adolescence. In: Lerner RM, Steingberg L, editors. Handbook of adolescent psychology. Vol. 2: Contextual influences on adolescent development, 3rd ed. Hoboken, NJ: John Wiley, 2009:444-91.

[6]   Dashiff C, DiMicco W, Myers B, Sheppard K. Poverty and adolescent mental health. J Child Adolesc Psychiatr Nurs 2009;22(1):23-32.

[7]   Leung JTY, Shek DTL. Poverty and adolescent developmental outcomes: a critical review. Int J Adolesc Med Health 2011;23(2):109-14.

[8]   Leung JTY, Shek DTL. Quantitative and qualitative approaches in the study of poverty and adolescent development: separation or integration? Int J Adolesc Med Health 2011;23(2):115-21.

[9]   Eamon MK. Influences and mediators of the effect of poverty on young adolescent depressive symptoms. J Youth Adolesc 2002;31(3):231-42.

[10]   Najman JM, Hayatbakhsh MR, Clavarino A, Bor W, O'Callaghan MJ, Williams GM. Family poverty over the early life course and recurrent adolescent and young adult anxiety and depression: a longitudinal study. Am J Public Health 2010;100(9):1719-23.

[11]   Hammack PL, Robinson WL, Crawford I, Li ST. Poverty and depressed mood among urban African-American adolescents: a family stress perspective. J Child Fam Stud 2004;13(3):309-23.

[12]   Phillips TM, Pittman JF. Identity processes in poor adolescents: exploring the linkages between economic disadvantage and the primary task of adolescence. Identity 2003;3(2):115-29.

[13]   Crocker J, Major B. Social stigma and self-esteem: the self-protective properties of stigma. Psychol Rev 1989;96(4):608-30.

[14]   Mickelson KD, Williams SL. Perceived stigma of poverty and depression: examination of interpersonal and intrapersonal mediators. J Soc Clin Psychol 2008;27(9):903-30.

[15]   Smith DE, Ashiabi GS. Poverty and child outcomes: a focus on Jamaican youth. Adolescence 2007;42(168):837-58.

[16]   Wadsworth ME, Raviv T, Reinhard C, Wolff B, Santiago CD, Einhorn L. An indirect effects model of the association between poverty and child functioning: the role of children's poverty-related stress. J Loss Trauma 2008;13(2-3):156-85.

[17]   Brook DW, Morojele NK, Zhang C, Brook JS. South African adolescents: pathways to risky sexual behavior. AIDS Educ Prev 2006;18(3):259-72.

[18]   Oberwittler D. The effects of neighbourhood poverty on adolescent problem behaviours: a multi-level analysis differentiated by gender and ethnicity. Housing Stud 2007;22(5):781-803.

[19]   Eamon MK. Poverty, parenting, peer, and neighborhood influences on young adolescent antisocial behavior. J Soc Serv Res 2002;28(1):1-23.

[20]   Wadsworth ME, Berger LE. Adolescents coping with poverty-related family stress: prospective predictors of copying and psychological symptoms. J Youth Adolesc 2006;35(1):57-70.

[21]   Elder Jr GH, Nguyen TV, Caspi A. Linking family hardship to children's lives. Child Dev 1985;56(2):361-75.

[22]   Shek DTL. Perceived parent control processes, parent-child relational qualities, and psychological well-being in Chinese adolescents with and without economic disadvantage. J Genetic Psychol 2005;166(2):171-88.

[23]   Shek DTL. A longitudinal study of perceived family functioning and adolescent adjustment in Chinese adolescents with economic disadvantage. J Fam Issues 2005;26(4):518-43.

[24]   Kwan YK. Life satisfaction and self-assessed health among adolescents in Hong Kong. J Happiness Stud 2010;11(3):383-93.

[25]   Catalano RF, Berglund ML, Ryan JAM, Lonczak HS, Hawkins JD. Positive youth development in the United States: research findings on evaluations of positive youth development programs. Ann Am Acad Pol Soc Sci 2004;591:98-124.

[26]   Shek DTL, Siu AMH, Lee TY. The Chinese Positive Youth Development Scale: a validation study. Res Soc Work Pract 2007;12(3):380-91.

[27]   Shek DTL, Ma CMS. Dimensionality of the Chinese Positive Youth Development Scale: confirmatory factor analyses. Soc Indic Res 2010;98(1):41-59.

[28]   Shek DTL. Paternal and maternal influences on the psychological well-being, substance abuse, and delinquency of Chinese adolescents experiencing economic disadvantage. J Clin Psychol 2005;61(3):219-34.

[29]   Shek DTL. Assessment of family functioning in Chinese adolescents: the Chinese family assessment instrument. In: Singh NN, Ollendick TH, Singh AN, editors. International perspectives on child and adolescent mental health. Netherlands: Elsevier, 2002:297-316.

[30]   Bolland JM. Hopelessness and risk behavior among adolescents living in high-poverty inner-city neighourhoods. J Adolesc 2003;26(2):145-58.

[31]   Shek DTL, Ma CMS. Consumption of pornographic materials among early adolescents in Hong Kong: profiles and psychosocial correlates. Int J Disabil Hum Dev 2012;11(2):143-50.

[32]   Shek DTL, Ma CMS, Tang CYP. Delinquency and problem behavior intention among early adolescents in Hong Kong: profiles and psychosocial correlates. Int J Disabil Hum Dev 2012;11(2):151-8.

[33]   Shek DTL, Yu L. Internet addiction in Hong Kong adolescents: profiles and psychosocial correlates. Int J Disabil Hum Dev 2012;11(2):133-42.

[34]   Duncan G, Brooks-Gunn J. Consequences of growing up poor. New York: Russell Sage Foundation, 1997.

[35]   Hong Kong Council of Social Service. Number of poverty by age. Accessed 2011 Aug 31. URL: http://www.poverty.org.hk/sites/default/files/shares/files/publications/No_of_Poverty_pop_by_age95-10_1stH.pdf

[36]   Jessor R. Successful adolescent development among youth in high-risk settings. Am Psychol 1993;48(2):117-26.

[37]   Shek DTL, Ma CMS. Impact of the Project P.A.T.H.S. in the junior secondary school years: individual growth curve analyses. ScientificWorldJournal 2011;11:253-66.

[38]   Shek DTL, Yu L. Prevention of adolescent problem behavior: longitudinal impact of the Project P.A.T.H.S. in Hong Kong. ScientificWorldJournal 2011;11:546-67.

Submitted: November 03, 2011. Revised: December 17, 2011. Accepted: December 21, 2011.

In: Child Health and Human Development Yearbook 2013   ISBN: 978-1-63117-939-6
Editor: Joav Merrick   © 2014 Nova Science Publishers, Inc.

Chapter 7

Post-lecture evaluation of a positive youth development subject for university students in Hong Kong

***Daniel TL Shek, PhD, FHKPS, BBS, SBS, JP**[*,1,2,3,4]*

[1]Department of Applied Social Sciences, The Hong Kong Polytechnic University,
Hong Kong, PRC
[2]Centre for Innovative Programmes for Adolescents and Families,
The Hong Kong Polytechnic University, Hong Kong, PRC
[3]Department of Social Work, East China Normal University, Shanghai, PRC
[4]Kiang Wu Nursing College of Macau, Macau, PRC

Abstract

The purpose of this study was to examine the post-lecture evaluation by the students taking a course ("Tomorrow's Leaders") that attempted to promote their leadership qualities and intrapersonal competencies at The Hong Kong Polytechnic University in Hong Kong. Except for the last lecture, students were invited to respond to a 12-item post-lecture questionnaire after each lecture. Results showed that the students had positive perceptions of the subject, class and teacher attributes, and they had positive global evaluation of the teacher and the subject. The post-lecture evaluation questionnaire was found to possess good psychometric properties. Multiple regression analyses showed that subject, class and teacher attributes were predictive of global evaluation of the lecture and the teacher. In conjunction with other evaluation findings, the present findings strongly suggest that students had positive perceptions of the attributes and benefits of "Tomorrow's Leaders".

* Correspondence: Professor Daniel TL Shek, PhD, FHKPS, BBS, SBS, JP, Associate Vice President (Undergraduate Programme), Chair Professor of Applied Social Sciences, Department of Applied Social Sciences, Faculty of Health and Social Sciences, The Hong Kong Polytechnic University, Room HJ407, Core H, Hunghom, Hong Kong, PRC. E-mail: daniel.shek@polyu.edu.hk.

Keywords: Positive youth development, university students, subjective outcome evaluation, post-lecture evaluation

Introduction

Client satisfaction or subjective outcome evaluation is a widely used evaluation method in human services. The common form of subjective outcome evaluation is to distribute a client feedback questionnaire to the clients which may have both quantitative rating items and open-ended questions. In the social welfare context, social workers normally invite the program participants to complete a client satisfaction questionnaire at the end of the program. For example, in the Project P.A.T.H.S. in Hong Kong, subjective outcome evaluation is used to capture the views of the program participants as well as the program implementers. For the program participants, a subjective outcome evaluation form (Form A) is used to gauge their perceptions of the program, instructors and effectiveness of the program. On the other hand, subjective outcome evaluation forms (Form B) are used to assess the perceptions of the program implementers on the program, implementers and effectiveness of the program. Previous research findings showed the value of subjective outcome evaluation strategies in assessing program effectiveness (1-4).

Subjective outcome evaluation is also commonly used in the education sector. For example, it is a common practice for universities throughout the world to evaluate the feedback of students using subjective outcome evaluation. A review of the literature shows that many measures have been developed and studies have been conducted to examine their psychometric properties in the Western world. For example, Cohen proposed that six dimensions of teaching (including skills, rapport, structure, difficulty, interaction and feedback) could be used to assess student feedback (5). With reference to the Students' Evaluations of Educational Quality (SEEQ), Marsh and Roche (6) identified nine dimensions of student feedback, including learning, teacher enthusiasm, organization, group interaction, individual rapport, breadth of coverage, examinations, assignments/readings and workload. The SEEQ was translated into Chinese and there was support for the validity of the assessment tool (7, 8). Kim, Damewood and Hodge (9) identified eight broad dimensions underlying course evaluation, including teacher character traits, management of the class, assignments, course design, testing, grading, feedback and course materials. Kember, Leung and Kwan (10) used the Student Feedback Questionnaire to evaluate teaching which included six dimensions. These dimensions were learning outcomes, interaction, individual help, organization and presentation, motivation and feedback.

Several observations can be highlighted from the literature review on course evaluation based on subjective outcome evaluation method. First, while different conceptual frameworks were adopted in different studies, there were similarities across studies. For example, many researchers proposed qualities of the teacher, objectives, teaching techniques and teacher-student relationship as the basic dimensions of evaluation in their frameworks. Second, exploratory and confirmatory factor analyses were commonly used to examine the underlying dimensions of different course evaluation instruments. Nevertheless, while factor analytic might yield findings that can support elegant statistical models, interpretation of the findings is not always simple. For example, with reference to the framework proposed by Kember and

Leung (11), although the proposed model provided an adequate fit to the data, items in the "Challenging Beliefs" and "Motivation" domains are not conceptually pure. Third, in contrast to the vast number of related studies in the West, there are very few studies on Chinese course evaluation questionnaires in different Chinese contexts. Fourth, different course evaluation questionnaires are used by different tertiary institutions in Hong Kong with different dimensions covered in the evaluation questionnaires. In fact, different institutions differ widely on the design of course evaluation questionnaires. Besides, psychometric properties of the instruments are rarely reported. Published scientific findings on the reliability, validity and norms of the course evaluation assessment tools are almost non-existent. As such, there is a need to document the psychometric properties of course evaluation tools. Finally, although there are questionnaires on course evaluation, effort to evaluate individual lecture (i.e., post-lecture evaluation) is comparatively weak.

While post-course evaluation can give a global picture about the quality of the course and teacher performance, it is argued that evaluation of individual lectures (i.e., post-lecture evaluation) is equally important for several reasons. First, post-lecture evaluation can give detailed information about the relevance of the lecture content and quality of lecture delivery. Such specific information is helpful for lecture improvement. Second, as post-course evaluation takes place at the end of a course, its timeliness in feedback is not quick. In contrast, post-lecture evaluation can yield immediate information that can be used by the instructor to plan for the next lecture. Finally, it can be argued that post-course evaluation may have greater bias because students respond according to their general impression only. Besides, memory decay and re-construction may affect the recalled information. On the other hand, post-lecture evaluation enjoys the advantage of immediacy where students can evaluate the lecture based on the information freshly acquired. Against this background, the present study attempted to carry out post-lecture evaluation of a course on positive youth development for university students in Hong Kong.

Under the new 4-year curriculum in The Hong Kong Polytechnic University, there are 30 credits in the General University Requirements (GUR) as follows: a) Language and Communication (9 credits); b) Freshman Seminar (3 credits); c) Leadership and Intrapersonal Development (3 credits); d) Service Learning (3 credits); e) Broadening Subjects chosen from 4 clusters (12 credits); and f) Healthy Life Style (Non-Credit Bearing). With specific reference to the requirement in Leadership and Intra-personal Development, a subject entitled "Tomorrow's Leaders" was developed by the author based on the positive youth development framework. The positive youth development constructs covered in the course included self-understanding, emotional competence, cognitive competence, resilience, spirituality, social competence, moral competence, positive identity, interpersonal communication, conflict resolution, relationship building and assertiveness. Through lectures, class activities and assignments, students are helped to understand the attributes of a successful leader, conduct personal reflections and cultivate their awareness of the importance of intrapersonal and interpersonal attributes of university students (see Appendix 1). Conceptually speaking, the topics covered in the course are based on the positive youth development framework which is also adopted in the Project P.A.T.H.S. in Hong Kong, with HK$400 million for the initial phase and HK$350 million for the extension phase. To date, evaluation findings based on different evaluation strategies showed two observations: a) different stakeholders generally had positive views of the program, implementers and effectiveness and such perceptions were consistent across different stakeholders; and b) compared with control participants, students in the experimental schools had better positive development and they displayed lower levels of substance abuse, delinquent behavior and intention to engage in risk behavior (12-16).

According to the subject syllabus, the objectives of the course are: a) to enable students to learn and integrate theories, research and concepts of the basic personal qualities (particularly intra-personal and interpersonal qualities) of effective leaders; b) to train students to develop and reflect on their intra-personal and interpersonal qualities; and c) to promote the development of an active pursuit of knowledge on personal qualities in leadership amongst students. On successfully completing this subject, it is expected that students will be able to: a) understand and integrate theories, research and concepts on the basic qualities (particularly intra-personal and interpersonal qualities) of effective leaders in the Chinese context; b) develop self-awareness and understanding of oneself; c) acquire interpersonal skills; d) develop self-reflection skills in their learning; and e) recognize the importance of active pursuit of knowledge on intra-personal and interpersonal leadership qualities.

The proposed subject was piloted in the second term of 2010/11 school year. To understand the effectiveness of the course, multiple evaluation strategies were used. First, objective outcome evaluation utilizing a one-group pretest-posttest design was used where pretest and posttest data were collected from the students taking the course. Second, post-course subjective outcome evaluation was conducted where students were invited to respond to a subjective outcome evaluation form including items assessing their perceptions of the course, instructor and perceived effectiveness of the program at the last lecture. Third, process evaluation via systematic observations was carried out by two trained colleagues to understand the program implementation details in 14 lectures as well as program adherence. Fourth, qualitative evaluation via focus groups involving students based on schools randomly selected from the participating schools was carried out. Finally, qualitative evaluation using reflection notes was conducted. In this paper, findings based on the quantitative data collected in post-lecture evaluation are reported.

Methods

The subject was offered to four classes of students, with a total of 268 students (65 in Class A, 68 in Class B, 66 in Class C and 69 in Class D). At the end of Lecture 1 to Lecture 13, students were invited to respond to a subjective outcome evaluation form on their perceptions of the content of the lecture and their views. There are 12 items and one open-ended question in the evaluation form. The items cover various areas of lecture, including design, atmosphere, peer interaction, student interest, student participation, opportunities for reflection, degree of helpfulness to personal development, instructor's mastery of lecture, instructor's use of teaching methods, helpful of the lecture to students, global evaluation of lecture and global evaluation of the lecturer. The respondents were required to respond on a six-point scale with "Strongly Disagree", "Disagree", "Slightly Disagree", "Slightly Agree", "Agree" and "Strongly Agree" as the response options. The items are as follows:

1 Item 1: The design of this lecture was very good.
2 Item 2: The classroom atmosphere of this lecture was very pleasant.

3   Item 3: There was much peer interaction amongst the students in this lecture.
4   Item 4: I am interested in the content of this lecture.
5   Item 5: There was much student participation in this lecture.
6   Item 6: There were many opportunities for reflection in this lecture.
7   Item 7: This lecture is helpful to my personal development.
8   Item 8: The lecturer had a good mastery of the lecture material.
9   Item 9: The lecturer used different methods to encourage students to learn.
10   Item 10: The lecturer in this lecture was able to help students understand the knowledge covered in the lecture.
11   Item 11: Overall speaking, I have very positive evaluation of the lecturer in this lecture
12   Item 12: Overall speaking, I have very positive evaluation of this lecture.

Conceptually speaking, it was hypothesized that items 1, 4, 6 and 7 are related to the attributes of the subject (Subject Attributes), items 2, 3 and 5 are related to the attributes of the class (Class Attributes) and items 8, 9 and 10 were related to the attributes of the teacher (Teacher Attributes). Item 11 and Item 12 are items that are designed to assess the global evaluation of the teacher and the course.

A total of 2,039 questionnaires were collected for all lectures throughout the course. On the day of data collection, the purpose of the evaluation was mentioned, and confidentiality of the data was repeatedly emphasized to all students. All participants responded to the items and question in the evaluation form in a self-administration format. Adequate time was provided for the participants to complete the questionnaire. In the present paper, focus would be put on the findings based on the quantitative data.

Data analysis

Percentage analyses were used to examine the perceptions of the students on the course and teacher performance. Factor analysis was performed for the Lecture 1 data (i.e., first batch of data) to examine the structure of Item 1 to Item 10 to see whether there was supported for the three dimensions – subject attributes, class attributes and teacher attributes. To examine whether subject attributes, class attributes and teacher attributes predicted the overall evaluation of the teacher (Item 11) and the subject (Item 12), multiple regression analyses were performed. All analyses were performed by using the Statistical Package for Social Sciences Version 16.0.

Results

A total of 2,039 post-lecture subjective outcome evaluation forms were collected after Lecture 1 to Lecture 13. The quantitative findings based on the closed-ended questions are presented in this paper, with the percentage findings presented in Table 1 and the mean findings presented in Table 2. Several observations can be highlighted from the percentage findings presented in Table 1. In the first place, most participants generally had positive perceptions of the course, including its design (item 1), student interest (item 4), reflection (item 6) and benefits (item 7). For example, 91% of the participants regarded the program design as positive; 85% of the participants agreed that class promoted reflection.

Table 1. Percentage findings based on subjective outcome evaluation of each lecture

Item	Percentage of positive responses for different lectures													
	1	2	3	4	5	6	7	8	9	10	11	12	13	Overall
1. Good lecture design	95.6	91.4	83.7	87.1	90.0	93.7	93.8	91.4	93.5	95.2	93.9	87.3	84.2	91.0
2. Atmosphere was very good	94.3	95.0	80.1	80.6	77.3	84.1	86.0	92.6	89.9	90.3	82.4	83.9	80.9	86.7
3. Much peer interaction	94.3	95.0	83.2	91.6	80.7	84.9	89.9	93.2	89.9	91.6	85.0	76.7	76.8	88.1
4. Interested in the content	88.5	88.2	84.7	76.8	87.2	92.1	89.1	93.2	86.9	92.4	85.8	87.3	83.2	87.4
5. Much student participation	93.8	95.9	85.1	84.5	76.6	82.5	86.8	86.3	91.1	91.7	81.1	75.4	74.7	86.3
6. Many opportunities for reflection	81.4	89.6	82.7	81.7	86.4	92.9	88.4	85.7	91.1	87.6	81.6	77.1	72.3	84.9
7. Helpful to my personal development	89.9	90.5	88.6	84.5	89.4	95.2	86.0	88.3	89.3	88.1	88.5	89.0	78.9	88.5
8. Lecturer had good mastery of lecture	95.2	94.1	93.1	89.7	90.8	96.0	93.8	91.4	93.4	96.6	89.9	86.3	86.3	92.4
9. Varied teaching methods used	93.0	96.8	89.6	92.9	84.4	87.2	90.6	90.1	92.3	90.3	91.2	84.7	86.3	90.6
10. Helpful to students (knowledge)	94.7	92.3	93.1	89.7	90.8	95.2	94.5	91.4	92.9	93.1	91.2	89.8	81.1	91.9
11. Very positive evaluation of the lecturer	95.6	95.0	91.1	92.9	90.8	94.4	96.9	95.1	94.0	92.4	92.6	87.3	83.2	92.9
12. Very positive evaluation of the lecture	93.0	93.2	86.6	87.7	89.4	92.9	88.4	94.4	92.8	93.1	89.2	89.0	80.0	90.4
Coefficient alpha for the 12-item scale	.93	.93	.94	.95	.95	.95	.94	.93	.94	.94	.94	.95	.97	.94
Mean inter-item correlation	.54	.52	.57	.59	.60	.62	.57	.53	.59	.57	.57	.63	.71	.58
Number of questionnaires collected	227	222	202	155	141	126	129	162	169	145	148	118	95	2039

Note: The cumulative percentage based on "Strongly Agree", "Agree" and "Slightly Agree" for an item is presented for each lecture.

Besides, students perceived the class atmosphere to be pleasant (item 2: 87%), with much peer interaction (item 3: 88%) and student participation (item 5: 86%). Finally, teachers were perceived to have good mastery of the course (item 8), used varied teaching methods (item 9) and were able to help students understand knowledge (item 10). Regarding global evaluation of the subject, 93% and 90% had positive evaluation of the teacher and subject, respectively.

Concerning the psychometric properties of the scale, reliability analysis showed that the 12-item scale was internally consistent in different lectures (Table 1). Both alpha and mean inter-item correlation coefficients were found to be in the high range. Regarding the factor structure of the 10 specific items, principal factor analysis followed by promax rotation showed that three factors could be meaningfully extracted, accounted for 75% of the variance. Factor I included items 1, 4, 6 and 7 and it was labeled a Subject Attributes factor (alpha = .85, mean inter-item correlation = .59). The second factor included items 2, 3 and 5 (alpha = .85, mean inter-item correlation = .66). Because these items are basically concerned with lecture delivery in class, this factor was labeled Class Attributes factor.

The third factor included items 8, 9 and 10 that could be labeled a Teacher Attributes factor (alpha = .83, mean inter-item correlation = .61). The pattern matrix can be seen in Table 3.

Table 2. Subjective outcome evaluation of each lecture

Item	Lecture 1	2	3	4	5	6	7	8	9	10	11	12	13	Mean
1. Good lecture design	4.59	4.56	4.31	4.36	4.55	4.63	4.52	4.50	4.58	4.54	4.49	4.33	4.23	4.48
2. Atmosphere was very good	4.77	4.75	4.26	4.26	4.26	4.37	4.43	4.59	4.53	4.50	4.36	4.23	4.18	4.42
3. Much peer interaction	4.86	4.92	4.36	4.48	4.34	4.34	4.57	4.70	4.54	4.52	4.40	4.16	4.09	4.48
4. Interested in the content	4.41	4.48	4.37	4.24	4.43	4.60	4.47	4.54	4.53	4.53	4.41	4.31	4.34	4.43
5. Much student participation	4.71	4.75	4.37	4.32	4.18	4.23	4.44	4.55	4.61	4.62	4.30	4.07	4.12	4.41
6. Many opportunities for reflection	4.19	4.37	4.22	4.37	4.54	4.68	4.53	4.35	4.60	4.37	4.29	4.21	4.01	4.36
7. Helpful to my personal development	4.39	4.44	4.36	4.32	4.50	4.72	4.41	4.42	4.53	4.43	4.44	4.38	4.19	4.42
8. Lecturer had good mastery of lecture	4.73	4.72	4.52	4.52	4.61	4.69	4.78	4.57	4.67	4.68	4.61	4.48	4.37	4.61
9. Varied teaching methods used	4.79	4.78	4.45	4.53	4.50	4.54	4.64	4.52	4.65	4.65	4.56	4.34	4.31	4.56
10. Helpful to students (knowledge)	4.52	4.58	4.41	4.43	4.52	4.62	4.62	4.45	4.58	4.51	4.52	4.41	4.14	4.49
11. Very positive evaluation of the lecturer	4.72	4.75	4.43	4.51	4.57	4.71	4.71	4.53	4.66	4.57	4.52	4.38	4.31	4.57
12. Very positive evaluation of the lecture	4.59	4.64	4.32	4.37	4.45	4.63	4.56	4.53	4.60	4.51	4.41	4.37	4.23	4.48
Number of questionnaires collected	227	222	202	155	141	126	129	162	169	145	148	118	95	2039

Table 3. Pattern matrix for the 10 specific items on different aspects of the lecture

Item	Subject Attributes	Class Attributes	Teacher Attributes
1. Good lecture design	**.426**	.377	.080
2. Atmosphere was very good	-.023	**.810**	.092
3. Much peer interaction	-.104	**.918**	-.050
4. Interested in the content	**.661**	.172	.015
5. Much student participation	.163	**.567**	.125
6. Many opportunities for reflection	**.795**	-.180	.111
7. Helpful to my personal development	**.865**	.011	-.120
8. Lecturer had good mastery of lecture	.151	.005	**.650**
9. Varied teaching methods used	-.170	.098	**.866**
10. Helpful to students (knowledge)	.187	-.030	**.663**
Variance Explained (%)	53.4	6.49	4.15

Table 4. Predictors of global evaluation of the teacher and global evaluation of the lecture

Analyses	Lecture													Overall
	1	2	3	4	5	6	7	8	9	10	11	12	13	
DV: Global Perception of the Teacher (Item 11):														
Predictors														
Subject Attribute	.32***	.28***	.53***	.34***	.36***	.56***	.32**	.16	.26**	.00	.40***	.25*	.21	.31***
Class Attribute	.06	.21**	.10	.07	.00	.15	.06	.26**	.06	.30***	.08	.18	.21	.12***
Teacher Attribute	.49***	.39***	.27***	.47***	.56***	.43***	.47***	.32**	.54***	.59***	.34***	.44***	.54***	.45***
R Square	.61	.59	.68	.65	.76	.66	.58	.45	.63	.65	.54	.65	.82	.63
DV: Global Perception of the Course (Item 12):														
Predictors														
Subject Attribute	.39***	.48***	.57***	.45***	.39***	.53***	.21*	.28**	.26**	.43***	.46***	.38**	.34*	.41***
Class Attribute	.14*	.07	.22***	.20**	.17*	.03	.42***	.26**	.19*	.24**	.18*	.11	.18	.19***
Teacher Attribute	.36***	.36***	.13*	.26***	.33***	.37***	.33***	.28**	.41***	.24**	.27***	.37***	.39***	.30***
R Square	.63	.66	.71	.67	.66	.68	.71	.56	.63	.67	.68	.65	.76	.66
Number of questionnaires collected	227	222	202	155	141	126	129	162	169	145	148	118	95	

Note: *** $p < .001$; ** $p < .01$; * $p < .05$.

To examine how the subject, class and teacher attributes contributed to the global evaluation of the teacher and the course, multiple regression analyses were carried out for the data collected from each lecture. Multiple regression analyses showed that subject, class and teacher attributes predicted global evaluation of the teacher and lecture (Table 4). Amongst these different aspects, findings showed that subject and teacher attributes showed greater influence on the global evaluation of the teacher and the class.

Discussion

The present paper examines the post-lecture subjective outcome evaluation of a subject entitled "Tomorrow's Leaders" offered at The Hong Kong Polytechnic University. Several observations can be highlighted from the present study. First, the students generally perceived the coursepositively in terms of the subject, class and teacher attributes. The findings also showed that very high proportions of the students had positive global evaluation of the teacher and the subject. Consistent with other forms of evaluation, the present findings showed that the students had positive evaluation of the subject.

Concerning the psychometric properties of the 12-item post-lecture subjective outcome evaluation form, reliability analyses showed that the scale was highly reliable in different lectures. Furthermore, consistent with the original conceptual model, factor analyses showed that three dimensions, including subject attributes, class attributes and teacher attributes were identified and reliability of the related subscales were on the high side. As there are very few published studies on post-lecture evaluation in different Chinese contexts, the present findings are interesting additions to the literature. As client satisfaction surveys are commonly criticized as invalid in the field of human service, there is a need to develop validated measures in this field. As pointed out by Royse (17), using validated measures of client satisfaction would "eliminate many of the problems found in hastily designed questionnaires" (p. 265). Hence, the present study is a positive response. Nevertheless, it is noteworthy that there are several limitations of the present study. First, as the present findings were based on small samples, there is a need to replicate the findings in large samples. Second, future studies should examine the validity of the 12-item post-lecture subjective outcome evaluation form. Third, as the sample size was small, the stability of the factors should be examined in future studies.

Finally, regarding predictors of perceived effectiveness of the course based on the data in different lectures, findings showed that subject, class and teacher attributes predicted global evaluation of the teacher, although subject and teacher attributes appeared to be stronger predictors. Similarly, although there are findings showing that subject, class and teacher attributes predicted global evaluation of the subject, subject and teacher factors were stronger predictors. These findings concur with the previous findings that program and implementer characteristics are important factors leading to program effectiveness (18). With specific reference to program implementers, Donnermeyer and Wurschmidt (19) asserted that implementers' "level of enthusiasm and support for a prevention curriculum influences their effectiveness because their attitudes are communicated both explicitly and subtly to students during the time it is taught and throughout the remainder of the school day" (p. 259-260). However, it is noteworthy that there are few studies of predictors of effectiveness of intervention programs. Berkel et al. (20) remarked that "program evaluations have rarely examined more than one dimension in a single study and thus have not untangled possible relations between them" (p. 24). Durlak and DuPre (21) further argued that most of the intervention studies failed to examine the relative importance of different predictors of program effectiveness. Hence, the present study is a constructive response to these criticisms.

Methodologically speaking, there may be queries on the use of multiple regression in looking at the relationships between the specific aspects and the global outcomes because it is expected that subject, student and class attributes are highly correlated. However, it is noteworthy that multiple regression analysis is frequently used to examine predictors of program effectiveness. For example, Byrnes et al. (22) showed that program adherence and quality of program implementation were significant predictors of participants' satisfaction towards the program. Of course, the use of structural equation modeling would give a clear picture on the factors affecting program effectiveness in future.

There are several limitations of this study. First, as only four classes of students were involved in this study, it would be desirable to include more students so that the generalizability of the findings could be enhanced. In addition, it would be helpful to examine the post-lecture evaluation findings in different groups of students. For example, it would be interesting to ask whether the subject has different impact for social science and non-social science students. Second, the limitations of using a quantitative approach to examine the subjective experiences of the informants should be noted. The use of qualitative techniques in this context would be very helpful. In the present study, data based on one open-ended question were collected and the findings would be reported in another study. Third, as there are many threats to the internal validity of a one-group pretest and posttest research design, addition of a control group can help to examine the impact of the intervention on the program participants. Despite these limitations, the present study is a ground-breaking study in different Chinese contexts and it is a good response to the appeal that psychosocial competencies should be promoted in university students (23).

Acknowledgments

An earlier version of this paper was presented at the "International Conference on Transitioning to Adulthood in Asia: Courtship, Marriage and Work" held at the Asia Research Institute, National University of Singapore on July 21-22, 2011 which was jointly organized by the Asia Research Institute, Faculty of Arts and Social Sciences of the National University of Singapore and the Ministry of Community Development, Youth and Sports. The author thanks Professor Jean Yeung for her invitation extended to the first author to give an invited paper at the conference. This work and the course on "Tomorrow's Leaders" are financially supported by The Hong Kong Polytechnic University. Members of the Curriculum Development Team include Daniel TL Shek, Rachel CF Sun, YH Chui, SW Lit, Yida YH Chung, Sowa SW Ngai, Yammy LY Chak, PF Tsui, Cecilia MS Ma, L Yu and Moon YM Law. This paper was originally published in The Scientific World Journal, Volume 2012, Article ID 934679, 8 pages doi: 10.1100/2012/934679.

References

[1] Shek DTL, Sun RCF. Subjective outcome evaluation based on secondary data analyses: the Project P.A.T.H.S. in Hong Kong. ScientificWorldJournal 2010;10:224-37.

[2] Shek DTL, Sun RCF. Development, implementation and evaluation of a holistic positive youth development program: Project P.A.T.H.S. in Hong Kong. Int J Disabil Hum Dev 2009;8:107-17.

[3] Shek DTL, Ma CMS. Subjective outcome evaluation findings: factors related to the perceived effectiveness of the tier 2 program of the Project P.A.T.H.S. ScientificWorldJournal 2010;10:250-60.

[4] Shek DTL, Ma HK. Subjective outcome evaluation of the Project P.A.T.H.S.: findings based on the perspective of the program participants. ScientificWorldJournal 2007;7:47-55.

[5] Cohen PA. Student ratings of instruction and student achievement: a meta-analysis of multi-section validity studies. Rev Educ Res 1981;51(3):281-309.

[6] Marsh HW, Roche LA. Making students' evaluations of teaching effectiveness effective: the critical issues of validity, bias and utility. Am Psychol 1997;52(11):1187-97.

[7] Marsh HW, Hau KT, Chung CM, Siu TLP. Students' evaluations of university teaching: Chinese version of the students' evaluations of educational quality (SEEQ) instrument. J Educ Psychol 1997;89:568-72.

[8] Marsh HW, Hau KT, Chung CM, Siu TLP. Confirmatory factor analysis of Chinese students' evaluations of university teaching. Struct Equ Modeling 1998;5(2):143-64.

[9] Kim C, Damewood E, Hodge N. Professor attitude: its effect on teaching evaluations. J Manage Educ 2000;24(4):458-73.

[10] Kember D, Leung DYP, Kwan KP. Does the use of student feedback questionnaires improve the overall quality of teaching?. Assess Eval High Educ 2002;27(5):411-25.

[11] Kember D, Leung DYP. Establishing the validity and reliability of course evaluation questionnaires. Assess Eval High Educ 2008;33(4):341-53.

[12] Sun RCF, Shek DTL. Life satisfaction, positive youth development and problem behaviour among Chinese adolescents in Hong Kong. Soc Indic Res 2010;95(3):455-74.

[13] Shek DTL, Ma CMS. Impact of the Project P.A.T.H.S. in the junior secondary school years: individual growth curve analyses. ScientificWorldJournal 2011;11:253-66.

[14] Shek DTL, Yu L. Prevention of adolescent problem behavior: longitudinal impact of the Project P.A.T.H.S. in Hong Kong. ScientificWorldJournal 2011;11:546-67.

[15] Shek DTL, Ng CSM. Early identification of adolescents with greater psychosocial needs: an evaluation of the Project P.A.T.H.S. in Hong Kong. Int J Disabil Hum Dev 2010;9:291-9.

[16] Shek DTL, Ng CSM, Tsui PF. Qualitative evaluation of the Project P.A.T.H.S.: findings based on focus groups. Int J Disabil Hum Dev 2010;9:307-13.

[17] Royse D. Research methods in social work. Pacific Grove, CA: Brooks/Cole-Thomson Learning; 2004.

[18] Gendreau P, Goggin C, Smith P. The forgotten issue in effective correctional treatment: program implementation. Int J Offender Ther Comp Criminol 1999;43(2):180-7.

[19] Donnermeyer JF, Wurschmidt TN. Educators' perceptions of the D.A.R.E. program. J Drug Addict Educ 1997;27(3):259-76.

[20] Berkel C, Mauricio AM, Schoenfelder E, Sandler IN. Putting the pieces together: an integrated model of program implementation. Prev Sci 2011;12(1):23-33.

[21] Durlak JA, DuPre EP. Implementation matters: a review of research on the influence of implementation on program outcomes and the factors affecting implementation. Am J Community Psychol 2008;41(3-4):327-50.

[22] Byrnes HF, Miller BA, Aalborg AE, Plasencia AV, Keagy CD. Implementation fidelity in adolescent family-based prevention programs: relationship to family engagement. Health Educ Res 2010;25(4):531-41.

[23] Shek DTL. Nurturing holistic development of university students in Hong Kong: where are we and where should we go. ScientificWorldJournal 2010;10:563-75.

Appendix 1. Topics covered in different lectures

Lecture	Subject Content
1	An overview of leadership theories and exploration of the meaning of 'effective leaders' and personal attributes constituting effective leadership. This overview also helps students understand how leadership studies are closely related to their own daily life experience and personal development.
2	Self-understanding: theories and concepts; personality traits; self-concept; self-esteem and personal identity; the role of self-understanding in effective leadership.
3	Emotional competence: awareness and understanding of emotions; emotional quotient (EQ); role of emotional management in effective leadership.
4	Cognitive competence: different types of thinking; higher-order thinking; experiential learning; role of cognitive competence in effective leadership.
5	Resilience: stresses faced by adolescents; life adversities; coping with life stresses; adversity quotient (AQ); role of resilience in effective leadership.
6	Spirituality: meaning in life and adolescent development; spirituality and mental health; role of spirituality in effective leadership.
7	Ethics and morality: moral issues and moral competence; role of ethics; morality and personal integrity in effective leadership.
8	Social competence: basic social competence skills; ability to build up positive human relationship; respecting the views of oneself and others; role of social competence in effective leadership.
9	Positive personal identity: develop healthy identity formation and achievement in youth; role of positive personal identity in effective leadership.
10	Interpersonal communication: theories, concepts and skills of interpersonal communication; role of communication skills in effective leadership.
11	Interpersonal conflict and assertiveness: theories of interpersonal conflict; conflict resolution skills; assertiveness and non-assertiveness; role of conflict resolution and assertive skills in effective leadership; student presentations (Group 1 and Group 2).
12	Relationship building and maintenance: tactics of building and maintaining relationship; relationship quality and effective leadership; student presentations (Group 3 and Group 4).
13	Team building: tactics and strategies of team building; identifying common goals in a team; maintaining morale and dealing with demoralization; student presentations (Group 5 and Group 6).
14	Wrapping up; summary of the course; evaluation; student presentations (Group 7 and Group 8).

In: Child Health and Human Development Yearbook 2013   ISBN: 978-1-63117-939-6
Editor: Joav Merrick   © 2014 Nova Science Publishers, Inc.

Chapter 8

Evaluation of the effectiveness of a positive youth development program for secondary students in Macau

Andrew L Luk, RN, PhD[*]*, *Ka Man Leong, BSc, MPH,* *and Annah ML Au, RN, MSc*

Kiang Wu Nursing College of Macau, Macau, PRC

Abstract

A well tested comprehensive Chinese positive youth development program (Project P.A.T.H.S.) developed in Hong Kong has been modified and adapted for use in Macau. This program aims to help adolescent school children develop positively and to be better prepared for their future. The present study investigated the effectiveness of the Tier 1 Program of "P.A.T.H.S." for Secondary 2 students of two pilot schools. Both subjective and objective outcomes were evaluated. Since there were 'repeating' and 'transferring' students joining the program, the effectiveness of the program on these particular groups of participants were also examined. The subjective outcome evaluations including participants' perceptions of the program, program instructors, benefits from the program and overall satisfaction were positive. Although the longitudinal data from the objective outcome evaluation did not show any notable improvement, the overall effect of the program was found to be positive to the new comers in the junior secondary years. The existing evaluation findings suggest that the Secondary 2 program is especially effective to those newly joining the program. In view of the paucity of youth studies in Macau, the present study can contribute to evidence-based youth work and provide baseline data for the program to be evaluated in the Secondary 3 periods in the future.

Keywords: Adolescents, positive youth development, P.A.T.H.S., objective outcome evaluation, subjective outcome evaluation

[*] Correspondence: Andrew L Luk, RN, PhD, Kiang Wu Nursing College of Macau, Est. Repouso No. 35, R/C, Macau, PRC. E-mail: luk@kwnc.edu.mo.

Introduction

Macau is a small city located near Hong Kong in South East Asia, famous for tourism and an increasing gaming industry. In 2010, the estimated population of Macau was 542,400, it has a comparatively young population with those aged between 10 and 24 years contributing 22 percents to the total population (1). The Macau Government opened the gaming licensure in 2002, this leads to a rapid development of this industry, generating a big increase of revenue and contributing to the economic growth of Macau. However, this may also bring with it potentially negative influences on adolescents. Due to employment opportunities and perks in the gaming industry, many adults work within the casinos, this requires them to work long and irregular hours. One potential implication of this development was highlighted in a recent government report which clearly identified the problem on lack of communication of parents with their children and the adverse effect on their adolescent development (2). The Youth Indicators published by Education and Youth Affairs Bureau in 2009 revealed that many teenagers lacked social norms and their participation in social functions/ affairs and the sense of belongingness to Macau had deteriorated in comparison to an earlier study conducted in 2006 (3). This research also reflects a dramatic increase in youths stress levels, originating from pressure at school as well as family conflicts. A recent study has revealed that over half of 744 respondents (54%) agreed that gambling was a common phenomenon in young people in Macau. It is suggested that by building up positive social norms and a sense of morality in adolescents a more harmonious society in Macau may be resulted (4).

A well structured local youth program can potentially help adolescents develop positive growth and ensure that they are better prepared for future challenges in life. At present, youth studies and theoretically sound and comprehensive programs for adolescent positive growth and development in Macau are lacking. (5, 6). Hong Kong and Macau share a similar Chinese culture; therefore, the well tested comprehensive Chinese positive youth development program "P.A.T.H.S." developed in Hong Kong (7, 8) has been modified and adapted for use in Macau. The acronym "P.A.T.H.S." denotes Positive Adolescent Training through Holistic Social Programs. There are two tiers of programs (Tier 1 and Tier 2) in this project. Tier 1 program is a universal positive youth development program in which students in Secondary 1 to 3 participate, normally 20 hours of duration, or at least with 10 hours of training of the core program during each academic year. With the support from the Education and Youth Affairs Bureau, a local research team was formed by the author and his colleagues who modified the program with some changes of the content relating to local terminology, government structure and indigenous customs (9). The team also monitored the implementation of the program and evaluated its effectiveness after the completion of the program for three consecutive academic years. Two secondary schools were invited to participate as pilot schools to run the program starting from their Secondary 1 students. Training for teachers and school social workers were also organized both in Hong Kong and Macau. The initial findings of this Secondary 1 program evaluation was completed during the academic year 2009 – 2010 and reported positively (9).

Macau has a history of a 15-year free non-tertiary education system with direct promotion from primary to secondary school without any public examination. Individual admission examination is required after secondary school education for entry into local universities. Consequently, there is a rather relaxed and less competitive learning atmosphere in the education system. It is not uncommon to see students repeating their studying in some classes in the primary and secondary schools if they find their academic performances unsatisfactory. It is roughly estimated that about 20% of students may repeat their studying in the junior secondary years in many schools (10). In this paper, the effectiveness of the Macau version of the Tier 1 Program of "P.A.T.H.S." for Secondary 2 students in 2 pilot schools during the academic year 2010- 2011 is evaluated. Both subjective and objective outcomes were measured. Since there were imported students either repeating the Secondary 2 class or transferred from other school joining the Secondary 2 classes of the pilot schools, the effectiveness of the program on these new participants was also examined.

Methods

The study participants included all Secondary 1 students in the two chosen schools, totally 232 starting from year 2009, these were followed up for three years up to Secondary 3. When this group of students was promoted to Secondary 2 year, 53 of them dropped out of their classes and 79 new students either repeating in Secondary 2 or transferred from other schools had joined the program. Data was collected at two time-points during each year. Firstly, before the program started, pre-test self-reported questionnaire were completed within 1-2 weeks after the start of the school year. The second data collection time-point occurred after the students finished the program at the end of that academic year. The pre-test data Wave 1 (W1) and posttest data Wave 2 (W2) of Secondary 1 had been collected and analyzed (9). This data was used as baseline for the longitudinal assessment for the Secondary 2 year. The pre-test data Wave 3 (W3) and posttest data Wave 4 (W4) of Secondary 2 were collected in this study to assess the effectiveness of the Secondary 2 program.

At pre- and post-tests, the participants were invited to complete a valid and reliable questionnaire including measures of positive youth development, life satisfaction, school adjustment, adolescent problem behaviors and demographic information. An identical questionnaire was used in the pre and post-tests, the paired-samples t test were performed to examine the pre- and post-test differences between the scales, providing an objective outcome measures for evaluation. After completion of the program each year, an evaluation questionnaire was also completed by the participants to assess their satisfaction with the course and perceived benefits of the program, providing subjective outcome measures for evaluation.

Instruments

The two set of questionnaires which were used in Year 1 were used again when the students were promoted to Year 2. The components in these questionnaires are described below.

The chinese positive youth development scale (CPYDS)
The Chinese Positive Youth Development Scale (CPYDS) is a self-administrated questionnaire developed by Shek et al. (11). It consists of 15 subscales (90 items) which address the 15 constructs of the program. These subscales include: Bonding (BO, 6 items),

Social Competence (SO, 7 items), Emotional Competence (EC, 6 items), Cognitive Competence (CC, 6 items), Behavioral Competence (BC, 6 items), Moral Competence (MC, 6 items), Self Efficacy (SE, 7 items), Prosocial Norms (PN, 5 items), Resilience (SE, 6 items), Self-Determination (SD, 5 items), Spirituality (SP, 7 items), Identity or Clear and Positive Identity (ID or CPI, 7 items), Beliefs in the Future (BF, 7 items), Prosocial Involvement (PI, 5 items), and Recognition for Positive Behavior (RP or PB, 4 items). The instrument had a good reliability (alpha = 0.91) and ranged from 0.63 to 0.86 (12). The Cronbach's alpha of the present study is 0.93 and ranged from 0.62 – 0.87. A higher score indicates a higher level of positive youth development.

Life satisfaction scale (LIFE)

Life satisfaction is another important indicator of positive youth development (13). The five-item LIFE was developed by Diener, Emmons, Larsen, and Griffin (14) to assess one's own global judgment of one's quality of life. The Chinese version was translated by Shek (15) with acceptable psychometric properties. The Cronbach's alpha of the present study is 0.80. A higher LIFE scale score indicates a higher level of life satisfaction.

Behavioral intention scale (BI)

The five-item scale were used to assess the adolescents' behavioral intention to engage in problem behavior, including drinking, smoking, taking drugs, having sex with others, and participation in gambling. The scale has a good reliability (alpha = 0.84) (16). The Cronbach's alpha of the present study is 0.71. A higher BI scale score indicates a higher behavioral intention.

School adjustment measures (SA)

The school adjustment measures include three items. Two items assess the participant's perception of his/her academic performance. The third item assesses the participant's perception of his/her conduct. Previous studies showed that these measures were temporally stable and valid (17, 18). The Cronbach's alpha of the present study is 0.84. In line with other measures, a higher scale score indicates a higher level of school adjustment in this study.

Subjective outcomes scale (Form A)

The Subjective Outcome Evaluation Form (Form A) was designed by Shek and Siu (19). The Form consists of totally 39 items and four open questions which are divided into five parts.

The first part asks for the participants' views on the program (10 items). The second part looks at the views of the participants towards those involved in delivering the program, including teachers and/or social workers (10 items). The third portion examines the participants' views about their perceived effectiveness of the program (16 items).

Three items ask about tendency of participants to join a similar program in the future, their overall satisfaction with the program and whether they would recommend the program to others.

The final part consists of four open questions on things that participants have learned and appreciated most, as well as opinions about the instructors and areas for improvement respectively. The Form had a good reliability on 39 items (alpha = 0.99, mean inter-item correlation = 0.80) (20). The present study has a Cronbach's alpha of 0.98 with mean inter-item correlation 0.55.

Results

Table 1. Number of participants and completed questionnaires collected at Year 1 (Wave 1 and Wave 2) and Year 2 (Wave 3 and Wave 4)

	Year 1		Year 2	
	Wave 1	Wave 2	Wave 3	Wave 4
Cases of 2 schools	239	242	268	244
Successfully match		232		236
Old participants			189	173
New Participants			79	63

Table 2. Participant Characteristics of P.A.T.H.S Secondary 2 Old and New Students

Variables	Old (n=189)	New (n=79)	Total (n=268)	*P* value
	n (%)	n (%)	n (%)	
Gender				
Male	120 (63.8)	45 (57.0)	165 (61.8)	0.292
Female	68 (36.2)	34 (43.0)	102 (38.2)	
Age				
12	5 (2.6)	0 (0.0)	5 (1.9)	**0.000**
13	86 (45.5)	0 (0.0)	86 (32.1)	
14	50 (26.5)	21 (26.6)	71 (26.5)	
15	28 (14.8)	37 (46.8)	65 (24.3)	
>=16	20 (10.6)	21 (26.6)	41 (15.3)	
Family Members				
1	1 (0.5)	0 (0.0)	1 (0.4)	0.349
2	6 (3.2)	7 (9.2)	13 (4.9)	
3	40 (21.2)	18 (23.7)	58 (21.9)	
4	90 (47.6)	35 (46.1)	125 (47.2)	
5	34 (18.0)	12 (15.8)	46 (17.4)	
>=6	18 (9.6)	4 (5.2)	22 (8.3)	
Parental marriage status				
Divorced	20 (10.7)	8 (10.5)	28 (10.6)	0.712
Separated	6 (3.2)	4 (5.3)	10 (3.8)	
Married	152 (81.3)	58 (76.3)	210 (79.8)	
Family happiness				
Very unpleasant	12 (6.4)	8 (10.4)	20 (7.5)	0.164
Unpleasant	19 (10.1)	15 (19.5)	34 (12.8)	
General	74 (39.4)	26 (33.8)	100 (37.7)	
Pleasant	57 (30.3)	21 (27.3)	78 (29.4)	
Very pleasant	26 (13.8)	7 (9.1)	33 (12.5)	
SSF				
Yes	15 (8.0)	5 (6.5)	20 (7.6)	0.689
No	172 (92.0)	71 (92.2)	243 (92.0)	

Note: SSF = Social Security Fund.

In total, there were 268 and 244 students who participated in the Wave 3 pre-test and Wave 4 post-test respectively. Out of 268 Secondary 2 students, almost one-third of them, 79 (29.48%) were students who were new to the program. Once invalid questionnaires were discarded, mainly due to missing data, 236 questionnaires were appropriately completed for analysis. There were 173 old participants and 63 new participants (Table 1). Results showed that, with the exception of age, there were no statistically significant differences in socio-demographic background between the old and new students using the chi-square test. The mean age of the new students ($\mu\pm SD = 15.08\pm0.87$) was higher than that of the old group ($\mu\pm SD= 13.87\pm1.11$). Details can be seen in Table 2.

Subjective outcome evaluation

Table 3. Findings from the Subjective Outcome Evaluation (n=257)

Your views towards the course(s)	Percentage of Responses (%)						
	1	2	3	A	4	5	6	B
1 The objectives of the curriculum are very clear.	0.4	6.5	13.8	**20.7**	31.0	39.1	7.3	**77.4**
2 The design of the curriculum is very good.	1.9	6.1	15.3	**23.4**	37.9	33.0	4.2	**75.1**
3 The activities were carefully planned.	1.5	6.9	17.6	**26.1**	33.7	33.3	5.0	**72.0**
4 The classroom atmosphere was very pleasant.	4.2	6.1	14.9	**25.3**	34.1	28.0	10.3	**72.4**
5 There was much peer interaction amongst the students.	3.8	7.7	11.9	**23.4**	28.7	31.0	13.0	**72.8**
6 I participated actively during lessons (including discussions, sharing, games, etc.).	1.9	6.1	11.9	**19.9**	38.7	28.0	11.1	**77.8**
7 I was encouraged to do my best.	3.8	8.0	15.3	**27.2**	37.2	27.6	5.4	**70.1**
8 The learning experience I encountered enhanced my interest towards the lessons.	3.4	6.5	15.7	**25.7**	36.0	29.5	6.5	**72.0**
9 Overall speaking, I have very positive evaluation of the program.	3.8	10.0	14.2	**28.0**	41.4	23.0	4.6	**69.0**
10 On the whole, I like this curriculum very much.	7.7	6.5	16.1	**30.3**	30.7	28.0	8.4	**67.0**
Your views towards the instructor(s)								
1 The instructor(s) had a good mastery of the curriculum.	0.8	4.6	13.0	**18.4**	27.6	39.5	13.0	**80.1**
2 The instructor(s) was well prepared for the lessons.	0.8	3.4	11.1	**15.3**	29.5	36.4	17.2	**83.1**
3 The instructor(s)' teaching skills was good.	1.9	5.0	11.9	**18.8**	28.7	39.5	11.5	**79.7**
4 The instructor(s) showed good professional attitudes.	1.9	2.7	8.8	**13.4**	31.0	36.4	17.2	**84.7**
5 The instructor(s) was very involved.	0.8	3.4	11.5	**15.7**	26.4	37.9	18.0	**82.4**
6 The instructor(s) encouraged students to participate in the activities.	0.4	3.1	8.0	**11.5**	29.9	35.2	21.5	**86.6**
7 The instructor(s) cared for the students.	0.0	3.8	10.0	**13.8**	25.3	37.2	22.2	**84.7**
8 The instructor(s) was ready to offer help to students when needed.	0.4	3.8	7.3	**11.5**	27.2	39.5	19.2	**85.8**
9 The instructor(s) had much interaction with the students.	1.1	5.7	11.5	**18.4**	26.1	35.6	18.4	**80.1**
10 Overall speaking, I have very positive evaluation of the instructors.	1.9	5.7	7.7	**15.3**	26.8	35.6	20.7	**83.1**

Remarks: 1=Strongly Disagree, 2= Disagree, 3=Slightly Disagree, 4=Slightly Agree, 5=Agree, 6=Strongly Agree. A= Sum of the disagree responses (1+2+3), B= Sum of the agree responses (4+5+6).

Table 3 highlights the participants' perception of the program and program instructors. Firstly, more than two-thirds of the participants viewed the program positively. For example, 77.4% of the students indicated that the objectives of the program were very clear; 77.8% felt that they had participated actively during the program; 69.0% had a very positive evaluation of the program. Secondly, more than four-fifths of the students provided a positive evaluation of their program instructors. The vast majority of participants, (84.7%) felt they were well cared for and 83.1% of them provided overall positive evaluation of the instructors. The participant's perception of the benefits of the Tier 1 program revealed the following findings. Firstly, more than two-thirds of the participants perceived the program was effective for their personal development and enhanced their psychosocial competences (Table 4). In addition they thought it also enriched their overall development (73.9%). Secondly, a majority of respondents (63.2%) indicated that they would recommend the program to their friends and, more than a half of them (51.3%) would join similar programs in the future (Table 5). Finally, more than two-thirds of the participants indicated that they were satisfied with the program (Table 5). The qualitative analysis of the four open-ended questions will not be reported in this paper.

Table 4. Perceptions on the extent to which the course has helped them (n=257)

The extent to which the course has helped you:	Percentage of Responses (%)						
	1	2	**A**	3	4	5	**B**
1 It has strengthened my bonding with teachers, classmates and my family.	8.8	20.3	**29.1**	41.0	25.7	2.3	**69.0**
2 It has strengthened my resilience in adverse conditions.	8.0	18.4	**26.4**	37.9	25.7	8.0	**71.6**
3 It has enhanced my social competence.	5.7	20.7	**26.4**	33.7	31.0	6.9	**71.6**
4 It has improved my ability in handling and expressing my emotions.	7.7	15.3	**23.0**	39.8	26.4	8.0	**74.3**
5 It has enhanced my cognitive competence.	8.4	13.4	**21.8**	36.8	30.7	9.2	**76.6**
6 My ability to resist harmful influences has been improved.	8.8	16.5	**25.3**	36.4	26.8	9.6	**72.8**
7 It has strengthened my ability to distinguish between the good and the bad.	7.3	14.6	**21.8**	35.6	31.4	9.2	**76.2**
8 It has increased my competence in making sensible and wise choices.	7.3	13.8	**21.1**	37.9	29.9	9.6	**77.4**
9 It has helped me to have life reflections.	10.0	13.0	**23.0**	32.2	29.9	12.6	**74.7**
10 It has reinforced my self-confidence.	13.4	13.0	**26.4**	35.2	25.7	10.7	**71.6**
11 It has increased my self-awareness.	10.0	16.1	**26.1**	32.6	29.1	10.0	**71.6**
12 It has helped me to face the future with a positive attitude.	7.7	15.3	**23.0**	37.2	28.7	8.0	**73.9**
13 It has helped me to cultivate compassion and care about others.	8.0	14.2	**22.2**	37.5	30.7	6.5	**74.7**
14 It has encouraged me to care about the community.	9.2	19.5	**28.7**	36.0	25.7	7.3	**69.0**
15 It has promoted my sense of responsibility in serving the society.	8.0	20.3	**28.4**	33.3	29.5	6.9	**69.7**
16 It has enriched my overall development.	10.3	13.8	**24.1**	37.5	26.8	9.6	**73.9**

Remarks: 1=Unhelpful, 2= Not Very Helpful, 3=Slightly Helpful, 4= Helpful , 5= Very Helpful. A= Sum of the unhelpful responses (1+2), B= Sum of the helpful responses (3+4+5).

Table 5. Other Aspects of Subjective Outcome Evaluation

	1	2	A	3	4	B
3 If your friends have needs and conditions similar to yours, will you suggest him/her to join this course?	11.9	21.8	33.7	51.7	11.5	63.2
4 Will you participate in similar courses again in the future?	16.1	29.1	45.2	42.9	8.4	51.3

Remarks: 1=Definitely will not, 2=Will not , 3= Will , 4=Definitely will. A= Sum of those will not (1+2), B= Sum of those will (3+4).

	1	2	3	A	4	5	6	B
5 On the whole, are you satisfied with this course?	4.6	3.8	14.9	23.3	46.0	19.9	8.4	74.3

Remarks:1=Very dissatisfied, 2=Moderated dissatisfied, 3= Slightly Dissatisfied, 4=Satisfied, 5= Moderately satisfied, 6=Very Satisfied. A= Sum of those will not satisfy (1+2+3), B= Sum of those will satisfy (4+5+6).

Objective outcome evaluation

The overall evaluation of all Secondary 2 students, using the paired t-test to compare the W3 and W4 data of the program, revealed that there was a non-significant decrease in the score of CYPDS, SA or increase of LIFE. Besides, there was a significant slightly increase in the score of BI (Table 6). To assess the continual effect of the program from Secondary 1 to Secondary 2, the W1 data of the Secondary 1 program was used as a baseline to measure the longitudinal effect after the participants had completed the Secondary 2 program. Only 189 participants completed Secondary 1 and Secondary 2 programs, using the repeated ANOVA for W1, W3 and W4 data revealed similar non-significant results.

Table 6. The Changes in the Secondary 2 Program Participants Based on the Different Scale

	Pre-test		Post-test		t value	P value
	Mean	SD	Mean	SD		
CYPDS	4.33	0.58	4.28	0.61	1.88	0.062
LIFE	3.66	1.01	3.70	1.13	-0.57	0.568
SA	3.01	0.67	2.96	0.72	1.038	0.300
BI	1.54	0.55	1.64	0.54	-3.13	**0.002**

Note: Significant. p values are in bold.

However, comparison between the W3 data of old participants with new participants revealed that the old students demonstrated better development, life satisfaction and school adjustment than the new students. Significant differences were reported within the sub-scales of CYPDS, LIFE and SA scores (Table 7). As there was a significant difference of age between the groups, analysis of covariance was conducted using age as a covariate. A statistical significant difference of ID subscale and LIFE score was also found. As shown in Table 8, when using the pair t-test to compare the W3 and W4 data of the new participants, results showed that there was significant improvement in EC, CC and ID subscales, LIFE and SA scores. However, there was a significant decrease in BO subscale and an increase of score of the BI scale.

Table 7. Comparison of the Old and New Participants in Wave 3 Data

	Old (n=189)		New (n=79)		*t* value	*P* value
	Mean	SD	Mean	SD		
BO subscale	4.59	0.74	4.38	0.86	2.024	**0.044**
RP subscale	4.14	0.92	3.86	0.93	2.268	**0.024**
EC subscale	4.21	0.85	3.92	0.88	2.526	**0.012**
CC subscale	4.35	0.81	4.12	0.78	2.148	**0.033**
ID subscale	4.07	0.79	3.74	0.77	3.191	**0.002**
BF subscale	4.21	0.89	3.96	0.79	2.137	**0.033**
PI subscale	4.21	0.93	3.87	1.03	2.671	**0.008**
SP subscale	4.76	1.25	4.31	1.30	2.671	**0.008**
CYPDS	4.34	0.59	4.14	0.61	2.513	**0.013**
LIFE	3.77	1.04	3.28	0.83	3.735	**0.000**
SA	3.07	0.61	2.85	0.84	2.071	**0.041**
BI	1.52	0.56	1.65	0.53	1.813	0.071
BI (item 1)	2.13	1.10	2.54	1.07	2.807	**0.005**
BI (item 2)	1.35	0.70	1.44	0.83	0.814	0.417
BI (item 4)	1.39	0.70	1.51	0.79	1.164	0.247

Note: BO=Bonding, RP=Recognition for Positive Behavior subscale, EC= Emotional Competence subscale, CC= Cognitive Competence subscale. ID= Clear and Positive Identity subscale, BF= Beliefs in the Future subscale, PI= Prosocial Involvement subscale, SP= Spirituality Subscale, CYPDS= mean of the 15 subscales, LIFE= Life Satisfaction Scale, SA= School Adjustment Measures, BI= Behavioral Intention Scale, BI (item 1) = Will you drink alcohol in the coming 2 years? BI (item 2) = Will you smoke cigarettes in the coming 2 years? BI (item 4) = Will you have sex in the future 2 years? Significant. p values are in bold.

Table 8. The changes of the New Participants based on the different objective indicators

	Pre-test		Post-test		*t* value	*P* value
	Mean	SD	Mean	SD		
New Participants (n=63)						
BO subscale	4.55	0.71	4.31	0.80	2.380	**0.020**
RP subscale	3.96	0.90	3.94	0.89	0.126	0.900
EC subscale	3.98	0.84	4.24	0.98	2.402	**0.019**
CC subscale	4.22	0.72	4.44	0.80	2.418	**0.019**
ID subscale	3.79	0.78	4.08	0.80	3.023	**0.004**
BF subscale	4.06	0.83	3.86	0.74	1.759	0.083
PI subscale	4.00	0.99	4.05	0.95	0.344	0.732
SP subscale	4.45	1.27	4.63	1.21	1.218	0.228
CYPDS	4.24	0.57	4.27	0.55	0.532	0.596
LIFE	3.32	0.81	3.62	1.09	2.138	**0.037**
SA	2.81	0.77	3.07	0.84	2.324	**0.023**
BI	1.62	0.50	1.91	0.51	4.376	**0.000**
BI (item 1)	2.57	1.06	2.90	1.00	2.490	**0.005**
BI (item 2)	1.35	0.74	1.70	0.91	3.017	**0.004**
BI (item 4)	1.49	0.78	1.94	1.00	3.727	**0.000**

Note: BO=Bonding, RP=Recognition for Positive Behavior subscale, EC= Emotional Competence subscale, CC= Cognitive Competence subscale. ID= Clear and Positive Identity subscale, BF= Beliefs in the Future subscale, PI= Prosocial Involvement subscale, SP= Spirituality Subscale, CYPDS= mean of the 15 subscales, LIFE= Life Satisfaction Scale, SA= School Adjustment Measures, BI= Behavioral Intention Scale, BI (item 1) = Will you drink alcohol in the coming 2 years? BI (item 2) = Will you smoke cigarettes in the coming 2 years? BI (item 4) = Will you have sex in the future 2 years? Significant. p values are in bold.

Discussion

In this study the participants' perception of the program and their program instructors were evaluated positively.

With regard to their perception to the effectiveness of the program and the overall satisfaction, results provided a positive feedback. Overall, subjective outcome evaluation generally supported positive perceptions to the program, program instructors, benefits from the program and overall satisfaction with the whole course, these findings are consistent with those reported in Hong Kong (20, 21). However, when asked about whether they would join similar program in the future, just over half of the participants replied positively. There may be several possible reasons for this dissociation between individuals' perception towards the program and their behavioral intention to participate.

Firstly, as suggested, students might think that similar programs may contain similar elements and not be motivated to join such programs again (20). In fact, the three year program is designed with the same 15 constructs but with more in-depth exploration of the constructs for senior classes. Secondly, presently students are more prone to be interactive in class. As revealed in the previous study by Luk (9) on the Secondary 1 students, many of them felt that the program was boring. Therefore, if they have a choice, they may not be willing to join even if it may be beneficial for them. Thirdly, when students move to Secondary 3 classes, there are likely to be higher academic demands placed on them. Moral class or personal growth courses like P.A.T.H.S. may not be seen by the students as a high priority.

With regard to the objective outcome evaluation, our findings showed no significant improvement in the Secondary 2 program at post-test, which is inconsistent with findings in Hong Kong (22). There may be several possible reasons. Firstly, the number of participants in this study is relatively small in comparison to the Hong Kong study which had 20 experimental schools with 2,784 students. This potentially increases the chances of sample bias in the study. Secondly, instructors in the Macau program included social workers and teachers, these professions are relatively new to this type of interactive youth program, which may affect their effectiveness in conducting the program. Thirdly, the instructors also have to adapt the modified program to meet their student needs, they may take time to practice and become familiarized with the program.

Finally, a certain number of students dropped out and exchanged with a group of new students joined in may affect the group cohesion which in turn may affect their involvement in the program.

However, when the W3 pre-test data of the old participants were compared with those of the new inexperienced participants, the findings generally showed that the old students performed better than the new ones. This was evidenced in terms of the global positive youth development and school adjustment indicators. Even with control for age, results still revealed that there was an improvement in positive identity sub-scale and life satisfaction scale. This comparison may demonstrate the effectiveness of the Secondary 1 program. Furthermore, when comparing the W3 and W4 data of this new group of students, significant improvement in different youth subscales, life satisfaction and school adjustment measures was noted. This evidence supports the effectiveness of the Secondary 2 program in this group of students. One possible explanation may relate to the non-academic nature of the program, so it may be more receptive to those whose academic performance is of average or below academic standard.

As this group of students is older than the students who were promoted from their original schools, most of them are probably of average or lower standard.

Another reason may relate to the fact that this is a new program and may attract their interest more than the older students. Conversely, the decrease in bonding score could be attributed to taking more time for them to develop new friendship, because of the repeating in Secondary 2 or adapting to a new school. More attention and further study are warranted in relation to the behavioral intention of alcohol consumption in this group.

Subjective outcome evaluation highlighted positive results from all participants. Although the longitudinal data from the objective outcome evaluation did not support any improvement, the effect of the program was found to be positive to the new comers in the junior secondary years. Therefore, in conjunction with the previous findings and based on the objective outcome evaluation the Secondary 2 program is effective, particularly for new comers of the program. There are several limitations of this study. Firstly, only two schools are involved and the sample size was relatively small, raising the potential for sample bias and it makes any generalization of the findings difficult. Secondly, the present study is based on a one-group pre/post-test design which may not be the most appropriate.

Other approaches such as the randomized control trial which can provide a more rigorous design to give more insight on the effectiveness of intervention program could have been considered. Thirdly, a comparative portion of students dropped out of the program which may affect longitudinal observation and observation of long-term effects.

Finally, if the program is more beneficial to those with below average academic performances, and if some of them may have to repeat studying in Secondary 1 and lose the chance to be followed up, the evaluation of the program will be incomplete.

Nevertheless, with the current paucity of youth studies in Macau, the present study can contribute to the understanding of the potential benefits of evidence-based youth work and provide further baseline data for evaluation of Secondary 3 periods in the future.

Acknowledgments

The research team would like to thank Professor Daniel Shek and his research team in Hong Kong for their support in launching this study in Macau. Furthermore, this study was financially supported by the Education and Youth Affair Bureau of the Macau Government.

References

[1]   Statistics and Census Services. Estimates of Macao resident population. Government of Macao Special Administrative Region. Accessed 2011 Oct 05. URL: http://www.dsec.gov.mo

[2]   Lo TW. The blueprint of youth problem and service development. Macau: Social Welfare of MSAR Government, 2005. (Chinese)

[3]   Education and Youth Affairs Bureau. Trend analysis of Youth Indicators of Macao 2008. Macau: Youth Indicators of Macao, 2009. (Chinese)

[4]   Loi HN, Soon IT, Tou C. Youth awareness on gaming in Macau. Macau: Macau Youth Research Association, 2008. (Chinese)

[5]   Anglican Macau Social Service. Review and development on youth studies. Macau: Anglican Macau Social Service, 2006. (Chinese)

[6]   Luk L. A review of the Positive Youth Development and Prevention Programs for Adolescents in Macau. Macau Journal of Nursing 2010;9(1):21-5.

[7]   Shek DTL. Conceptual framework underlying the development of a positive youth development program in Hong Kong. Int J Adolesc Med Health 2006;18(3):303-14.

[8]   Shek DTL, Siu A, Lee TY, Cheung CK, Chung R. Effectiveness of the Tier 1 Program of project P.A.T.H.S.: Objective outcome evaluation based on a randomized group trial. ScientificWorldJournal 2008;8:4-12.

[9]   Luk AL, Au A, Leong KM, Zhu M, Lau GB, Wong T, Lei N. Effectiveness of a positive youth development program for Secondary 1 students in Macau: A pilot study. ScientificWorldJournal 2011;11:1089–1100.

[10]   Anglican Youth Leadership Development Center. Survey report on "My school life". Macau: Anglican Macau Social Service. (Chinese) Accessed 2011 Oct 05. URL: http://www.dsej.gov.mo/rejm/db.html

[11]   Shek DTL, Siu A, Lee TY, Cheng H, Tsang S, Lui J, Lung D. Development and validation of a positive youth development scale in Hong Kong. Int J Adolesc Med Health 2006;18(3):547-58.

[12]   Shek DTL, Siu A, Lee TY. The Chinese youth development scale: A validation study. Res Soc Work Pract 2007;17:380-391.

[13]   Damon W. What is positive youth development? Ann Am Acad Political Soc Sci 2004;591(1):13-24.

[14]   Diener E, Emmons RA, Larsen RJ, Griffin S. The satisfaction with life scale. J Pers Assess 1985;49(1):71-5.

[15]   Shek DTL. Chinese cultural beliefs about adversity: Its relationship to psychological well-being, school adjustment and problem behavior in Hong Kong adolescents with and without economic disadvantage. Childhood 2004;11(1):63-80.

[16]   Lam CW, Shek DTL, Ng HY, Yeung KC, Lam OB. An innovation in drug prevention programs for adolescents: the Hong Kong Astro Project. Int J Adolesc Med Health 2005;17(4):343-53.

[17]   St Pierre TL, Mark MM, Kaltreider DL, Aikin KJ. Involving parents of high-risk youth in drug prevention: a three-year longitudinal study in boys and girls clubs. J Early Adolesc 1997;17:21-50.

[18]   Shek DTL. The relation of family functioning to adolescent psychological well-being, school adjustment, and problem behaviour. J Gene Psychol 1997;158:467-79.

[19]   Shek DTL, Siu A. Evaluation of a positive youth development program in Hong Kong: issues, principles and design. Int J Adolesc Med Health 2006;18(3):329-39.

[20]   Ma HK, Shek DTL. Subjective outcome evaluation of a positive youth development program in Hong Kong: Profiles and correlates. ScientificWorldJournal 2010;10:192-200.

[21]   Shek DTL, Sun R, Chan C. Evaluation of project P.A.T.H.S. (Secondary 2 program) by the program participants: findings based on the Experimental implementation phase. ScientificWorldJournal 2008;8:526-35.

[22]   Shek DTL. Effectiveness of the Tier 1 Program of Project P.A.T.H.S.: findings based on the first 2 years of program implementation. ScientificWorldJournal 2009;9:539–47.

In: Child Health and Human Development Yearbook 2013   ISBN: 978-1-63117-939-6
Editor: Joav Merrick   © 2014 Nova Science Publishers, Inc.

Chapter 9

Measurement of prosocial reasoning among Chinese adolescents

*Frank HY Lai[1], Andrew MH Siu, PhD[*1], Chewtyn CH Chan, PhD[1], and Daniel TL Shek, PhD, FHKPS, BBS, JP[2]*

[1]Department of Rehabilitation Sciences
[2]Department of Applied Social Sciences,
The Hong Kong Polytechnic University, Hunghom, Kowloon, Hong Kong, PRC

Abstracts

This study attempted to develop a standardized instrument for assessment of prosocial reasoning in Chinese populations. The Prosocial Reasoning Objective Measure (PROM) was translated and a two-stage study was conducted to evaluate the psychometric properties of the translated instrument. The content validity, cultural relevance, and reading level of the translated instrument were evaluated by an expert panel. Upon revisions according to the expert opinions, the Chinese PROM demonstrated good content validity, "good-to-very good test-retest" reliability and internal consistency. However, only partial support to the convergent validity of the Chinese PROM was found. In the first stage of the study (n = 50), the PROM scores had high positive correlations with empathy and negative correlations with personal distress and fantasy. These results were consistent with theoretical expectations, although this is also a concern that empathy had a close-to-unity correlation with PROM score in the small sample study of Stage 1. In the second stage of the study (n = 566), the relationship between PROM scores and prosocial behavior appeared to be weak. Results suggest that there were many personal, family, or social factors that were linked to prosocial behavior, and prosocial reasoning might only contribute to a small proportion of variation in prosocial behavior among adolescents.

Keywords: Prosocial, Reasoning, Moral, Measure, Chinese

* Correspondence: Dr. Andrew MH Siu, Department of Rehabilitation Sciences, The Hong Kong Polytechnic University, Hunghom, Kowloon, Hong Kong, PRC. E-mail: a.siu@polyu.edu.hk.

Introduction

Moral reasoning is defined as the process of judging right and wrong, and is regarded as the force behind moral action (1). As a child progresses to adolescence, and their moral reasoning changes from the 'self-focused' or 'self-centered' status / mentality ('what feels good to me is right') to a stance in which social approval guides both reasoning about justice and about doing good. Moral reasoning becomes more sophisticated as a child reaches adolescence, an empathic orientation stage in which they often express sympathetic concerns for others. The empathic orientation could further develop into the internalized value orientation stage in late adolescence or early adulthood, which is defined as an "orientation to an internalized responsibility, duty, or need to uphold the laws and accepted norms or values (2,3). The young person eventually develops an individualized ethics code for directing their moral behavior.

Eisenberg adopted the stages of moral development of Kohlberg and examined how prosocial (moral) reasoning is linked to prosocial behavior like sharing, cooperating, helping, volunteering and comforting others (4). Based on the theories of moral development (1) and empirical studies, Eisenberg further refined the five stages of prosocial reasoning (5): 1) Hedonistic (self-focused) Orientation: The respondent only cares for oneself, and any apparent altruistic behavior is motivated by selfishness, e.g. 'I'll help them because they'll help me in future' (reciprocity), or simply because the child likes the person they are helping, 2) "Needs of Others" Orientation: It addresses the needs of others who are being recognized only to a limited extent. The needs of the specific situation are being addressed without a genuine sense of empathy, 3) Stereotyped, and Approval-focused Orientation: Adolescent acts in a way that will make them popular or liked by others, for example lending a helping hand in order to impress others. When they are asked to explain their behavior, they tend to use stereotyped portrayals of good and bad behavior, 4a) Empathic Orientation: Adolescent starts to show genuine empathy by putting themselves in the shoes of others and begins to report feelings of genuine guilt when considering their own actions, 4b) Transitional Level: Adolescents explain their actions by referring to wider social values and the need to protect the dignity and self-esteem of others, 5) Internalized Orientation: The adolescent has a comprehensive set of values and understands their responsibilities towards others. They harbor self-respect that they can only maintain by behaving with a duty of care towards others. The person's desire to live up to their own set of principles is also a motivating factor.

The assessment of moral reasoning was often conducted by using moral dilemmas - hypothetical situations in which people are required to make difficult decisions. During the assessment, it is more significant to examine the reasoning behind rather than the actual choice made. In line with the approach used by Kohlberg (1), Eisenberg and associates (5, 6) presented ethical dilemmas for assessing the stage of development of the prosocial moral reasoning in children and adolescents. They asked respondents to take up the role of someone else and decide whether to act out of self-interest or in the interests of others.

To date, many of the previous studies on prosocial moral reasoning were conducted by using interview measures of moral reasoning. In recent years, some self-completed measures of moral reasoning have been designed to assess prosocial reasoning, which could be more efficiently and effectively administered to larger research samples (7-9).Based on Eisenberg's prosocial moral reasoning interview measure (2), Carlo and associates developed a paper-and-pencil measure named Prosocial Reasoning Objective Measure (PROM) (10).The PROM is a self-completed questionnaire which assess prosocial reasoning using moral dilemmas, in which a person's needs/desires conflict with those of needy others, with formal obligations minimal or absent (11). It is one of the few standardized instruments designed for measuring prosocial reasoning, which takes approximately 20 to 30 minutes to complete.

The original English PROM has been administered to child, adolescent, and adult samples, and its psychometric properties were promising (12). The test-retest reliability of the standard 5-story version was good, with coefficients ranging from .70 to .79 (10). Internal consistency was fair to acceptable, with Cronbach's α ranging from 56 to.78. For the 7-story version, internal consistency (α) ranged from .61 to .85 for the five types of reasoning, but no test-retest reliability was reported (11).

Studies of construct validity of the 5-stories version showed that sympathy was positively associated with higher levels of prosocial moral reasoning in PROM and tended to be negatively related to lower levels of moral reasoning (i.e. hedonistic and approval -oriented reasoning). These findings are consistent with prior empirical findings (11, 13,14) that self-reflective types of moral reasoning often reflect other-oriented cognitions and feelings. These psychometric studies provided evidence that the 5-story version PROM is a reliable and valid measure of prosocial moral reasoning for adolescents.

The PROM has been translated into Portuguese, Spanish, Korean, and Tagalog (Philipino), and there were slight modifications of the test stories for different language versions. A Chinese version of 5-story PROM had also been developed in Taiwan, but no validation study of the Chinese version has been completed so far. Culture plays an important part in how people understand and define prosocial behavior in a society. It is therefore essential to examine the cultural relevance and validity of the PROM if it is used within a Chinese population.

This study attempted to evaluate the psychometric properties of the Chinese Prosocial Reasoning Measure (Chinese PROM), i.e. to assess whether the Chinese version PROM is culturally relevant, reliable, internally consistent, and valid. The convergent validity of PROM will be investigated by studying its relationships with measures of empathy and prosocial as well as antisocial behavior.

There are several reasons in developing a standardized instrument for measuring prosocial reasoning. First, the stage theory of prosocial moral reasoning has long been used in describing moral development. It is of empirical interest to examine if measures of prosocial reasoning (like the PROM) could be developed by using the stage theories. Second, there is a growing research interest in studying the factors underlying the development of prosocial behavior (15,16), but the lack of a standardized instrument for efficient assessment of prosocial reasoning could be a major barrier to further research in this area (17). Third, the testing of moral reasoning has long been assessed through ethical or moral dilemmas by using the semi-structured interview format.

The PROM replaces the interview method with self-completed questionnaire format, and there is a need to examine if this format assessment could be as valid and reliable as in the interviews. Fourth, there is a need to examine the cultural relevance and psychometric properties when the PROM is used with Chinese adolescents. Culture clearly makes a substantial contribution to the development of prosocial development in Chinese populations (18,19).

Methods

This study attempted to conduct a validation study of a Chinese version of Prosocial Reasoning Objective Measure (Chinese PROM).The study comprises two stages. In the first stage, we evaluated the content validity and cultural relevance through expert panel review, and estimated test-retest reliability and internal consistency of the Chinese version of PROM by using a small sample ($n = 50$). We also examine the relationship between PROM scores and empathy. In the second stage, we collected a large sample ($n = 566$) to examine the validity of the PROM by correlating its scores with prosocial and antisocial behavior.

Study 1

Expert Panel Review

The original English version of the PROM was translated into Chinese by a professional translator. A group of 5 experts in youth development research was invited to review the translated Chinese PROM. On a self-completed questionnaire, the experts were requested to use a five-point scale (from "strongly disagree" to "strongly agree") to rate how far the test scenarios and items were relevant to testing prosocial reasoning, and how representative of these five scenarios in assessing prosocial reasoning in young people. A second expert panel, which was composed of three secondary school teachers and two social workers, assess the clarity of presentation of the test scenarios and evaluate if the story contents could be easily understood by young people at a reading level of grade 6 or above.

   For both expert panel reviews, a mean score of 4.0 (agree) was selected as the criterion for the cut-off score of a clear presentation, good-content understandability and the selected scenario is relevant to young people. Justifications would be requested for items that are considered irrelevant, and recommendations on modifications of items that needed revision would also be requested. Refinement and finalization of items were made according to opinions of these panels' reviews.

Study of reliability and convergent validity

Participants

A convenient sample of young people from early to mid-adolescence was recruited through parents' network and a youth service agency, if they are Chinese, aged between12 and 16 years old, are full time secondary school students, can read and write Chinese. The participants were recruited. A sample of 50 participants (25 males and 25 females) was recruited. Their mean age is 13.5 (SD = 1.43), and they were Secondary 1 to 5 students. Twenty four of them were in junior high school, while 26 subjects were in high school. They came from 10 different schools.

Instruments

Prosocial reasoning. The Prosocial Reasoning Objective Measure (PROM) was used to examine prosocial moral reasoning in young people and adults (10).The PROM requested respondents to read stories about people who need help from others and then decide whether they would offer help and the reasoning behind it. The dilemmas in the stories are designed to invoke a conflict between the actor's needs, wants and desires and those of another (or others).The Chinese short version uses 5 stories that are translated from the short version of the English PROM: 1) Donating blood to needy others versus losing time and money at work and school, 2) Choosing to get an injured child's parents versus going to a friend's party, 3) Continuing to stay and play in one's own backyard versus going to try and stop a bully that is picking on a peer, 4) Helping disabled children strengthen their legs by teaching them to swim versus practicing for a swimming contest to win the prize in cash, 5) Keep food after a flood versus giving some food to others who had none.

After reading each story, respondents were asked to rate on a scale of one to five (from "greatly important" to "not important") on how important each of the five reasons was in deciding what the character should do. The five reasons reflected the five types of prosocial reasoning of Hedonistic, Needs-oriented, Stereotyped, Approval- orientated, and Internalized. The overall weighted PROM score is an overall score that reflects the development or maturity of prosocial moral reasoning. According to the PROM manual, the overall weighted PROM score is the sum of proportion scores of internalized reasoning multiplied by 3, needs-oriented and stereotypic reasoning multiplied by 2, and hedonistic and approval-oriented reasoning.

PROM stories were slightly modified for use with different age groups and cultural groups (5,12).The psychometric properties of PROM have been reported in studies with students from middle-childhood to early adulthood. The results have been well elaborated (20). The test-retest reliability of PROM ranged from .70 to .79, while Cronbach's α ranged from .56 to.78 (10).

Empathy and related constructs. The 21-item Chinese Interpersonal Reactivity Index (C-IRI) is a self-reported questionnaire consisting of 3 subscales measuring empathy and related constructs: 1) The Fantasy Scale (FS) that measures the tendency to imaginatively transpose oneself into fictional situations, 2) The Empathy Scale (ES) that measure the tendency to experience feelings for sympathy and perspective/role taking, 3) Personal Distress Scale (PDS) that measures the tendency to experience distress and discomfort in response to extreme distress in others. Participants are requested to indicate the degree they agree with each item by using a 5-point Likert-type scale, which varied from 0 (*does not describe me well*) to 4 (*describes me very well*). A higher score in the three subscales represents a higher tendency in each aspect of empathy. The C-IRI possessed acceptable psychometric properties in Chinese adolescent samples (21), and empathy-related constructs can be conceptualized as a convergent construct with prosocial moral reasoning.

Procedures

A cover letter, a research information sheet, and a consent form were sent to the potential participants. The documents described the background and purpose of the study. The participants were instructed to sign on a consent form if they agreed to participate in this study, and returned the completed questionnaires to their teachers or parents.

To assess test-retest reliability, 25 of the 50 participants completed the Chinese PROM twice, with an interval of one week in between. The internal consistency estimates (Cronbach's α) were obtained from the data set of all participants ($n = 50$). For the data collection on convergent validity, a group of 50 full time secondary school students was recruited using the same selection criterion. The participants were requested to complete the Chinese PROM and the C-IRI. Correlations between the two measures were estimated.

Study 2

This stage of the study aims to recruit a larger sample for studying convergent validity between PROM scores, adolescent prosocial and antisocial behavior, and also sex differences in PROM scores.

Instruments

The Prosocial Reasoning Objective Measure (PROM), that was used in stage 1, was also used in this Stage of the study.

Prosocial behavior. The Adolescent Behavior Questionnaire (ABQ) is generic Chinese instrument designed for measuring the prosocial and antisocial behavior of adolescents (22). The Prosocial scale assesses normative acts and altruistic acts, while the Antisocial scale covers rule-breaking, challenging, or aggressive behavior in school, home, and social settings. The respondents were asked to report the frequency of 65 behaviors performed in the past year on a 7-point Likert type scale (1 = none, 2 = 1-2 times, 3 = 3-4 times, 4 = 5-6 times, 5 = 7-8 times,6 = 9-10 times, and 7 = more than 10 times). The ABQ possesses two general scales of Antisocial/Delinquent Behavior (DB) scale and Prosocial Behavior (PB) scale. The Adolescent Behavior Questionnaire (ABQ) score is the difference between the mean scores of Prosocial Behavior and Antisocial Behavior scales. It indicates how far a young person's behavior is antisocial (negative scores) or prosocial (positive scores).

Participants

A convenient sample of 566 young people in mid- to late adolescence was recruited from 36 secondary schools. The ages of the participants ranged from 14 to 22 years old ($M = 16.2$, $SD = 1.1$), but 79% were between 15 and 17 years old. There were more females (67.7%) than males (32.3%) in the sample. Most of the participants were studying Secondary 4 (52.2%) or Secondary 5 (42.3%), and a few were studying Secondary 6 (5.4%).Teachers help to carry out the study. It may involve to a certain extent of social desirability and the ethical consideration.

Procedures

All potential participants were given a briefing on the objective and information of the study (based on a research information sheet) by class teachers. All participants (students) who were willing to participate in the study are requested to sign on a consent form for volunteer participation in the study. For potential participants who are younger than 18 years, an invitation letter would be sent to their parents. Parents who endorsed their children to join the study are requested to sign on and return a consent form to the school. Ethical approval of this study had been obtained from the Departmental Research Committee of our university. The school sent all the consent forms and completed questionnaires back to the researchers for record and analysis.

Results

A total of 11 content experts were invited to comment on the content validity, cultural relevance, and reading level of the translated instrument (Chinese PROM). The experts are professionals in education, social work, clinical psychology and education. Six of the experts are academics and experienced researchers on the youth development in Hong Kong. Five of the experts were frontline workers in providing educational, social work, or counseling service to young people.

On the whole, the experts agreed that the contents of five test scenarios were relevant to assessment of prosocial reasoning (mean rating of 4.46 out of 5), and representativeness of stories for testing prosocial reasoning (mean rating of 4.49 out of 5).However, the experts found that the reading level and cultural relevance of Scenario 2 were not satisfactory (mean rating were 3.73 and 3.76 respectively). The experts suggested that most adolescents in Hong Kong have a mobile phone, and the young person in Scenario 2 could seek help by using his/her mobile. Thus, the story was changed from "going to her home and told her parent to come for help" to "stay with her till her parent comes". The experts also gave a number of suggestions to further improve the presentation of the test scenarios, including: 1) Use of terms that can be more easily understood by young people, 2) Improve the quality of translation,3) Simplification of sentences, 4) Clarification of meaning, and 5) Amend grammatical errors.

Reliability

The internal consistency of the PROM subscales and the weighted total ranged from .74 to .93 (Cronbach's α), while the test-retest reliability ranged from .75 to .88 (ICCs) (Table 1).The reliability estimates are regarded as ranging from "acceptable" to "satisfactory". The reliability estimates were much higher than that reported in the study by Carlo in 1992(10).

Table 1. Reliability study of the Chinese PROM

PROM scale and subscales	Test-retest (ICC) (n = 25)	Internal Consistency	
		This study (n = 50)	Carlo (1992) study (n = 27)
Hedonistic	.83	.91	.72
Needs-oriented	.88	.93	.56
Approval-oriented	.75	.74	.78
Stereotypic	.81	.89	.67
Internalized	.88	.93	.70
PROM weighted total	.88	.89	#

Note.[#] not reported.

Relationship between PROM scores and C-IRI

Based on the small sample collected in Stage 1 ($n = 50$), the results showed that the PROM scales and subscales had significantly correlations with the C-IRI subscales (Table 2). The hedonistic and approval-oriented subscales in PROM had a different pattern of correlations from the other three subscales. Both the hedonistic and approval-oriented subscales had significantly positive correlations with fantasy ($r_{hedonistic} = .55$, $r_{approval-oriented} = .61$) and personal distress subscales ($r_{hedonistic} = .61$, $r_{approval-oriented} = .68$). The pattern of correlation of these two subscales was opposite to that between the needs-oriented, stereotypic, and internalized subscales with the C-IRI subscales. These three subscales had significant negative correlations with fantasy and personal subscales of C-IRI, and significant positive correlation with empathy subscale of the C-IRI. The overall weighted PROM score had significant negative correlation with fantasy ($r = -.77$) and personal distress ($r = -.80$) subscales of C-IRI and significant positive correlation with empathy subscales ($r = .92$). Relationship between PROM scores and prosocial/antisocial behavior. On the whole, PROM scores were not strongly related to antisocial, prosocial or adolescent behavior (Table 3).Among the five subscales, only hedonistic and internalized reasoning subscales showed low significant correlations with adolescent behavior. Hedonistic reasoning subscale had significant positive correlation with antisocial behavior ($r = .14$, $p < .01$), and negative correlations with prosocial behavior ($r = -.10$, $p < .05$) and adolescent behavior ($r = -.17$, $p < .01$). Internalized reasoning subscale had low significant correlation with adolescent behavior ($r = .10$, $p < .05$). Overall weighted PROM score had significant correlations with prosocial behavior ($r = .10$, $p < .05$) and adolescent behavior ($r = .12$, $p < .05$).

Table 2. Correlation between the Chinese PROM and the C-IRI (measure of empathy and related constructs) ($n = 50$)

PROM scales &Subscales	Chinese C-IRI subscales		
	Fantasy Scale	Empathy Scale	Personal Distress Scale
Hedonistic	.55 **	-.78 **	.61 **
Needs-oriented	-.71 **	.72 **	-.72 **
Approval-oriented	.68 **	-.76 **	.69 **
Stereotypic	-.67 **	.77 **	-.65 **
Internalized	-.78 **	.92 **	-.82 **
PROM weighted overall	-. 77 **	.92 **	-.80 **

Note.* $p < .05$, ** $p < .01$.

Table 3. Correlation between Prosocial Moral Reasoning and Prosocial/Antisocial Behaviorin Adolescents ($n = 566$)

PROM subscales and Weighted Overall	Antisocial Behavior	Prosocial Behavior	Adolescent Behavior
Hedonistic	.14**	-.10*	-.17**
Need-oriented	.05	.06	.04
Approval-oriented	-.09	-.04	.00
Stereotypic	-.06	.04	.07
Internalized	-.06	.07	.10*
Overall Weighted	-.05	.10*	.12*

Note.* $p < .05$, ** $p < .01$.

Gender Differences

Multivariate ANCOVA was conducted to examine gender differences in PROM weighted total and subscales, with age as covariate (Table 4). Multivariate test results showed that age was not a significant covariate, and there were no differences in the profile of five PROM subscales between males and females. There were, however, significant differences in hedonistic and stereotypic reasoning subscales between males and females. Males had significant higher hedonistic reasoning ($F = 13.06$, $p< .001$) than females and females had significantly higher needs-oriented reasoning ($F = 7.54$, $p< .01$) than males.

Table 4. Comparison of Prosocial Reasoning between Males and Females, with Age as Covariate

Variables	Male[a] (n = 182)		Female[a] (n = 379)		*F*
	M	*SE*	*M*	*SE*	
Hedonistic	.176	.002	.168	.001	13.06***
Needs-oriented	.206	.002	.212	.001	7.54**
Approval-oriented	.183	.002	.184	.001	.49
Stereotypic	.219	.002	.220	.001	.00
Internalized	.216	.001	.216	.001	.08
PROM Overall Weighted	1.86	.004	1.86	.003	2.33

Note: * $p< .05$, ** $p< .01$, *** $p< .001$.
[a] Estimated marginal means and standard errors were presented, adjusted for age effects.

Discussion

A Chinese version of the PROM was developed in this study for measuring prosocial moral reasoning in young people. Through an expert panel review, the translated instrument had good-content relevance and representativeness. The expert panel also identified some issues in the translation, presentation, and reading level of the test scenarios, and modifications were done according to the expert opinions. The Chinese PROM weighted overall and subscales had "acceptable" to "very good" test-retest reliability and internal consistency, which is significantly higher than studies of the original English version. The results supported that the Chinese PROM has good -content validity and reliability.

The study of convergent validity yields mixed results. High levels of prosocial reasoning (PROM weighted overall) were associated with high levels of empathy but low levels of fantasy and personal distress. In particular, the correlation between empathy and PROM weighted overall score was close to unity. This implies that young persons with high empathy are very likely to reach an internalized stage of prosocial reasoning. It is interesting to find that hedonistic and approval-oriented reasoning is strongly and negatively associated with empathy while all other reasoning types had positive correlation with empathy. This implies young persons with high hedonistic or approval-oriented reasoning are less likely to apply empathy. Since the developmental theories postulated that empathy precedes the development of higher level of prosocial reasoning (23-25), the results support that hedonistic and approval-oriented are the less mature types of prosocial reasoning. Self-reflective types of moral reasoning are often elicited by the tendency to feel concerned for others. The positive relationship between need-oriented and empathy is not consistent with theoretical expectations or empirical findings in a Western culture. Need-oriented is also regarded as a less mature type or reasoning in the stage theories of prosocial development, but it could be regarded as a socially desirable response to the needs of others in Chinese culture. On the other hand, undertaking prosocial behavior due to the needs of the specific situation could be regarded as socially desirable in the Chinese culture. In fact, a needs-oriented type of reasoning could exist with or without a genuine sense of empathy.

Personal distress is considered as primitive and self-focused empathic reaction (25). Our findings echoed previous findings that personal distress was negatively related to both stereotypic and internalized reasoning whilst positively related to approval-oriented reasoning (10, 23). Fantasy has a pattern of correlation with prosocial reasoning that is similar to that of personal distress. Fantasy could be a precursor to empathy, but it could be a barrier to apply empathy or moral reasoning if fantasy stays very strong in social interaction. It is therefore reasonable that fantasy has a negative correlation with overall score of prosocial reasoning and positive correlations with hedonistic and approval-oriented reasoning. In general, the results indicate a high level of personal distress and fantasy is associated with lower levels of maturity in prosocial reasoning. It appears that personal distress and fantasy, as emotional and imaginative aspects of reacting to others, could be barriers to the application of prosocial reasoning.

The low correlations between PROM scores and measures of antisocial or prosocial behavior did not provide strong support to the convergent validity of PROM. The PROM overall weighted score was low but had significant correlations with prosocial and overall adolescent behavior (a score of mean prosocial behavior minus antisocial behavior). Among the subscales, only hedonistic reasoning had significant and low positive correlation with antisocial behavior, and low negative correlations with prosocial and overall adolescent behavior. Internalized reasoning had low and significant correlation with overall adolescent behavior. The first implication of the results is that prosocial reasoning may have little influence on prosocial behavior. Adolescent prosocial behavior could be shaped by a wide range of family and social factors, as well as their own development in interpersonal competence (26). Further research on predicting prosocial behavior may need to include social influence factors other than prosocial reasoning. Second, the studies also showed that proportions of using the five types of reasoning were quite similar (varying from .17 to .22) in this sample of high school students. There is a slightly higher proportion of scores (.21 to .22) for the needs-oriented, stereotypic, and internalized, but only slightly higher than hedonistic and approval-oriented reasoning (.17 to .18). Contrary to expectations of stage theory, the more mature types of prosocial reasoning were not widely adopted by the participants in this late adolescence sample (23, 25). Further longitudinal studies of prosocial development will be needed to examine the validity of the stage theory, i.e. if internalized reasoning increases as young people grow older.

This study is a useful addition to current literature on prosocial reasoning and development. First, it is one of the few studies that investigate the measurement of prosocial reasoning. The PROM is found to be reliable measure of prosocial reasoning. Second, the study also explored how prosocial reasoning is related to convergent constructs of empathy-related constructs and prosocial behavior. The results only provide partial support to the validity of PROM. The results are not consistent with studies conducted in Western cultures, and may point to the differences in conceptualization of what is prosocial among cultures. Prosocial reasoning may also not be as important predictor of prosocial behavior in collectivist cultures. The results indicate a need for further replication of the present study. The development of the Chinese PROM enables professionals and researchers to assess prosocial reasoning among young people in an objective and efficient manner. The scale can also be used to evaluate the outcomes of youth development programs.

There are several limitations in this study. First, because of practical limitations, the test-retest interval in the reliability test was one week only. Further study should try to use longer periods of test-retest reliability i.e. two to four weeks. Second, the sample in first stage of study was small ($n = 50$). For the second stage of study, most of the participants were from Secondary 4 and 5 and a narrow age band. This is a possible reason why age effects were insignificant, which is not in line of results of longitudinal studies of prosocial reasoning conducted in the US. Third, items for monitoring social desirability responses were not utilized in this study. The original full and brief versions include a 6th question in addition to the five items on prosocial reasoning for each test scenario. The items were removed as many expert panel members regarded it is not necessary and confusing to potential respondents. However, we believe it is likely that social desirability can greatly influence responses to a test of prosocial reasoning. Future studies should try to include these items and estimate how far respondents are trying to tell people that they are prosocial.

In summary, the results indicate that the Chinese PROM had good -content validity and reliability. The quality of translation, cultural relevance, and reading level have been satisfactorily revised for use with adolescents. There is, however, partial support to the convergent validity of the Chinese PROM. The PROM scores had high positive correlations with empathy, and negative correlations with personal distress and fantasy. These results were consistent with theoretical deductions, although it is also a concern that empathy had a close-to-unity correlation with PROM score in the small sample study of Stage 1. The relationship between PROM scores and prosocial behavior tends to be weak. It appears that there are many personal, family, or social factors that are linked to prosocial behavior, and prosocial reasoning which may only contribute to a small proportion of variation in prosocial behavior among adolescents.

References

[1]   Kohlberg L. Essays on moral development: Volume two. The psychology of moral development. San Francisco, CA: Harper Row, 1984:3-19,170-81,640-51.

[2]   Eisenberg N. Altruistic emotion, cognition, and behavior. Hillsdale, NJ: Lawrence Erlbaum, 1986.

[3]   Krebs DL. Altruism: An examination of the concept and review of the literature. Psychol Bull 1970;73:258-572.

[4]   Carlo G, Okun MA, Knight GP, de Guzman M. The interplay of traits and motives on volunteering: Agreeableness, extraversion and prosocial value motivation. Pers Individ Dif 2005;38:1293–305.

[5]   Eisenberg-Berg N. Development of children's prosocial moral judgment. Dev Psychol 1979;15:128-37.

[6]   Eisenberg N, Shell R, Pasternack J, Lennon R, Beller R, Mathy RM. Prosocial development in middle childhood: a longitudinal study. Dev Psychol 1987;23:712-18.

[7]   Gibbs JC, Arnold KD, Morgan RL,Schwartz ES, Gavaghan MP, Tappan MB. Construction and validation of a multiple-choice measure of moral reasoning. Child Dev1984;55:527-36.

[8]   Kurtines WM, Pimm JB. The moral development scale: A Piagetian measure of moral judgment. Educ Psychol Meas 1983;43:89-105.

[9]   Rest J. Morality. In: Mussen P, Flavell JH, Markman E, eds. Handbook of child psychology. New York: Wiley, 1983:556-629.

[10]   Carlo G, Eisenberg N, Knight GP. An objective measure of prosocial moral reasoning. J Res Adolesc 1992;2:331-49.

[11]   Carlo G, Koller SH, Eisenberg N, Da Silva MS, Frohlich CB. A cross-national study on the relations among prosocial moral reasoning, gender role orientations and prosocial behaviors. Dev Psychol 1996;32:231-40.

[12]   Carlo G, Knight GP, McGinley M, Zamboanga BL, Jarvis L. The multidimensionality of prosocial behaviors: Evidence of measurement invariance in early Mexican American and European American adolescents. J Res Adolesc 2010;4:489-512.

[13]   Eisenberg N, Shell R, Pasternack J, Lennon R, Beller R, Mathy RM. Prosocial development in middle childhood: a longitudinal study. Dev Psychol 1987; 23:712-18.

[14]   Eisenberg N, Miller PA, Shell R, McNalley S, Shea C. Prosocial development in adolescence: a longitudinal study. Dev Psychol 1991;27:849-57.

[15]   Carlo G, Da Silva MS, Eisenberg N, Frohlich CB, Koller SH. A cross-national study on the relations among prosocial moral reasoning, gender role, orientations, and prosocial behaviours. Dev Psychol 1996;32:2231-40.

[16]   Fabes RA, Carlo G, Kupanoff K, Laible D. Early adolescence and prosocial/moral behaviorI: The role of individual processes. J Early Adolesc 1999;19:5–16.

[17]   Colby A, Kohlberg L. The Measurement of Moral Judgment: Volume1. Theoretical Foundations and Research Validation. Cambridge: Cambridge University Press, 1987.

[18]   Ma HK. The relation of academic achievement, family and classroom social environment, and peer interactions to prosocial and antisocial behaviour of Chinese children. Psychologia 2003;46:163-73.

[19]   Ma HK, Leung MC. The relation of altruistic orientation to family social environment in Chinese children. Psychologia 1995;38:109-15.

[20]   Carlo G, Knight GP, McGinley M, Zamboanga BL, Jarvis L. The multidimensionality of prosocial behaviors: Evidence of measurement invariance in early Mexican American and European American adolescents. J Res Adolesc 2010;4:489-512.

[21]   Siu AMH, Shek DTL. Validation of the Interpersonal Reactivity Index in a Chinese Context. Res Soc Work Pract 2005;15:118-26.

[22]   Ma HK. Adolescent Behavior Questionnaire: An introduction. (Unpublished manuscript). Hong Kong: Chinese University Hong Kong, 1988.

[23]   Eisenberg N, Miller PA, Shell R, McNalley S, Shea C. Prosocial development in adolescence: a longitudinal study. Dev Psychol 1991;27:849-57.

[24]   Eisenberg N, Carlo G, Murphy B, Van Court P. Prosocial development in late adolescence: A longitudinal study. Child Dev 1995;66:1179-97.

[25]   Hoffman ML. Development of prosocial motivation: Empathy and guilt. In: Eisenberg N, Eds.The Development of Prosocial Behavior. New York: Academic Press, 1982:218–231.

[26]   Siu AMH, Cheng HCH, Leung MCM. Prosocial norms as a positive youth development construct: Conceptual bases and implications for curriculum development. Int J of Adolesc Med Health 2006;18:451-57.

In: Child Health and Human Development Yearbook 2013   ISBN: 978-1-63117-939-6
Editor: Joav Merrick   © 2014 Nova Science Publishers, Inc.

Chapter 10

Predictors of prosocial behavior among Chinese high school students in Hong Kong

Andrew MH Siu, PhD[*1]*, Daniel TL Shek, PhD, FHKPS, BBS, JP*[2]*, and Frank HY Lai, MSc*[1]

[1]Department of Rehabilitation Sciences
[2]Department of Applied Social Sciences,
The Hong Kong Polytechnic University, Hunghom, Kowloon, Hong Kong, PRC

Abstract

This study examined the correlates and predictors of prosocial behavior among Chinese adolescents in Hong Kong. A sample of 518 high school students responded to a questionnaire containing measures of antisocial and prosocial behavior, prosocial norms, pragmatic values, moral reasoning, and empathy. Preliminary analyses showed that there were gender differences in some of the measures. While correlation analyses showed that parental education, prosocial norms, pragmatic values, moral reasoning, and empathy were related to prosocial behavior, regression analyses showed that prosocial norms, pragmatic values, and empathy dimensions (personal distress and empathy) were key predictors of it. The findings are largely consistent with theoretical predictions and previous research findings, other than the negative relationship between personal distress and prosocial behavior. The study also underscores the importance of values and norms in predicting prosocial behavior, which has been largely neglected in previous studies.

Keywords: Prosocial behavior, adolescence, Chinese adolescents

---

[*] Correspondence: Dr. Andrew MH Siu, Department of Rehabilitation Sciences, The Hong Kong Polytechnic University, Hunghom, Kowloon, Hong Kong, PRC. E-mail: a.siu@inet.polyu.edu.hk.

Introduction

Prosocial behaviors are actions that aim to fulfill another person's need for support, or to promote and sustain a positive benefit for them [1,2]. In everyday life, this involves actions such as donating, sharing, comforting, expressing sympathy, helping, and providing physical assistance and support to others, often at a cost to oneself [3,4]. Interestingly, individual prosocial behavior contributes not just to others' well-being, but also one's own. Many studies show that through helping and volunteering, young people can satisfy their own needs, learn about and express their values, understand the world, gain career-related experience, and strengthen social competence and relationships [4-7]. Accordingly, interest in the study of prosocial behavior is growing around the world.

The cultivation of prosocial behavior has long been an important objective of compulsory education and youth development programs. Prosocial development is closely linked to various positive developmental outcomes for young people including academic success, positive self-worth, positive relationships with others, and higher social competence [4-6]. On the community or societal level, prosocial behavior such as cooperation, taking responsibility, and team work are crucial to the effective functioning of work and social interactions. Prosocial and altruistic behavior like volunteering or care giving could be a major source of a society's human capital.

In contrast to the abundance of Western research on adolescent prosocial behavior, very few studies have been done with Chinese adolescents. In addition, while there are many studies on antisocial and deviant behaviors among adolescents, comparatively fewer look at prosocial behavior, including the predictors of it in adolescents. For example, Ma and colleagues [8,9] show that several factors influence prosocial behavior in adolescents, including peer and teacher influences; family, school, and social environment; and individual achievement. Although these studies are pioneering, they did not explore intrapersonal competencies such as prosocial norms, pragmatic values, moral reasoning, and empathy.

It is likely that prosocial development has largely taken shape by mid to late adolescence. By then, young people are likely to have developed a set of values to guide their behavior. Unfortunately, few studies have examined how personal values may influence prosocial behavior among young people. In this study, it is hypothesized that the adoption of prosocial norms and rejection of pragmatic values will play a part in determining prosocial behavior of young people. Prosocial norms are standards and beliefs, or the set of shared social expectations of healthy, ethical, appropriate, and culturally-desirable actions, that promote prosocial behavior and minimize health risks [10,11].The label pragmatic values is used in this study to refer to values that are self-centered, materialistic, and instrumental in achieving one's own ends rather than others', such as one's own achievement, satisfaction, happiness, security, or power [12,13]. Furthermore, as moral reasoning is intimately related to prosocial behavior, it can also be hypothesized that a higher level of the former will be related to a higher level of the latter.

There are also theoretical accounts proposing that individual differences in prosocial development are closely linked to empathy-related constructs like sympathy, personal distress, perspective and role taking, social awareness, and moral reasoning [3,14,15]. Many of these competencies emerge in early life and continue to develop over childhood and adolescence. By the time young people reach late adolescence, they have passed the peak of their physical growth and become sexually mature, and are starting to consolidate their identity. The rapid development of executive functioning, such as deductive reasoning and information processing, enables them to become more proficient in perspective and role taking, emotional expression, and social awareness. They develop greater self-awareness and the ability to manage their emotional expression and social behavior [16]. Based on the existing literature, it can be proposed that empathy-related constructs (such as empathy, personal distress, and fantasy) will be related to prosocial behavior in later adolescence.

Finally, one might ask how socio-demographic factors such as age, gender, and level of parental education related to adolescent prosocial behavior and the attributes which may be associated with it (such as prosocial norms, pragmatic values, moral reasoning, and empathy constructs). In terms of age, since adolescents develop better moral reasoning as they get older, it may be expected that age is linearly related to prosociality. On the other hand, some theorists may also argue that as an increase in age may not necessarily lead to an advancement of moral values, there may be no relationship between these factors. Since there is not much data in this area, the present study attempts to examine the relationship between age and prosocial behavior. Furthermore, as females tend to show more empathy and to be more relationship oriented, it may also be expected that they will demonstrate higher levels of prosocial norms, moral reasoning, and prosocial behavior, and lower levels of pragmatic values. Finally, as parental education implies greater social capital (such as better parenting and more involvement), it can also be predicted that parental education levels will be positively related to adolescent prosocial behavior. Against this background, the specific objectives of this study were; a) to examine the correlations between basic demographic factors (age and gender) and adolescent prosocial behavior and its related attributes (including prosocial norms, pragmatic values, moral reasoning and empathy-related constructs); b) to study the correlates of prosocial behavior, including prosocial norms, pragmatic values, prosocial reasoning, and empathy-related constructs; and c) to identify the key predictors of prosocial behavior among late adolescents. A cross-sectional survey was conducted using a sample of high school students in Hong Kong.

Methods

The participants in this study were recruited from a group of high school students (Secondary Four to Six) who attended a one-day "Teen Talk" event organized by the Hong Kong Law Society. The event was titled "Love Yourself, Love Others" and its purpose was to engage young people in a whole day of discussion about their own core values as well as those of society. As well as this, the event attempted to increase participants' understanding of legal and social issues.

A total of 533 participants completed and returned survey questionnaires through their schools, giving a response rate of around 35.5%. Fifteen questionnaires were not included in the analysis either because more than 10% of items were in complete or because they were extreme outliers. After discarding these questionnaires, 518 remained in the dataset. The participants were all full-time students aged 14-22 (M = 16.2, SD = 1.1). There were more females (69.6%) than males (30.4%). They were recruited from 36 secondary schools and studying in Secondary 4 (54.0%), 5 (40.2%), or 6 (5.8%). When asked about their educational achievements compared to classmates, more than one third (37.1%) regarded themselves as better than average, and around half (48%) said they were average. A large proportion of participants regarded their conduct as better than average (48%) or very much better than average (14.3%).

Most of the participants were the only child in their family (72.4%) and 23.7% had one sibling. The median education level of both respondents' parents was Secondary Three. Financially, only 7.8 %(n=46) of these households were supported by social security benefits. Most of the respondents' fathers were employed full time (85.6%) or part-time (4.1%), with 50.8%of mothers working full time.

Procedures

Ethical approval for this study was obtained beforehand from the Departmental Research Committee of The Hong Kong Polytechnic University. After access had been obtained, the schools which had participated in the Teen Talk event helped to distribute the questionnaires, invitation letters, and consent forms. If potential participants were under 18, an invitation letter was also sent to their parents. Parents who were willing to allow their child to join the study were asked to sign a consent form and return it to the school. All participants were also requested to sign a consent form for voluntary participation. The schools sent the completed questionnaires and consent forms back to the researchers.

Instruments

Prosocial behavior. The Adolescent Behavior Questionnaire (ABQ) is a generic Chinese-language instrument designed to measure the pro- and antisocial behavior of adolescents [17]. Respondents are asked to report the frequency of 65 behaviors performed in the past year on a 7-point Likert-type scale (1 = none, 2 = 1-2 times, 3 = 3-4 times, 4 = 5-6 times, 5 = 7-8 times,6 = 9-10 times, and 7 = more than 10 times). The ABQ has two general subscales; the Antisocial/Delinquent Behavior (DB) and Prosocial Behavior (PB) scales. The PB scale assesses normative and altruistic acts, while the DB scale covers rule-breaking, challenging, or aggressive behavior at school, home, and in social settings. The ABQ total score is the difference between the mean scores of the PB and DB scales. It indicates how far a young person's behavior is anti- (negative scores) or prosocial (positive scores).

Prosocial norms. Three items were taken from the Chinese Youth Positive Development scale (CYPDS) to measure how willing participants were to provide help to the needy, participate in volunteer work, and follow school rules. The reliability and validity of the CYPDS have been demonstrated in previous validation studies [18,19].

Pragmatic values. The items used in a youth opinion poll titled "Young People's Outlook on Life"[20] were used here to assess respondents' pragmatic values. Respondents were asked to rate how far they agreed with eight pragmatic values in the local culture (such as "money can purchase happiness" and "a person must work very hard in order to be successful"). In the present study, factor analysis revealed two stable factors which explained 47.51% of the total variance. The first had two items (factor loadings ranging from .62 to .78) which focused on intention to abide by the law. The second comprised seven items (factor loadings ranging from .53 to .69) which focused on values reflecting a materialistic and "smart" mentality – in other words, pragmatic values. The second factor (containing seven items) is used in this study to indicate how far the respondent identifies with pragmatic values.

Prosocial reasoning. The Chinese version of the Prosocial Reasoning Objective Measure (PROM) was used to assess participants' prosocial reasoning. The PROM is a measure assessing prosocial moral reasoning in young people and adults [21]. Respondents are invited to read stories about people who need help from others, and then decide whether they would offer such help and the reasoning behind their response. The dilemmas in the stories are designed to invoke a conflict between the actor's needs, wants, and desires and those of another (or others). The Chinese short version uses five stories translated from the short version of the English PROM. After reading each one, the respondents are asked to rate on a scale from 1 to 5(that is, from most to least important) how important each of the five reasons are in deciding what the character should do. The five reasons reflect the five types of prosocial reasoning: Hedonistic, Needs-oriented, Stereotyped, Approval-oriented, and Internalized. An overall weighted PROM score provides an indicator of the development of the respondent's prosocial reasoning. The PROM stories can be slightly modified for use with different age and cultural groups [22]. Its psychometric properties have been reported in studies based on participants from middle childhood to early adulthood with promising results [13]. The test-retest reliability of PROM ranged from .70 to .79, while Cronbach's α ranged from .56 to.78 [21].

Empathy. The 21-item Chinese Interpersonal Reactivity Index (C-IRI) is a self-report questionnaire consisting of three subscales: Fantasy (FS), Empathy (ES), and Personal Distress (PD). The participants were asked to indicate the degree to which each item described them using a 5-point Likert-type scale, which varied from 0 (does not describe me well) to 4 (describes me very well). A higher score in a subscale represents a higher functioning in each aspect of empathy. The C-IRI has acceptable psychometric properties in Chinese adolescent samples [23], and can be used as a valid instrument for assessing empathy.

Results

A multivariate analysis of variance (MANOVA) was conducted to examine gender and age differences in prosocial behavior and its related attributes. The sample was stratified into 4 age groups; 14-15 (n = 157), 16 (n = 191), 17 (n = 104), and 18 and above (n = 62) (4 cases had missing age data). The results showed that there was a significant gender difference (Wilks' Lambda = 9.59, $p < .001$) but no significant differences between age groups (Wilks' Lambda = 1.58, n.s.).

Further analyses using univariate ANOVAs showed that males reported more antisocial behavior than females, but that there were no significant gender differences in prosocial behavior. However, using the overall ABQ scores as the outcome indicator, females were significantly more prosocial than males (F = 23.77, $p < .001$). Consistent with our predictions, females had higher levels of prosocial norms (F = 12.79, $p < .001$), pragmatic values (F = 6.67, $p < .05$), and prosocial reasoning (F = 20.47, $p < .001$). Furthermore, they had higher levels of empathy than males in several empathy-related constructs, including personal distress ($F = 20.03$, $p < .001$), fantasy ($F = 11.01$, $p < .01$), and empathetic concerns ($F = 10.92$, $p < .01$). These findings are shown in Table 1.

Table 1. Sex Differences in Prosocial Behavior and its Correlates

Variable[a]	Sex	M	SE	95% CI Lower	95% CI Upper	F	η^2
Antisocial behavior	M	3.46	.22	3.03	3.88	20.64***	.04
	F	2.25	.15	1.95	2.55		
Prosocial behavior	M	3.31	.14	3.02	3.59	.49	.00
	F	3.43	.10	3.23	3.63		
ABQ score	M	-.15	.22	-.59	.29	23.77***	.03
	F	1.18	.16	.87	1.49		
Prosocial norms	M	4.65	.05	4.54	4.75	12.79***	.03
	F	4.88	.04	4.81	4.95		
Pragmatic values	M	2.72	.04	2.63	2.81	6.67*	.01
	F	2.86	.03	2.80	2.92		
PROM overall weighted	M	6.46	.08	6.31	6.61	20.47***	.04
	F	6.88	.05	6.77	6.99		
Personal Distress subscale	M	1.98	.05	1.88	2.07	20.03***	.06
	F	2.28	.03	2.22	2.35		
Fantasy subscale	M	2.07	.06	1.95	2.19	11.01**	.02
	F	2.32	.04	2.24	2.41		
Empathy subscale	M	2.45	.04	2.36	2.52	10.92**	.02
	F	2.60	.03	2.54	2.65		

Note. [a] Estimated marginal means are shown.
* $p < .05$; ** $p < .01$; *** $p < .0001$.

Correlations of prosocial behavior

Table 2. Correlations between potential predictors and adolescent antisocial and prosocial behavior

Potential Predictors	Antisocial Behavior	Prosocial Behavior	Adolescent Behavior
Age	.06	.05	-.02
Parent education	-.08	.18***	.19***
Prosocial norms	-.28***	.30***	.46***
Pragmatic values	.32***	-.09*	-.36***
PROM overall weighted	-.16***	.09*	.21***
Personal Distress subscale	.11*	.02	-.09*
Fantasy subscale	.10*	.14***	-.00
Empathy subscale	-.18***	.32***	.39***

Correlation analyses were conducted to identify potential predictors of prosocial behavior (Table 2). Both the PB and overall ABQ scores showed a similar pattern of correlations, with the latter having a generally higher correlation with the predictors than the former. As well as this, prosocial norms, pragmatic values, prosocial reasoning, and different constructs related to empathy were all associated with prosocial behavior and/or overall ABQ scores. As a result of this analysis, prosocial norms, pragmatic values, overall weighted PROM total, and the ES and PD subscale scores from the C-IRI were selected as potential predictors in the regression analysis. Parental education, calculated as the mean level of education of fathers and mothers, was not included in the further analysis because of the large amount of missing data (n = 454, $n_{missing} = 64$). Many participants appeared to be unsure about their parents' educational background.

Predictors of prosocial behavior in adolescents

The findings on the predictors of prosocial behavior in adolescents are shown in Table 3. The predictors were able to predict a significant proportion of the variance in prosocial behavior as represented by the ABQ score ($R^2 = .31$, Adjusted $R^2 = .30$). All variables, except the PROM score (p = .24), were found to be significant predictors of ABQ score. Comparing the sizes of β's, the relative importance of the predictors is as follows: prosocial norms (β = .32), pragmatic values (β = -.19), empathetic concern (β = .18), and personal distress (β = -.14). Increased scores in prosocial norms and empathy, and decrease in pragmatic values and personal distress, are associated with increases in prosocial behavior. Preliminary collinearity analysis using tolerance and VIF revealed no major concerns. However, analysis using the Condition Index showed that the PROM score shared significant variance proportions with both empathy and prosocial norms in two dimensions. Multi collinearity among these three variables may therefore force the PROM score to become an insignificant predictor. Nevertheless, removing it did not result in a significant reduction in the accuracy of the prediction ($R^2 = .30$, Adjusted $R^2 = .29$).

Table 3. Prediction of prosocial behavior (ABQ) among adolescents (N = 516)

Predictors	b	SE	β	t	p	Collinearity Statistics	
						Tolerance	VIF
Pragmatic values	-.90	.20	-.19	-4.52	<.001	.81	1.23
Prosocial norms	1.28	.17	.32	7.53	<.001	.75	1.33
Prosocial reasoning (PROM overall weighted)	.13	.11	.05	1.17	.24	.84	1.19
Empathy subscale	.98	.25	.18	3.97	<.001	.68	1.46
Personal Distress subscale	-.63	.17	-.14	-3.59	<.001	.92	1.08

Note. $R^2 = .31$, Adjusted $R^2 = .30$.

There were some differences in the results of the regression analyses conducted for the male (n = 155) and female (n = 355) subsamples (see Table 4). Prediction was stronger for girls ($R^2 = .34$, Adjusted $R^2 = .33$) than boys ($R^2 = .29$, Adjusted $R^2 = .27$). The significant predictors for females were the same as those for the whole sample, but only personal distress, empathetic concern, and prosocial norms were significant for the male subsample.

Table 4. Prediction of prosocial behavior (ABQ score) among males and females

Variables		b	SE	β	t	p
Males[a]	Personal distress	-1.45	.35	-.29	-4.12	<.001
	Empathy	1.05	.46	.17	2.27	.02
	Prosocial norms	1.15	.27	.31	4.30	<.001
	PROM overall weighted	.19	.19	.07	1.00	.32
	Pragmatic values	-.60	.34	-.13	-1.77	.08
Females[b]	Personal distress	-.48	.20	-.11	-2.37	.02
	Empathy	.82	.29	.16	2.81	.01
	Prosocial norms	1.48	.22	.35	6.77	<.001
	PROM overall weighted	.04	.14	.01	.26	.80
	Pragmatic values	-1.02	.24	-.21	-4.25	<.001

Note. For male subsample (n = 155), R^2 = .29, Adjusted R^2 = .27; for female subsample (n = 355), R^2 = .34, Adjusted R^2 = .33.

Discussion

In terms of socio-demographic correlates, while the findings do not reveal any age effect, they demonstrate significant gender differences in ABQ scores, prosocial norms, pragmatic values, prosocial reasoning, and empathy (personal distress, fantasy, and empathetic concern). These findings are generally consistent with those reported in the literature as well as with the hypotheses of this study.

Consistent with the original expectations, several factors are related to prosocial behavior in both the correlation and regression analyses. Higher levels of empathy and prosocial norms as well as a lower level of pragmatic values are associated with a higher level of prosocial behavior. These three predictors remain significant in separate regression analyses with the male and female subsamples. These results are highly consistent with theoretical predictions and previous empirical results [24,25]. They also underscore the role of pragmatic values as a predictor of prosocial behavior, which has seldom been explored in previous studies. The present study suggests that agreement with pragmatic values (associated with materialism and self-centeredness) could hamper prosocial behavior. Based on this conjecture, further work should be conducted to examine how different values may promote or inhibit prosociality. The present findings indicate a significant association between personal distress and prosocial behavior, but the relationship is negative rather than positive in nature.

Most previous studies show that higher levels of personal distress and sympathy are associated with more prosociality towards persons in need [26,27].The result in this study contradicts the proposed hypothesis as well as previous research findings. Since empathy is a multidimensional construct, while sympathy, personal distress, and perspective taking may make unique contributions to prosocial behavior, they can also interact with each other in predicting it [28]. For example, while personal distress may elicit a motivation to help, it could also inhibit prosocial actions when fear, tension, or distress is too high. As such, further research is needed to examine the relationship between empathy-related responses and prosocial behavior.

While prosocial reasoning assessed by the PROM score is correlated significantly with prosocial behavior, it fails to predict prosocial behavior in the regression analyses. This may be due to the significant collinearity among prosocial reasoning, empathy, and prosocial norms. Analysis using Condition Indices shows that these three variables share significant variance proportions in several dimensions. Nevertheless, it is noteworthy that prosocial reasoning only explained a small proportion of variation in prosocial behavior (4.5%) when it was entered as the only predictor in the regression.

The four significant predictors, including empathetic concern, prosocial norms, pragmatics values, and personal distress, were able to predict around 30% of variation in prosocial behavior. The variance explained was a bit higher for the female (33%) than male (27%) sample. The percentage of variance explained was statistically significant, but much of the variation was not accounted for. In future studies, it will be a good idea to add predictors involving social influences such as peer and teacher influence, parent and school socialization, school discipline and encouragement for prosocial involvement, or interpersonal competence [9,29].

These findings should be interpreted with reference to several factors. Firstly, while the sample was large, it was a convenience sample recruited from high schools with the age range largely limited to late adolescence (age 15-18). Secondly, the students involved had been nominated by their schools to take part in the "Teen Talk." Since it is likely that schools will prefer to have students with better academic or conduct records to take part in these types of community events, the sampled group may have displayed better previous conduct. Thirdly, we found that the range of prosocial behaviors in the ABQ could be expanded further. While it covers prosocial acts in home, school, and social situations, additional items could be added to sample a wider range of prosocial behaviors like providing support or assistance to people one knows or does not know; sharing, listening, and comforting; appreciating others; working in a team; and involvement in prosocial groups (such as service teams or religious groups)[30].

In summary, this study has shown that empathetic concern, personal distress, prosocial norms, and pragmatic values are key predictors of prosocial behavior among older adolescents in Hong Kong. These results are largely consistent with theoretical expectations and the findings of previous work, other than the negative relationship between personal distress and prosocial behavior. Further study is needed to examine the unique and combined effect of empathy-related constructs (empathy, sympathy, perspective taking, and personal distress) on prosocial development. This study also provides support for the importance of values and norms in predicting prosocial behavior, which has seldom been explored in previous studies. While prosocial reasoning shows a significant correlation with prosocial behavior, it is not a significant predictor of it. This is probably a result of the collinearity of prosocial reasoning with empathy and prosocial norms. In further studies looking at predictors of prosocial behavior, it will be necessary to design or employ a standardized measure that provides a wider coverage of such activity. It will also be necessary to select and measure additional predictors which reflect peer, family, and school influences on prosocial development.

References

[1]   Bar-Tal D. Sequential development of helping behavior: a cognitive-learning model. Dev Rev 1982;2:101-24.

[2]   Eisenberg N, Fabes RA. Prosocial development. In: Damon W, ed. Handbook of child psychology. Social, emotional, and personality development. New York: Wiley, New York, 1998:701-78.

[3]   Zahn-Waxler C, Smith D. The development of prosocial behavior. In: VanHasselt VB, Hersen M, eds. Handbook of social development. A life-span perspective. New York: Pleum, 1992:229-56.

[4]   Penner LA, Dovidio JF, Piliavin JA, Schroeder DA. Prosocial behavior: multilevel perspectives. Annu Rev Clin Psychol 2005;56:365-92.

[5]   Schwartz CE, Keyl PM, Marcum JP, Bode R. Helping others shows differential benefit on health and well-being for male and female teens. J Happiness Stud 2009;4:431-48.

[6]   Wentzel KR, McNamar CC. Interpersonal relationships, emotional distress, and prosocial behavior in middle school. J Early Adolesc 1999;19:114-25.

[7]   Weinstein N, Ryan RM. When helping helps: autonomous motivation for prosocial behavior and its influence on well-being of helper and recipient. J Pers Soc Psychol 2010;2:222-44.

[8]   Ma HK. The relation of academic achievement, family and classroom social environment, and peer interactions to prosocial and antisocial behaviour of Chinese children. Psychol 2003;46:163-73.

[9]   Ma HK, Shek DTL, Cheung PC, Lee RYP. The relation of prosocial and antisocial behavior to personality and peer relationships of Hong Kong Chinese adolescents. J Genet Psychol 1996;157:255-66.

[10]   Hawkins JD, Catalano RF. Communities that Care. San Francisco, CA: Jossey-Bass, 1992.

[11]   Siu AMH, Cheng HCH, Leung MCM. Prosocial norms as a positive youth development construct: conceptual bases and implications for curriculum development. Int J Adolesc Med Health 2006;18:451-57.

[12]   Chaplin LN, John DR. Growing up in a material world: age differences in materialism in children and adolescents. J Consum Res 2007;34:480-93.

[13]   Chaplin LN, Roedder D. Interpersonal influences on adolescent materialism: a new look at the role of parents and peers. J Consum Res 2009;20:176-84.

[14]   Eisenberg N. Meta-analytic contributions to the literature on prosocial behavior. Pers and. Soc Psychol Bull 1991;17(3):273-82.

[15]   Eisenberg N, Carlo G, Murphy B, Van Court P. Prosocial development in late adolescence: a longitudinal study. Child Dev Res 1995;66:1179-97.

[16]   Steinberg L. Cognitive and affective development in adolescence. Trends Cogn Sci 2005;9:69-74.

[17]   Ma HK. Adolescent Behavior Questionnaire: An Introduction. (Unpublished manuscript). The Chinese University of Hong Kong: Hong Kong, 1988.

[18]   Shek DTL, Siu AMH, Lee TY. The Chinese PositiveYouthDevelopment Scale: a validation study. Res Soc Work Pract 2007;17:380-91.

[19]   Shek DTL, Ma CMS. Dimensionality of the Chinese Positive Youth Development Scale: confirmatory factor analyses. Soc Indic Res 2009;98:41-59.

[20]   The Hong Kong Federation of Youth Groups. Young people's outlook on life (II) 2000:78. URL:http://yrc.hkfyg.org.hk/eng/p78.html.

[21]   Carlo G, Eisenberg N, Knight GP. An objective measure of prosocial moral reasoning. J Res Adolesc 1992;2:331-49.

[22]   Eisenberg N, Shell R, Pasternack J, Lennon R, Beller R, Mathy RM. Prosocial development in middle childhood: a longitudinal study. Dev Psychol 1987;23:712-18.

[23]   Siu AMH, Shek DTL. Validation of the interpersonal reactivity index in a Chinese context. Res Soc Work Pract 2005;15:118-26.

[24]   Carlo G, Eisenberg N, Koller SH, Da Silva MS, Frohlich CB. A cross-national study on the relations among prosocial moral reasoning, gender role orientations, and prosocial behaviors. Dev Psychol 1996;32:231-40.

[25]   Eagly AH. The his and hers of prosocial behavior: an examination of the social psychology of gender. Am Psychol 2009;64(8):644-58.

[26] Batson CB, Fultzand J, Schoenrade PA. Distress and empathy: two qualitatively distinct vicarious emotions with different motivational consequences. J Pers 2006;55(1):19-39.

[27] Eisenberg N, Fabes RA, Miller PA,Fultz J,Shell R, Mathy RM, Reno RR, Relation of sympathy and personal distress to prosocial behavior: a multimethod study. J Pers Soc Psychol 1989;57(1):55-66.

[28] Carlo G, Okun MA, Knightand GP, de Guzman MRT. The interplay of traits and motives on volunteering: agreeableness, extraversion and prosocial value motivation. Pers Individ Dif 2005;38:1293-305.

[29] Ma HK,Leung MC. The relation of altruistic orientation to family social environment in Chinese children. Psychol1995;38(2):109-115.

[30] Carlo G, Randall BA. The development of a measure of prosocial behaviors for late adolescents. J Youth Adolesc 2002;32(1):31-44.

In: Child Health and Human Development Yearbook 2013   ISBN: 978-1-63117-939-6
Editor: Joav Merrick   © 2014 Nova Science Publishers, Inc.

Chapter 11

Classroom misbehavior in the eyes of students: A qualitative study

Rachel CF Sun, PhD[*1], and *Daniel TL Shek, PhD,
FHKPS, BBS, JP*[2,3,4,5,6]

[1]Faculty of Education, The University of Hong Kong,
Hong Kong, PRC
[2]Department of Applied Social Sciences,
The Hong Kong Polytechnic University, Hong Kong, PRC
[3]Public Policy Research Institute, The Hong Kong Polytechnic University,
Hong Kong, PRC
[4]Department of Social Work, East China Normal University,
Shanghai, PRC
[5]Kiang Wu Nursing College of Macau, Macau, PRC
[6]Division of Adolescent Medicine, Department of Pediatrics,
Kentucky Children's Hospital, University of Kentucky College of Medicine,
Lexington, Kentucky, United States of America

Abstract

Using individual interviews, this study investigated perceptions of classroom misbehaviors among secondary school students in Hong Kong (N=18). Nineteen categories of classroom misbehaviors were identified, with talking out of turn, disrespecting teacher, and doing something in private being most frequently mentioned. Findings revealed that students tended to perceive misbehaviors as those actions inappropriate in the classroom settings and even disrupting teachers' teaching and other students' learning. Among various misbehaviors, talking out of turn and disrespecting teacher were seen as the most disruptive and unacceptable. These misbehaviors were unacceptable because they disturbed teaching and learning, and violated the values of

* Correspondence: Assistant Professor Rachel CF Sun, PhD, Faculty of Education, The University of Hong Kong, Pokfulam Road, Hong Kong, PRC. E-mail: rachels@hku.hk.

respect, conformity, and obedience in the teacher-student relationship within the classroom. The frequency and intensity of misbehaviors would escalate if students found it fun, no punishment for such misbehaviors, or teachers were not authoritative enough in controlling the situations. Implications for further research and classroom management are discussed.

Keywords: Student misbehavior, students' perceptions, Chinese students, classroom management, Hong Kong

Introduction

There are numerous studies examining the definitions and range of student misbehaviors. For example, in the United Kingdom and Australia, researchers defined classroom misbehaviors as behaviors which are disruptive to classroom order and cause trouble to teachers, such as making non-verbal noise, disobedience, talking out of turn, idleness/slowness, non-punctuality, hindering others, physical aggression, untidiness, out of seat, and verbal abuse (1-3). In the United States, James (4) conceived students misbehaved when they "either did what they were not supposed to do or did not do what they were supposed to do" (page 9), ranging from fooling around as mild misbehavior to fighting as severe misbehavior. In the Caribbean contexts, student misbehaviors in classroom included those disruptive behaviors which hampered teaching and learning, such as classroom disconformity, verbal and physical hostility, defiance of authority, task avoidance, inappropriate use of school property, inconsiderate interpersonal relationships, over-reactions to normal situations, and technological related factors (5).

While classroom misbehavior is generally interpreted as disruptive and improper behavior that adversely affects the order, teaching and learning in classroom, it is noteworthy that the range of student misbehavior varies across cultures (6, 7). Particularly, as respect for authority, conformity, and obedience are highly valued in the Chinese school context (8), some student behaviors would be considered as problematic or unacceptable in Chinese classroom but not elsewhere. For example, in the traditional Chinese culture, students who kept on asking questions would be regarded as "troublesome" students whereas students strictly followed teachers' orders were regarded as excellent students. However, in contrast to the studies conducted in the Western cultural contexts, there have been very limited research findings on student misbehavior in the Chinese cultural contexts (9, 10), particularly in Hong Kong (11, 12). Therefore, it is necessary to understand more about the definition and conception of student misbehavior in Hong Kong. This need is particularly acute when we realize that adolescent behavior has changed tremendously with the advance in technology. Through the Internet, it does not take long to popularize certain misbehavior in young people.

Against the above background, a recent study was conducted in Hong Kong Chinese schools by Sun and Shek (13), which showed that most of the classroom misbehaviors reported by the teachers included doing something in private, talking out of turn, verbal aggression, disrespecting teachers, non-attentiveness/daydreaming/idleness, sleeping, habitual failure in submitting assignments, and out of seat. These findings suggest that classroom misbehaviors can be defined as those behaviors that involve rule-breaking, violating the implicit norms or expectations, being inappropriate in the classroom settings and upsetting teaching and learning. The findings also matched with the categorization of misbehavior as off-task, disruptive, and unruly behaviors (14). Off-task behaviors like doing things irrelevant to the class learning, or daydreaming and sleeping are regarded as classroom misbehaviors. These misbehaviors would become disruptive if their frequency and intensity escalated. Similar to those obvious disruptive behaviors such as talking out of turn and out of seat, they impede teachers' teaching and students' learning. Failing one's responsibility in handing homework on time, and lacking respect to classmates and teachers by showing verbal and physical aggressiveness are definitely breaking the conventional rules and values in Chinese classroom. Among the various forms of misbehaviors, "talking out of turn" was constantly rated by teachers as the most frequent and troublesome misbehavior across contexts (15). However, it is doubtful whether behaviors considered as problematic, inappropriate, disturbing or unruly in the eyes of teachers are necessarily shared by the students.

One serious limitation of the research on student misbehavior is that most of the existing studies on school misbehavior were primarily based on teachers' perceptions and ratings (e.g., 1, 9, 11, 12). However, it can be criticized that teachers usually have a dissimilar conception of school misbehavior with their students due to differences in social roles and values (16). Moreover, teachers and students might have different degree of tolerance in judging whether a particular action is a misbehavior or not, or in rating the intensity of disruptiveness on the same misbehavior (17). Hence, it is argued that findings simply based on teachers' responses might be partial or biased, and the perceptions of students should also be included. Nevertheless, there are scant research studies investigating students' perceptions of classroom misbehavior (4, 18). Although a study was conducted in Hong Kong to examine misbehavior from the students' perspective (19), it focused on students' explanations of their school misbehavior and effective means to deal with student misbehavior. However, it can be argued that any meaningful intervention would not be possible if students' conceptions and definitions of classroom misbehavior are not thoroughly examined before the intervention. Thus, the present study attempted to examine classroom misbehavior from the students' point of views, and to understand what are the most common, disruptive, and unacceptable misbehaviors in the eyes of students. The overarching goal of this study was to examine classroom misbehavior from the perspective of students in junior secondary school settings in Hong Kong. In this study, classroom misbehavior was regarded as a kind of problem behavior (20-22). It is a descriptive and exploratory qualitative research study which attempted to identify and categorize classroom misbehaviors reported by a group of Grade 7 to 9 students. By understanding the issue from the students' perspective, the present findings would contribute to the existing literature and shed a light to teaching, discipline or guidance work in the school context.

A qualitative research method was adopted in this study. This method can enrich our understanding of the problem area because most of the studies in this area are quantitative in nature. By listening to the voices of the students, it is expected that the findings can help generate findings that cannot be adequately captured by those based on the teachers. A general qualitative study orientation (i.e., no particular qualitative research strand was adhered to) was adopted, with the following elements intrinsic to the study. First, voices of the students instead of the "experts" or "adults" were heard. Second, narratives of the students were focused upon. Third, individual interviews were conducted in non-artificial setting. As it is an exploratory study, a general qualitative orientation close to a post-positivistic tradition (qualitative data collection with coding and thematic analyses) was sufficient for this purpose.

Methods

The informants were 18 junior secondary school students from three schools, with each school admitting students having low, medium, or high academic competencies. In each school, six students (one boy and one girl in Grade 7, Grade 8 and Grade 9) were randomly selected by their teachers and they were invited to join an individual interview on a voluntary basis. The informants comprised nine boys and nine girls, with a mean age of 13.9 years old (range = 12-17 years old). Although there is no "sacred number" in qualitative research, an engagement of 18 participants could be regarded as on the high side. Also, recruitment of students from schools with different academic abilities and gender could ensure that a wide range of experiences would be examined. Written consent from the school principals and the informants, as well as passive parental consent from the student informants were obtained prior to data collection. At the beginning of each interview, anonymity and confidentiality of the study were clearly explained to the informants. Before conducting this research, ethical approval was obtained from the Human Research Ethics Committee, The University of Hong Kong.

Instruments

A self-constructed semi-structured interview guide was used for each individual interview. In the interview guide, questions and prompts were used to explore the informants' perceptions of students' problem behaviors and teachers' management strategies in the classroom and school contexts.

The informants were asked to define "problem behaviors" based on their own understanding and interpretation. They were invited to use real-life examples to further illustrate their views. The average time for an interview was 48 minutes (range = 33-71 minutes). Each interview was conducted by two trained interviewers in Cantonese (the mother tongue of both the interviewers and interviewees). The interviews were audio-taped with informants' prior consent, and transcribed in verbatim after the interviews.

As many open-ended questions were covered in the interview guide, only data related to the following questions were analyzed in this paper. Interested readers can write to the first author to obtain the full list of interview questions.

- In the classroom, what student problem behaviors are there? Please list out as many as possible and describe them.
- Among these problem behaviors, which one(s) is/are the most common?
- Among these problem behaviors, which one(s) is/are the most disruptive to teaching and learning?
- Among these problem behaviors, which one(s) is/are the most unacceptable? Please illustrate.

Data analysis

The data were analyzed by general qualitative analyses techniques (23), in which codes and categories of misbehavior were inductively derived from the data. A colleague who has a Bachelor degree in Psychology and teaching experiences conducted the first-level coding to cluster semantically similar words, phrases, and/or sentences that formed meaningful units in each conclusion at the raw response level. The first author further checked and carried out second-level coding and categorization, in which similar codes were grouped to reflect higher-order categories of themes. The coding and categorization were finalized with consensus among the coders, and agreed by another colleague with a Bachelor degree in Psychology and professional counseling training.

The researchers were aware of their possible biases in their conceptions of student misbehavior because they had worked in the education field for some time. Therefore, checking procedures were carried out to look at the consistency in the coding process without the involvement of the authors. Both intra- and inter-rater reliability on the coding were calculated to ensure the credibility of the findings. Intra-rater reliability tests were conducted by the two coders independently, whereas inter-rater reliability tests were conducted by two colleagues (one has a Master degree and several years of teaching experience and one has a Bachelor degree) independently.

In each reliability test, 20 raw responses were randomly selected for each rater to code without referring to the original codes.

Results of the reliability analyses were on the high side: intra-rater agreement percentages were both 100% for both coders; inter-rater agreement percentages were 80% and 90% for each coder when they coded the analyses of the counterpart. To enhance the quality of the research, audit trails were developed and data analyses processes were systematically documented.

Results

Table 1 summarizes the categorization of responses based on students' perceptions of problem behaviors inside classroom reported by 18 student informants. The 107 responses could be classified into 19 main categories and six of them could further be divided into subcategories. The frequently reported classroom misbehaviors were: "talking out of turn", "disrespecting teachers", "doing something in private", "verbal aggression", "out of seat", "sleeping", "playing", "clowning/making fun", "(habitual) failure in submitting assignments", "non-attentiveness/looking out of window" and "non-verbal communication". Among them, "talking out of turn" and "out of seat" were viewed as the most common misbehaviors in the classroom. "Talking out of turn" and "disrespecting teachers" were rated as the most disruptive and unacceptable problem behaviors.

Talking out of turn

The informants perceived that students usually talked out of turn, such as *"don't put up their hands before answering questions"* and *"shout the answer out"* (Student A05). This kind of calling out, as well as asking nonsense questions without teacher permission, were regarded as disturbing. As mentioned by Student B08:

> "No one likes to hear people speaking too loudly. It will affect the learning environment. The class is often distracted by this kind of noise. Also the noise will largely affect each student psychologically. I mean student may be annoyed by the noise. They will become more agitated, easily lose their temper and become inattentive in class. It is fine if you make noise but you should not disturb others."

They also revealed that "conversation among students" was the most common and annoying. Student B10 described:

> "When the teacher is teaching, students at the back talk to each other... Sometimes they are not too excessive, but sometimes they speak too loudly that we can hardly hear what the teacher is saying... There are not just two (students) but sometimes a cluster... just like to kick up a fuss, because sometimes you won't sit next to your friend. Your friend may sit far away from you at the diagonal corner. You have to speak out loudly in order to let your friend hear you. Then, other students will hear you and all of them will laugh together. This is like ripple effect."

"Talking out of turn", especially chatting among students, was perceived as the most disruptive to teachers' teaching and students' learning. Student C10 explained:

> "Chatting will disturb teaching. If they chat very loudly or do not listen to the teacher, they and other students will miss some new knowledge. Also the teacher may think that you do not have motivation to learn which may make him/her unhappy."

It was perceived as unacceptable when the misbehavior becomes so noisy and uncontrollable that it adversely affects other students' learning. Student A10 revealed:

> "It is acceptable if you chat in a low voice. But the point is you chat louder and louder despite being asked to stop. This is the most distracting behavior which makes others unable to concentrate in class."

Disrespecting teacher

Behaviors that were disrespectful to teachers, such as disobedience, refusing to follow instructions, rudeness, talking back, arguing with teacher, offending or attacking teachers, were reported as an obvious problem behavior in the classroom. Student B08 described how students used some subtle way to offend their teachers:

"The students do not respect their teacher. Sometimes they do not treat their teacher as a person. Generally speaking, they do not care about him/her. They may pretend to be good, but in fact, they behave differently at the back of their teacher."

On the other hand, some students would attack teachers directly. Student A06 recalled:

"Such as our class teacher, when teaching, some boys offended him/her for no reason. It is because the teacher does not know how to scold the students. That's why those boys like to assault him/her."

Arguing with teachers could disrupt teaching and learning because it was time-consuming. Student C07 commented that *"if the teacher scolds us, we will argue back, and then the teacher will scold us even much more. It uses up all the time"*. Student B08 also considered it as an unacceptable behavior: *"I think politeness of a student is very important. Sometimes if the teacher asks you to do something, you need to show your politeness in addition to respect... A person's virtue is more important than his/her knowledge."*

Doing something in private

Students liked to do something unrelated to classroom learning, such as doing homework of other subjects, dealing with personal stuff, having irrelevant drawing, or using mobile phone. However, not all informants would regard "doing something in private" as a kind of problem behavior. For example, Student C09 explained,

"some students use mobile phone to text when the teacher is not looking at them... Actually, I think using mobile phone or pushing classmates are not problematic. It will not affect the learning atmosphere... playing mobile phone only affects the individual...a person's learning attitude... and usually the teacher does not see them so that it affects nothing."

Out of seat and sleeping

The informants also pointed out that "out of seat" (including changing seats and wandering around the classroom) and "sleeping" were other problem behaviors in the classroom. Moreover, these problem behaviors would become more serious and spread over if without proper teacher control. Some students also considered that both of these behaviors would affect classroom teaching and learning. As two students described:

"The teacher sometimes is not aware of students who are out of seat, and also he/she may be dealing with the students who are making noise...so he/she is not able to handle those who leave their seats." (Student A06)

"When the students, who are very tired but try to endure the sleepiness, find their classmate is sleeping, they will begin to lay on the table, sleep or do other things because they realize that the sleeping student will not be punished, that means they are allowed to do so." (Student A09)

Table 1. A Summary of Students' Perceptions of Student Problem Behaviors inside Classroom (N=18)

Category	Subcategory	No. of responses	No. of responses regarding on the most common problem behavior	No. of responses regarding on the most disruptive behavior	No. of responses regarding on the most unacceptable problem behavior
Talking out of turn	Asking nonsense question	1	0	1	0
	Calling out	5	1	1	0
	Having disruptive conversation	15	6	9	3
	Subtotal	21	7	11	3
Disrespecting teacher	Disobedience / Refusing to carry out instructions	4	0	2	1
	Rudeness / Talking back / Arguing with teacher	4	1	2	3
	Offending / Attacking teacher	3	0	0	0
	Subtotal	11	1	4	4
Doing something in private	Dealing with personal stuff	4	0	0	0
	Doing homework	3	0	0	0
	Using electronic device (texting, playing games, surfing webpages, listening to music)	1	2	0	0
	Irrelevant drawing	2	0	0	0
	Subtotal	10	2	0	0
Verbal aggression	Attacking classmates	2	0	0	0
	Gossiping	2	0	0	0
	Quarrelling with classmates	1	0	0	0
	Speaking foul language	0	0	0	1
	Teasing classmates	3	0	0	0
	Subtotal	8	0	0	1
Out of seat	Changing seats	1	0	0	0
	Wandering around the classroom	6	4	2	1
	Subtotal	7	4	2	1
Sleeping		7	0	2	0
Playing		6	0	1	0
Clowning / Making fun		5	2	2	0
(Habitual) failure in submitting assignments		5	1	0	0
Non-attentiveness/ Looking out of window		5	1	1	0
Non-verbal communication	Via body language, papers	5	0	1	1

Category	Subcategory	No. of responses	No. of responses regarding on the most common problem behavior	No. of responses regarding on the most disruptive behavior	No. of responses regarding on the most unacceptable problem behavior
Physical aggression	Attacking classmates	1	0	1	1
	Destroying things	1	0	0	0
	Pushing classmates	1	0	0	0
	Striking classmates	1	1	0	1
	Subtotal	4	1	1	2
Isolating classmates		3	0	0	1
Making noise	E.g., rocking chair, paper-playing, singing	2	1	0	0
Copying homework		2	0	0	0
Forget to bring textbook and other learning materials to class		2	1	0	0
Disturbing other classmates		2	0	0	0
Invasion of privacy		1	0	0	0
Intimate physical contact		1	1	0	0
Total responses		107	22	25	13

Verbal aggression and physical aggression

"Verbal aggression" (including attacking classmates, quarrelling with classmates, speaking foul language, teasing classmates, and gossiping) and "physical aggression" (including striking, attacking and pushing classmates, and destroying things) were reported as problem behaviors. Student might feel bad and even threatening when there was hostility. As Student C09 expressed, *"I feel hurt when I saw my classmate was struck by others... We are classmates, we are friends... I don't dare to stop them because I'm afraid that they will strike me too."*

Other forms of misbehaviors

As shown in Table 1, there were other problem behaviors reported by the informants. They were "playing", "clowning / making fun", "failure in submitting assignments" (and in a habitual manner), "non-attentiveness" (also including looking out of window), "non-verbal communication" (via body language or passing papers), "making noise" (like rocking chair and singing), "isolating classmates", "copying homework", "forget to bring textbook and other learning materials to class", and "disturbing other classmates" (e.g., pulling classmate's braid, tickling others, messing up other's things). Individual informants also reported that "invasion of privacy" (tried to sneak a quick look of other personal stuffs) and "intimate physical contact" (likes touching and hugging during class) were problem behaviors in the classroom.

Discussion

The present study attempted to examine classroom misbehaviors perceived by junior secondary school students in Hong Kong. A total of 19 problem behaviors were mentioned by the students, including talking out of turn, disrespecting teachers, doing something in private, verbal aggression, out of seat, sleeping, playing, clowning/making fun, (habitual) failure in submitting assignments, non-attentiveness/looking out of window, non-verbal communication, physical aggression, isolating classmates, making noise, copying homework, forget to bring textbook and other learning materials to class, disturbing other classmates, invasion of privacy and intimate physical contact (see Table 1). The present findings showed that many of the misbehavior categories are similar to those reported in the studies conducted in the Western and Chinese cultural contexts (1, 9, 11), and they are consistent with those reported by teachers and students as well (4, 13). The findings generated from the Chinese students' perspective lent support to the previous research findings that "talking out of turn" is the most common and disruptive misbehavior inside the classroom (15).

In conjunction with the previous study conducted by the authors (13), the present study showed that the views of both the teachers and students were complementary in understanding the definition and types of student misbehaviors inside classroom. In terms of the categorization of the classroom misbehavior, there was a consensus in some of the misbehaviors, though some differences were also identified. While teachers perceived lateness to class, eating/drinking, and passive engagement in class were problem behaviors, students did not regard these to be misbehaviors. On the other hand, while students reported that disturbing classmates, intimate physical contact, invasion of privacy, isolating classmates and making noise were problem behaviors, their teachers did not mention these behaviors in their narratives.

There are two explanations for the discrepancies in the conceptions of misbehavior between teachers and students. First, some misbehaviors may be more easily identified among students than by teachers such as those misbehaviors performed at the back of the teacher inside the classroom. It was mentioned by the students that teachers were not aware of some misbehaviors when they were concentrated in teaching or dealing with other problem behaviors in the classroom. Second, the discrepancies might be due to different levels of tolerance between the students and teachers. For example, some students did not perceive some off-task behaviors as problematic as they considered that these behaviors would not cause disturbances to others. Moreover, students and teachers might view the same thing through different lens. For example, students who had not brought textbook to class were perceived as "forgetfulness" in the eyes of the students but perceived as "unprepared for learning" by the teachers. Both "forgetfulness" and "unpreparedness" refer to a lack of responsibility in the expected role of students, but the level of accusation for "unprepared for learning" seemed to be more serious than that for "forgetfulness". Obviously, the present study shows that collecting students' views can help provide a more comprehensive picture in describing various types of student misbehaviors.

In the present findings, all the reported misbehaviors were actually off-task and inappropriate behaviors inside classrooms. This observation is in line with the assertion that misbehavior is behavior "students either did what they were not supposed to do or did not do what they were supposed to do" (4, page 9). It is noteworthy that some of these misbehaviors are disruptive to teaching and learning as well. For instance, asking nonsense questions and fighting with teachers are wasting the time which is timetabled for valuable learning. Students who are running out of seat and playing would disturb others. Students would learn nothing if they fell asleep in class, and the worse was more students would slumber as a result of imitation. Interestingly, some misbehaviors, such as chatting in a low voice and doing irrelevant things in private, were perceived as non-problematic as they simply affected one's own learning and did not disturb other students, or when these behaviors were not detected by the teachers and thus did not disturb teachers' teaching. This observation may be due to the fact that contemporary young people have become more egocentric (i.e., not really caring about others' feelings) and pragmatic (i.e., less emphasis on moral principles).

Among various misbehaviors reported in this study, both talking out of turn and disrespecting teachers were rated as the most unacceptable problem behaviors. Obviously, these behaviors, particularly if uncontrollable, are disruptive to classroom learning and thus unacceptable. Moreover, it is interesting to note that some students found these misbehaviors as intolerable, when they upheld the personal virtues of politeness and respect, and the Chinese values of conformity and obedience, in the teacher-student relationship within the school context (8). Therefore, they regarded misbehaviors as those behaviors that were impolite, challenging, noncompliant, and rebellious behaviors because they violated the hierarchical teacher-student relationship as well as the order and organization of the classroom (24). Also, attacking and striking classmates, though rarely happened, were unacceptable because they upset the harmonious peer relationship and classroom atmosphere. All these misbehaviors would elicit negative emotions, such as annoying, hurtful and even threatening, that in turn affected learning adversely.

Some students also mentioned that the frequency and intensity of misbehaviors, such as chatting, sleeping, and out of seat, would escalate if they found it fun, or no punishment for such misbehaviors, or teachers were not authoritarian enough in controlling the situations. Dreikurs (25) stated that student misbehavior is a purposeful endeavor to gain social recognition, while Glasser (26) stated that student misbehavior is a response to the classroom context or instruction that cannot satisfy their basic needs of love, belongingness, self-worth, freedom, fun, and survival. Thus, misbehavior usually occurs when there is a mismatch between the school and student needs (27). It was suggested that having caring teachers who are willing to cater for students needs might be one of the helpful means to deal with student misbehavior (19). Research findings also showed that a combination of care and behavioral control (28), school wide/whole-school positive behavior support (29, 30), character education (31), social skills training (32), and positive youth development programs (33-35), were effective in mitigating students' problem behavior. In particular, positive youth development programs such as the Project P.A.T.H.S. would help to reduce misbehavior in class. The existing evaluation findings showed that this program was able to promote psychosocial competencies (which may eventually lower classroom misbehavior) and reduce adolescent delinquency (36-39).

The present findings underscore the importance to view student misbehavior through the lens of students. Practically, they shed lights on managing student behavior and enhancing student learning and development via identifying students' needs and matching up with the classroom context. It is equally important for future research to further explore the reasons behind student misbehaviors and the effective means of managing student behaviors from both students' and teachers' perspectives. As mentioned above, there are few studies looking at both the perspectives of the teachers and students. Theoretically, it is important to look at the discrepancies between teachers and students on student misbehavior and understand how such differences may affect school policies on school discipline and counseling. For researchers adopting an interpretive perspective, the social reality is fluid in nature. Hence, it is important to look at things from different angles and hear voices of different parties. For critical theories, it is even more important to understand the views of different stakeholders so that we can empower them.

There are several limitations in this study. First, it was a small-scale exploratory study with 18 students from three secondary schools recruited via convenience sampling. Hence, representativeness of the findings should be viewed with caution. However, it is noteworthy that the informants were randomly selected from the students. Second, as the informants were junior secondary school students, generalization of the findings to other age-groups, like upper secondary or elementary school students, needs further validation. Third, only a one-shot interview was conducted for each informant. It would be ideal if more interviews over a longer period of time can be conducted. Finally, it may be criticized that the students may share the ideologies of the teachers. However, as the students were randomly selected, this possibility is not too high. Regardless of these limitations, this study is a good endeavor to understand the issue of classroom misbehavior from the perspectives of students, which helps to give a fuller picture of the phenomenon of classroom misbehavior, particularly in Hong Kong Chinese school context.

To what extent the present study is an acceptable qualitative study? Based on the criteria proposed by Shek, Tang and Han (40) to evaluate the quality of qualitative research, the present study can be regarded as having good quality. First, there was an explicit statement of the philosophical base of the study (Criteria 1). Second, the number and nature of the participants of the study were justified (Criteria 2). Third, the data collection procedures were given in details (Criteria 3). Fourth, biases and preoccupations of the researchers were discussed (Criteria 4) and how such biases were handled (Criteria 5) are described. Sixth, inter-rater reliability and intra-rater reliability procedures were used (Criteria 6) and the present findings were triangulated with those collected from the teachers (Criteria 7). Seventh, the researchers were consciousness of the importance and development of audit trails (Criteria 9). Eighth, alternative explanations for the observed findings were discussed (Criteria 10). Ninth, negative evidence was accounted for (Criteria 11). Finally, limitations of the study were examined (Criteria 12). Because of time and manpower constraints, the researchers were not able to include peer checking and member checking procedures (Criteria 8), which should be carried out in future studies.

Acknowledgments

The authorship of this paper is equally shared by both authors. The research and preparation for this paper was financially supported by the Faculty Research Fund, Faculty of Education, The University of Hong Kong. Special thanks to Ms. Katrina Cheung and Ms. Evana Lam for their assistance in data collection and analysis.

References

[1] Houghton S, Wheldall K, Merrett F. Classroom behavior problems which secondary school teachers say they find most troublesome. Br Educ Res J 1988;14(3):297-312.

[2] Wheldall K, Merrett F. Which classroom behaviors do primary school teachers say they find most troublesome. Educ Rev 1988;40(1):13-27.

[3] Little E. Secondary school teachers' perceptions of students' problem behaviours. Educ Psychol 2005;25(4):369-77.

[4] James AR. Perceptions of misbehavior in middle school physical education. J Phys Educ Recreation Dance 2004;75(1):9.

[5] Thompson B. Disruptive behaviours in Barbadian classrooms: implications for universal secondary education in the Caribbean. J Eastern Caribbean Stud 2009;34(3):39-58.

[6] Ho IT. A comparison of Australian and Chinese teachers' attributions for student problem behaviors. Educ Psychol 2004;24(3):375-91.

[7] Weisz JR, Chaiyasit W, Weiss B, Eastman KL, Jackson EW. A multimethod study of problem behavior among Thai and American children in school: teacher reports versus direct observations. Child Dev 1995;66(2):402-15.

[8] Hue MT. The influence of Chinese culture in Hong Kong classrooms. In: Hue MT, Li WS. Classroom management: creating positive learning environment. Hong Kong: Hong Kong University Press, 2008:21-44.

[9] Ding M, Li Y, Li X, Kulm G. Chinese teachers' perceptions of students' classroom misbehaviour. Educ Psychol 2008;28(3):305-24.

[10] Shen J, Zhang N, Zhang C, Caldarella P, Richardson MJ, Shatzer RH. Chinese elementary school teachers' perceptions of students' classroom behaviour problems. Educ Psychol 2009;29(2):187-201.

[11] Ho C, Leung J. Disruptive classroom behaviors of secondary and primary school students. Educ Res J 2002;17(2):219-33.

[12] Leung J, Ho C. Disruptive classroom behavior perceived by Hong Kong primary school teachers. Educ Res J 2001;16(2):223-37.

[13] Sun RCF, Shek DTL. Student classroom misbehavior: an exploratory study based on teachers' perceptions. ScientificWorldJournal, 2012. doi: 10.1100/2012/208907.

[14] Winter J. Managing classroom behavior. In: Biggs J, Watkins D. Classroom learning: educational psychology for the Asian teacher. Hong Kong: Pearson, 1995:51-65.

[15] Beaman R, Wheldall K, Kemp C. Recent research on troublesome classroom behavior: a review. Australasian J Spec Educ 2007;31(1):45-60.

[16] Supaporn S, Dodds P, Griffin L. An ecological analysis of middle school misbehavior through student and teacher perspectives. J Teaching Phys Educ 2003;22(3):328-49.

[17] Robinson SL, Griesemer SMR. Helping individual students with problem behavior. In: Evertson CM, Weinstein CS. Handbook of classroom management: research, practice, and contemporary issues. New Jersey: Lawrence Erlbaum, 2006:787-802.

[18] Supaporn S. High school students' perspectives about misbehavior. Phys Educ 2000;57(3):124-35.

[19] Yeung OY. Resistance at school: a sociological study of student misbehaviour in two Hong Kong secondary schools. Dissertation. Hong Kong: The University of Hong Kong, 1999.

[20] Jessor R, Jessor SL. Problem behavior and psychosocial development: a longitudinal study of youth. New York: Academic Press, 1977.

[21] Jessor R, Turbin MS, Costa FM, Dong Q, Zhang H, Wang C. Adolescent problem behavior in China and the United States: a cross-national study of psychosocial protective factors. J Res Adolesc 2003;13(3):329-60.

[22] Vazsonyi AT, Chen P, Jenkins DD, Burcu E, Torrente G, Sheu CJ. Jessor's problem behavior theory: cross-national evidence from Hungary, the Netherlands, Slovenia, Spain, Switzerland, Taiwan, Turkey and the United States. Dev Psychol 2010;46(6):1779-91.

[23] Miles MB, Huberman AM. Qualitative data analysis: a sourcebook of new methods. CA: Sage, 1994.

[24] Hue MT, Li WS. Classroom management: creating positive learning environment. Hong Kong: Hong Kong University Press, 2008.

[25] Dreikurs R. Discipline without tears: how to reduce conflict and establish cooperation in the classroom. Mississauga, Ontario: John Wiley & Sons, 2004.

[26] Glasser W. Choice theory in the classroom. Rev. Ed. New York: Harper Collins, 1998.

[27] Maag JW. Behavior management: from theoretical implications to practical applications. Belmont, CA: Wadsworth/Thomson Learning, 2004.

[28] Nie Y, Lau S. Complementary roles of care and behavioral control in classroom management: the self-determination theory perspective. Contemporary Educ Psychol 2009;34(3):185-94.

[29] Anderson CM, Kincaid D. Applying behavior analysis to school violence and discipline problems: schoolwide positive behavior support. Behav Anal 2005;28(1):49-63.

[30] Luiselli JK, Putnam RF, Handler MW, Feinberg AB. Whole-school positive behaviour support: effects on student discipline problems and academic performance. Educ Psychol 2005;25(2-3):183-98.

[31] Parker DC, Nelson JS, Burns MK. Comparison of correlates of classroom behavior problems in schools with and without a school-wide character education program. Psychol Sch 2010;47(8):817-27.

[32] Mathur SR, Rutherford RB. Is social skills training effective for students with emotional or behavioral disorders? Research issues and needs. Behav Disorders 1996;22(1):21-8.

[33] Lewin-Bizan S, Bowers EP, Lerner RM. One good thing leads to another: cascades of positive youth development among American adolescents. Dev Psychopathol 2010;22(4):759-70.

[34] Sun RCF, Shek DTL. Life satisfaction, positive youth development, and problem behaviour among Chinese adolescents in Hong Kong. Soc Indic Res 2010;95(3): 455-74.

[35] Shek DTL, Sun RCF. Effectiveness of the tier 1 program of project P.A.T.H.S.: findings based on three years of program implementation. ScientificWorld Journal 2010;10:1509–19.

[36] Shek DTL, Ng CSM, Tsui PF. Qualitative evaluation of the project P.A.T.H.S.: findings based on focus groups. Int J Disabil Hum Dev 2010;9:307-13.

[37] Shek DTL. Subjective outcome and objective outcome evaluation findings: insights from a Chinese context. Res Soc Work Pract 2010;20(3):293-301.

[38] Shek DTL, Merrick J. Eds. Special issue: positive youth development and training. Int J Adolesc Med Health 2010;21:341-447.

[39] Shek DTL, Ma CMS. Subjective outcome evaluation findings: factors related to the perceived effectiveness of the Tier 2 Program of the project P.A.T.H.S.. ScientificWorldJournal 2010;10:250-60.

[40] Shek DTL, Tang VMY, Han XY. Evaluation of evaluation studies using qualitative research methods in the social work literature (1990-2003): evidence that constitutes a wake-up call. Res Soc Work Pract 2005;15(3):180-94.

Submitted: November 06, 2011. *Revised:* December 17, 2011.
Accepted: December 23, 2011.

In: Child Health and Human Development Yearbook 2013   ISBN: 978-1-63117-939-6
Editor: Joav Merrick   © 2014 Nova Science Publishers, Inc.

Chapter 12

Associations between pathological gambling and psychiatric comorbidity among help-seeking populations in Hong Kong

Daniel TL Shek, PhD, FHKPS, BBS, SBS, JP[*1,2,3,4],
Elda ML Chan[5,6] *and Ryan HY Wong*[5]

[1]Department of Applied Social Sciences,
The Hong Kong Polytechnic University, Hong Kong, PRC
[2]Centre for Innovative Programmes for Adolescents and Families,
The Hong Kong Polytechnic University, Hong Kong, PRC
[3]Department of Social Work, East China Normal University, Shanghai, PRC
[4]Kiang Wu Nursing College of Macau, Macau, PRC
[5]Tung Wah Group of Hospitals, Integrated Centre on Addiction Prevention and
Treatment, Hong Kong, PRC
[6]Melbourne Graduate School of Education, University of Melbourne, Australia

Abstract

Problem gambling is complex and often comorbid with other mental health problems. Unfortunately, gambling studies on comorbid psychiatric disorders among Chinese communities are extremely limited. The objectives of this study were to: a) determine the prevalence of comorbid psychiatric disorders among treatment-seeking pathological gamblers; b) compare the demographic profiles and clinical features of pathological gamblers with and without comorbid psychiatric disorders; - c) explore the associations between pathological gambling and psychiatric disorders and their temporal relationship.

* Correspondence: Professor Daniel TL Shek, PhD, FHKPS, BBS, SBS, JP, Associate Vice President (Undergraduate Programme), Chair Professor of Applied Social Sciences, Department of Applied Social Sciences, The Hong Kong Polytechnic University, Room HJ407, Core H, Hunghom, Hong Kong, PRC E-mail: daniel.shek@polyu.edu.hk.

Participants (N = 201) who sought gambling counseling were examined by making Axis-I diagnoses including mood disorders, schizophrenia spectrum disorders, substance use disorders, anxiety disorders, and adjustment disorder. Results showed that 63.7% of participants had lifetime comorbid psychiatric disorder. The most common comorbid psychiatric mental disorders were mood disorders, adjustment disorders and substance use disorders. Pathological gamblers with psychiatric comorbidities were significantly more severe in psychopathology, psychosocial functioning impairment, and gambling problems than those without the disorders.

Keywords: Pathological gamblers, Hong Kong, psychiatric disorders, comorbidity

Introduction

Pathological gambling can have a wide range of adverse effects on individuals, families, and society. The negative consequences include financial and debt problems, marital conflict, criminal behavior, family violence and breakdown, as well as severe emotional and mental health problems (1-3). In Hong Kong, a study conducted in 2008 showed that the prevalence of probable problem gambling and pathological gambling was 2.2% and 1.8%, respectively (4). These figures were comparable with other cities such as Macau (2.5% probable problem gambling and 1.8% pathological gambling (5)) and Singapore (2% probable problem gambling and 2.1% pathological problems (6)).

In Hong Kong, the development of pathological gambling treatment and research is still at an early stage. One of the neglected areas in the literature is the comorbid conditions of pathological gambling. International studies have reported that pathological gambling was highly comorbid with mental health disorders such as anxiety disorders, depression and affective disorders, and substance use disorders (7-10). There are research findings showing that patients with multiple diagnoses were more impaired and less responsive to treatment than those with a single diagnosis (11). A number of epidemiological studies have been carried out to investigate the prevalence of comorbid mood disorders, anxiety disorders, substance use disorders and other psychiatric disorders among pathological gamblers. Although comparisons between studies are difficult due to differences in samples, inclusion criteria, and assessment tools used, these studies generally showed a high psychiatric comorbidity among pathological gamblers identified from the general population sample (9, 12, 13).

Kessler and colleagues (12) reported a significant prevalence rate of 55.6% of mood disorders among pathological gamblers whereas Petry et al. (9) reported a prevalence rate of 49.6%. Regarding anxiety disorders, Petry and colleagues (9) found a prevalence rate of 41.3% among problem gamblers whereas Kessler et al. (12) reported an even higher rate of 60.3%. Besides, the risk of experiencing moderate/high severity gambling was shown to be 1.7 times higher for people with anxiety disorder. Regarding substance use disorders, Petry and colleagues (9) found alcohol use disorder among almost three quarters (73.2%) of pathological gamblers, whereas drug use disorder and nicotine dependence were found among 38.1% and 60.4% of pathological gamblers respectively. El-Guevaly et al. (13) also reported that people with substance or alcohol dependence had 2.9 times higher risk having gambling problems compared to people without the disorder. Unfortunately, there is no data on comorbid schizophrenia spectrum disorders from existing epidemiological studies on pathological gamblers.

Several studies have also reported a high prevalence of comorbid psychiatric disorders among pathological gamblers seeking treatment (8, 14, 15). Ibáñez et al. (8) and Kausch (15) reported that 50% of treatment seeking pathological gamblers had a clinical diagnosis of mood disorders in their lifetime. Anxiety disorders are also common, with the lifetime prevalence estimated to range between 4.3% and 8.5% (8, 14, 15). Kausch (15) reported a prevalence rate of 66.4% of substance abuse or dependence among treatment-seeking gamblers. The reported rate of comorbid alcohol abuse or dependence was 8.5% and 23.2% across studies (14, 15). As for schizophrenia spectrum disorders, the prevalence rate reported was 4.3% to 6% (14, 15). Based on these findings, it can be conjectured that psychiatric comorbidity has a high rate among pathological gamblers identified both in the community sample and treatment seeking sample.

Some researchers argued that the high comorbidity of psychiatric disorders among pathological gamblers suggested an association between these conditions (8, 9, 12, 13). However, studies on their temporal relationships are limited. Researchers have generated a number of hypotheses regarding the pattern of temporal priority in onset. For example, some psychiatric disorders might be viewed as risk factors for pathological gambling, while others as consequences of pathological gambling (12). Some researchers suggested that patients with major depressive disorder resorted to gambling as a means of escaping from the depressive symptoms. People with depressive symptoms often suffered from an underlying anhedonic state such as an inability to experience pleasure from normal pleasurable life events. Excessive gambling activity might offer an escape or a feeling of reward pursued to compensate the feeling of flat and lacking pleasure (16). In contrast, other studies reported that depression observed in pathological gamblers was not primary to underlying gambling symptoms, but constituted a secondary reaction to the negative consequence of pathological gambling such as family breakdown or financial problems (17, 18).

Blum and colleagues (19) argued that there are underlying psychological mechanisms linking pathological gambling and other addictive behaviors. They proposed a concept of reward deficiency syndrome that links all the addictive, compulsive and impulsive behaviors. Under this hypothesis, persons at risk for one addiction could be viewed as having a higher risk for other addictions. Therefore, people with pathological gambling behavior are more likely to develop other addictive, compulsive or impulsive, and dysfunctional behaviors. McCormick (20) suggested that a high degree of impulsivity and a high level of negative affection make pathological gamblers particularly vulnerable to feelings of helplessness and hopelessness. This idea was supported by the high rate of suicidal attempts among treatment-seeking pathological gamblers (15).

A search of the literature showed that very few studies had addressed the temporal relationship between pathological gambling and its cooccurring psychiatric disorders. It has been reported that the onset and maintenance of pathological gambling could be predicted by some preexisting psychiatric disorders such as anxiety, mood, and substance use disorders. At the same time, pathological gambling could predict the onset of generalized anxiety disorder, posttraumatic stress disorder, and substance dependence (12). In another study on the temporal relationship between gambling and mood disorders (21), it was reported that 70% of participants had mood disorder before the development of their gambling problems. The onset of gambling behavior was found to be earlier in men with major depressive disorders than in women (21). Individuals in the "mood first" group had higher rates of substance dependence while individuals in the group "gambling first" had higher rates of anxiety disorders like panic disorder and generalized anxiety disorder (21). Studies on substance use reported that alcohol problems, tobacco use, and marijuana use tended to occur before gambling problems (22).

Kessler and colleagues (12) reported findings on the temporal relationship between psychiatric disorders and problematic gambling behaviors in their epidemiological study. Among people with lifetime comorbidity of pathological gambling and other psychiatric disorders, the onsets of mood disorder (65.1%), anxiety disorder (82.1%), and substance use disorder (57.4%) were reported to be earlier than the onset of pathological gambling (12). Although published researches provided some data on the prevalence of psychiatric comorbidity and pathological gambling, little information was available regarding the cultural effects, temporal relationship, clinical as well as social significance of the observed conditions. Most of the available comorbidity research studies on pathological gambling were conducted on Caucasian study samples. There is a severe lack of studies on the prevalence and relationship of pathological gambling and mental health disorders and other comorbid conditions in the Chinese community. The lack of Chinese dominance sample studies may limit the applicability of the available findings.

Against the above background, this is the first study to report prevalence rates of comorbid psychiatric disorders among Chinese pathological gamblers in Hong Kong. This study will provide valuable data on the temporal relationships between psychiatric disorders and pathological gambling, severity of gambling problems and psychiatric symptoms, and level of functional impairment among Chinese treatment-seeking pathological gamblers in Hong Kong. The objectives of the current study were to: (a) determine the prevalence of comorbid psychiatric disorders among pathological gamblers seeking treatment in Hong Kong; (b) compare the demographic profiles and clinical features of pathological gamblers with and without comorbid psychiatric disorders; (c) assess the associations of pathological gambling with comorbid psychiatric disorders, as well as its temporal relationship.

Methods

Participants and procedures

As a first step, an extensive literature review on the prevalence and relationship between psychiatric disorders and pathological gambling as well as their temporal relationship was conducted. Based on the research findings and clinical experiences, a comprehensive design of our study was formulated. All research personnel collecting the data in this study received training and supervision at Hong Kong Mood Disorders Centre on how to use the psychiatric research instrument (i.e., Chinese version of Structured Clinical Interview for DSM-IV: SCID) before conducting research interview.

The data collection period for this study was from June 2009 to February 2010. Inclusion criteria for the participants of this study were age 18 or older, and meeting five or more DSM-IV diagnostic criteria for pathological gambling. Exclusion criteria adopted in the study were manifestation of signs of cognitive impairments or imminent suicidal risk, as well as inability to read Chinese characters or to speak Cantonese. Clients who met the inclusion criteria and sought services from the Tung Wah Group of Hospitals Even Centre and Zion Social Services Yuk Lai Hin Counselling Centre within the data collection period were invited to join the study during the intake process. The purpose and procedure of this research and interview were explained to all eligible participants. Participants were reassured that all individual identifiable information would be treated as confidential and would not be released to anyone outside this research project. Written informed consent was obtained from participants prior to joining the study.

The participants were first provided with a self-administered questionnaire which attempted to collect their demographic data, gambling characteristics, and psychiatric symptoms. They were then interviewed face-to-face by trained health professionals such as social workers or clinical psychologists who administered the SCID and other instruments to assess participants' psychiatric comorbidities, gambling problems, and functional impairment. Both parts of the self-administrated questionnaire and semistructured interview took about 1 hour and 30 minutes. Upon the completion of the interview, participants received a HK$100 supermarket voucher as an incentive. During the data collection period, a total of 201 interviews (182 men and 19 women) were successfully completed.

Instruments

The information collected from the participants is as follows:

Demographic information
The participants were asked to provide information about their current age, gender, marital status, educational attainment, living arrangement, type of housing, economic status, occupation, and personal income.

Psychiatric symptoms
The Brief Symptom Inventory (BSI) is a self-administered 53-item inventory used to measure respondents' psychiatric symptoms experienced in the previous week (23, 24). Each item in the BSI is rated on a 5-point Likert scale ranging from 0 to 4, reflecting the intensity of distress experienced in the past week from "not at all present" to "extremely present". These 53 items measure a variety of problems and complaints in nine primary symptom dimensions including depression, somatization, obsessive-compulsive, anxiety, psychoticism, hostility, phobic anxiety, interpersonal sensitivity, and paranoid ideation. Nine subscale scores are derived and profiled according to these dimensions.

In addition to the individual subscales, three global measures of psychological distress are derived from the BSI: General Severity Index (GSI), Positive Symptom Total Score (PST), and Positive Symptom Distress Index (PSDI). The GSI indicates the overall level of psychological distress, the PST reveals the number of symptoms endorsed, and the PSDI quantifies the average intensity of distress the participant experienced. Higher scores stand for greater severity of symptoms. Adequate reliability and validity has been demonstrated in the BSI (23, 25) and its Chinese version has shown good internal consistency in previous studies in Hong Kong (26, 27) and convergent validity for Chinese samples (28).

Psychiatric comorbidities

The Structured Clinical Interview for DSM-IV Axis I Disorders (SCID-I; (29)) is a semistructured instrument assessing major Axis I diagnoses described in DSM-IV (30). The modules of the SCID-I selected for this research included mood disorders (modules A and D), schizophrenia spectrum disorders (modules B and C), substance use disorders (module E), anxiety disorders (module F), adjustment disorder (module I), and optional module (module J). The modules on somatoform disorders (module G) and eating disorders (module H) were not administered due to their lack of relevance to our study. Supplementary questions on nicotine dependence were added in the module of substance use disorders. Age at onset for any particular psychiatric disorder diagnosed was recorded to examine the temporal relationship between psychiatric disorders and pathological gambling. The current Chinese version of the SCID was developed in the 1970s and revised by The Chinese University of Hong Kong in 1996. The Chinese version of the SCID was found to be a reliable diagnostic instrument for the diagnosis of mood disorders, adjustment disorders, anxiety disorders, and schizophrenia spectrum disorders for outpatients (31, 32). The non-patient version of SCID-I used in this study is largely similar to the patient version of SCID-I.

Gambling characteristics

The Addiction Severity Index (ASI)–Gambling Section-is a standardized and semistructured instrument which is widely used to evaluate the intake status for clients seeking substance use treatment (33, 34). The instrument measures the severity of multiple domains which are commonly affected by substance misuse, such as medical, psychiatric, employment, family/social, legal, alcohol, and drug problems in the previous month. The ASI has demonstrated excellent reliability and validity in various substance-abusing populations (33, 35), the severely mentally ill (36), as well as pathological gamblers seeking treatment (37).

In this study, the gambling section was developed as a supplement to the traditional ASI to assess the severity of gambling problems (38, 39). Items related to the frequency and amount spent on gambling, number of days gambling more than was affordable, and the number of days experiencing gambling problems, perceived trouble towards the gambling problems, and perceived importance towards gambling treatment were calculated to derive composite scores with a value ranging from 0 to 1. Higher composite scores indicate a greater severity of gambling problems. The gambling subscale has also shown reliability and validity in populations of pathological gamblers (38-40).

Severity of nicotine problems

The severity of nicotine dependence was assessed by a widely used measure, Fagerstrom Test for Nicotine Dependence (FTND) (41). FTND has a revised scoring for Fagerstrom Tolerance Questionnaire (FTQ) which was developed to measure the dependency on nicotine (42). The FTND includes six items, which are scored dichotomously and rankly, and produces a total score ranged from 0 to 10, with higher scores indicating greater severity of nicotine addiction. The FTND was translated into Chinese by the Bureau of Health Promotion of the Department of Health in Taiwan. Previous studies have demonstrated that the FTND, and its Chinese version, has shown satisfactory validity and reliability (41, 43).

Level of psychosocial functional impairment

The Range of Impaired Functioning Tool (LIFE-RIFT) is a valid and reliable semistructured instrument for assessing functional impairment (44). It was derived from items that were included in the Longitudinal Interval Follow-up Evaluation (LIFE; (45, 46)). The LIFE-RIFT items focus on the assessment of functioning in various domains including work (with different scales for employment, household duties, and student work), interpersonal relations, global satisfaction, and recreation. The LIFE-RIFT requires some clinical judgment from a trained interviewer such that supplementary questions with the guidance of behavioral anchors would be asked before giving the ratings. Scores on each domain range from 1 to 5 with higher scores indicating poorer functioning. The total score of LIFE-RIFT was obtained by summing the subscale scores from four domains. Response of 0 (not applicable) and 6 (no information) were coded as missing items and would not be used for total score calculation. A total score would be derived only if there was no missing response in any of those four domains. In the "work" and "interpersonal" domains, the subscore would be the highest score among the multiple items addressing the domain (i.e., employment, household duties, and student work in "work" domain; interpersonal relations with spouse, children, relatives, and friends in "interpersonal relations" domain).

Data analytic strategies

Differences in demographic characteristics, gambling-related variables, and clinical correlates between pathological gamblers with and without comorbid psychiatric disorders were determined by independent sample *t*-tests for continuous variables (e.g., ASI), and chi-square tests for categorical variables (e.g., marital status). Chi-square was also used to examine prevalence estimates of pathological gambling and psychiatric comorbidities. Multiple regression analyses were then performed to investigate whether comorbid psychiatric disorders were predictive of severity of gambling problems. Presence of any comorbid psychiatric disorder and demographic characteristics were entered as fixed factors, while ASI composite score was entered as dependent variable, because young adults (47), male gender (38), being divorced or separated (48), lower education attainment (49, 50), being unemployed or on a low income (50) are risk factors for development of pathological gambling (47). SPSS for Windows, version 17.0, was used to conduct all statistical analysis. All tests were two-tailed with statistical significance set at $p<0.05$.

Results

Based on the DSM-IV operational definition, people who endorsed 5 or more symptoms were regarded as "pathological gamblers". A total of 201 participants who met the criteria of pathological gambling were included in the present study, with a mean clinically rated DSM-IV score of 7.3. Among them, 128 participants (63.7%) had comorbid psychiatric disorders in their lifetime, whereas 90 participants (44.8%) had at least one comorbid psychiatric disorder at the time of evaluation.

Table 1 showed that about nine-tenths of 201 participants were men. Most of them were in the stages of early and middle adulthood, and reached secondary school level of educational attainment. Around 60% of the participants were married or cohabitating.

Compared with those without current comorbid psychiatric disorder, results of chi-square test showed that a greater proportion of participants with current comorbid psychiatric disorder were divorced, separated or widowed. Regarding the living arrangement, most of them lived with family members and there were a greater proportion of participants with current comorbid psychiatric disorder living alone than those without current comorbid psychiatric disorder.

In terms of economic status and personal income, most of the participants were employed on either a full-time or part-time basis, and earned within the range of HK$5,001 and HK$15,000 per month. Generally speaking, greater proportions of participants with both lifetime and current diagnosis of comorbid psychiatric disorders were unemployed than those without the psychiatric disorders. Moreover, greater proportions of participants with lifetime comorbid psychiatric disorder had no income than those without psychiatric comorbidities, but the difference was not found to be statistically significant in current diagnosis.

Table 2 showed the results for gambling behavior on both the lifetime and current diagnoses between participants with and without comorbid psychiatric disorders. It was found that most participants started gambling involving money in their early twenties, with the average age of 19.9. More than 80% of participants with both lifetime and current comorbid psychiatric disorders reported that they had debts at the time of study, compared to about 75% of participants without comorbid psychiatric disorders. *t*-tests analysis showed that there were significantly more participants with current psychiatric comorbidities with debt (86.7%) than those without current psychiatric comorbidities (74.8%), while comparison for lifetime diagnosis did not reach statistically significant level.

On the other hand, severity of gambling problems assessed by ASI composite scores (which ranged from 0 to 1) with higher scores reflecting more severe gambling problems showed a mean ASI gambling scale composite score for participants was 0.38. For both lifetime and current diagnosis, the mean scores for participants with comorbid psychiatric disorders were significantly higher than those without the disorders, and reflecting greater severity of gambling problems (Table 2).

Psychiatric symptoms experienced by the participants in the past week were examined by the BSI. Participants with comorbid psychiatric disorders in general scored significantly higher than those without the disorders in all nine psychiatric symptom dimensions including depression, somatization, obsessive-compulsive, anxiety, psychoticism, hostility, phobic anxiety, interpersonal sensitivity, and paranoid ideation. Moreover, there were significant differences in the overall level of psychological distress, number of symptoms endorsed and the average intensity of distress experienced between participants with and without lifetime comorbid psychiatric disorders in general (Table 2).

The LIFE-RIFT was developed specifically to assess functional impairment with a range from 4 to 20. A higher score indicates more severe psychosocial dysfunction. Since 11 participants reported "not applicable" or "no information" for a particular domain of LIFE-RIFT, no total score could be calculated for these participants and they were coded as missing. Of the remaining 190 participants, results showed that participants with comorbid psychiatric disorders in general had significantly higher LIFE-RIFT score than those without the disorders (Table 2).

Table 1. Differences between pathological gamblers with and without lifetime and current psychiatric disorders in demographic characteristics

Variable	Lifetime psychiatric disorders					Current psychiatric disorders				
	With MI (N = 128)	Without MI (N = 73)	χ^2	df	p	With MI (N = 90)	Without MI (N = 111)	χ^2	df	p
Demographic characteristics										
Gender										
Male	89.8%	91.8%	0.204	1	0.652	86.7%	93.7%	2.867	1	0.090
Female	10.2%	8.2%				13.3%	6.3%			
Age										
20 or below	0.8%	1.4%				1.1%	0.9%			
21-30	18.8%	17.8%	0.268	4	0.992	16.7%	19.8%	0.996	4	0.915
31-40	27.3%	28.8%				30.0%	26.1%			
41-50	29.6%	30.1%				27.7%	31.5%			
51 or above	23.4%	21.9%				24.4%	21.6%			
Marital status										
Never married	28.9%	28.8%				27.8%	29.7%			
Married	56.3%	65.8%	4.266	2	0.179	53.3%	64.9%	9.069	2	0.011
Widowed or separated or divorced	11.4%	5.5%				18.9%	5.4%			
Education										
Lower secondary school or below	28.1%	17.8%				30.0%	19.8%			
Upper secondary school	42.2%	42.5%	3.436	2	0.179	42.2%	42.3%	3.622	2	0.163
Sixth form or above	29.7%	39.7%				27.8%	37.8%			
Economic status										
Employed	73.4%	90.4%				70.0%	87.4%			
Homemakers, retired, or students	6.3%	2.7%	8.297	2	0.016	6.7%	3.6%	9.437	2	0.009
Unemployed	20.3%	6.8%				23.3%	9.0%			
Personal income										
$0	17.2%	8.2%				18.9%	9.9%			

Table 1. (Continued)

Variable	Lifetime psychiatric disorders					Current psychiatric disorders				
	With MI (N = 128)	Without MI (N = 73)	χ^2	df	p	With MI (N = 90)	Without MI (N = 111)	χ^2	df	p
$1 - $5,000	8.6%	15.1%				7.8%	4.5%			
$5,001– $10,000	21.9%	21.9%				22.2%	21.6%			
$10,001 - $15,000	24.2%	24.7%	14.160	7	0.048	21.1%	27.0%	11.487	7	0.119
$15,001 - $20,000	14.1%	13.7%				17.8%	10.8%			
$20,001 - $25,000	3.9%	11.0%				3.3%	9.0%			
$25,001 - $30,000	3.9%	4.1%				3.3%	4.5%			
$30,001 or above	6.3%	15.1%				5.6%	12.6%			
Living arrangement										
Living alone	12.5%	4.1%				15.5%	4.5%			
With spouse	14.1%	20.5%	5.195	3	0.158	12.2%	19.8%	9.467	3	0.024
With family members	68.8%	72.6%				66.7%	73.0%			
With friends, in hostels, or in unstable homes	4.7%	2.7%				5.5%	2.7%			

Table 2. Differences between pathological gamblers with and without lifetime and current psychiatric disorders in gambling and clinical characteristics

Variable	Lifetime psychiatric disorders					Current psychiatric disorders				
	With MI (N = 128) mean(SD)	Without MI (N = 73) mean(SD)	χ^2	df	p	With MI (N = 90) mean(SD)	Without MI (N = 111) mean(SD)	χ^2	df	p
Gambling characteristics										
Age of first gambling	20.0 (8.1)	19.6 (6.2)	-0.378	199	0.706	20.3 (8.5)	19.5 (6.6)	-0.773	199	0.441
Presence of debt (%)	82.0%	76.7%	0.825	1	0.364	86.7%	74.8%	4.409	1	0.036
ASI-G[a] composite score	0.42 (0.21)	0.32 (0.17)	-3.174	199	0.002	0.45 (0.22)	0.33 (0.17)	-4.351	199	0.000
Clinical characteristics										
Brief Symptom Inventory										

Variable	Lifetime psychiatric disorders					Current psychiatric disorders				
	With MI (N = 128) mean(SD)	Without MI (N = 73) mean(SD)	χ^2	df	p	With MI (N = 90) mean(SD)	Without MI (N = 111) mean(SD)	χ^2	df	p
Somatization	0.78 (0.78)	0.38 (0.47)	-3.973	199	0.000	0.87 (0.83)	0.44 (0.53)	-4.429	199	0.000
Obsessive-complusive	1.47 (0.82)	0.90 (0.78)	-4.765	199	0.000	1.60 (0.83)	0.99 (0.77)	-5.371	199	0.000
Interpersonal sensitivity	1.39 (0.84)	0.78 (0.59)	-5.453	199	0.000	1.53 (0.85)	0.88 (0.65)	-6.143	199	0.000
Depression	1.61 (1.02)	0.85 (0.79)	-5.540	199	0.000	1.79 (0.99)	0.96 (0.87)	-6.363	199	0.000
Anxiety	1.25 (0.95)	0.72 (0.71)	-4.154	199	0.000	1.44 (0.98)	0.75 (0.69)	-5.766	199	0.000
Hostility	0.94 (0.76)	0.61 (0.69)	-3.061	199	0.003	1.02 (0.78)	0.67 (0.69)	-3.343	199	0.001
Phobic anxiety	0.74 (0.74)	0.31 (0.47)	-4.439	199	0.000	0.82 (0.80)	0.39 (0.51)	-4.660	199	0.000
Paranoid ideation	0.87 (0.74)	0.48 (0.55)	-3.865	199	0.000	0.90 (0.77)	0.58 (0.60)	-3.331	199	0.001
Psychoticism	1.14 (0.84)	0.62 (0.61)	-4.719	199	0.000	1.25 (0.86)	0.71 (0.66)	-5.044	199	0.000
GSI[a]	1.15 (0.71)	0.64 (0.53)	-5.398	199	0.000	1.27 (0.72)	0.71 (0.56)	-6.135	199	0.000
PST[a]	32.4 (13.6)	21.8 (14.7)	-5.153	199	0.000	34.0 (13.6)	24.0 (15.4)	-5.032	199	0.000
PSDI[a]	1.78 (0.61)	1.44 (0.39)	-4.194	199	0.000	1.89 (0.64)	1.46 (0.41)	-5.612	199	0.000
Psychosocial impairment										
LIFE-RIFT[a]	11.93 (3.28)	8.96 (2.60)	-6.444	188	0.000	12.72 (3.11)	9.30 (2.80)	-8.004	188	0.000
Severity of nicotine problem										
FTND[a]	4.56 (3.00)	2.03 (2.46)	-3.979	93	0.000	5.00 (2.86)	2.39 (2.70)	-4.558	93	0.000

a ASI-G: Addiction Severity Index-Gambling Section; GSI: General Severity Index; PST: Positive Symptom Total Score; PSDI: Positive Symptom Distress Index; LIFE-RIFT: Longitudinal Follow-up Evaluation-Range of Impaired Functioning Tool; FTND: Fagerstrom Test for Nicotine Dependence

Table 3. Prevalence rates of lifetime and current comorbid psychiatric disorders in 201 pathological gamblers

Variable	Lifetime psychiatric disorders					Current psychiatric disorders				
	N	%	PG first [a]	MI first [b]	Same year [c]	N	%	PG first [a]	MI first [b]	Same year [c]
Any psychiatric disorder	128	63.7	34.9%	55.8%	9.3%	90	44.8	30.0%	58.9%	11.1%
Mood disorders										
Any mood disorder	59	29.4	62.7%	23.7%	13.6%	43	21.4	65.9%	20.5%	13.6%
Major depressive disorder	43	21.4	60.5%	25.6%	14.0%	30	14.9	63.3%	23.3%	13.3%

Table 3. (Continued)

Variable	Lifetime psychiatric disorders					Current psychiatric disorders				
	N	%	PG first [a]	MI first [b]	Same year [c]	N	%	PG first [a]	MI first [b]	Same year [c]
Bipolar disorder	4	2.0	75.0%	0%	25.0%	2	1.0	50.0%	0%	50.0%
Dysthymic disorder	13	6.5	76.9%	15.4%	7.7%	13	6.5	76.9%	15.4%	7.7%
Schizophrenia spectrum disorder										
Any schizophrenia spectrum disorder	5	2.5	40.0%	60.0%	0%	3	1.5	66.7%	33.3	0
Schizophrenia	4	2.0	50.0%	50.0%	0%	3	1.5	66.7%	33.3	0
Substance use disorder										
Any substance use disorder	62	30.8	15.9%	74.6%	9.5%	46	22.9	8.7%	78.3	13.0
Alcohol abuse or dependence	23	11.4	30.4%	60.9%	8.7%	16	8.0	25.0%	62.5	12.5
Nicotine dependence	49	24.4	16.3%	75.5%	8.2%	41	20.4	12.2%	78.0	9.8
Any drug abuse or dependence	10	5.0	50.0%	40.0%	10.0%	9	4.5	55.6%	33.3	11.1
Anxiety disorder										
Any anxiety disorder	19	9.5	36.8%	57.9%	5.3%	17	8.5	35.3%	58.8	5.9
Panic disorder	5	2.5	50.0%	25.0%	25.0%	4	2.0	66.7%	25.0	33.3
Agoraphobia	2	1.0	100.0%	0%	0%	1	0.5	100.0%	0	0
Social phobia	1	0.5	0%	100.0%	0%	0	0	0	0	0
Specific phobia	8	4.0	25.0%	75.0%	0%	1	0.5	16.7	86.3	0
Obsessive compulsive disorder	4	2.0	0%	100.0%	0%	1	0.5	0	100.0	0
Posttraumatic stress disorder	4	2.0	50.0%	50.0%	0%	4	2.0	50.0	50.0	0
Generalized anxiety disorder	4	2.0	100.0%	0%	0%	4	2.0	100.0	0	0
Adjustment disorder	42	20.9	64.3%	21.4%	14.3%	28	13.9	60.7	21.4	17.9

[a] "PG First" refers to onset of pathological gambling preceded onset of comorbid psychiatric disorder.
[b] "MI First" refers to onset of comorbid psychiatric disorder preceded onset of pathological gambling.
[c] "Same Year" refers to both pathological gambling and comorbid psychiatric disorder developed in the same year.

Regarding nicotine problems, 104 (51.7%) participants reported that they ever smoked in their lifetime. Nine of them reported they were former smokers whereas 95 reported to be current regular tobacco users. Participants with comorbid psychiatric disorders in general had significantly higher FTND score than those without comorbid psychiatric disorders (Table 2).

Table 3 summarizes the prevalence rates for lifetime and current comorbidity of DSM-IV Axis I psychiatric disorders, including mood disorders, schizophrenia spectrum disorders, substance use disorders, anxiety disorders, and adjustment disorders, whereas Table 4 shows the number of comorbid psychiatric disorders possessed by pathological gamblers. All disorders were screened by detailed and structured interview of SCID by trained social workers or clinical psychologists. In Table 3, lifetime comorbid psychiatric disorders included mood disorders (n = 59; 29.4%), schizophrenia spectrum disorders (n = 5; 2.5%), substance use disorders (n = 62; 30.8%), anxiety disorders (n = 19; 9.5%) and adjustment disorders (n = 42; 20.9%). The most common comorbid psychiatric disorders for lifetime diagnosis were nicotine dependency (n = 49; 24.4%), major depressive disorder (n = 43; 21.4%), adjustment disorders (n = 42; 20.9%), and alcohol abuse or dependency (n = 23; 11.4%).

Similarly, current comorbid psychiatric diagnoses included mood disorders (n = 43; 21.4%), schizophrenia spectrum disorders (n = 3; 1.5%), substance use disorders (n = 46; 22.9%), anxiety disorders (n = 17; 8.5%), and adjustment disorders (n = 28; 13.9%). Similar to the results for lifetime diagnosis, the most common current psychiatric comorbidities were major depressive disorders (n = 30; 14.9%), nicotine dependency (n = 41; 20.4%), adjustment disorders (n = 28; 13.9%), and alcohol abuse or dependency (n = 16; 8.0%).

In Table 3, for those 128 participants with lifetime comorbid psychiatric disorders, 55.8% of them reported that the onset of psychiatric disorder was prior to the onset of pathological gambling. With respect to specific disorders, most of them reported the onset of any substance use disorders (74.6%) and anxiety disorders (57.9%) prior to the onset of pathological gambling, whereas the onset of mood disorders (62.7%) and adjustment disorders (64.3%) was later than the onset of pathological gambling.

As shown in Table 4, about two-thirds of participants (N = 128, 63.7%) had at least one lifetime Axis I disorder other than pathological gambling. Among them, 73 participants had one lifetime comorbid disorder, 33 participants had at least two disorders, and 22 participants had three disorders or more in their lifetime. For those participants who had lifetime comorbid psychiatric disorders, the average number of psychiatric comorbidity was 1.7. On the other hand, 90 participants (44.8%) had at least one current Axis I disorder other than pathological gambling. Among them, 69 participants had only one current comorbid psychiatric disorder, 12 of them had two disorders, and 9 of them had three disorders or more. For those participants who had current comorbid psychiatric disorders, the average number of psychiatric comorbidity was 1.36 (Table 4).

Previous research findings showed that participants with comorbid psychiatric disorders had significantly greater severity in gambling problems and psychiatric symptoms, level of impairment in psychosocial functioning as well as nicotine problems. Further analysis of the relationship between these clinical correlates and the presence of comorbid psychiatric disorder was conducted. Multiple regression analyses were then performed to investigate whether comorbid psychiatric disorders were predictive of severity of gambling problems (Table 5).

The ASI was treated as the outcome variable, and presence of any comorbid psychiatric disorder, gender, education, and income were regarded as predictors. For both lifetime and current diagnosis, results of multiple regression analyses showed that the association between psychiatric comorbidity and gambling severity (ASI composite score) remained significant after adjusting for other demographic variables (lifetime morbidity: beta = 0.239, p < 0.001; current morbidity: beta = 0.300, p < 0.001).

Table 4. Number of lifetime and current comorbid psychiatric disorders for pathological gamblers seeking treatment

Variables	Lifetime psychiatric disorders (N = 128)		Current psychiatric disorders (N = 90)	
Number of psychiatric disorders	N	%	N	%
1	73	57.0	69	76.7
2	33	25.8	12	13.3
3 or above	22	17.2	9	10.0
	Mean = 1.70; SD = 1.05		Mean = 1.36; SD = 0.72	

Table 5. Lifetime and current psychiatric disorder and demographic predictors of gambling severity

Variables	Lifetime psychiatric disorders (N = 128)		Current psychiatric disorders (N = 90)	
	Beta	p	Beta	p
Presence of lifetime psychiatric disorder	0.239**	0.001	0.300***	0.000
Age (20 or below as reference)				
21-30	0.094	0.741	0.138	0.622
31-40	0.271	0.412	0.304	0.350
41-50	0.282	0.445	0.344	0.342
50 or above	-0.174	0.052	-0.188	0.033
Gender (male as reference)				
Female	0.129	0.102	0.100	0.196
Marital status (single as reference)				
Married or cohabitated	-0.050	0.571	-0.041	0.642
Divorced or separated or widowed	-0.014	0.874	-0.034	0.693
Education (lower secondary school or below as reference)				
Upper secondary school	-0.197*	0.040	-0.183	0.052
Sixth form or above	-0.106	0.288	-0.090	0.361
Economic status (employed as reference)				
Retired/ homemaker/ student	0.036	0.722	-0.032	0.708
Unemployed	0.206	0.732	0.016	0.876
Income (5,000 or below as reference)				
5,001 – 10,000	0.206	0.087	0.190	0.106
10,001 – 15,000	0.170	0.180	0.159	0.199
15, 001 or above	0.239	0.085	0.192	0.156
	Adjusted R^2 = 0.073; F (15, 185) = 2.048*		Adjusted R^2 = 0.104; F (15, 185) = 2.543**	

Note. * $p < 0.05$, ** $p < 0.01$, *** $p < 0.001$. Beta is the standardized regression coefficient.

Discussion

This study provides valuable information for clinical practice as well as research directions in future. In particular, it provides original findings on comorbid psychiatric disorders among pathological gamblers in Hong Kong using a clinical sample and structured diagnostic instruments to assess the prevalence of comorbid psychiatric disorders.

The present study showed that psychiatric comorbidity was related to the socio-demographic characteristics of pathological gamblers. Regarding marital status, compared with those without current comorbid psychiatric disorders, those with current comorbid psychiatric disorders had a significantly lower proportion of married/cohabitating status, but a greater proportion being single, divorced, separated or widowed. This result was consistent with the characteristic of living arrangement that participants with comorbid psychiatric disorders had a relatively higher proportion of living alone than those without comorbid psychiatric disorders. One observation of these findings was that participants with comorbid psychiatric disorders had comparatively weaker supportive networks from family or the society and could experience emotional loneliness and a sense of helplessness. This result is consistent with the Western literatures that prior psychiatric disorders were associated with a substantially higher risk of divorce(51), and higher comorbidity rates of mood and anxiety disorders were found in individuals who were living alone (52).

With respect to the economic status and personal income of pathological gamblers, those with lifetime psychiatric comorbidities had significantly greater proportions of being unemployed and having no income than those without psychiatric comorbidities. The effects of a psychiatric disorder may cause significant distress or impairment in social, occupational, or other important areas of functioning. This further leads to an inability to fulfill work tasks and consequential financial hardship. The results supported the previous study which suggested that work impairment was one of the adverse consequences of psychiatric disorders (53).

In our study group, pathological gamblers with psychiatric comorbidities displayed more severe gambling problems than those without psychiatric disorders in general. They received a higher composite score in ASI gambling subscale and a much greater proportion of percentage for those with comorbid psychiatric disorders in general had a debt problem. These findings are consistent with previous studies on pathological gamblers in Western cultures showing that the existence of comorbid psychiatric problems was associated with more severe gambling behavior and longer term of gambling problems (8, 16, 54, 55). One possible explanation for the findings is that the effects of comorbid psychiatric disorders may contribute to the persistence of pathological gambling. For example, some depressive symptoms such as diminished interest in anything or indecisiveness might lead to the increased use of maladaptive coping strategies such as excessive gambling to escape from the underlying anhedonic state. This pattern will form a vicious cycle that could complicate and hinder the treatment and recovery process for clients with both disorders.

Consistent with the previous study conducted by Ibáñez and his colleagues (8), the presence of comorbid disorders was associated with greater gambling severity as assessed by ASI scale. That means that multiple and recurrent comorbid psychiatric disorders might increase the severity in gambling. The results support the associations between psychiatric disorders and pathological gambling in which they might be counterproductive to each other and might intensify the gambling problem and the comorbid condition. For example, some participants in our study reported that they tended to engage in excessive smoking when they were involved in gambling activities. The previous study also revealed that daily tobacco smoking in pathological gamblers was common and associated with more severe gambling and financial problems (56). Some participants reported that they tended to spend a longer time and a greater amount of money on gambling activities in order to deal with depressed moods and to pursue excitement. This is consistent with previous results that excessive gambling activity may offer an escape or a feeling of reward for depressed individuals, in order to compensate for their feeling of flat and lacking pleasure (16). The findings of the current study suggest that comorbid psychiatric disorders could intensify pathological gambling behavior and produced further negative impacts on the individuals.

In terms of the clinical correlates, pathological gamblers with lifetime and current comorbid psychiatric disorders reported more severity in psychopathology, impairment in psychosocial functioning and nicotine problems compared to those without lifetime and current psychiatric disorder, respectively. For example, they had higher scores on BSI's nine dimensions–depression, somatization, obsessive-compulsive, anxiety, psychoticism, hostility, phobic anxiety, interpersonal sensitivity, and paranoid ideation. They also reported higher overall level of psychological distress, more psychiatric symptoms endorsed, and more intense distress experienced. These results are in line with previous comorbidity studies that pathological gamblers with comorbid psychiatric disorders had higher severity of depression and more trait and state anxiety (8). In addition, pathological gamblers with psychiatric comorbidity experienced more severe symptoms of paranoid ideation, obsessive–compulsive thoughts and behaviors, hostility, interpersonal sensitivity or psychoticism. This pattern suggested that they may be more withdrawn and isolated, may feel inferior, and experience more distorted thinking initiated by delusional or projective thoughts. This study also showed that participants with comorbid psychiatric disorders were markedly impaired in at least one major areas of functioning such as occupational or academic achievement and interpersonal relations. These findings are consistent with the previous studies that people with multiple disorders were more impaired than those with a single diagnosis (57). With respect to the comparison of severity of nicotine problems between groups, pathological gamblers with comorbid psychiatric disorders in general had significantly higher scores on FTND than those without comorbid psychiatric disorders. That means pathological gamblers with comorbid psychiatric disorders had experienced more severe nicotine problems.

Consistent with previous prevalence studies on psychiatric comorbidity, the current study showed that there were high prevalence rates (63.7% for lifetime diagnosis and 44.8% for current diagnosis) and wide ranges of comorbid psychiatric disorders among pathological gamblers seeking treatment. It has been well demonstrated in both community and clinical sample studies that pathological gamblers have high prevalence rates of comorbid mood disorder, anxiety disorder, and substance use disorders (8, 9, 12-15). Similar findings were found in our study with the most common psychiatric comorbidities reported including major depressive disorders, adjustment disorders, nicotine dependency and alcohol abuse or dependency for both lifetime and current diagnosis.

Among the participants who suffered from lifetime comorbid mood disorder, most of them suffered from major depressive disorder (21.4%), dysthymic disorder (6.5%), and bipolar disorder (2.0%). This is consistent with the previous literature showing a close link between pathological gambling and mood disorders (7, 48). Around 63% of pathological gamblers with comorbid mood disorders reported that their mood disorders appeared after pathological gambling. This observation could be explained by the fact that some pathological gamblers suffered from depressive symptoms, such as loss of interests and pleasures, as a consequence of financial and psychological distress associated with gambling.

However, about one-fourth of the participants with comorbid mood disorders in our study reported that the onset of mood disorders was prior to the onset of pathological gambling. The findings suggested that gambling in some cases could be underlying to mood disorders while the longitudinal clinical course of pathological gambling may be influenced by the clinical course of an underlying mood disorder (54). It was not uncommon for an individual with depression to develop pathological gambling as a way of escaping from and coping with depressive symptoms. Excessive gambling would provide them with feelings of reward and excitement which they repeatedly pursued to compensate for their flattened mood (16).

There are very few comorbidity studies on the prevalence rates of schizophrenia spectrum disorders among pathological gamblers in both community and clinical samples. In line with the findings of previous studies (7, 14, 15), the current study found a very low rate of lifetime comorbid schizophrenia spectrum disorder (2.5%). Previous studies suggested that genetics, early environment, neurobiology, psychological and social processes were important factors in schizophrenia spectrum disorders while the onset typically occurs between the late teens and the mid-30s (30). Due to the low prevalence rates reported in our study and the inconclusive findings in the literature, there is little evidence to suggest that pathological gamblers were more likely to develop any schizophrenia spectrum disorder, or vice versa. Petry (58) argued that results from treatment-seeking samples may underestimate the association of pathological gamblers with severe mental health problems such as schizophrenia, since they may be less likely to receive treatment for another coexisting disorder such as pathological gambling. Therefore, further studies to examine pathological gambling among patients diagnosed with schizophrenia spectrum disorders are needed.

Results from previous studies on clinical samples have indicated that substance use disorders were prevalent in treatment seeking pathological gamblers with lifetime prevalence rates ranging from a quarter to two-thirds across studies (8, 14, 15). The current study similarly showed the high lifetime prevalence rates for substance use disorder (30.8%) in pathological gamblers. The high prevalence rates of nicotine (24.2%) and alcohol use disorder (11.4%) among pathological gamblers could be explained by the fact that as alcohol consumption and tobacco use were not prohibited in gambling venues like casinos, it is common for pathological gamblers to engage in excessive drinking and smoking as integral parts of gambling experience. They may also model such behavior from other gamblers. Blum and associates (19) suggested that there were similar underlying psychological mechanisms associated with different drives such as pathological gambling and substance use. Thus, individuals with an addiction would have a higher tendency to develop other addictive, compulsive, or impulsive dysfunctional behaviors.

Regarding the early onset of substance use disorder among the participants with comorbid psychiatric disorders, almost three-quarters of them stated that onset of substance use disorders preceded the development of pathological gambling. Blum and colleagues (19) hypothesized a shared underlying psychological mechanism between substance abuse and pathological gambling linking all the addictive, compulsive and impulsive behaviors. Thus, individuals with one addiction could be viewed as being at a higher risk for another kind of addiction. With reference to this hypothesis, people with substance use disorder are more likely to develop other addictive and dysfunctional behaviors such as pathological gambling. Further studies to examine how much a person's cognitive functioning may be affected under the influence of substance use during the process of gambling will be helpful in the development of responsible gambling policy.

Our results on the lifetime prevalence rate of anxiety disorders (9.5%) corroborate earlier clinical sample studies which have generally found that pathological gamblers seeking treatment have a prevalence of lifetime anxiety disorders of less than 10%. However, the prevalence rates of specific types of anxiety disorder in the current study were generally lower than those reported in previous studies. For example, the current study showed lifetime generalized anxiety disorder (GAD) rates of 2.0%, which was much lower than the 7.2% reported by Ibáñez et al.(8), and 40% by Black and Moyer (7). Black and Moyer (7) also reported a prevalence rate for panic disorder of 10% whereas our study only revealed a rate of 2.5%.

A relatively high prevalence rate of current adjustment disorder (13.9%) was found in our study, which was slightly lower than the current rate of 17.4% reported in the previous study conducted by Ibáñez and his associates (8). According to the descriptions of DSM-IV (30), one of the important features of adjustment disorder is that there is an identifiable stressor that develops clinically significant emotional or behavioral symptoms in an individual, in which the stressor is significantly indicated by marked distress in excess of what would be expected or by significant impairment in social or occupational functioning. In our samples of pathological gamblers seeking treatment, most of them reported that their significant psychological distress was due to specific negative life events. These life events experienced by pathological gamblers were significantly related to gambling which exhibited deleterious effects on their lives. The adverse consequence of excessive gambling activities included marital and family problems and breakdown, job loss, unmanageable debt, and legal problems that easily led to depressed mood and anxiety. This explanation is supported by the temporal relationship between onset of adjustment disorder and pathological gambling in our study, with 60.7% of pathological gamblers with current comorbid adjustment disorders reporting that adjustment disorders appeared after pathological gambling.

Recommendation and Conclusion

The present findings showed that pathological gambling was significantly associated with the presence of comorbid psychiatric disorders among pathological gamblers seeking treatment. In Hong Kong, pathological gambling is treated in specialized gambling counseling centres mainly staffed by social workers, and counselors. Lesieur and Blume (38) reported that it would be more effective to treat individuals with dual mental health problems and addictions such as pathological gambling and alcohol abuse simultaneously to avoid encumbrance of treatment progress. To accomplish the above objective, it is necessary to achieve a joint effort from helping professionals in both gambling counseling services and mental health services and to develop accurate assessment measures. Based on the findings of the study, recommendations of the study are outlined in the following paragraphs.

Use of an integrative approach involving a multidisciplinary team

To ensure both pathological gambling and comorbid psychiatric disorders are treated effectively, it is recommended to establish a multidisciplinary team which includes professionals such as psychiatrists, clinical psychologists, social workers, and gambling counselors. Multidisciplinary professionals can work closely and collaboratively to formulate treatment plans and to attend regular case conferences in order to monitor clients' progress and adjust the treatment plans and strategies when necessary. A multi-dimensional and holistic treatment approach should also be used which include psychotherapy and counseling, medication, group counseling, financial education, family therapy, psychoeducation, relapse prevention, vocational counseling, and continuing care. There is a need to strengthen multi-disciplinary and cross-sectional collaboration in the treatment of addictions such as pathological gambling. Using substance abuse as an example, there are substance abuse clinics under the Hospital Authority where patients with both substance abuse and other psychiatric problems are treated. In contrast, there is no such service for pathological gamblers.

Professional training on psychiatric issues for gambling counselors

Treatment-seeking pathological gamblers with comorbid psychiatric disorders reported increased severity of gambling problems, psychiatric symptoms and functional impairment than those without comorbid psychiatric disorders. As such, early detection can minimize the risk of further harmful effects, reduce prolonged health care costs, and optimize treatment outcomes. Hence, it is important for counselors to be sensitive to psychiatric symptoms during the intake and treatment process as most of the gamblers would focus on the presenting problems related to gambling. It is recommended to provide professional training on psychiatric issues to gambling counselors with knowledge for early detection.

Comprehensive assessment during the intake process

In order to establish an appropriate treatment program for pathological gamblers with psychiatric comorbidities, it is recommended to adopt a comprehensive intake assessment during the admission process. Some semistructured or structured psychiatric diagnostic interviews such as Structural Clinical Interview for DSM-IV (SCID; (29)) and Composite International Diagnostic Interview (CIDI; (59, 60)) are some of the available diagnostic assessments on comorbid psychiatric disorders for pathological gamblers.

Differentiation of primary or secondary disorder to inform treatment priority

In the present study, the temporal relationship between pathological gambling and comorbid psychiatric disorders was examined. This contributes to our understanding on the etiological associations between pathological gambling and comorbid psychiatric disorders among pathological gamblers. Winters and Kushner (61) pointed out that there are several ways to conceptualize this etiological association since pathological gambling could serve as either the cause or consequence of comorbid disorders. They also highlighted some general clinical guidelines which have been derived from previous comorbidity studies. It was suggested that the sequence of treating addictions such as pathological gambling and comorbid psychiatric disorder could depend on the severity of active psychiatric problems. If psychiatric symptoms of a client are not assessed as severe, counselors could first treat their pathological gambling while continuously observing the psychiatric symptoms. Until the client is no longer experiencing the distress as a result of pathological gambling, reassessment of psychiatric comorbidity could be conducted to inform the need for separate treatment for the comorbid psychiatric disorder. Nunes and his associates (62) further recommended treating the comorbid psychiatric disorder while managing gambling behavior concomitantly through a series of psychoeducational and behavioral modifications on the problem gambling behavior. It is believed that conjoint treatment strategy will be beneficial to pathological gamblers who use gambling as a way of coping with their psychiatric symptoms.

Collaboration between mental health services and pathological gambling services

Joint efforts from mental health services and pathological gambling services are necessary to ensure that individuals with dual diagnosis of pathological gambling and psychiatric disorders would be treated effectively. It is recommended that gambling counseling centres could collaborate with other mental health agencies to implement a wide range of new and enhanced services including individual and group counseling, workshops, community programs, screening protocol, and referral system.

Community education of the relationship between pathological gambling and psychiatric disorders

There is a need to increase public awareness of the intimate link between psychiatric problems and pathological gambling. Such understanding may have two important effects. First, the moral labeling of pathological gamblers will be reduced. Second, relatives and friends of individuals who suffer from mental disorders can pay particular attention to the gambling behavior. They should note that gambling is not a good coping strategy for mental patients. Psychoeducation on the risk of using gambling to cope with emotional and mental health problems is vital.

Establishment of an addiction practice, research, and training centre in the Asia Pacific region

It is common for clinicians and researchers to treat different excessive behaviors, such as pathological gambling and substance abuse, as distinct disorders, but evidence from recent literatures and clinical experiences started to support the view that many commonalities occur across different expressions of addictions.

Shaffer and colleagues (63) proposed the syndrome model of addiction that a distinctive addiction might express the same underlying addiction syndrome and reflect shared etiology. Thus, addiction should be understood as a syndrome with multiple opportunistic expressions. In order to facilitate evidence-based practice and to link research, practice, and training collectively in the Asia Pacific region, it is recommended to establish an Asia Pacific addiction centre. The centre can create a platform for coordinating addiction research, practice, and professional training in an integrated fashion that will help researchers and clinicians better understand and provide effective treatment. Moreover, the centre can develop international linkage with other addiction services and academic institutions in Hong Kong and in the Asia Pacific region to advance local knowledge and to encourage interdisciplinary collaborations in the field of addictions.

There are several limitations of the present study. First, the cross-sectional nature and retrospective design of the present study does not allow us to understand the causal relationship between pathological gambling and comorbid psychiatric disorders. Future studies using a longitudinal course of gamblers would help to further clarify the temporal priority and causal relationship between these disorders, and help understand how comorbid psychiatric disorders affect the gambling treatment outcomes. Second, as a nonrandom clinical sample was used, participants seeking gambling treatment may have higher level of emotional distress and functional impairment. Therefore, whether pathological gamblers in the community show different characteristic is a question remains to be examined. Third, as information on psychiatric morbidity was based on the self-report data of the participants, there is no access to medical records. In future, collaboration with relevant psychiatric services can give a fuller picture of the problem areas. Finally, due to limited time and financial resources, not all psychiatric disorders were assessed in the present study. Other disorders such as conduct disorder (CD), attention deficit/hyperactivity disorder (ADHD) and personality disorders to be associated with pathological gambling in previous studies (9, 12) will remain for further studies. Despite the above limitations, the present study is an important addition to the literature.

Acknowledgments

The current study was financially supported by Ping Wo Fund and Tung Wah Group of Hospitals (TWGHs) Board of Directors. The authors would like to sincerely thank Professor Howard Jeffrey Shaffer from Division on Addictions, Cambridge Health Alliance, a teaching affiliate of Harvard Medical School for his prompt and helpful advice throughout the study. They wish to thank Professor Lee Sing and Mr. Tsang Cheuk-him Adley from Hong Kong Mood Disorders Centre for allowing and providing training for us to use the Chinese version of the Structured Clinical Interview of DSM-IV. They would like to thank all the respondents from TWGHs Even Centre and Zion Social Services Yuk Lai Hin Counselling Centre for taking part in this research project. Without their participations and truthful responses to the research questions, this study would have not been made possible. "This paper was originally published in The Scientific World Journal, Volume 2012, Article ID 571434, 15 pages doi:10.1100/2012/571434."

References

[1]   Abbott MW. What do we know about gambling and problem gambling in New Zealand? Report number seven of the New Zealand gaming survey. Wellington, New Zealand: The Department of Internal Affairs, 2001.

[2]   Krishnan M, Orford J. Gambling and the family: from the stress-coping-support perspective. Int Gambl Stud 2002;2:339-409.

[3]   Black DW, Monahan PO, Temkit M, Shaw M. A family study of pathological gambling. Psychiatr Res 2005;141(3):295-303.

[4]   The Hong Kong Polytechnic University. Evaluation study on the impacts of gambling liberalization in nearby cities on Hong Kong peoples' participation in gambling activities and development of

counselling and treatment services for problem gamblers 2008. Hong Kong: The Hong Kong Polytechnic University, 2008. Accessed 2014 Apr 08. URL: http://www.hab.gov.hk/en/publications_and_press_releases/reports.htm

[5]   Fong KC, Ozorio B. Gambling participation and prevalence estimates of pathological gambling in a far-east gambling city: Macao. UNLV Gaming Res Rev J 2005;9(2):15-27.

[6]   Ministry of Community Development, Youth and Sports Singapore Government. More than half of Singapore gambles; but only 2 in 100 at risk of gambling addiction. Ministry of Community Development, Youth and Sports Singapore Government, 2005. Accessed 2014 Apr 08. URL: http://app.msf.gov.sg/Portals/0/Summary/pressroom/SporeGambles.pdf

[7]   Black DW, Moyer T. Clinical features and psychiatric comorbidity of subjects with pathological gambling behavior. Psychiatr Serv 1998;49(11):1434-9.

[8]   Ibáñez A, Blanco C, Donahue E, et al. Psychiatric comorbidity in pathological gamblers seeking treatment. Am J Psychiatry 2001;158(10):1733-5.

[9]   Petry NM, Stinson FS, Grant BF. Comorbidity of DSM-IV pathological gambling and other psychiatric disorders: results from the national epidemiologic survey on alcohol and related conditions. J Clin Psychiatry 2005;66(5):564-74.

[10]   Pietrzak RH, Morasco BJ, Blanco C, Grant BF, Petry NM. Gambling level and psychiatric and medical disorders in older adults: results from the national epidemiologic survey on alcohol and related conditions. Am J Geriatr Psychiatry 2007;15(4):301-13.

[11]   Petersen T, Andreotti CF, Chelminski I, Young D, Zimmerman M. Do comorbid anxiety disorders impact treatment planning for outpatients with major depressive disorder. Psychiatr Res 2009;169(1):7-11.

[12]   Kessler RC, Hwang I, LaBrie R, et al. The prevalence and correlates of DSM-IV pathological gambling in the national comorbidity survey replication. Psychol Med 2008;38:1351-60.

[13]   El-Guebaly N, Patten SB, Currie S, et al. Epidemiological associations between gambling behavior, substance use & mood and anxiety disorders. J Gambl Stud 2006;22(3):275-87.

[14]   Choi YS, Park JH, Hong GH. Psychiatric comorbidity and the clinical characteristics of pathological gamblers seeking admission treatment. Eur Neuropsychopharmacol 2007;7:S561.

[15]   Kausch O. Patterns of substance abuse among treatment-seeking pathological gamblers. J Subst Abuse Treat 2003;25(4):263-70.

[16]   Thomsen KR, Callesena MB, Linnet J, Kringelbach ML, Møller A. Severity of gambling is associated with severity of depressive symptoms in pathological gamblers. Behav Pharmacol 2009;20:527-36.

[17]   Becoña E, Lorenzo MDC, Fuentes MJ. Pathological gambling and depression. Psychol Rep 1996;78(2):635-40.

[18]   Thorson JA, Powell FC, Hilt M. Epidemiology of gambling and depression in an adult sample. Psychol Rep 1994;74(3):987-94.

[19]   Blum K, Cull JG, Braverman ER, Comings DE. Reward deficiency syndrome. Am Sci 1996;84(2):132-45.

[20]   McCormick RA. Disinhibition and negative affectivity in substance abusers with and without a gambling problem. Addict Behav 1993;18(3):331-6.

[21]   McIntyre R, O'Donovan C, Milev R, Melledo JML, Bisserbe JC, Zimmerman M. Frequency and correlates of gambling problems in depressed and bipolar outpatients. Final report to OPGRC - Proposal#2280. Ontario, Canada: Ontario Problem Gambling Research Centre, 2008.

[22]   Cho MJ, Hahm BJ, Suh T, Suh GH, Cho SJ, Lee CK. Comorbid mental disorders among the patients with alcohol abuse and dependence in Korea. J Korean Med Sci 2002;17(2):236-41.

[23]   Derogatis LR. The Brief Symptom Inventory (BSI): administration, scoring, and procedures manual-II 2nd ed. Baltimore, Minneapolis, MN: Clinical Psychometric Research, 1992.

[24]   Derogatis, LR. BSI, Brief Symptom Inventory: administration, scoring, and procedures manual. Minneapolis, MN: National Computer Systems, 1993.

[25]   Morlan KK, Tan SY. Comparison of the brief psychiatric rating scale and the brief symptom inventory. J Clin Psychol 1998;54:885-94.

[26]   Wong DFK. Differential impacts of stressful life events and social support on the mental health of mainland Chinese immigrant and local youth in Hong Kong: a resilience perspective. Br J Soc Work 2008;38(2):236-52.

[27]   Wong DFK, Lam D, Yan P, Hung M. The impacts of acculturative stress and social competence on the mental health of mainland Chinese immigrant youth in Hong Kong. Br J Soc Work 2004;34(7):1009-24.

[28]   Wong DFK, Song HX. The resilience of migrant workers in Shanghai China: the roles of migration stress and meaning of migration. Int J Soc Psychiatry 2008;54(2):131-43.

[29]   First MB, Spitzer RL, Gibbon M, Williams JBW. Structured clinical interview for DSM-IV-TR Axis I disorders, research version, non-patient edition (SCID-I/NP). New York: New York State Psychiatric Institute, Biometrics Research, 2002.

[30]   American Psychiatric Association. Diagnostic and statistical manual of mental disorders: text revision (4th ed.). Washington, DC: American Psychiatric Association, 2000.

[31]   So E, Kam I, Leung CM, Pang A, Lam L. The Chinese-bilingual SCID-I/P project: stage 2–reliability for anxiety disorders, adjustment disorders, and 'no diagnosis'. Hong Kong J Psychiatry 2003;13(1),19-40.

[32]   So E, Kam I, Leung CM, Chung D, Liu Z, Fong S. The Chinese-bilingual SCID-I/P project: stage 1-reliability for mood disorders and schizophrenia. Hong Kong J Psychiatry 2003;13(1):7-39.

[33]   McLellan AT, Luborsky L, Cacciola J, et al. New data from the addiction severity index:reliability and validity in three centers. J Nerv Ment Dis 1985;173(7):412-23.

[34]   McLellan AT, O'Brien CP, Metzger DS, Alterman AI, Cornish J, Urschel H. How effective is substance abuse treatment-compared to what? In: O'Brien CP, Jaffe JH (Ed). Addictive states. Research publications: Association for Research in Nervous and Mental Disease. New York, NY: Raven Press, 1992;70:231-52.

[35]   Leonhard C, Mulvey K, Gastfriend DR, Schwartz M. The addiction severity index: a field study of internal consistency and validity. J Subst Abuse Treat 2000;18:129-35.

[36]   Appleby L, Dyson V, Altman E, Luchins DJ. Assessing substance use in multiproblem patients: reliability and validity of the addiction severity index in a mental hospital population. J Nerv Ment Dis 1997;185:159-65.

[37]   Petry NM. Concurrent and predictive validity of the addiction severity index in pathological gamblers. Am J Addict 2007;16(4):272-82.

[38]   Lesieur HR, Blume SB. Evaluation of patients treated for pathological gambling in a combined alcohol, substance abuse and pathological gambling treatment unit using the addiction severity index. Br J Addict 1991;86(8):1017-28.

[39]   Lesieur HR, Blume SB. Modifying the addiction severity index for use with pathological gamblers. Am J Addict 1992;1:240-7.

[40]   Petry NM. Validity of a gambling scale for the addiction severity index. J Nerv Ment Dis 2003;191(6):399–407.

[41]   Heatherton TF, Kozlowski LT, Frecker RC, Fagerstrom KO. The fagerstrom test for nicotine dependence: a revision of the fagerstrom tolerance questionnaire. Br J Addict 1991;86(9):1119-27.

[42]   Fagerstrom KO, Schneider NG. Measuring nicotine dependence: a review of the fagerstrom tolerance questionnaire. J Behav Med 1989;12(2):159-82.

[43]   Huang CL, Lin HH, Wang HH. The psychometric properties of the Chinese version of the fagerstrom test for nicotine dependence. Addict Behav 2006;31(12):2324-7.

[44]   Leon AC, Solomon DA, Mueller TI, Turvey CL, Endicott J, Keller MB. The Range of Impaired Functioning Tool (LIFE-RIFT): a brief measure of functional impairment. Psychol Med 1999;29(4):869-78.

[45]   Keller MB, Lavori PW, Friedman B, Nielsen E, Endicott J, McDonald-Scott P. The longitudinal interval follow-up evaluation: a comprehensive method for assessing outcome in prospective longitudinal studies. Arch Gen Psychiatry 1987;44:540-8.

[46]   Warshaw MG, Keller MB, Stout RL. Reliability and validity of the longitudinal interval follow-up evaluation for assessing outcome of anxiety disorders. J Psychiatr Res 1994;28(6):531-45.

[47]   Shaffer HJ, Hall MN, Vander Bilt J. Estimating the prevalence of disordered gambling behavior in the United States and Canada: a research synthesis. Am J Public Health 1999;89(9):1369-76.

[48]   Cunningham-Williams RM, Cottler LB, Compton WM, Spitznagel EL. Taking chances: problem gamblers and mental health disorders-results from the St. Louis Epidemiologic Catchment Area study. Am J Public Health 1998;88(7):1093-5.

[49]   Volberg RA. Gambling and problem gambling in Mississippi: a report to the Mississippi Council on compulsive gambling. Mississippi State, MS: Mississippi State University, Social Science Research Centre, 1997.

[50]   Petry NM, Oncken C. Cigarette smoking is associated with increased severity of gambling problems in treatment-seeking gamblers. Addict 2002;97(6):745-53.

[51]   Kessler RC, Walters EE, Forthofer MS. The social consequences of psychiatric disorders, III: probability of marital stability. Am J Psychiatry 1998;155(8):1092-6.

[52]   Lépine JP, Gasquet I, Kovess V, et al. Prevalence and comorbidity of psychiatric disorders in the French general population. Encephale 2005;31(2):182-94.

[53]   Kessler RC, Frank RG. The impact of psychiatric disorders on work loss days. Psychol Med 1997;27(4):861-73.

[54]   Kim SW, Grant JE, Eckert ED, Faris PL, Hartman BK. Pathological gambling and mood disorders: clinical associations and treatment implications. J Affect Disord 2006;92(1):109-16.

[55]   Hodgins DC, Peden N, Cassidy E. The association between comorbidity and outcome in pathological gambling: a prospective follow-up of recent quitters. J Gambl Stud 2005;21(3):255-71.

[56]   Grant JE, Kim SW, Odlaug BL, Potenza MN. Daily tobacco smoking in treatment-seeking pathological gamblers: clinical correlates and co-occurring psychiatric disorders. J Addict Med 2008;2(4):178-84.

[57]   Feigelman W, Wallisch LS, Lesieur HR. Problem gamblers, problem substance abusers, and dual-problem individuals: an epidemiological study. Am J Public Health 1998;88(3):467-70.

[58]   Petry NM. Substance abuse, pathological gambling, and impulsiveness. Drug Alcohol Depend 2001;63(1):29-38.

[59]   Kessler RC, Abelson J, Demler O, et al. Clinical calibration of DSM-IV diagnoses in the World Mental Health (WMH) version of the World Health Organization (WHO) Composite International Diagnostic Interview (CIDI). Int J Methods Psychiatr Res 2004;13(2):122-39.

[60]   Kessler RC, Üstün TB. The World Mental Health (WMH) survey initiative version of the World Health Organization (WHO) Composite International Diagnostic Interview (CIDI). Int J Methods Psychiatr Res 2004;13(2):93-117.

[61]   Winters KC, Kushner MG. Treatment issues pertaining to pathological gamblers with a comorbid disorder. J Grambl Stud 2003;19(3):261-77.

[62]   Nunes EV, Deliyannides D, Donovan S, McGrath PJ. The management of treatment resistance in depressed patients with substance use disorders. Psychiatr Clin North Am 1996;19(2):311-27.

[63]   Shaffer HJ, LaPlante DA, LaBrie RA, Kidman RC, Donato AN, Stanton MV. Toward a syndrome model of addiction: multiple expressions, common etiology. Harv Rev Psychiatr 2004;12(6):367-74.

Submitted: November 06, 2011. *Revised:* December 17, 2011. *Accepted:* December 23, 2011.

In: Child Health and Human Development Yearbook 2013   ISBN: 978-1-63117-939-6
Editor: Joav Merrick   © 2014 Nova Science Publishers, Inc.

Chapter 13

Internet addiction phenomenon in early adolescents in Hong Kong

*Daniel TL Shek, PhD, FHKPS, BBS, SBS, JP[*1,2,3,4], and Lu Yu, PhD[1]*
[1]Department of Applied Social Sciences, The Hong Kong Polytechnic University,
Hong Kong, PRC
[2]Centre for Innovative Programmes for Adolescents and Families,
The Hong Kong Polytechnic University, Hong Kong, PRC
[3]Department of Social Work, East China Normal University, Shanghai, PRC
[4]Kiang Wu Nursing College of Macau, Macau, PRC

Abstract

The present study investigated the prevalence and demographic correlates of Internet addiction in Hong Kong adolescents as well as the change in related behavior at two time points over a one-year interval. Two waves of data were collected from a large sample of students (Wave 1: 3,328 students, age = 12.59 ± 0.74 years; Wave 2: 3,580 students, age = 13.50 ± 0.75 years) at 28 secondary schools in Hong Kong. Comparable to findings at Wave 1 (26.4%), 26.7% of the participants met the criterion of Internet addiction at Wave 2 as measured by Young's 10-item Internet Addiction Test. The behavioral pattern of Internet addiction was basically stable over time. While the predictive effects of demographic variables including age, gender, family economic status, and immigration status were not significant, Internet addictive behaviors at Wave 1 significantly predicted similar behaviors at Wave 2. Students who met the criterion of Internet addiction at Wave 1 were 7.55 times more likely than other students to be classified as Internet addicts at Wave 2. These results suggest that early detection and intervention for Internet addiction should be carried out.

[*] Correspondence: Professor Daniel TL Shek, PhD, FHKPS, BBS, SBS, JP, Associate Vice President (Undergraudate Programme), Chair Professor of Applied Social Sciences, Department of Applied Social Sciences, Faculty of Health and Social Sciences, The Hong Kong Polytechnic University, Room HJ407, Core H, Hunghom, Hong Kong, PRC. E-mail: daniel.shek@polyu.edu.hk.

Keywords: Chinese adolescents, early adolescents, Hong Kong, Internet addiction, longitudinal design

Introduction

The use of the Internet has brought a variety of convenience to our modern life. Nonetheless, negative impact is also created by addictive behaviors to the Internet pervasively on one's academic and working performance, family life, social relationships, physical health, and psychological well-being (1-3). Although there are different views on the term, "Internet addiction" or "pathological use of the Internet" usually refers to the phenomenon that an individual is unable to control his or her use of the Internet (including any online-related, compulsive behavior) which eventually causes one's marked distress and functional impairment in daily life (4). With the soaring number of Internet users, it has been reported that Internet addiction is becoming a serious problem across the world, especially for adolescents. Scholars have also warned that Internet addiction could bring substantial loss of productivity in schools and companies where no Internet governance policies are implemented (5, 6). As there are few related studies on Internet addiction in Hong Kong, the present study investigated the occurrence and demographic correlates of Internet addiction among a group of Hong Kong adolescents and examined the stability of the phenomenon by comparing the prevalence findings between two time points with a one-year interval.

In the past few decades, several studies have examined the prevalence of youth Internet addiction, with the reported data varying across different areas of the world (7). It has been found that the occurrence rate of Internet addiction among adolescents ranges from 1.98% to 35.8% in Western and Eastern societies (8-10). Even in different Chinese communities, prevalence findings of Internet addiction were inconsistent. For example, in Chou and Hsiao's study, 5.9% of Taiwan college students were classified as having Internet addiction (11), whereas Wu and Zhu reported that 10.6% of university students in Mainland China could be identified as Internet addicts (12). While a study on high school students in Changsha showed a prevalence rate of 2.4% (13), another study in Shanxi revealed that 6.44% of first-year university students were addicted to the Internet (14). In Hong Kong, using Young's 20-item questionnaire to examine Internet addiction among youth, 61.4% of senior primary school students, 35.2% of Secondary 1 to 3 students, 18.8% of Secondary 4 to 5 students, 35.8% of Secondary 6 to 7 students, and 37.0% of college students were identified as highly at risk of Internet addiction (15). There were also findings showing that 13.8% of a sample of high school adolescents in Taiwan met the criterion of Internet addiction and had different psychological and psychiatric problems (16).

These inconsistent findings may be explained by several factors on the conceptual and methodological levels. First, various instruments for assessing Internet addiction were used. In Taiwan, researchers tended to use a 40-item Chinese Internet-Related Addictive Behavior Inventory to assess Internet addiction in adolescents (15). However, Young's questionnaires were usually adopted by scholars in Mainland China and Hong Kong (14, 16). Second, inconsistent diagnostic criteria and cut-off scores were employed in different studies. Although most researchers followed Young's proposed cut-off (i.e., having 4 out of 10 symptoms as the threshold of being classified as Internet addiction), other researchers used a higher cutoff score. Third, some prevalence studies were based on small and unrepresentative samples which limited the generalizability of the findings. Fourth, most of the existing studies utilized cross-sectional designs and thus cannot provide a complete understanding of how Internet addiction developed over time. These problems point to the urgent need to conduct methodologically sound research on youth Internet addiction, particularly in Chinese contexts, where few validated measures exist (17).

Another important puzzle in Internet addiction research is whether an individual's tendency of displaying Internet addictive behaviors remains the same or change over time. On the one hand, some researchers claimed that Internet addiction is a short-term phenomenon which would gradually diminish as time passes (18, 19). For example, Widyanto and McMurran (18) proposed that Internet addiction is "a temporary phenomenon for some individuals, likely related to the initial novelty of the Internet and wearing off with increased familiarity" (p. 444). Young reported that over half of self-identified "Internet-dependent" had been online for less than one year, suggesting that new users may be more inclined to develop addictive behaviors associated with Internet use (20). In fact, more than two-thirds of "non-Internet-dependent" subjects in Young's study had been online for over a year, which seems to indicate that excessive use of the Internet could be a transient phenomenon that wears off over time in most individuals. There are also perspectives suggesting that real-life difficulties may contribute to Internet addiction because Internet provides an escape for the individual from stressful life events (21). Once the problems in reality are solved, Internet addictive behaviors would gradually taper off.

On the other hand, another school of thoughts and empirical studies support the stability and persistence of Internet addiction where pathological use of the Internet is believed to be associated with personality factors and other problems. In one study, individuals who were self-reliant, emotionally sensitive, reactive, vigilant, nonconformist, and have low self-disclosure were found to be more likely to become Internet dependent (1). Amiel and Sargent found that the use of the Internet gave highly neurotic subjects a sense of belonging and made them feel informed, while extraverts tended to use the Internet for instrumental purposes (22). The comorbidity of Internet addiction and other psychosocial problems provides extra support to expect stability in Internet addiction, although there is no consensus regarding whether Internet addiction should be considered a cause or an effect. It was found that lonely individuals used the Internet more frequently and were more likely to use the Internet for emotional support than non-lonely people (23). All these findings seem to indicate the stability of Internet addiction tendency. However, the studies are severely limited by their cross-sectional design, which collected data only one time and/or examined stability of Internet addiction through retrospective recall technique. Hence, such an approach could only provide a snapshot of Internet addiction. To determine whether Internet addictive behaviors are temporary or stable among adolescents, longitudinal studies examining data across different time points are necessary.

Against the above background, there were two purposes of the present study. The first purpose was to investigate the occurrence rate of Internet addiction and its demographic correlates among a large sample of Hong Kong adolescents using a validated instrument, Young's 10-item Internet Addiction Test (17). As part of a large longitudinal study on youth development, for which two waves of data have been collected, this paper focuses on data collected at the second wave.

Results regarding the first wave of data have been reported elsewhere (24). To establish causal relationships between different demographic factors and Internet addiction, demographic information (age, gender, family economic status, and immigration) collected at Wave 1 was used to predict youth Internet addictive behaviors at Wave 2. The second purpose was to examine the stability of Internet addiction over time by comparing the occurrence rates of different types of Internet addictive behaviors in the same sample of students at the two time points (Wave 1 and Wave 2). The predictive effect of Internet addiction at Wave 1 on participants' behaviors at Wave 2 was also evaluated after controlling for other demographic variables.

Methods

The present paper reports findings on participants' Internet addictive behavior collected at the second wave of the longitudinal study. There were 28 secondary schools in Hong Kong participated in this study. Details about the study as well as findings of the first wave of data can be seen in Shek and Yu's paper (24).

Participants

In the school year of 2010-2011, all Secondary 2 students in the selected 28 schools, who participated in the first wave of data collection in the school year of 2009-2010 when they were at Secondary 1 level, were invited to attend the second wave of data collection. There were 3,580 students responding to the questionnaire, including 1,864 males (52.1%) and 1,716 females (47.9%). The mean age of the participants was 13.64 years (SD = 0.75). Local students accounted for 78.6% of the participants; 19.3% of them were born in Mainland China and 2.0% were from other places. The demographic information of the participants is summarized in Table 1. From Wave 1 to Wave 2, data of 2904 students were successfully matched, indicating an acceptable attrition rate of 12%.

Procedures

The participants were invited to respond to a comprehensive youth development questionnaire including both existing instruments and scales developed by the first author. The questionnaire survey was conducted by a trained research assistant in classroom settings with standardized instructions. At each measurement occasion, the purposes of the study were introduced and confidentiality of the data collected was repeatedly ensured to all participants.

School, parental and student consent had been obtained before data collection. Participants responded to the questionnaires in a self-administered format. The research assistant was present throughout the administration process to answer possible questions from the participants.

Table 1. Descriptive statistics about participants

Categorical variables	n	%		
Gender				
Male	1,864	52.1%		
Female	1,716	47.9%		
Place of birth				
Hong Kong	2,806	78.6%		
Mainland China	690	19.3%		
Others	73	2.0%		
Parental marital status				
First marriage	2,985	82.7%		
Divorced	256	7.1%		
Separated	78	2.2%		
Remarried	168	4.7%		
Others (not first marriage)	122	3.4%		
Family economic status				
Receiving CSSA	208	5.8%		
Not receiving CSSA	2,932	81.2%		
Others (don't know)	472	13.1%		
Continuous variables	Mean	SD	Range	Cronbach's α
Age	13.64	.75	10-17	-
NET-Wave 1	1.23	.24	1-2	.79
NET-Wave 2	1.24	.25	1-2	.80

Notes: CSSA = Comprehensive Social Security Assistance.
NET-Wave 1 = Internet Addiction Test scale score at wave 1.
NET-Wave 2 = Internet Addiction Test scale score at wave 2.

Instruments

The questionnaire used in this study comprises questions about participants' Internet addictive behaviors, demographic information, participants' family environment, different measures of youth development constructs, and other problem behaviors. For family factors, participants responded to questions regarding paternal presence, maternal presence, parental marital status, paternal educational level, maternal educational level, and family economic status.

Family economic status is indexed by the question of whether the family of the participant is receiving Comprehensive Social Security Assistance (CSSA), a financial aid provided by Hong Kong Government for low-income populations, at the time of survey. The scales used to assess Internet addiction and positive youth development constructs are introduced below.

Young's 10-item Internet Addiction Test (IAT)

Young developed several instruments to assess Internet addiction, among which the 10-item Internet Addiction Test was validated by Shek, Tang and Lo (17) for Chinese populations and was selected to measure youth Internet addictive behavior in this study. The 10-item IAT asks respondents to answer "Yes" or "No" as to whether they have the listed Internet addictive behaviors in the past one year. Example items include "feeling a need to spend more and more time online to achieve satisfaction" and "feeling restless or irritable when attempting to cut down or stop online use".

A person is classified as "Internet addiction" if he/she shows 4 or more of the listed behaviors. Cronbach's alpha of IAT for the present sample was 0.79 and 0.80 at Wave 1 and Wave 2, respectively.

Chinese Positive Youth Development Scale (CPYDS)

The CPYDS consists of 15 subscales which are listed as follows:

1. Bonding Subscale (three items)
2. Resilience Subscale (three items)
3. Social Competence Subscale (three items)
4. Emotional Competence Subscale (three items)
5. Cognitive Competence Subscale (three items)
6. Behavioral Competence Subscale (three items)
7. Moral Competence Subscale (three items)
8. Self-Determination Subscale (three items)
9. Self-Efficacy Subscale (two items)
10. Beliefs in the Future Subscale (three items)
11. Clear and Positive Identity Subscale (three items)
12. Spirituality Subscale (three items)
13. Prosocial Involvement Subscale (three items)
14. Prosocial Norms Subscale (three items)
15. Recognition for Positive Behavior Subscale (three items)

Although the administered questionnaire includes the CPYDQ, findings regarding this scale will be reported elsewhere. The present paper only focused on the descriptive profile of Internet addictive behavior and its demographic correlates as well as the change of behavior over time.

Data analytic plan

First, to examine the prevalence of Internet addiction among Hong Kong adolescents, numbers and percentages of adolescents who reported different addictive behaviors associated with Internet use at Wave 2 were computed. Secondly, to investigate the stability or change in participants' Internet addiction over a one-year interval, the percentages of participants showing Internet addictive behaviors at Wave 2 were compared with the percentages found at Wave 1 by using related-samples McNemar Tests, a statistic method examining the difference between paired proportions. Participants' IAT scale score at the two waves were also compared with a paired-samples t-test.

Thirdly, to investigate the predictive effects of different demographic variables and Internet addictive behaviors at Wave 1 on participants' Internet addiction at Wave 2, both multiple regression analysis and logistic regression analysis were performed. Specifically, in the multiple regression analysis, participants' scale score on IAT at Wave 2 served as the dependent variable. For independent variables, gender and age were entered in the first block; family economic status and immigration status were entered in the second block; and participants' score on IAT at Wave 1 was input in the third block. For the logistic regression model, whether the participant met the criterion of Internet addiction at Wave 2 was entered as dependent variable; independent variables and their order of input were the same as those in the linear regression model, except that in the third block participants' IAT score was replaced by their eligibility of being classified as Internet addiction at Wave 1 as the predictor.

As immigrant youth from other places than Mainland China only accounted for 2.0% of the participants, they were not included in the regression analyses. In other words, the present study only focused on comparing local and immigrant adolescents from Mainland China on their Internet addictive behaviors.

Results

Descriptive profiles on Internet addictive behavior

Numbers and percentages of participants who displayed Internet addictive behaviors in the past one year are summarized in Table 2. Several observations can be highlighted from the findings. First, signs of Internet addiction were still common among Secondary 2 students in Hong Kong. There were 41.1% of the respondents reporting "feeling preoccupied with the Internet or online services and think about it while offline"; 46.6% of the students "stay online longer than originally intended"; 31.6% of the participants "feeling a need to spend more and more time online to achieve satisfaction". Second, according to Young's criterion, 26.7% of the respondents could be classified as Internet addicted.

Third, psychosocial problems related to excessive Internet use were observed: 20.2% of the participants reported to "go online to escape problems or relieve feelings such as helplessness, guilt, anxiety or depression"; 19.4% of the students were found to "lie to family members or friends to conceal excessive Internet use". These observations suggest that Internet addiction is a serious and widespread problem in Secondary 2 students in Hong Kong which requires more public attention from the Hong Kong society.

Comparison of internet addiction over one year

The differences in percentages of participants with different Internet addictive behaviors on IAT were examined between the two waves of data collection.

As can be seen in Table 2, the occurrence rates for eight out of ten Internet addictive behaviors were similar among students at Wave 1 and Wave 2. No significant differences were found in the percentages of students displaying these behaviors. The proportion of students who met the criterion of Internet addiction at Wave 2 (26.7%) was also comparable to that of last year (26.4%). In addition, the result of paired-samples t-test showed there was no significant difference ($p > .05$) in students' mean scores on IAT at Wave 1 (Mean = 1.23) and Wave 2 (Mean = 1.24). Overall, these figures suggest that adolescent Internet addiction is a relatively stable phenomenon as opposed to wearing off over time. It should be noted that for two individual items, significant differences were detected, with a larger proportion of students at Wave 2 reported that they "stay online longer than originally intended" ($p < .001$) and "risk the loss of a significant relationship, job, or educational or career opportunity because of online use" ($p = .02$) than at Wave 1.

Such an increasing tendency may serve as a warning for researchers and practitioners in the field that without effective intervention/prevention strategies, it is possible that Internet addiction in adolescents would deteriorate with the increasingly wide application of the Internet in youth life.

Prediction of internet addictive behavior

The predictive effects of participants' demographic variables and prior Internet addictive behaviors on pathological use of Internet at Wave 2 were examined. Table 3 and Table 4 present the results of multiple regression analysis and logistic regression analysis, respectively. Several findings can be observed from the results of multiple regression analysis. First, participants' age failed to predict Internet abuse behaviors. Second, gender was not related to adolescent Internet addiction: boys and girls had similar IAT scale scores. Third, both family economic status and immigration status had no significant influence on participants' addictive behaviors associated with Internet use. Fourth, after controlling for the demographic variables, participants' pathological use of Internet at Wave 1 significantly predicted Internet addictive behavior at Wave 2. The whole model explained 31% of the variance in adolescents' IAT scores at Wave 2, which was almost all from participants' prior Internet addictive behaviors. Using the probability of being classified as Internet addiction as the dependent variable, results of logistic regression analysis again showed that previous Internet addiction was the only significant predictor of whether a participant would meet Young's criterion of Internet addiction at Wave 2 (B = 2.02, odds ratio = 7.55, $p < .001$). In other words, students who met the criterion of Internet addiction at Wave 1 were 7.55 times more likely to be identified as having Internet addiction at Wave 2. The non-significant findings regarding demographic predictors indicated that for the present sample of students, the occurrence of Internet addiction was unrelated to their age, gender, family economic status, and immigration status. These findings are consistent with the results of linear regression analysis.

Discussion

This study investigated the prevalence and demographic correlates of Internet addictive behaviors in Hong Kong adolescents and examined stability and change in pathological use of Internet as measured by Young's 10-item Internet Addiction Test.

Table 2. Percentage of participants with Internet addiction behavior in two years

Internet use behaviors in the past year	No (Wave 2) Number	Percent	Yes (Wave 2) Number	Percent	Yes (Wave 1) Number	Percent	Related-Samples McNemar Tests Statistics	p
1. Feeling preoccupied with the Internet or online services and think about it while offline	2141	58.9%	1494	41.1%	1324	39.9%	1.50	.22
2. Feeling a need to spend more and more time online to achieve satisfaction	2484	68.4%	1147	31.6%	1072	32.3%	1.11	.29
3. Unable to control your online use	2765	68.1%	866	23.9%	752	22.7%	.54	.46
4. Feeling restless or irritable when attempting to cut down or stop online use	3119	85.9%	511	14.1%	484	14.6%	.04	.85
5. Stay on-line longer than originally intended	**1937**	**53.4%**	**1691**	**46.6%**	**1404**	**42.4%**	**14.82**	**.00**
6. Risk the loss of a significant relationship, job, or educational or career opportunity because of online use	**2821**	**77.7%**	**809**	**22.3%**	**644**	**19.5%**	**5.89**	**.02**
7. Lie to family members or friends to conceal excessive Internet use	2925	80.6%	703	19.4%	651	19.7%	.51	.48
8. Go online to escape problems or relieve feelings such as helplessness, guilt, anxiety or depression	2892	79.8%	732	20.2%	633	19.2%	1.63	.20
9. Showing withdrawal when offline, such as increased depression, moodiness, or irritability	3151	77.6%	477	13.1%	395	12.0%	1.40	.24
10. Keep on using Internet even after spending too much money on online fees	3219	89.0%	399	11.0%	331	10.1%	.10	.75
Participants can be classified as Internet addiction (Young's criteria)	2663	73.3%	972	26.7%	869	26.4%	.10	.76

Note: Related-Samples McNemar Tests were conducted to examine whether the difference between the distribution of students with Internet addictive behaviors in Wave 1 and Wave 2 is significant.

Table 3. Multiple regression analyses on students' Internet use behavior

	B	Beta	Sig	R^2	R^2 change
First block					
Age	-.01	-.03	.11		
Gender	.00	.00	.89	.00	.00
Second block					
Immigration status	-.01	-.01	.51		
Family economic status	-.01	-.02	.31	.00	.00
Third block					
NET-Wave 1	**.57**	**.56**	**.00**	**.31**	**.31****

Notes: * $p < .01$, ** $p < .001$.

Dependent variable: NET-Wave 2 = Internet Addiction Test scale score at wave 2.

Gender: 1 = female; 0 = male.

Immigration status: 1 = immigrant student; 0 = local student.

Family economic status: 1 = Receiving Comprehensive Social Security Assistance (CSSA); 2 = not receiving CSSA.

NET-Wave 1 = Internet Addiction Test scale score at wave 1.

Table 4. Logistic regression analyses on students' Internet addiction

	B	Odds ratio	p
First block			
Age	-.04	.96	.59
Gender	-.13	.88	.18
Second block			
Immigration status	.19	1.21	.17
Family economic status (CSSA)	.09	1.10	.66
Third block			
IA-Wave 1	**2.02**	**7.55**	**.00**

Notes:

Dependent variable: IA-Wave 2 = whether the student meets the criterion of Internet addiction at wave 2.

Gender: 1 = female; 0 = male.

Immigration status: 1 = immigrant students; 0 = local student.

Family economic status: 1 = Receiving Comprehensive Social Security Assistance (CSSA); 2 = not receiving CSSA.

IA-Wave 1: 1 = the student met the criterion of Internet addiction at wave 1; 0 = the student did not meet the criterion of Internet addiction at wave 1.

A sample of more than 3,000 secondary school students was assessed twice over one year. The results showed that Internet addiction appeared to be a common problem in Hong Kong adolescents which may need more public attention and resources to develop effective prevention/intervention strategies. The two-wave longitudinal findings lent support for stability in Internet addiction as opposed to wearing off over time. Specifically, the percentages of participants who met the criterion of Internet addiction were comparable across one year. While none of the demographic variables in the present study predicted Internet addiction, one's earlier pathological use of the Internet significantly affected the individual's later Internet addictive behaviors and the probability of being classified as Internet addicts. Clearly, these findings suggest the importance of early detection and intervention for Internet addiction in Chinese adolescents in Hong Kong.

Consistent with the findings at Wave 1 (24), more than one-fourth of the participants (26.7%) at Wave 2 were identified as having Internet addiction based on Young's criterion. The percentages of adolescents showing various Internet misuse behaviors ranged from 11.0% to 46.6%. When the two-wave comparison was made, no significant differences were detected for most addictive behaviors and for participants' IAT scale scores. These findings support the stability in Internet addiction. In other words, adolescents' Internet addictive behavior is not a transient phenomenon that will naturally disappear as adolescents grow older. As such, effective strategies must be developed and implemented to help youth control excessive use of the Internet and form healthy habit associated with Internet use. At the same time, it should be noted that the occurrence rate of Internet addiction found in this study is higher than previously reported prevalence data on Hong Kong adolescents by other researchers (17, 25). Also, there were more students at Wave 2 reported that they "stay online longer than originally intended" (46.6%) and "risk the loss of a significant relationship, job, or educational or career opportunity because of online use" (22.3%), as compared to Wave 1. This appears to be a worrying tendency. As the Internet has increasingly become an important part of adolescent life, the risk of youth being addicted to the Internet also increases. In the present study, the findings that more adolescents reported excessive time spent on Internet activities and showed impaired social relationships caused by Internet use after one year actually suggest a growing severity of the issue. To solve the problem, researchers, educators, parents, and policy makers must work together and act promptly. For example, school-based prevention programs that involve the participation of parents, teachers and students should be implemented. The government could promote public awareness of the seriousness of Internet addiction and its effects on society through major media and provide support for different agencies to conduct scientific research and develop effective strategies to prevent Internet addiction.

There are both good and bad implications regarding the relatively stable Internet addiction picture in Secondary 1 and Secondary 2 students in Hong Kong. With specific reference to the "good" implication, stability in the level as well as the prevalence of Internet addiction suggests that there is no further deterioration of the situation, which is quite unlike other adolescent risk behaviors, such as substance abuse, delinquency and intention to engage in problem behavior in the future. Theoretically, there is a need to understand why Internet addiction does not deteriorate in adolescents over time. Is it due to the fact that the baseline prevalence is already very high, as compared to other youth risk behaviors, or that adolescents would start to have more self-control as they become more mature? Concerning the "bad" implication, adolescents' maintenance of relatively same rate of Internet addiction over time suggests that developmental maturation alone may not be able to reduce Internet addictive behavior. Apparently, if we want to reduce the severity of the problem, there is a need to provide additional intervention strategies.

Interestingly, all demographic variables, including gender, age, immigration status, and family economic status, failed to predict youth Internet addiction in this study. This means that students with different demographic background are at similar risk of developing Internet addictive behaviors. Except for the prediction of age on Internet addiction, the present finding further confirmed the results obtained from the same sample of students one year ago (24). The study on Wave 1 data showed that older students displayed more pathological use of the Internet, which can be explained by older students' greater developmental dynamics, such as a stronger need to develop a sense of identity, and more access to the Internet, than younger students when they first entered into secondary schools. It may be that after one-year secondary school life, such discrepancies between older and younger students are reduced. Besides, participants in the present study were all at the same grade. The variance in student age was relatively small, which may also contribute to the non-significant effect of age on Internet addictive behaviors. Future studies should recruit participants of a wider range of age to further establish the relationship between age and Internet addiction. In addition, in contrast to other addictive behaviors where males usually show a higher level of addictive behavior than do females, the occurrence of Internet addictive behavior appeared to be similar for both adolescent boys and girls. It is suggested that future studies should be conducted to examine gender differences over a longer period of time. In fact, in view of the lack of significant findings for all sociodemographic correlates, it would be important to examine whether this observation could be replicated across time and populations.

Adolescents' prior addictive behaviors associated with the Internet (Wave 1) significantly predicted their Internet addiction after one year, with all possible influence of demographic factors being excluded. The effect size was quite large. Students who met the criterion of Internet addiction at Wave 1 were 7.55 times more likely to be classified as Internet addict one year later. This further suggests that Internet addiction is a relatively stable behavioral pattern. As with other addictive behaviors, once the pattern of pathological use of the Internet is established, it may not be easily changed. The implication is that Internet addiction must be treated and prevented as early as possible. Researchers have proposed different intervention strategies to treat Internet addiction, such as cognitive behavior therapy and motivational enhancement therapy (26). For example, in cognitive behavior therapy, addicts are taught to identify the distorted thoughts that trigger Internet addictive behaviors and are provided coping strategies trainings to help them effectively deal with real or perceived problems. Motivational enhancement therapy allows the Internet abusers and therapists to collaborate on treatment plans and set achievable goals (26). Young (4) also suggested several specific treatment techniques, like construct new schedule for using the Internet, set clear and achievable goals to give the addicts a sense of control, provide social support to decrease addicts' dependence on the Internet, and family therapy.

While these techniques have been demonstrated to be effective in treating Internet addicts, what is more important is to prevent adolescents who have not met the criterion of Internet addiction to develop such a behavioral pattern.

Based on the problem behavior theory that Internet addiction is an intersection of multiple physical, psychological, and technological phenomena instead of a single problem, it has been suggested that prevention programs directed at the organization of different problem behaviors (e.g., substance use, delinquency) may be more appropriate than those target at specific behaviors alone (3), such as promoting positive youth development among adolescents. In fact, based on a longitudinal randomized controlled group trial, researchers have reported that participants of the Project P.A.T.H.S., a program that aims to promote holistic positive development among adolescents, displayed stronger ability to control Internet use than did the comparison group (27).

It seems that positive youth development program represents a promising direction for youth Internet addiction prevention in the future (28, 29). In the recent longitudinal study including eight waves of data collected in the Project P.A.T.H.S. (a positive youth development program in Hong Kong), results showed that relative to the control group participants, students in the experimental schools (i.e., students participated in the Project P.A.T.H.S.) showed higher levels of psychosocial competencies and less problem behaviors.

It is argued that promotion of psychosocial competencies may help to protect young people from risk behavior by enhancing their inner strengths (30-32). Besides, as different youth risk behaviors tend to co-exist, reduction of other problem behaviors, such as intention to engage in risk behavior, may also lower the risk of developing Internet addiction in the long run (33, 34).

Several limitations of this study should be noted. First, Internet addictive behaviors were assessed at only two time points over a relatively short period. Long-term developmental tendency of the behavior cannot be determined. Second, participant age varied within a small range, which limits the investigation of the relationship between age and Internet addiction. Third, single items were used to assess demographic variables, such as family economic status and immigration status. The demographic background of the students may not be fully reflected by these indicators.

Ideally, future studies should collect multiple waves of data from adolescents at different age groups, such as students at different secondary school grades, and use more specific demographic index, like monthly family income or years of living in Hong Kong for immigrant students. Fourth, only ten items with dichotomous responses were used to assess Internet addiction, which may produce a less discriminating response profile. More comprehensive measures on Internet addiction may be employed in further research. Despite of the limitations, the present findings provide a useful addition to existing literature of Internet addiction in Hong Kong adolescents.

Acknowledgment

The preparation for this paper and the Project P.A.T.H.S. were financially supported by The Hong Kong Jockey Club Charities Trust. This paper was originally published in The Scientific World Journal, Volume 2012, Article ID 104304, 9 pages doi:10.1100/2012/104304

References

[1]   Young KS, Rogers RC. The relationship between depression and internet addiction. Cyberpsychol Behav 1998;1(1):25-8.

[2]   Kaltiala-Heino R, Lintonen T, Rimpelä A. Internet addiction? Potentially problematic use of the internet in a population of 12-18 year old adolescents. Addict Res Theory 2004;12(1):89-96.

[3]   Yen JY, Ko CH, Yen CF, Wu HY, Yang MJ. The comorbid psychiatric symptoms of Internet addiction: attention deficit and hyperactivity disorder (ADHD), depression, social phobia, and hostility. J Adolesc Health 2007;41(1):93-8.

[4]   Young KS. Internet addiction: symptoms, evaluation, and treatment. In: Van de Creek L, Jackson T, editors. Innovations in clinical practice: a source book, Vol. 17. Sarasota, FL: Professional Resource Press, 1999:19-31.

[5]   Young KS, de Abreu CN, editors. Internet addiction: a handbook and guide to evaluation and treatment. Hoboken, NJ: John Wiley, 2010.

[6]   Yellowlees PM, Marks S. Problematic internet use or internet addiction? Comput Hum Behav 2007;23(3):1447-53.

[7]   Beard KW. Internet addiction: a review of current assessment techniques and potential assessment questions. Cyberpsychol Behav 2005;8(1):7-14.

[8]   Aboujaoude E, Koran LM, Gamel N, Large MD, Serpe RT. Potential markers for problematic internet use: a telephone survey of 2,513 adults. CNS Spectr 2006;11(10):750-5.

[9]   Niemz K, Griffiths M, Banyard P. Prevalence of pathological internet use among university students and correlations with self-esteem, the General Health Questionnaire (GHQ), and disinhibition. Cyberpsychol Behav 2005;8(6):562-70.

[10]   Johansson A, Götestam KG. Internet addiction: characteristics of a questionnaire and prevalence in Norwegian youth (12-18 years). Scand J Psychol 2004;45(3):223-9.

[11]   Chou C, Hsiao MC. Internet addiction, usage, gratifications, and pleasure experience – the Taiwan college students' case. Comput Educ 2000;35(1):65-80.

[12]   Wu HR, Zhu KJ. Path analysis on related factors causing internet addiction disorder in college students. Chin J Pub Health 2004;20(1363):1364.

[13]   Cao FL, Su LY. Internet addiction among Chinese adolescents: prevalence and psychological features. Child Care Health Dev 2007;33(3):275-81.

[14]   Ni X, Yan H, Chen S, Liu Z. Factors influencing internet addiction in a sample of freshmen university students in China. Cyberpsychol Behav 2009;12(3):327-30.

[15]   Chinese YMCA of Hong Kong. Study on adolescents' internet using behaviors. Hong Kong: Tsuen Wan Centre, Chinese YMCA of Hong Kong, 2004.

[16]   Yang SC, Tung CJ. Comparison of internet addicts and non-addicts in Taiwanese high school. Comput Hum Behav 2007;23(1):79-96.

[17]   Shek DTL, Tang VMY, Lo CY. Internet addiction in Chinese adolescents in Hong Kong: assessment, profiles, and psychosocial correlates. ScientificWorldJournal 2008;8:776-87.

[18]   Widyanto L, McMurran M. The psychometric properties of the internet addiction test. Cyberpsychol Behav 2004;7(4):443-50.

[19]   Kraut R, Patterson M, Lundmark V, Kiesler S, Mukopadhyay T, Scherlis, W. Internet paradox: a social technology that reduces social involvement and psychological well-being? Am Psychol 1998;53(9):1017-31.

[20]   Young KS. Internet addiction: the emergence of a new clinical disorder. Cyberpsychol Behav 1998;1(3):237-44.

[21]   Armstrong L, Philips JG, Saling LL. Potential determinants of heavier internet usage. Int J Hum Comput Stud 2000;53(4):537-50.

[22]   Amiel T, Sargent SL. Individual differences in internet usage motives. Comput Hum Behav 2004;20(6):711-26.

[23]   Morahan-Martin J, Schumacher P. Loneliness and social uses of the internet. Comput Hum Behav 2003;19(6):659-71.

[24]   Shek DTL, Yu L. Internet addiction in Hong Kong adolescents: profiles and psychosocial correlates. Int J Disabil Hum Dev 2012;11(2):133-42.

[25]   Chan TCF. Cyber risk of Hong Kong youngsters. J Youth Stud 2004;7(2):155-68.

[26]   Orzack MH, Orzack DS. Treatment of computer addicts with complex co-morbid psychiatric disorders. Cyberpsychol Behav 1999;2(5):465-73.

[27]   Shek DTL, Yu L. Prevention of adolescent problem behavior: longitudinal impact of the Project P.A.T.H.S. in Hong Kong. ScientificWorldJournal 2011;11:546-67.

[28]   Shek DTL, Ng CSM. Early identification of adolescents with greater psychosocial needs: an evaluation of the Project P.A.T.H.S. in Hong Kong. Int J Disabil Hum Dev 2010;9(4):291-9.

[29]   Shek DTL, Ng CSM, Tsui PF. Qualitative evaluation of the Project P.A.T.H.S.: findings based on focus groups. Int J Disabil Hum Dev 2010;9(4):307-13.

[30]   Sun RCF, Shek DTL. Life satisfaction, positive youth development, and problem behaviour among Chinese adolescents in Hong Kong. Soc Indic Res 2010;95(3):455-74.

[31]   Shek DTL, Merrick J, editors. Special issue: positive youth development and training. Int J Adolesc Med Health 2010;21:341-447.

[32]   Shek DTL. Subjective outcome and objective outcome evaluation findings: insights from a Chinese context. Res Soc Work Pract 2010;20(3):293-301.

[33]   Shek DTL, Ma CMS. Impact of the Project P.A.T.H.S. in the junior secondary school years: objective outcome evaluation based on eight waves of longitudinal data. ScientificWorldJournal 2012, Article ID 170345, 12 pages doi:10.1100/2012/170345.

[34]   Shek DTL, Yu L. Longitudinal impact of the Project P.A.T.H.S. on adolescent risk behavior: what happened after five years? ScientificWorldJournal 2012, Article ID 316029, 13 pages doi:10.1100/2012/316029.

Submitted: November 08, 2011. *Revised:* December 20, 2011. *Accepted:* December 27, 2011.

In: Child Health and Human Development Yearbook 2013   ISBN: 978-1-63117-939-6
Editor: Joav Merrick   © 2014 Nova Science Publishers, Inc.

Chapter 14

Consumption of pornographic materials among Hong Kong early adolescents: A replication

Daniel TL Shek, PhD, FHKPS, BBS, SBS, JP[*1,2,3,4], and Cecilia MS Ma, PhD[1]

[1]Department of Applied Social Sciences, The Hong Kong Polytechnic University, Hong Kong, PRC
[2]Centre for Innovation Programmes for Adolescents and Families, The Hong Kong Polytechnic University, Hong Kong, PRC
[3]Department of Social Work, East China Normal University, Shanghai, PRC
[4]Kiang Wu Nursing College of Macau, Macau, PRC

Abstract

Consumption of pornographic materials was examined in 3,638 Secondary 2 students in Hong Kong. Results showed that over 80% of the respondents had never consumed pornographic materials in the past year. Internet pornography was the most common medium that adolescents used when viewing pornographic materials. Males reported a higher level of pornography consumption than did females. Participants who were born in mainland China were more likely to consume pornographic materials than their Hong Kong counterparts. Regardless of the types of pornographic materials, the levels of pornography consumption significantly increased over time. Results also showed that higher levels of positive youth development and better family functioning were concurrently related to a lower level of pornography consumption at Secondary 2. The relative contribution of positive youth development and family factors to pornographic material consumption was also explored.

* Correspondence: Professor Daniel TL Shek, PhD, FHKPS, BBS, SBS, JP, Associate Vice President (Undergraduate Programme), Chair Professor of Applied Social Sciences, Department of Applied Social Sciences, Faculty of Health and Social Sciences, The Hong Kong Polytechnic University, Room HJ407, Core H, Hunghom, Hong Kong, PRC. E-mail: daniel.shek@polyu.edu.hk.

Keywords: Chinese adolescents, positive youth development, family functioning, Project P.A.T.H.S., pornographic material consumption

Introduction

Research has shown that mass media, particularly the Internet, is one of the most popular channels through which young people obtain sexual information (1-4). This might be related to the easy accessibility, affordability and anonymity of the Internet (5). Young people often use the Internet for non-recreational (e.g., doing homework and project) and recreational purposes (e.g., playing online video games, watching videos, and visiting social networking sites). As prior research on pornography investigating sexually explicit materials mainly focused on the traditional form of print pornography, health practitioners have raised the concern about the potential harms of Internet pornography. This is further supported by the growing number of online pornography among youths in the recent studies (6). Given the fact that early exposure to pornography is a significant risk factor associated with problematic sexual behavior (7-9), early detection of the signs of consumption of sexual materials and exploring the determinants of this behavior are necessary.

Gender has been commonly examined in mainstream pornography research (10-12). Compared to females, males reported higher levels of pornography consumption, and were more attracted to hardcore pornography and more sexually excited after viewing pornography (11, 13). However, few studies have examined such differences in Chinese samples. Given the majority of studies were conducted in Western contexts, more attention to studying the correlates of pornography consumption in non-Western contexts is warranted. There are two reasons why Chinese adolescents should be studied. First, Chinese people constitute roughly one-fifth of the world's population. Second, sex was a "taboo" and socially inhibited in the traditional Chinese culture. With rapid Westernization and modernization, it is expected that there might be some changes in sexual attitudes amongst Chinese adolescents. Hence, there is a need to understand consumption of pornographic materials in adolescents in this area.

Family processes play an important role in adolescent problem behavior. There is evidence that weak parental monitoring and lack of parental warmth and poor family functioning were conducive to adolescent problem behavior (7, 8). In the local context, Shek (14) also showed that poor parenting and family dysfunction predicted adolescent problem behavior. Similar observations are also shown in young people sexual behavior. Family factors, such as family structure, parental monitoring, and parental trust were associated with young people sexual behavior (15-17). However, it is not clear whether perceived family functioning is related to pornographic material consumption. Besides, it would be important to look at how attributes of adolescents such as self-concept, resilience would be related to pornographic material consumption. The present study attempted to address these research gaps.

Given the majority of the pornography studies are cross-sectional in nature (13, 18, 19), it would be helpful to study the changes in the pattern of pornography consumption over time. Researchers highlighted the need to understand the interplay of factors related to pornography consumption (20). As argued by Fisher and Barak (21), future research should focus on "a) personality characteristics that incline individuals to seek out sexually explicit materials...b) the effects of contact with sexually explicit media on individuals who chose to consume such material" (p. 315). In view of the proliferation of sexual information, more attention in this area is needed. This information will provide insights and guidelines regarding the design of effective youth programs that could help young people achieve a sexually healthy adulthood.

Shek and Ma (22) examined the consumption of pornographic materials in 3,328 Secondary 1 students in Hong Kong. Results showed that most Secondary 1 students had not consumed pornographic materials in the past year. In addition, gender was related to the level of exposure to pornographic materials. Different measures of positive youth development and family functioning were significant predictors to adolescents' consumption of pornographic materials. In the present study, we extended previous research in several ways. First, we examined the profiles of pornography consumption as well as the psychosocial correlates among Chinese adolescents in their Secondary 2 school year. Second, to replicate the findings observed at Time 1, we examined the linkages between personal and family factors and consumption of pornographic materials in Secondary 2 students. Lastly, we explored the changes of pornography consumption over a year.

Methods

The data reported in this paper were derived from the second wave of a six-year longitudinal study of adolescent development and their families in Hong Kong (Wave 1: academic year 2009-10; Wave 2: academic year 2010-11). The longitudinal study is a component of the extension phase of the Project P.A.T.H.S. which is financially supported by the Hong Kong Jockey Club Charities Trust. A total of 3,638 Secondary 2 students (Grade 8) from 28 schools participated in this study. Among the participants, 1,864 (52%) were boys and 1,716 (48%) were girls, with 58 of them did not respond to the questionnaire. The mean age of the participants was 13.6 years old (*SD* = .75). The demographic information of the participants is shown in Table 1.

During data collection, the purpose of the study was mentioned and confidentiality of the collected data was assured. School, parental and student consent had been obtained prior to data collection. All participants responded to all scales in the questionnaire in a self-administration format. Adequate time was provided for the participants to complete the questionnaire. A trained research assistant was present throughout the administration process.

Table 1. Demographic information of the respondents (N = 3,638)

	n	%
Gender*		
Male	1,864	52
Female	1,716	48
Place of birth		
Hong Kong	2,806	79
Mainland China	690	19
Others	73	2
Location of schools		
Hong Kong Island	5	18
Kowloon	7	25
New Territories	16	57

Table 1. (Continued)

	n	%
Parents' marital status		
Married	2,985	83
Divorced/Separated	334	9
Remarried	168	5
Others	122	3
Receiving financial aids		
Yes	208	6
No	2,932	81
Others	472	13

*58 respondents did not identify their gender.

Instruments

The Chinese Positive Youth Development Scale (CPYDS)

The Chinese Positive Youth Development Scale (CPYDS) (23) was developed to assess positive youth development. The CPYDS has 15 subscales, including bonding (BO), resilience (RE), social competence (SC), recognition for positive behavior (PB), emotional competence (EC), cognitive competence (CC), behavioral competence (BC), moral competence (MC), self-determination (SD), self-efficacy (SE), clear and positive identity (SI), beliefs in the future (BF), prosocial involvement (PI), prosocial norms (PN) and spirituality (SP). The details of the items can be seen in Shek et al. (23). A 6-point Likert scale (1 = strongly disagree to 6 = strongly agree) was used to assess the responses of the participants.

Using multi-group confirmatory factor analyses (MCFA), Shek and Ma (24) showed that the 15 basic dimensions of the CPYDS could be subsumed under four higher-order factors, including cognitive-behavioral competencies (CBC), prosocial attributes (PA), positive identity (PID) and general positive youth development qualities (GPYDQ). Evidence of factorial invariance in terms of configuration, first-order factor loadings, second-order factor loadings, intercepts of measured variable, and intercepts of first-order latent factor, was found. In short, existing research findings showed that the CPYDS is a valid and reliable instrument.

The Chinese Family Assessment Instrument (CFAI)

The Chinese Family Assessment Instrument (CFAI) was used to assess family functioning. In the present study, three subscales, including mutuality (mutual support, love and concern among family members), communication (frequency and nature of interaction among family members), conflicts and harmony (presence of conflicts and harmonious behavior in the family) were examined. The five response options were "very similar," "somewhat similar," "neither similar nor dissimilar," "somewhat dissimilar," and "very dissimilar." A higher total score on the subscales indicated a higher level of positive family functioning. The reliability and validity of the CFAI were supported in previous studies (14, 25-27). Furthermore, multi-group confirmatory factor analyses (MCFA) showed the existence of two higher order factors (i.e., family interaction and parenting) and factorial invariance of the CFAI across gender and subgroups (28).

Exposure to pornographic materials

Twelve items were used to assess the consumption of two types of pornographic materials during the last year. They were Internet pornography (e.g., pornographic stories, pictures, videos and websites) and traditional pornography (e.g., pornographic movies, rental films, movies on cable TV, magazines, books and comics). Participants answered on a 6-point Likert scale (0 = never; 1 = less than 1 time a week; 2 = 1-3 times a week; 3 = about 1 time a week; 4 = several times a week; 5 = daily). A composite score was calculated by averaging all twelve item scores in order to obtain the mean of the overall exposure to pornographic materials. The same method was used to calculate the mean consumption scores of traditional and Internet pornographic materials.

Family background characteristics

An item was asked to assess whether participants received financial aids (known as CSSA-comprehensive social security assistance) from the government of Hong Kong. For example *"Is your family now receiving CSSA?"* (1 = Yes, 0 = No). Another item was used to assess the immigrant status of the participants (0 = Hong Kong, 1 = mainland China, 2 = others).

Results

Reliability analyses showed that all subscales had acceptable internal consistency at Time 2 (Table 4). The prevalence of pornography consumption among Hong Kong adolescents is shown in Tables 2 and 3. Over 80% of adolescents reported they had never consumed pornographic materials over the past year. The degree of adolescents' exposure to the Internet pornographic materials was significantly higher than those found in the traditional pornographic materials (mean rank = 236.50, Z = -18.69, $p < .01$).

A Chi-square (Pearson's test of independence) analysis was performed to examine the relationships between respondents' characteristics (i.e., gender, immigrant status and family economic background) and pornography consumption. Significant relationships were found for gender and immigrant status, but not for family economic background (Table 5). Males were more likely to consume different types of pornographic materials than did females (χ^2 (1, N = 3,580) = 85.68, $p <.01$). Participants who were born in mainland China were more likely to expose to pornography consumption than those who were born in Hong Kong (χ^2 (1, N = 3,601) = 14.92, $p <.01$). It is noteworthy that the relation between family economic background and pornography consumption was not significant.

Analyses based on Pearson correlation showed that all positive youth development and family functioning measures were negatively correlated (ranging from -.05 to -.18) with the overall pornography exposure at Time 2. In general, higher levels of positive youth development and family functioning were related to lower levels of positive youth development and family functioning were related to lower levels of pornography consumption (Table 4).

To further examine whether there was a significant change in the consumption of pornographic materials across time, a series of paired t-tests were performed (Table 6). Regardless of the types of pornographic materials, higher levels of pornography exposure were found over time (Overall: t (2,851) = -7.80, $p <.01$; Internet: t (2,830) = -8.59, $p < .01$; Traditional: t (2,856) = -3.96, $p <.01$).

Table 2. Past year exposure to Internet and traditional pornographic materials

	Never (%)	Less than 1 time a month (%)	1-3 times a month (%)	About 1 time a week (%)	Several times a week (%)	Daily (%)
Internet						
Pornographic stories	89.8	6.3	1.7	.8	.9	.6
Pornographic pictures (exposed genitals)	88.5	7.5	1.5	.8	1.0	.6
Pornographic videos (exposed genitals)	88.4	6.4	2.2	1.1	1.1	.7
Sexual intercourse pictures (including comics)	90.2	5.5	1.6	.9	1.2	.6
Sexual intercourse videos (including cartoons)	89.6	5.8	2.0	.9	1.0	.6
Pornographic website	91.5	4.9	1.3	.8	.8	.7
Traditional						
Pornographic movies	98.3	1.0	.2	.1	.1	.3
Pornographic rental films	98.5	.7	.2	.1	.1	.4
Pornographic movies on cable TV	97.7	1.3	.2	.1	.2	.5
Pornographic magazines	97.6	1.3	.3	.2	.2	.5
Pornographic books	96.7	1.8	.5	.2	.3	.5
Pornographic comics	95.0	3.0	.8	.2	.4	.5

Table 3. Past year exposure to Internet and traditional pornographic materials by gender

	Attempted (%)	
Internet	Male	Female
Pornographic stories	12.2	8.1
Pornographic pictures (exposed genitals)	16.6	6.0
Pornographic videos (exposed genitals)	17.6	5.4
Sexual intercourse pictures (including comics)	13.2	6.2
Sexual intercourse videos (including cartoons)	14.6	6.0
Pornographic website	3.1	3.1
Traditional		
Pornographic movies	2.4	1.0
Pornographic rental films	2.0	1.0
Pornographic movies on cable TV	2.9	1.6
Pornographic magazines	3.4	1.4
Pornographic books	4.0	2.7
Pornographic comics	5.2	4.7

Table 4. Correlations among variables in the model

	M (SD)	α (mean)[#]	Overall Pornography (α = .95)	Internet pornography (α = .96)	Traditional pornography (α = .94)
Subscales based on primary-order factors					
BO	4.60 (.90)	.77 (.53)	-.14**	-.12**	-.12**
RE	4.57 (.90)	.81 (.59)	-.11**	-.09**	-.10**
SC	4.67 (.89)	.88 (.71)	-.09**	-.08**	-.06**
PB	4.20 (.95)	.77 (.53)	-.14**	-.13**	-.11**
EC	4.27 (.90)	.74 (.49)	-.10**	-.10**	-.07**

	M (SD)	α (mean)#	Overall Pornography (α = .95)	Internet pornography (α = .96)	Traditional pornography (α = .94)
CC	4.35 (.86)	.83 (.62)	-.11**	-.09**	-.10**
BC	4.49 (.82)	.76 (.52)	-.11**	-.10**	-.10**
MC	4.38 (.87)	.75 (.50)	-.14**	-.13**	-.10**
SD	4.41 (.88)	.78 (.55)	-.09**	-.08**	-.06**
SE	4.33 (.93)	.68 (.51)	-.06**	-.06**	-.04**
SI	4.06 (1.01)	.80 (.57)	-.02	-.02	-.02
BF	4.26 (1.06)	.85 (.66)	-.07**	-.07**	-.06**
PI	4.26 (.98)	.82 (.59)	-.11**	-.11**	-.07**
PN	4.50 (.95)	.72 (.47)	-.18**	-.18**	-.12**
SP	4.99 (1.30)	.89 (.73)	-.09**	-.09**	-.07**
Subscales based on second-order factors					
CBC	4.42 (.74)	.84 (.65)	-.12**	-.10**	-.10**
PA	4.38 (.86)	.75 (.60)	-.16**	-.16**	-.12**
GPYDQ	4.51 (.71)	.88 (.49)	-.15**	-.14**	-.11**
PID	4.16 (.96)	.84 (.73)	-.05**	-.05**	-.04*
Subscales based on family functioning					
Mutuality	3.80 (.90)	.88 (.72)	-.12**	-.12**	-.09**
Harmony	2.27 (.93)	.78 (.55)	-.10**	-.11**	-.09**
Communication	3.41 (.96)	.81 (.59)	-.09**	-.10**	-.06**

** $p < .01$; * $p < .05$. Note. BO: bonding; RE: resilience; SC: social competence; PB: recognition for positive behavior; EC: emotional competence; CC: cognitive competence; BC: behavioral competence; MC: moral competence; SD: self-determination; SE: self-efficacy; CPI: clear and positive identity; BF: beliefs in the future; PI: prosocial involvement; PN: prosocial norms; SP: spirituality; CBC: cognitive-behavioral competencies second-order factor; PA: prosocial attributes second-order factor; GPYDQ: general positive youth development qualities second-order factor; PID: positive identity second-order factor. ** $p < .01$. # Mean inter-item correlations.

Table 5. The Chi-square test of independence among different types of pornographic materials by gender, immigrant status and family economic background

	Overall pornography		Internet pornography		Traditional pornography	
	%^	χ^2	%^	χ^2	%^	χ^2
Gender						
Male	26	85.68**	24.4	85.64**	7.9	3.35**
Female	13		12.3		6.3	
Immigrant status						
Hong Kong	18.4	14.92**	17.2	12.24**	6.8	2.08
Mainland China	24.5		22.7		8.2	
Receiving financial aids						
No	23.1	1.63	21.5	1.46	7.7	.96
Yes	19.5		18.2		6.9	

** $p < .01$.
^The observed percentage.

Table 6. Paired t-test results among different types of pornographic materials by wave

	Wave 1	Wave 2		
	M (SD)	M (SD)	t	d
Overall pornography	1.05 (.22)	1.10 (.40)	-7.80**	.15
Internet pornography	1.08 (.32)	1.16 (.57)	-8.59**	.17
Traditional pornography	1.02 (.15)	1.04 (.29)	-3.96**	.09

** $p < .01$.

Discussion

The goal of the current study was to examine the prevalence and psychosocial correlates of pornography consumption among Secondary 2 students in Hong Kong. Similar to the data collected at the Secondary 1 year, most of the participants (over 80%) reported that they had never read or watched pornographic materials in the past 12 months. Compared to the findings in the Western studies (13, 29, 30), the results of our present study were generally lower. There are two possible explanations for this observation. First, it may be related to the fact that this sample was generally younger than those employed in the previous studies. Second, as there is a strong cultural sanction against sexual permissiveness in the Chinese culture, socialization against consumption of pornographic materials might also account for the low levels of exposure to pornography among the Chinese youths.

Consistent with the Wave 1 data, pornographic materials were mostly consumed via the Internet. In particular, there was a steady increase in the consumption of pornographic materials over a year. During this period of risk-taking, young people are inclined to experiment and engage in problem behaviors, such as substance use and teenage pregnancy in order to find their own identity (31). The prevalence of pornography is also in line with Ybarra and Mitchell's findings (32) that adolescents reported a higher degree of online pornography exposure than traditional print medium (e.g., magazine, books, and comics). Among them, males (24%) were significantly more likely to consume online pornography than their female counterparts (12%), and this is consistent with prior studies (13, 33). This result deserves our attention as research findings suggested that young people who viewed online pornography were susceptible to emotional challenge and interpersonal problems (32, 34). Perhaps, this might be related to the decrease in social interaction with frequent use of the Internet. This is further supported by Lam and Chan (35) who examined the potential impact of Internet pornography exposure among Chinese young adults. Focusing exclusively on men, they found that prolonged exposure to Internet pornography was related to premarital sexual permissiveness and proclivities towards sexual harassment. Given the prevalence of pornography exposure, comprehensive sex education that focuses on the development of correct attitudes and values towards sexual behavior and contemporary pornography is important.

An interesting finding was that immigrant status, but not family socioeconomic background, was associated with pornography consumption. This finding suggests that adolescents' demographic background, rather than their family financial status, plays an important role on their pornography consumption. Furthermore, results showed that mainland Chinese reported higher levels of pornographic exposure than did their Hong Kong counterpart. Perhaps, compared to Hong Kong adolescents, mainland adolescents expressed higher curiosity towards sexuality and stronger needs to satisfy their sexual desire due to the limited availability of pornographic materials, especially on the Internet, in mainland China. Furthermore, it is possible that young people from the mainland may use pornographic consumption as a way to cope with stress. Our findings highlight the need for research specifically examining the sexual background factors and their effects on pornography consumption and individuals' psychological well-being.

The present findings support earlier findings of the beneficial effects of positive youth development attributes and better family functioning on lower levels of pornography consumption among early Chinese adolescents (22). The correlation results, though the magnitudes were not high, reinforced the notion that higher levels of positive youth development qualities would predict lower levels of youth health risk behavior (36, 37). It is important to note that the link between one of the attributes, clear and positive identity and pornography consumption was not significant. This finding is inconsistent with previous results based on the same sample at Secondary 1 (22). Perhaps, this may be related to the unique characteristics of Secondary 2 students. This observation underscores the importance of looking at the phenomenon using longitudinal data.

The present study attempted to explore the linkage between family functioning and pornography consumption. Three features of family functioning, mutuality, communication and harmony, were negatively related to pornography consumption. Prior studies showed that parental monitoring, parental control and quality of parent-child relationship were associated with the decrease of externalizing behaviors, delayed sexual intercourse, and substance use (38-41). Our findings extend the pornography literature by providing useful additional evidence on the predictors of pornography consumption among Chinese adolescents. In addition, the observation for Secondary 1 students was replicated for Secondary 2 students.

One of the unique characteristics of the present study is the examination of pornography exposure among Chinese adolescents across two waves of data. Our results support the notion that there is an increasing tendency of pornography consumption with age. As most studies on pornography consumption were cross-sectional in nature (13, 29, 35), little is known about the developmental changes of pornographic material consumption over time. Research in this area is important because risk and protective factors for pornography consumption might vary from one culture to another (20). The current study overcomes these limitations by using a longitudinal design based on Chinese adolescents. It sheds light on designing appropriate programs for Chinese adolescents.

Because our findings were based on Hong Kong Chinese adolescents, caution should be taken when they are generalized to other Chinese cultures, such as mainland China and Taiwan. Despite the emphasis on anonymity and confidentiality, social desirability and other biases cannot be eliminated in the study. Furthermore, the reliance on self-report data is another limitation. This might explain the low prevalence of pornography consumption as found in the study. However, this approach is commonly used in this field of research and under-reporting is expected. Of course, the present findings require replication using a three-wave design to understand the related changes over time.

In the present study, the effect of early exposure to pornography was not examined. It would be desirable to investigate the potential harm of this premature exposure to pornography. As noted by Zillmann (12), "next to nothing is known about the consequences of the steadily increasing amount of such exposure" (p. 41). Clearly, more research in understanding the impact of this exposure among young people is warranted. Also, future study should include other factors, such as reasons for exposure, social context of use and sexual socialization, which have been widely examined in previous pornography studies (42, 43).

Despite the above limitations, the present study basically replicated the correlates of pornography consumption among Hong Kong early adolescents. The proliferation of pornographic materials and the emergence of a "pornified" world (44) through the Internet become an integral part of lives and contemporary cultures among adolescents (11). Therefore, more efforts in promoting media literacy among this population should be emphasized. As positive youth development programs such as the Project P.A.T.H.S. can promote adolescent development and reduce adolescent risk behavior (45-49), it would be exciting to see whether such programs can reduce adolescent pornographic behavior. Furthermore, as pointed out by Hald (13), "future research (should) focus on these situational, interpersonal, and behavioral characteristics of pornography consumption in addition to actual prevalence rates of consumption in different cultures" (p. 584).With reference to this suggestion, the present study represents a positive response to this request and adds to the growing literature on pornography consumption. Furthermore, as mentioned by Hubbard and Vetter (50), "replication and extension research can play a major role in ensuring the integrity of a discipline's empirical results" (p. 153). The present study basically replicated the findings based on Secondary 1 students.

Acknowledgments

The preparation for this paper and the Project P.A.T.H.S. were financially supported by The Hong Kong Jockey Club Charities Trust. This paper was originally published in The Scientific World Journal, Volume 2012, Article ID 406063, 8 pages doi: 10.1100/2012/406063.

References

[1]   Duncan D. Pornography as a source of sex information for students at a private northeastern university. Psychol Reports 1991;68:782.

[2]   Duncan D, Nicholsson T. Pornography as a source of sex information for students at a southeastern state university. Psychol Reports 1991;68:802.

[3]   Griffiths M. Excessive Internet use: implications for sexual behavior. Cyper Psychol Behav 2000;3(4):537-52.

[4]   Trostle L. Pornography as a source of sex information for university students: some consistent findings. Psychol Reports 1993;72:407-12.

[5]   Cooper ML, Shaver PR, Collins NL. Attachment styles, emotion regulation and adjustment in adolescence. J Person Soc Psychol 1998;74(5):1380-97.

[6]   Wolak J, Mitchell K, Finkelhor D. Unwanted and wanted exposure to online pornography in a national sample of youth Internet users. Pediatrics 2007;119:247-57.

[7]   Kanuga M, Rosenfeld WD. Adolescent sexuality and the Internet: the good, the bad, and the URL. J Pediatr Adolesc Gynecol 2004;17(2):117-24.

[8]   Malamuth NM, Impett EA. Research on sex in the media: what do we know about effects on children and adolescents? In: Singer DG, Singer J, editors. Handbook of children and the media. Thousand Oaks, CA: Sage, 2001:269-87.

[9]   Rich M. Sex screen: the dilemma of media exposure and sexual behavior. Pediatrics 2005;116(1):329-31.

[10]   Svedin CG, Åkerman I, Priebe G. Frequent users of pornography: a population based epidemiological study of Swedish male adolescents. J Adolesc 2011;34(4):779-88.

[11]   Traeen B, Spitznogle K, Beverfjord A. Attitudes and use of pornography in the Norwegian population 2002. J Sex Res 2004;41(2):193-200.

[12]   Zillmann D. Influence of unrestrained access to erotica on adolescents' and young adults' dispositions toward sexuality. J Adolesc Health 2000;27(2):41-4.

[13] Hald GM. Gender differences in pornography consumption among young heterosexual Danish adults. Arch Sex Behav 2006;35(5):577-85.

[14] Shek DTL. Family functioning and psychological well-being, school adjustment, and substance abuse in Chinese adolescents: are findings based on multiple studies consistent? In: Shohov SP, editor. Advances in psychology research. New York: Nova Science, 2003:163-84.

[15] Cohen DA, Farley TA, Taylor SN, Martin DH, Schuster MA. When and where do youths have sex? the potential role of adult supervision. Pediatrics 2002;110(6):e66.

[16] Huebner AJ, Howell LW. Examining the relationship between adolescent sexual risk-taking and perceptions of monitoring, communication, and parenting styles. J Adolesc Health 2003;33(2):71-8.

[17] Kiernan K. Lone motherhood, employment and outcomes for children. Int J Law Policy Family 1996;10(3):233-49.

[18] Rosenthal DA, Smith AMA, de Visser R. Personal and social factors influencing age at first sexual intercourse. Arch Sex Behav 1999;28(4):319-33.

[19] Weinberg MS, Williams CJ, Kleiner S, Irizarry Y. Pornography, normalization, and empowerment. Arch Sex Behav 2010;39(6):1389-401.

[20] Boislard PMA, Poulin F. Individual, familial, friends-related and contextual predictors of early sexual intercourse. J Adolesc 2011;34(2):289-300.

[21] Fisher WA, Barak A. Internet pornography: a social psychological perspective on Internet sexuality. J Sex Res 2001;38(4):312-23.

[22] Shek DTL, Ma CMS. Consumption of pornographic materials among early adolescents in Hong Kong: profiles and psychosocial correlates. Int J Disabil Hum Dev 2012;11(2):143-50.

[23] Shek DTL, Siu AMH, Lee TY. The Chinese Positive Youth Development Scale: a validation study. Res Soc Work Prac 2007;12(3):380-91.

[24] Shek DTL, Ma CMS. Dimensionality of the Chinese Positive Youth Development Scale: confirmatory factor analyses. Soc Indic Res 2010; 98:41-59.

[25] Shek DTL. Assessment of family functioning in Chinses adolescents: the Chinese version of the Family Assessment Device. Res Soc Work Prac 2002;12:502-24.

[26] Shek DTL. Assessment of family functioning Chinese adolescents: the Chinese Family Assessment Instrument. In: Singh NN, Ollen-dick T, Singh AN, editors. International perspectives on child and adolescent mental health. Amsterdam: Elsevier, 2002:297-316.

[27] Siu AMH, Shek DTL. Psychometric properties of the Chinese Family Assessment Instrument in Chinese adolescents in Hong Kong. Adolescence 2005;40(160):817-30.

[28] Shek DTL, Ma CMS. The Chinese Family Assessment Instrument (C-FAI): hierarchical confirmatory factor analyses and factorial invariance. Res Soc Work Prac 2010;20(1):112-23.

[29] Braun-Courville DK, Rojas M. Exposure to sexually explicit web sites and adolescent sexual attitudes and behaviors. J Adolesc Health 2009;45(2):156-62.

[30] Peter J, Valkenburg PM. The use of sexually explicit Internet material and its antecedents: a longitudinal comparison of adolescents and adults. Arch Sex Behav 2011;40(5):1015-25.

[31] Burtney E, Duffy M. Young people and sexual health: individual, social and policy contexts. Bristol: Plagrave Macmillan, 2004.

[32] Ybarra ML, Mitchell KJ. Exposure to Internet pornography among children and adolescents: a national survey. Cyber Psychol Behav 2005;8(5):473-86.

[33] Janghorbani M, Lam TH, The Youth Sexuality Study Task Force. Sexual media use by young adults in Hong Kong: prevalence and associated factors. Arch Sex Behav 2003;32(6):545-53.

[34] Kazdin AE, Marchiano PL. Childhood and adolescent depression. In: Mash EJ, Barkley RA, editors. Treatment of childhood disorders, 2nd ed. New York: The Guilford Press, 1998:211-48.

[35] Lam CB, Chan DKS. The use of cyberpornography by young men in Hong Kong: some psychosocial correlates. Arch Sex Behav 2007;36(4):588-98.

[36] Catalano RF, Berglund ML, Ryan JAM, Lonczak HS, Hawkins JD. Positive youth development in the United States: research findings on evaluations of positive youth development programs. Ann Am Acad Polit SS 2004;591(1):98-124.

[37]   Gavin LE, Catalano RF, David-Ferdon C, Gloppen KM, Markham CM. A review of positive youth development programs that promote adolescent sexual and reproductive health. J Adolesc Health 2010;46(3):S75-91.

[38]   Boislard PMA, Poulin F, Kiesner J, Dishion TJ. A longitudinal examination of risky sexual behaviors among Canadian and Italian adolescents: considering individual, parental, and friend characteristics. Int J Behav Dev 2009;33(3):265-76.

[39]   Dittus PJ, Jaccard J. Adolescents' perceptions of maternal disapproval of sex: relationship to sexual outcomes. J Adolesc Health 2000;26:268–78.

[40]   Smith LH, Guthrie BJ. Testing a model: a developmental perspective of adolescent male sexuality. J Spec Pediatric Nurs 2005;10(3):124-38.

[41]   Capaldi DM, Stoolmiller M, Clark S, Owen LD. Heterosexual risk behaviors in at-risk young men from early adolescence to young adulthood: prevalence, prediction, and association with STD contraction. Dev Psychol 2002;38(3):394-406.

[42]   Wallmyr G, Welin C. Young people, pornography, and sexuality: sources and attitudes. J Sch Nurs 2006;22(5):290-5.

[43]   Peter J, Valkenburg PM. Adolescents' exposure to sexually explicit online material and recreational attitudes toward sex. J Commun 2006;56(4):639-60.

[44]   Paul P. Pornified: how pornography is transforming our lives, our relationships, and our families. New York: Times Books, 2005.

[45]   Shek DTL, Ng CSM, Tsui PF. Qualitative evaluation of the Project P.A.T.H.S.: findings based on focus groups. Int J Disabil Hum Dev 2010;9(4):307-13.

[46]   Shek DTL, Ma CMS. Impact of the Project P.A.T.H.S. in the junior secondary school years: individual growth curve analyses. ScientificWorldJournal 2011;11:253-66.

[47]   Shek DTL, Yu L. Prevention of adolescent problem behavior: longitudinal impact of the Project P.A.T.H.S. in Hong Kong. ScientificWorldJournal 2011;11:546-67.

[48]   Shek DTL, Ng CSM. Early identification of adolescents with greater psychosocial needs: an evaluation of the Project P.A.T.H.S. in Hong Kong. Int J Disabil Hum Dev 2010;9(4):291-9.

[49]   Shek DTL, Sun RCF. Qualitative evaluation of the Project P.A.T.H.S. (Secondary 1 Program) based on the perceptions of the program implementers. Int Pub Health J 2009;1(3),255-65.

[50]   Hubbard R, Vetter DE. An empirical comparison of published replication research in accounting, economics, finance, management, and marketing. J Bus Res 1996;35(2):153-64.

Submitted: November 08, 2011. *Revised:* December 20, 2011. *Accepted:* December 31, 2011.

Section two –
Child and adolescent health

In: Child Health and Human Development Yearbook 2013   ISBN: 978-1-63117-939-6
Editor: Joav Merrick   © 2014 Nova Science Publishers, Inc.

Chapter 15

Multi-level determinants of regional variations in infant mortality in India: A state level analysis

*Shamindra Nath Roy, MA, MPhil**

Centre for the study of Regional Development,
School of Social Sciences, Jawaharlal Nehru University,
New Delhi, India

Abstract

The present study attempts to identify the key factors determining the interregional variations of infant mortality in India at different levels of operations and examines some of the relevant relationships between those factors based on a cross-section analysis of NFHS III data. Appropriate Bi-Variate analyses are worked out to see the gross effect of different level factors (namely individual, household and community level) over infant mortality. Multivariate analysis is worked out to show the net effect of selected individual, household and community level factors over infant mortality. Here a distinction have been made between Neo-natal and Post neo-natal mortality to demonstrate that the determinants of these two types of mortality are different, and that the use of the overall infant mortality rate masks some of these important differences. Results show that the gross effect of all the individual level factors like percentage women having all kinds of recommended antenatal care or index of vaccination have higher gross effect on infant deaths, although the net effects of all these factors are lower because many of them are linearly related to the next level, i.e. household or community level factors. Both gross and net effect of the household level factors like mother's empowerment and poverty is very high over infant deaths as many of these factors often controls household's access to different community level facilities as well as individual's ability to shield against infant deaths. Hence, the study concludes that the interplay of

---

* Correspondence: Shamindra Nath Roy, Doctoral Scholar, Room No: 241, Jhelum Hostel, JNU, New Delhi-67. E-mail: writeshami@gmail.com.

both kinds of factors at different levels of child birth can take major role in reducing infant mortality.

Keywords: Human Development, Infant Mortality, Multi-Level Factors, Mother's Empowerment

Introduction

Health status of new-born children has been regarded as one of the premier ingredient of the Human development achievements in a developing country like India. Clearly, children have not benefitted to the same extent as adults from the improvements in food supply, and from the preventive and curative measures implemented so far. Identification of effective strategies to reduce infant mortality requires a better understanding of the determinants of infant mortality, and of factors responsible for the observed regional variations in infant mortality levels in India.

The present study attempts to identify the key factors determining the interregional variations of infant mortality in India at different levels of operations and examines some of the relevant relationships between those factors based on a cross-section analysis of state level data. An attempt has been made to build an analytical framework, which shows infant mortality as a function of multi-level factors operating at different stages of child birth, namely pre-natal, peri-natal and post natal periods.

The present study mainly attempts to enquire the effect of multi-level (individual, household and community level) factors over infant death during different periods of child birth as the independent effect of all the factors are not equal at different periods of child birth.

Another major objective to observe the independent effect of all the different level factors differently over neo-natal (the probability of dying at the first month of life) and post neo-natal mortality (the probability of dying after the first month of life but before the first birthday) that will trace out the fact that the determinant of these two types of mortality are different which is often shaded by infant mortality. However, the study attempts to develop an analytical framework on the basis of segmenting the wide range of factors affecting infant mortality and by measuring their partial and independent effects.

The proposition of the present study primarily based on the objective statements mentioned above. The central question would be how the interplay between multi-level factors may influence infant mortality at different stages and what would be the relative importance of these factors?

Methods

In the analytical framework used in the present analysis factors are distinguished at three different levels: *Community, Household and Individual* (Figure 1). They are arranged in ascending order according to their proximity to the dependent variable of interest- in the present case, the death of an infant. The individual-level factors are closest to the dependent variable. Next come the household-level factors, and the community level factors are the most distant.

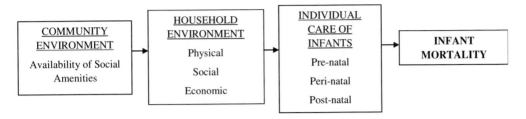

Figure 1. Schematic Representation of relationships among Multi-Level Factors and IMR.

Individual level factors

Excluding endogenous genetic factors at the individual level, it is assumed that the chances of infant survival depend upon the degree of care with which the infant is brought up. Broadly visualized, care, starting from conception to the first birthday, i.e. during 21 months of life, is important for an understanding of the determinants of infant mortality. Pre-natal care, for example vaccination of the pregnant mother against tetanus, can virtually eliminate deaths from neo-natal tetanus.

Proper medical care at delivery can reduce the risk of death from birthday injury and tetanus. Post natal care in the form of breastfeeding, immunization, and timely and appropriate medical treatment in case of illness can reduce the risk of death during infancy. Hence, two important dimensions of individual level factors affecting infant mortality are:

- Timing
- Type of Care

Timing can be divided into three categories:

- Pre-natal
- Peri-natal
- Post-natal

Type of care can be divided into two main groups:

- Medical
- Non-medical

Medical care includes immunization, treatment of illness and medical attention at birth. Non-medical care includes feeding practices, protection from environmental insults and general cleanliness. The two main dimensions of care yield the following six individual-level factors which determine the levels of infant mortality in a population.

1. Pre-natal Medical Care- immunization of pregnant mothers and treatment of infections during pregnancy.
2. Pre-natal non-medical care- maternal health including nutrition during pregnancy.
3. Peri-natal medical care- general hygiene including the deliveries occurred under trained health personnel.
4. Post-natal non-medical child care- infant feeding practices, for example breastfeeding for at least six months.
5. Post-natal preventive medical child care- immunization.
6. Post-natal curative medical child care- incidence and treatment of illness and effectiveness of treatment.

These factors are not arranged in any order of priority. Their relative importance may vary from population to population and for the same population at different times. But I put forward the hypothesis that household and community level factors would affect the chances of infant survival through one or more of these proximate determinants.

Household level factors

The second group of factors consists of the physical, social and economic environment of the household. Physical environment is reflected by the condition of the house, toilet facilities, crowding, quality of drinking water and source of fuel and lighting; social environment factors include mother's empowerment in terms of decision making and maternal education or intervals between birth; and economic conditions by factors such as household income.

Community level factors

The third group of factors concerns physical, social and economic environment at the community level. These are basically institutional laden factors, reflected the availability of Government medical facilities, ICDS services, schools and adult literacy centres, contact with health workers etc. The use made of these facilities varies in different households within the same community. For this reason, the primary effects of these factors on infant mortality will be transmitted through changes in household level factors.

The effect of community level factors on infant mortality will be transmitted through individual level factors, if all households in a community are equally affected- for example, if all pregnant women or infants in a community were immunized in a programme organized at the community level, or if all members of the community were to drink contaminated (or clean) water from the same source. If a community-level factor were to affect infant mortality independently the model is not completely specified, i.e. it does not include some of the relevant factors at the household and individual levels.

It is notable that even under the worst conditions; there are considerable variations at the individual level in the probability of an infant's survival. The reasons for these variations are not known.

Within a community, they could reflect differences between households, but they are most probably due to genetic differences between individuals. The individual factors mentioned above thus cannot explain all the differences in individual's chances of survival; their *relative contributions* would depend upon the level of infant mortality in a population; and would vary in different populations.

Databases required for the present study have been taken from the National Family Health Survey III Reports, published at 2005-'06. The databases regarding combined poverty estimates have been collected from the Planning Commission URP (Uniform Recall Period) poverty estimates of 2004-'05.

Table 1. Levels and trends in infant mortality in India during three NFHS rounds

STATES	IMR PER THOUSAND LIVE BIRTHS			CHANGES	
	NFHS I	NFHS II	NFHS III	NFHS I & II	NFHS II & III
Andhra Pradesh	70.4	65.8	53.5	-4.6	-12.3
Arunachal	40	63.1	60.7	23.1	-2.4
Assam	88.7	69.5	66.1	-19.2	-3.4
Bihar	89.2	72.9	37.5	-16.3	-35.4
Chhattisgarh	-	-	70.8	-	-
Delhi	65.4	46.8	39.8	-18.6	-7.0
Goa	31.9	36.7	15.3	4.8	-21.4
Gujarat	68.7	62.6	49.7	-6.1	-12.9
Haryana	73.3	56.8	41.7	-16.5	-15.1
Himachal Pradesh	55.8	34.4	36.1	-21.4	1.7
Jammu & Kashmir	45.4	65	44.7	19.6	-20.3
Jharkhand	-	-	68.7	-	-
Karnataka	65.4	51.5	43.2	-13.9	-8.3
Kerala	23.8	16.3	15.3	-7.5	-1
Madhya Pradesh	85.2	86.1	69.5	0.9	-16.6
Maharashtra	50.5	43.7	37.5	-6.8	-6.2
Manipur	42.4	37	29.7	-5.4	-7.3
Meghalaya	64.2	89	44.6	24.8	-44.4
Mizoram	14.6	37	34.1	22.4	-2.9
Nagaland	17.2	42.1	38.3	24.9	-3.8
Orissa	112.1	81	64.7	-31.1	-16.3
Punjab	53.7	57.1	41.7	3.4	-15.4
Rajasthan	72.6	80.4	65.3	7.8	-15.1
Sikkim	-	43.9	33.7	-	-10.2
Tamilnadu	67.7	48.2	30.4	-19.5	-17.8
Tripura	75.8	N.A.*	51.5	-	-
Uttar Pradesh	99.9	86.7	72.7	-13.2	-14
Uttaranchal	-	-	41.9	-	-
West Bengal	75.3	48.7	48	-26.6	-0.7
India	78.5	67.6	57	-10.9	-10.6
CV	29.1	32.5	32.3		

Source: NFHS I, II and III.
*N.A. refers to Data not available.

i. Selection of indicators at the individual level

The individual level factors, as mentioned above, can be categorized into six different subsets determining their timing and type of care. However, the present study attempts to take into consideration five out of these six factors. In the case of pre-natal medical care, percentage of women who received all kinds of antenatal care has been taken into consideration. Percentage of mothers got supplementary foods from ICDS centres during pregnancy reflects the extent of pre-natal care within the individuals, whereas it can be denoted as an important community level factor reflecting institutional measure for infant care which is transmitted through the individuals at different rates. The peri-natal factor is represented through percentage of deliveries assisted by trained health personnel, which reflects the awareness of individuals for safe medication during the delivery processes. Post-natal non-medical care is represented by percentage of children (less than six months of age) breastfed six plus times in 24 hours. The post-natal preventive medical care is represented by an index of immunization, which is composed of percentage of children received all kinds of basic vaccinations (BCG, Measles, and three doses each of DPT and polio vaccine).

ii. Selection of indicators at the household level

As noted earlier, the physical and social environment of the household and its economic conditions strongly influence the probability of infant death. These factors are larger in number and the relative contribution of any them on infant death is not negligible. Hence, it is better to measure the association of these of these factors with infant death in an aggregative manner rather than considering them individually. Hence, a physical infrastructure index of household have been constructed which represents the physical status of living of the household with the help of a number of indicators, namely percentage of households having electricity, improved source of drinking water, toilet facility, percentage household using solid fuel for cooking, percentage household living in pucca house, and the mean number of persons per room used for sleeping as separate rooms and enough space is required during delivery and post-natal phases to prevent infections to the child.

Like the physical infrastructure index of the household, a separate mother's empowerment index have been constructed representing the currently married women's autonomy and decision making ability within the household which have quantum effect in controlling birth preferences in terms of number of children to have, birth interval and gender preferences in child birth, all of which have significant association with infant mortality. The adult literacy rate for women is the most crucial element of this index as, according to Caldwell and Mcdonald (1), 'schooling brings in a new family system in which children (and women) are awarded higher priorities in terms of care and consumption than in the traditional system.' Other elements of the index are percentage of adult women having exposure to some kind of mass media which increases the married women's awareness regarding the process of child birth in a healthy and hygienic environment and increases their decision making power regarding preferences in child birth. The other indicators are all pertain to currently married women's decision making ability, namely percentage of currently married women who alone or jointly with their husbands decide how their own earnings are used, percentage men who say that wives should have the final say alone or jointly with the husband in five major decisions (major household purchases, purchases for daily household needs, visits to the wives' family or relatives, what to do with the money the wife earns, & how many children to have), percentage of female headed households, and percentage of mothers allowed going to market alone. The economic condition of the household is being reflected by the percentage of people existing above the poverty line in both rural and urban India. It may be mentioned that percentage of people above the poverty line has been taken into consideration instead of percentage of people below the poverty line because of making the indicators unidirectional.

iii. Selection of indicators at the community level

Association of institutional factors with infant mortality have been worked out with reference to the indicators reflecting the Government initiatives in developing infant, maternal and child care like percentage of lactating mothers getting health and nutritional education from ICDS, percentage of households using Government health facilities, and percentage of women having any contact with a health worker, i.e. the initiatives of Government health workers to have contact with pregnant and lactating mothers.

In terms of methodology, the First Principal Component Analysis (PCA) have been taken into consideration for creating the composite index of household physical infrastructure and mother's empowerment, which represents the maximum sum of square of correlations of all the aggregated values (i.e. index values) with the indicators taken. The process, thus, creates an index value for each observation which is the best representative of all the indicators taken. PCA assigns weightages to each indicators depending upon the correlations within them, i.e. higher the correlation, higher will be the weightages provided to an indicator. It in this way, removes all kinds of indicators which doesn't show much association with other indicators, i.e. not so relevant to the context. The percentage of variations explained by the first principal component essentially depends upon the degree of correlations between the indicators, i.e. higher the correlations, higher will be the variation explained by the first principal component.

Appropriate Bi-Variate analyses are worked out to see the gross effect of different level factors over infant mortality. Separate correlation matrices have been worked out to show the inter association among IMR and other factors pertained to individual, household and community level. Multivariate analysis using the OLS estimates is worked out to show the net effect of selected individual, household and community level factors over infant mortality. Here a distinction have been made between Neo-natal and Post neo-natal mortality to demonstrate that the determinants of these two types of mortality are different, and that the use of the overall infant mortality rate masks some of these important differences. For example, some factors of individual level are much more important than any other community or household level factors for neo-natal mortality. To capture the net or independent effects of all these factors separately on neo-natal, post neo-natal mortality and gross IMR and to measure their differential contributions in each of the kind of infant death, separate models have been worked out for neo-natal, post neo-natal and aggregative IMR.

Results

Cross-sectional analysis of NFHS III data

This analysis have been carried out for twenty nine states (unlike only 16 major states) using NFHS III data of 2005-'06. In case of total IMR, at the all India level 57 infant deaths are used to be caused in per thousand live births, out of which 39 were occurred within one month of birth (neo-natal deaths) and the remaining 18 were occurred between the first month and first birthday of the child (post neo-natal death). The third quartile calculated for total IMR, neo-natal and post neo-natal mortality for all India reveals the fact that 25% of the states still have an IMR of nearly 61 per thousand live births during NFHS III, where the neo-natal mortality accounts 40 per thousand live births and the post neo-natal mortality accounts for the rest 21 infant deaths. Highest IMR can be found in U.P. (72.7 per thousand live births), followed by Chhattisgarh, M.P, Jharkhand and Assam. Lowest infant deaths are characteristics of the states Kerala (15.3 per thousand live births), followed by Goa, Manipur, Tamilnadu, Sikkim, Mizoram, Himachal Pradesh and Maharashtra. Figure 2a represents the spatial variation in infant mortality across the Indian states during NFHS III. In terms of male IMR, highest infant deaths are found in Orissa (71.4 per thousand live births), followed by U.P., Assam, M.P. and Bihar. (ranging from 58-72 per thousand live births). The third quartile calculated for male IMR is 60.1 per thousand live births, indicating that 25% of the states have a male IMR of 60 or more.

In terms of female IMR, highest female IMR is found in Rajasthan (77.4 per thousand live births), followed by U.P., M.P., Bihar, Assam (63-75 per thousand live births); lowest occurrence was found in Kerala (12 per thousand live births), associated by Tamilnadu, Himachal, Maharashtra, and Karnataka (ranging from 12-39 per thousand live births).

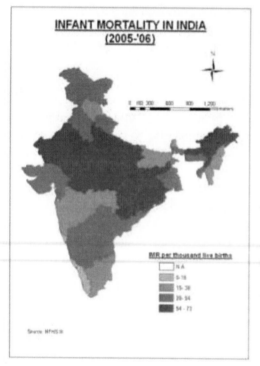

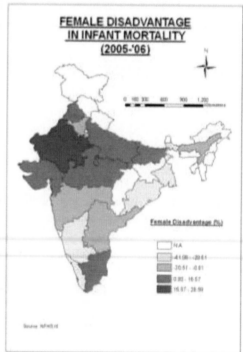

Figure 2a.   Figure 2b.

In terms of female disadvantage in IMR, highest discrimination against female children can be shown in Rajasthan (29.59%), followed by Tamilnadu, M.P., Punjab, Gujarat and Bihar. Lowest female disadvantage is evident in West Bengal (-41.06%), followed by Kerala, Orissa, Karnataka and Assam. During NFHS III, in terms of female disadvantage in infant deaths, nine states have more female disadvantage than the national average, whereas seven states have lesser female disadvantage than national average. Figure 2a and 2b shows the regional distribution of IMR as a whole and female disadvantage of IMR across India during NFHS III.

Individual level factors and IMR

Out of the five factors (representing five possible subsets of determinants at the individual level, Table 2a) used to show the gross effect of individual level determinants on infant deaths, three have shown strongly negative and statistically significant association with IMR, namely percentage women who received all recommended kinds of antenatal care, percentage deliveries assisted by health personnels and percentage of children received all kinds of basic vaccinations. All these factors have shown strongly negative correlation (-0.681 for percentage women, who received all recommended kinds of antenatal care, -0.740 for percentage deliveries assisted by health personnel and -0.697 for percentage of children received all kind of basic vaccinations), all of which are statistically significant at 1% level of significance. These factors, however, have higher inter-association within them, and hence their gross effect on IMR is also very high. However, all of these factors are at some level determined by household or community level factors, which will be evident in later discussions. Results of association between individual level factors and infant deaths are represented in Table 2b.

Table 2a. Individual level factors and IMR (2005-'06)

STATES	IMR PER THOUSAND LIVE BIRTHS	a	b	c	d	e	RANKING OF STATES ACCORDING TO IMR
Uttar Pradesh	72.7	4.1	9.6	27.2	96.5	23	1
Chhattisgarh	70.8	11.3	64.1	41.6	96.5	48.7	2
Madhya Pradesh	69.5	7.2	31	32.7	98.8	40.3	3
Jharkhand	68.7	7.5	34.7	27.8	96.6	34.2	4
Assam	66.1	9.6	12.7	31	99.3	31.4	5
Rajasthan	65.3	8.6	17	41	94.6	26.5	6
Orissa	64.7	18.4	44.6	44	98.5	51.8	7
Bihar	61.7	5.8	0.6	29.3	98	32.8	8
Arunachal	60.7	6.5	9	30.2	98.8	28.4	9
Andhra Pradesh	53.5	28.2	22.9	74.9	99.8	46	10
Tripura	51.5	10.6	6.8	48.8	96.8	49.7	11
Gujarat	49.7	25.6	19.1	63	95.5	45.2	12
West Bengal	48	12.3	23.1	47.6	95.6	64.3	13
Jammu & Kashmir	44.7	17.5	6.3	56.5	92.1	66.7	14
Meghalaya	44.6	8.1	36.1	31.1	98.5	32.9	15
Karnataka	43.2	29.6	30.3	69.7	95.9	55	16
Uttaranchal	41.9	16.1	18.9	38.5	88.7	60	17
Haryana	41.7	14.7	11	48.9	97.8	65.3	18
Punjab	41.7	19.6	7.5	68.2	95.9	60.1	19
Delhi	39.8	29	5.3	64.1	89.4	63.2	20
Nagaland	38.3	1.9	5.4	24.7	97.2	21	21
Maharashtra	37.5	21.6	25.8	68.7	95.5	58.8	22
Himachal Pradesh	36.1	17.4	33.6	47.8	93.4	74.2	23
Mizoram	34.1	8.7	54.5	65.4	98.4	46.5	24
Sikkim	33.7	27.2	24.6	53.7	98.1	69.6	25
Tamilnadu	30.4	34	50.4	90.6	99.2	80.9	26
Manipur	29.7	10.5	3.7	59	97.1	46.8	27
Goa	15.3	55.7	46.4	94	89.9	78.6	28
Kerala	15.3	63.6	15.8	99.4	100	75.3	29

Definition of indicators

a	% of women who received all recommended kinds of antenatal care
b	% of mothers got supplementary foods from ICDS centres during pregnancy
c	% of deliveries assisted by health personnel
d	% of children got breastfed 6+ times in 24 hours
e	% of children received all kinds of basic vaccinations

Source: NFHS III Report.

Ranking done in a descending manner, e.g. higher IMR, higher ranking.

Table 2b. Association between the individual level factors and IMR

CORRELATION MATRIX						
INDICATORS	IMR	a	b	c	d	e
IMR	1	-.681**	-0.032	-.740**	0.231	-.697**
a		1	0.193	.879**	-0.167	.726**
b			1	0.231	0.085	0.261
c				1	-0.101	.748**
d					1	-0.328
e						1

** Correlation is Significant at 1% level (Two-tailed).

Household level factors and IMR

The factors at household level, as explained above, are discussed in a more aggregative manner rather than the individual or community level factors in order to trace out their gross effect on infant deaths (Table 3a). These household level factors usually transmit their effects on IMR through the operation of individual level factors. For example, the effect on pre, peri or post natal care on infant deaths would be more or less controlled by mother's level of education or levels of empowerment. On the other hand, household level factors strongly depend upon the community level factors to operate, such as the level of maternal education in any village are determined by the availability of schools or adult literacy centres in the village. Basically, household level factors lead the most crucial role in determining infant deaths by acting as a bridging gap between the individual and community level factors.

The index of physical infrastructure of the household created to show the physical standard of living of the household consists of a set of six highly correlated indicators. Out of the six indicators, two shows negative correlations with others, namely percentage households using solid fuel for cooking and mean numbers of persons per room used for sleeping.

Except the last one, rest of the indicators has shown high correlations among them (as most of them are same kind of indicators). Weightages provided to the indicators have been shown in Table 3c. The first principal component in the index explains 45.1% of variance.

The mother's empowerment index created to show the decision making power of the married women in the household in terms of child care and child birth consists of six different kinds of factors including adult women literacy, percentage of adult women's exposure to mass-media, percentage of female headed households, percentage of mothers allowed going to market alone, percentage of currently married women having independent decision making ability for using their own earnings and percentage of married men's allowance to their wives to take five major decisions. Out of all these six factors, excluding the last two indicators, the rest of the indicators show moderate to high correlation among themselves in determining an aggregative measure of mother's empowerment. Weightages assigned to all these indicators depending upon the degree of correlations between them have been depicted in Table 3d.

Adult women literacy and women's exposure to mass media are regarded two most important indicators in determining mother's empowerment, which were assigned higher weightages. The percentage of variance explained by the first principal component is 46.31%.

Correlation matrix worked out to show the inter-association among the infant deaths and the indicators of household's economic and social well-being (physical infrastructure index, mother's empowerment index, and percentage of people above the poverty line) shows very good relation between the dependent and the independent variables (Table 3b). All the three determinants show strongly negative correlations with infant deaths, all of which are statistically significant at 1% level of significance.

Table 3a. Household level factors and IMR (2005-'06)

STATES	IMR PER THOUSAND LIVE BIRTHS	a	b	c	RANKING OF STATES ACCORDING TO IMR
Uttar Pradesh	72.7	-0.933	-0.979	67.2	1
Chhattisgarh	70.8	-1.066	-1.445	59.1	2
Madhya Pradesh	69.5	-0.895	-1.241	61.7	3
Jharkhand	68.7	-1.826	-1.765	59.7	4
Assam	66.1	-1.193	-0.618	80.3	5
Rajasthan	65.3	-0.415	-1.364	77.9	6
Orissa	64.7	-1.328	-0.704	53.6	7
Bihar	61.7	-1.436	-0.248	58.6	8
Arunachal	60.7	-0.204	-0.285	82.4	9
Andhra Pradesh	53.5	0.479	-0.001	84.2	10
Tripura	51.5	-0.755	0.634	81.1	11
Gujarat	49.7	0.907	-0.365	83.2	12
West Bengal	48	-0.459	0.152	75.3	13
Jammu & Kashmir	44.7	0.452	-0.132	94.6	14
Meghalaya	44.6	-0.606	0.088	81.5	15
Karnataka	43.2	0.408	-0.086	75	16
Uttaranchal	41.9	0.299	-0.251	60.4	17
Haryana	41.7	0.626	-0.873	86	18
Punjab	41.7	1.234	-0.206	91.6	19
Delhi	39.8	2.480	0.400	85.3	20
Nagaland	38.3	-0.635	-0.149	81	21
Maharashtra	37.5	0.817	0.121	69.3	22
Himachal Pradesh	36.1	0.439	0.727	90	23
Mizoram	34.1	0.780	1.727	87.4	24
Sikkim	33.7	0.653	0.197	79.9	25
Tamilnadu	30.4	0.776	1.014	77.5	26
Manipur	29.7	-0.647	1.406	82.7	27
Goa	15.3	1.381	1.797	86.2	28
Kerala	15.3	0.669	2.445	85	29

Definition of variables

a	Physical Infrastructure Index of Household
b	Mother's Empowerment Index
c	% People Above the Poverty Line(URP estimates)

Source: NFHS III Report & Planning Commission Poverty Estimates, 2005.
Ranking done in a descending manner, e.g. higher IMR, higher ranking.

Table 3b. Association between the household level factors and IMR

CORRELATION MATRIX				
INDICATORS	IMR	a	b	c
IMR	1	-.692**	-.864**	-.588**
a		1	.518**	.631**
b			1	.535**
c				1

**Correlation is Significant at 1% level (Two-tailed).

Table 3c. Components of physical infrastructure index of household

INDICATORS	WEIGHTAGES
% of Households having ELECTRICITY	0.839
% of Households having IMPROVED SOURCE OF DRINKING WATER	0.471
% of Households having TOILET FACILITY	0.448
% of Households using SOLID FUEL FOR COOKING	-0.895
% of Households living IN A PUCCA HOUSE	0.833
MEAN NUMBER OF PERSONS PER ROOM USED FOR SLEEPING	-0.09

Table 3d. Components of mother's empowerment index

INDICATORS	WEIGHTAGES
Adult Women Literacy(15-49 years)	0.852
% of Adult women having exposure to some kind of mass media (15-49 years)	0.808
% of Currently married women who alone or jointly with their husbands decide how their own earnings are used	0.324
% of Men who say that wives should have the final say alone or jointly with the husband in five major decisions**	-0.197
% of Female headed households	0.621
% of Mothers allowed going to market alone	0.544

Extraction Method: Principal Component Analysis.
Rotation Method: Varimax with Kaiser Normalization.
**Decisions include major hh purchases, purchases for daily hh needs, visits to the wives' family or relatives, what to do with the money the wife earns, & how many children to have.

Importance of household's physical infrastructure and general hygiene situation is undisputedly one of the proxies for households' standard of living, which also reflects households' general awareness regarding the hygiene during the pre and peri-natal cares of new born babies and pregnant mothers as well as preventive to the ailments and morbidity of the children initially after birth from infections. The index of physical infrastructure, however, transmits its effects to the individual level by the pre, peri and post-natal cares of the child such as usage of sterilized instruments to cut the umbilical cord.

Out of the three household level determinants, the mother's empowerment index calculated to show the decision making ability of women regarding child birth and infant care have shown the most strong negative correlation with infant mortality. The strongest element of this index is the adult women literacy, which is the chief determinant of married women's autonomy in the household and their decision making ability regarding child birth. At a general level, it is useful to distinguish between the influences of female education on: (1) desired family size, (2) the relationship between desired family size and planned number of births, and (3) ability to achieve the planned number of births. According to Dyson and Moore (8), educated women are most likely to voice resentment at the burden of repeated pregnancies and to take action to lighten that burden. This may occur because educated women have other sources of prestige and fulfillment besides reproductive performance, more control over household resources and personal behavior, and greater involvement in reproductive decisions. The correlation between all these factors have been represented by the correlation matrix prepared for creating the mother's empowerment index through PCA (0.794 with media exposure by current women, 0.457 with women's decision making ability to spend their own earnings, 0.594 with mother's who are allowed to go to market alone, the first and the last is significant at 1% level, whereas the other is significant at 5% level).Second, educated women have higher aspirations for their children, combined with lower expectations from them in terms of labour services provided (United Nations, 1993). This may reduce number of births if there is a perceived tradeoff between the number of children and their personal achievements. Third, the opportunity cost of time tends to be comparatively high for educated women, and this creates an incentive to minimize such time-intensive activities as childbearing and childrearing, as opined by Dreze, Guio and Murthi (7), especially in urban areas. Moreover, educated women are likely to be more knowledgeable about nutrition, hygiene, and health care, and this awareness is transmitted through the individual level pre, peri and post natal care. In addition, basic education can be important in helping mothers to demand adequate attention to children's needs by other members of the household, to take advantage of public health care services, and generally to pursue their aspirations (including the wellbeing of children) in the family and society in a more informed and effective way. The final household level factor found to be associated with infant deaths is poverty, and the relationship between the duos requires careful examination. It can be noted that although poverty has a moderately strong positive relationship with IMR, but there is also a good deal of colinearity between poverty and similar kind of factors like households' physical standard of living, number of earning women or female literacy etc. The multivariate analysis can only reveal the independent effect of poverty on IMR.

However, figure 3a represents a very good picture of spatial correlation between levels of mother's empowerment and infant mortality. The problem regions of infant death, mainly centered on Mid-Indian belt, comprising the states of Rajasthan, Bihar, U.P., M.P., Chhattisgarh and Orissa, have also shown very low level of female autonomy and decision making abilities. However, such kind of low level of mother's empowerment can be ascribed to poverty and low access to resources, which can also be signified when plotting the poverty condition over the composite picture of IMR and mother's empowerment level.

The figure 3b clearly represents the fact that states which have more number of people below the national average of above poverty line estimates (i.e. poorer states) have lower level of mother's empowerment, thus resulting higher level of infant deaths and vice-versa.

Community level factors and IMR

Availability of amenities in the community level appears to make a difference in infant mortality because they are the sole determinants of all kinds of factors discussed above. The availability of well-organized Government health facilities and Anganwadi services, for example, are more acceptable and affordable to those people who lies below the poverty line, thereby affecting the quality of pre, peri and post natal cares taken at the individual level.

Table 4b shows the correlation between three community level factors and infant mortality. None of the relationships are found to be significant, even at 10% level. No correlations are found at all between the community level determinants and IMR, which is little bit confusing. This suggests the fact that the effects of community level factors have been overshadowed to some extent by the factors at individual and household level.

Table 4a. Community level factors and IMR (2005-'06)

STATES	IMR	a	b	c	RANKING OF STATES ACCORDING TO IMR
Uttar Pradesh	72.7	0.7	15.3	19.8	1
Chhattisgarh	70.8	24.6	36.3	19.4	2
Madhya Pradesh	69.5	17.5	37.4	16.9	3
Jharkhand	68.7	12.2	22.3	14.7	4
Assam	66.1	2.1	65.2	8.9	5
Rajasthan	65.3	3.2	70.2	11.7	6
STATES	IMR	a	b	c	RANKING OF STATES ACCORDING TO IMR
Orissa	64.7	16.7	76	22.6	7
Bihar	61.7	0.3	6.7	19.2	8
Arunachal	60.7	1.4	82.5	9.6	9
Andhra Pradesh	53.5	12.8	25.7	9	10
Tripura	51.5	4.6	79.9	14.4	11
Gujarat	49.7	8.4	27.5	27.3	12
West Bengal	48	10.8	28.8	23.3	13
Jammu & Kashmir	44.7	1.7	62.9	4.1	14
Meghalaya	44.6	25.7	64.8	7.6	15
Karnataka	43.2	12.5	36	19.9	16
Uttaranchal	41.9	4.8	44.4	18.7	17
Haryana	41.7	2.7	27.7	11.2	18
Punjab	41.7	2.5	19.2	11.9	19
Delhi	39.8	2.7	29.3	2.9	20
Nagaland	38.3	0.1	52.1	4.5	21
Maharashtra	37.5	10.4	29.7	16.5	22
Himachal Pradesh	36.1	12.5	82.7	9.1	23
Mizoram	34.1	14.4	90.6	6.2	24
Sikkim	33.7	9.9	91.8	13.2	25
Tamilnadu	30.4	29.1	53	15.2	26
Manipur	29.7	0.9	79	4.6	27
Goa	15.3	20.8	29.6	14.5	28
Kerala	15.3	6.8	50	22.6	29

Definition of indicators

a	% of Mothers got health & nutritional education from ICDS during breastfeeding
b	% of households using Govt. health facilities
c	% of Women have any contact with a health worker

Source: NFHS III Report.
Ranking done in a descending manner, e.g. higher IMR, higher ranking.

Table 4b. Association between the community level factors and IMR

CORRELATION MATRIX				
INDICATORS	IMR	a	b	c
IMR	1	-0.1	-0.178	0.2
a		1	0.045	0.225
b			1	-.395**
c				1

**Correlation is Significant at 5% level (Two-tailed).

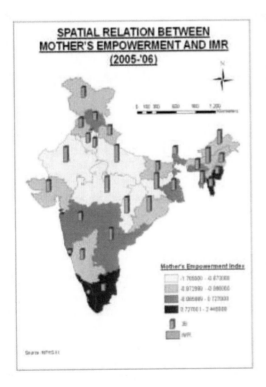

Figure 3a.

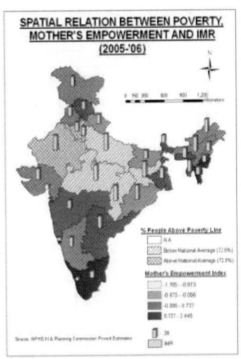

Figure 3b.

The multivariate model

In order to trace out the independent effects of three different level factors separately on IMR, neo-natal mortality and post neo-natal mortality, three separate multivariate models have been used. Indicators are selected from all the three levels depending upon their gross pattern of relationship with infant mortality done in the previous sections. This exercise is mainly carried out to investigate the relative and independent contributions of all these different level factors at infant death as a whole as well as at different levels of infant death, i.e. neo-natal and post neo-natal mortality (as it is previously hypothesized that the effect of different level factors are different in the case of neo-natal and post neo-natal mortality, which is often shadowed by the gross IMR estimates). The model is based on the analytical framework presented above and described by the following set of equations:

$$Y = y_1 + y_2 \tag{1}$$

$$y_1 = \alpha_1 + \beta_1 x_1 + \beta_2 x_2 + \beta_3 x_3 + \beta_4 x_4 + \beta_5 x_5 + \beta_6 x_6 + \beta_7 x_7 + u_1 \tag{2}$$

$$y_2 = \alpha_2 + \beta_1 x_1 + \beta_2 x_2 + \beta_3 x_3 + \beta_4 x_4 + \beta_5 x_5 + \beta_6 x_6 + \beta_7 x_7 + u_2 \tag{3}$$

where,

Y= Overall Infant Mortality
y_1= Neo-natal Mortality
y_2= Post neo-natal Mortality
α_1, α_2= Intercept
β_1.......β_7= Slope Co-efficients
x_1= % of women who received all recommended kinds of antenatal care
x_2= % of deliveries assisted by health personnel
x_3= Mother's Empowerment Index
x_4= % People above the Poverty Line (URP estimates)
x_5= % of mothers got health & nutrition education from ICDS during breastfeeding
x_6= % of children received all kinds of basic vaccinations
x_7= % of household using Government health facilities

Results of all the equations have been displayed in Table 5 together. In case of IMR as a whole, independent relations are depicted in the first column of the table. It can be observed that in case of the model as a whole, the R^2 value is 0.855, with an adjusted R^2 of 0.806, i.e. the independent variables explains almost 85.5% variation of the infant death, or the explanatory power of the independent variables is very high. The F-statistic, for the first model is significant at 1% level, i.e. the model is overall significant at 1% level. Results show that the mother's empowerment level has very significant and highly negative effect over the infant deaths, or more precisely, the independent effect of the levels of mother's empowerment is much higher on infant deaths than any other factors. The slope coefficient for mother's empowerment is -9.884, referring to the fact that about nine fold increase in the autonomy of married women is beneficial to reduce one unit variation in infant deaths. Apart from mother's empowerment level, the poverty indicator at the household level also has significant independent effect on infant mortality as a whole (-0.276). The negative independent effect of poverty on infant mortality can be observed probably due to the different dietary habits of mothers which influence their nutrition level during pregnancy and also affects the nutritional and curative care of the child after the birth. However, the net effect of these factors on neo-natal and post neo-natal mortality separately will be able to illustrate the different roles of poverty in different levels of infant deaths. Moreover, the levels of female autonomy have also shown to be positively associated with the levels of poverty (correlation co-efficient calculated between the duo is 0.534, significant at 1% level), suggesting the indirect role of poverty to determine some of the individual level factors like child vaccination through a higher enhancement of female autonomy. Effect of vaccination is found to be also significant on infant deaths; it has a negative independent effect on gross estimate of infant deaths (-0.191). The Durbin-Watson d statistic calculated for the first model is 2.480 for all 29 observations and seven independent variables, which lies within the 'zone of indecision' (between 4-d_u and 4-d_l); hence no conclusion can be done regarding the autocorrelation parameter of the model.

The second model analyses the independent relationship between the selected multi-level factors with neo-natal mortality, which used to occur within the first month of the child birth and constitutes almost 60% of the infant deaths. It is previously hypothesized that the factors affecting neo-natal mortality at different levels of childhood care is different from post neo-natal mortality, which is often shaded by the gross estimation of infant mortality.

It is found that one of the important peri-natal factors like deliveries assisted by the trained health personnel has a negative significant effect on neo-natal mortality (-0.507), which was not evident when we discussed the infant death as a whole. However, the effect of mother's empowerment level has also a negative and statistically significant effect on the variations in neo-natal mortality (-7.821). Such a factor ascribe to the fact that the negative effect of adult women literacy and other empowerment measure is transmitted to neo-natal mortality by an increase in the percentage of births attended by trained health personnel.

Table 5. Summary of multiple regression analysis of the effect of individual, household and community level factors on infant mortality and its components, NFHS III (2005-'06)

BACKGROUND VARIABLES	DEPENDENT VARIABLE		
	IMR	NEO-NATAL MORTALITY	POST NEO-NATAL MORTALITY
CONSTANT	33.916 (0.674)	0.145 (.004)	46.738 (1.493)***
a	-0.057 (-0.359)	-0.040 (0.367)	-0.123 (-1.248)
b	-0.446 (0.905)	-0.507 (1.488)***	-0.152 (-0.495)
c	-9.884 (-4.774)*	-7.821 (-5.460)*	-1.081 (-0.840)
d	-0.276 (-1.825)**	-0.117 (-1.121)	-0.114 (-1.211)
e	0.015 (0.077)	0.041 (0.311)	-0.051 (-0.437)
f	-0.191 (-1.528)**	-0.215 (-2.491)*	-0.087 (-1.117)
g	0.031 (0.486)	0.026 (0.594)	-0.024 (-0.145)
R^2	0.855	0.873	0.598
ADJUSTED R^2	0.806	0.830	0.464
F	17.640*	20.553*	4.468*
N	29	29	29
DURBIN-WATSON d STATISTIC	2.480	2.272	1.623

t-ratios in parentheses.
* Significant at 1% level (Two-tailed).
** Significant at 5% level (Two-tailed).
*** Significant at 10% level (Two-tailed).

Definition of variables

a	% of women who received all recommended kinds of antenatal care
b	% of deliveries assisted by health personnel
c	Mother's Empowerment Index
d	% People Above the Poverty Line(URP estimates)
e	% of mothers got health & nutrition education from ICDS during breastfeeding
f	% of children received all kinds of basic vaccinations
g	% of households using Government health facilities

However, the poverty indicator which was found to have an significant negative effect on total infant deaths, has also a negative effect on neo-natal mortality, although not statistically significant, indicating the fact that as a whole it can be an important determinant of infant mortality, but judging at the neo-natal level the independent effect of poverty is not so much evident, although it transmits some of its influence through the dietary practice of the mothers during pregnancy, i.e. non-medical pre-natal care or through vaccination of the child or percentage of deliveries assisted by the health personnels (correlation co-efficient calculated between poverty indicator and index of vaccination is 0.320, significant at 5% level). Another factor which affects the neo-natal death significantly is the index of vaccination, which has a negative effect on neo-natal mortality (-0.215), i.e. the neo-natal mortality decreases by 0.215 units with a unit increase in vaccination, which in turn reflects mother's awareness in post natal medical childhood care that have been ascribed through a higher level of female autonomy (the correlation coefficient calculated between mother's empowerment level and index of vaccinations is 0.551, significant at 1% level, supports the argument). The three significant indicators along with others explain almost 87.3% variation in neo-natal mortality. The F- statistic calculated for the model is significant at 1% level, referring a fairly well-explanation of the model by the explanatory variables, which is statistically significant. The Durbin-Watson d statistic calculated to trace out the autocorrelation parameter of the model is 2.272, which also falls within the 'zone of indecision'; hence no comment can be made regarding the autocorrelation parameter of the model.

The third and final model explains the effect of the multi-level determinants on post neo-natal mortality. Here the result is little bit confusing because no significant effect can be found in case of any of the factors on post neo-natal mortality. However, the independent effect of mother's empowerment index on post neo-natal mortality is also very high, although not significant. No significant effect of post-natal nutritional education of mothers or index of vaccination can be found on post neo-natal mortality, although the gross effect of all these factors on post neo-natal mortality is very high (correlation coefficient calculated between post neo-natal nutritional education of mothers and post neo-natal mortality is -0.420, significant at 5% level, the same calculated between index of vaccination and post neo-natal mortality is -0.643, significant at 1% level). Such factors signify low independent effects of all these factors on post neo-natal mortality. The explanatory variables together are able to explain about 60% regional variation in post neo-natal mortality, with an significant F-statistic at 1% level, referring the joint effect of all independent variables are statistically significant. The Durbin-Watson d statistic calculated to trace out the autocorrelation parameter of the model is 1.623, lies within d_u and d_l, referring to the 'zone of indecision'; hence no conclusion can be made regarding the autocorrelation parameter of the model.

In summary, the mother's empowerment level, poverty and index of vaccination are the three important determinants of infant mortality as a whole, whereas the role of percentage deliveries assisted by the trained health personnels along with mother's empowerment level and index of vaccination is regarded as two important determining factors having their independent effect on neo-natal mortality. The independent effect of poverty indicator on neo-natal mortality is not evident, although the gross and independent effect is much higher. In the case of post neo-natal mortality, none of the factors have significant independent effect but the gross effect of some of the post natal factors like vaccination or mother's nutritional education from ICDS remains important. Factors like poverty and mother's empowerment continues to remain their higher independent effect on post neo-natal mortality, although not significant.

Discussion

The crucial findings traced out from the study are:

- Most of the states which have recorded positive changes between NFHS I and NFHS II have recorded negative changes between NFHS II and NFHS III and vice versa. Notable changes have been observed in case of Himachal Pradesh (-21.4 points changes between NFHS I and II, but recorded 1.7 point change between NFHS II and III), Meghalaya, Punjab etc.
- Regarding Male, Female and Female Disadvantage in IMR, conditions have been much not improved between NFHS II and NFHS III, rather significant changes can be observed between the first two rounds.
- The gross effect of individual level factors like percentage women having all kinds of recommended antenatal care, percentage deliveries assisted by trained health personnels or index of vaccination have higher gross effect on infant deaths, although the net effects of all these factors are lower because many of them are linearly related to the next level, i.e. household or community level factors.
- The gross effect of household level factors like mother's level of empowerment or poverty is high on infant deaths, whether the net effect of mother's empowerment is also very high as it largely controls the individual's decision making regarding pre, peri and post natal care as well as reflects the availability of basic social amenities at the community level, i.e. number of schools in the community or Government health facilities taken by households. The same argument can be also taken in favour of poverty which has high linear association from the demand side, i.e. it's a large controlling variable of the demand side constraints like household's awareness during pre-natal dietary practices for pregnant women or general standard of living of the household.
- In terms of supply and demand side viewpoint, both supply and demand side factors found to be significant in determining infant deaths as a whole and at different levels. Demand side constraints like poverty or mother's empowerment level have significant effects, either directly or indirectly over infant deaths in the form of individual care or medical attentiveness whereas supply side factors like facility

indicators of Government health facilities, Anganwadi services or household's physical infrastructure have direct effects that often work in response to the demand side indicators.

- Clear-cut regional differentiation can be found in the distribution of IMR level over India. However, well-marked spatial correlations can be traced out between the major determinants of IMR like levels of mother's empowerment or poverty levels which signify the fact that regional differentiation in infant death is ascribed to poorer social and economic conditions in same places.
- There are significant differences observed between factors affecting neo-natal mortality and the determinants of post neo-natal mortality, especially at the individual level. Pre and peri-natal factors have a higher effect on neo-natal deaths whereas post-natal medical and non-medical cares have larger effect on post neo-natal deaths.

As discussed above, a number of literatures have suggested the fact that the interplay of three different level factors determines the levels and trends of infant deaths and its components in any spatial context. Some of these literatures have been suggested that in the absence of modern health and education services, levels of female autonomy may influence the patterns of child care, and hence infant mortality. However, the present analysis partially supports this hypothesis as far as mother's empowerment level is concerned. The levels of mother's empowerment directly and indirectly through its association with the individual level care determines the levels of infant deaths during both pre and post natal period. However, the effect of economic development indicators cannot be overlooked as it is already shown that poverty is seemed to have an independent effect on infant mortality as a whole. Household's social and economic circumstances, e.g. level of maternal education or general standard of living largely captures the family resources that affects child survival. Hence, the present analysis clearly demonstrates the importance of both medical and non-medical factors at different levels in explaining the observed regional differences in infant mortality in India. However, the relative importance of these two types of factors varies from state to state but only an effective interplay of both kinds of factors at different levels of child birth can take major role in reducing infant mortality. Simultaneous improvements in women's education and general economic conditions of the household would enhance the effect of preventive medical interventions by taking them more acceptable and by improving the use made of available medical services for curative purposes.

Acknowledgments

I am grateful to my parents, my brother, my dear friend Ritwika and Awadhesh for supporting me while working on this paper. I also acknowledge my warm gratitude to Prof. B.S.Butola, Prof. Sararswati Raju, Dr. Atul Sood and Dr. Nilanjan Patra for technical and informative supports while preparing the paper.

References

[1]   Caldwell JC, Mcdonald P. Influence of maternal education on infant and child mortality: levels and causes. Proceedings of IUSSP Conference in Manila 1982;2:79-95.

[2]   Caldwell JC. Education as a factor in mortality decline: an examination of Nigerian data. Popul Stud (Camb) 1979;33(3):395-413.

[3]   Celeste MS et al. Neo-natal Mortality in South Asia: The Special Role of Tetanus. Popul Stud (Camb) 1980;34(2):321-35.

[4]   Das Gupta Monica, Mari Bhat PN. Fertility decline and increased manifestation of sex bias in India. Popul Stud (Camb) 1997;51(3):307-15.

[5]   Das Gupta Monica. Selective discrimination against female children in rural Punjab, India. Popul Dev Rev 1987;13(1):77-100.

[6]   Dreze, Jean, Sen A. India: Economic Development and Social Opportunity. Delhi: Oxford University Press, 1995.

[7]   Dreze Jean, Murthi M, Guio AC. Fertility, Mortality and Gender Bias in India: A District Level Analysis. Popul Dev Rev 1995;21(4):745-82.

[8]   Dyson Tim, Moore M. On Kinship structure, female autonomy, and demographic behavior in India. Popul Dev Rev 1983;9(1):35-59.

[9]   Gulati SC. Developmental determinants of demographic variables in India: A district level analysis. J Quant Econ 1992;8(1):157-72.

[10]   Mosley WH, Chen LC. An analytical framework for the study of child survival in developing countries. In Mosley, Chen (ed.) Child survival: strategies for research. Popul Dev Rev 1984;Suppl 10:25-45.

[11]   Nag Moni. Impacts of social development and economic development on mortality: A comparative study of Kerala and West Bengal. Econ Polit Wkly 1983;18:877-900.

Submitted: November 01, 2011. *Revised:* December 27, 2011. *Accepted:* January 01, 2012.

In: Child Health and Human Development Yearbook 2013   ISBN: 978-1-63117-939-6
Editor: Joav Merrick   © 2014 Nova Science Publishers, Inc.

Chapter 16

Assessment of energy and nutrient intakes among Saharawi children hosted in Spain

Gloria Domènech, BSND, Sabina Escortell, BSND, Rosa Gilabert,
BSND, Manuel Lucena, BSND, Ma C Martínez, BSND,
Jordi Mañes, PhD, and Jose M Soriano, PhD[*]

Observatory of Nutrition and Food Safety in Developing Countries,
Faculty of Pharmacy, University of Valencia,
Burjassot, Spain

Abstract

The objective was to examine anthropometric measurements and to evaluate the daily energy and nutrient intakes of Saharawi children of Tindouf (Algeria) hosted in Spain. To date, it is the first report about energy and nutrient intakes in these hosted children. Study group: Saharawi children of refugees camp in Tindouf (Algeria) aged 4-13 years (n =270), hosting in Spanish families during summertime. Methods: Anthropometric measures and energy and nutrient intakes for a 7-day periods using the weighed food intake method were evaluated in these children and compared with the values of Institute of Medicine. Results: The highest value of BMI was obtained for girls aged from 9 to 13 (20.2 kg m-2). Mean energy intake was ranged from 8.0 to 9.0 MJ day-1 for girls aged from 4 to 8, and for boys aged from 9 and 13, respectively. The highest value of the carbohydrate and fat intakes were for Saharawi boys aged from 9 to 13, but the highest value of protein intake were Saharawi girls aged from 9 to 13. The PUFA/SFA ratio is lower than 0.5 and the (PUFA+MUFA)/SFA values are <2 for studied Saharawi children. Five (vitamin D and E, potassium, calcium and iodine) out of twenty-three micronutrients intakes below than the recommended values, being the low value of iodine an advantage for these children due to that suffer goitre for excessive intake of iodine in their refugee

[*] Correspondence: Jose M Soriano, PhD, Observatory of Nutrition and Food Safety in Developing Countries, Faculty of Pharmacy, University of Valencia, Av. Vicent Andres Estelles s/n, 46100 Burjassot, Spain. E-mail: jose.soriano@uv.es.

camps. Conclusions: Our study reflected in some nutrients an inadequately intakes for these hosted children.

Keywords: Saharawi children, energy intakes, macronutrients, micronutrients, anthropometric measurements

Introduction

The Saharawi refugee camps is located in four remotely camps (Dakhla, Smara, Al-'Uyun and Awsard), since 1976, in a territorial zone set up in the harsh Algerian desert 30 km from the westernmost town of Tindouf (1). There are also some smaller satellite camps, called the "February 27", serving as a boarding school for women.

The headquarters of Polisario Front, which is a Saharawi rebel movement working for the independence of Western Sahara from Morocco, with the government in exile of the Saharawi Arab Democratic Republic (SADR), are headquartered in Rabouni, a camp dedicated to administration (2). According to the United Nations High Commission for Refugees (3), approximately estimated 165.000 Saharawi refugees currently live in a hostile environment that make difficult to deliver and impede refugee self-sufficiency. International aid groups provide most of the consumed food, medicine and other basic supplies by camp residents (4,5) and around 2.987 children attend school in the camps around Tindouf, supported by 78 education personnel, mostly volunteers, working in 40 educational units, including 28 primary schools (1, 2). Today, nearly 90% of Saharawi refugees are able to read and write, the number having been less than 10% in 1975, and several thousands have received university educations in foreign countries as part of aid packages (mainly Algeria, Cuba and Spain).

Some of these Saharawi children between the ages of eight and thirteen are hosted by Spanish families in their homes for a two-month period during the summer according to the "Holidays in Peace" program organized by a national Spanish Non-Governmental Organization.

As part of this action, between 7.000 and 10.000 Saharawi children arrives in Spain to spend the summer with host families and allows receive medical examinations and treatment, as well as gifts of clothes, toys, and money which they take back with them to the camps and many of them return year after year to the same host homes. Additionally, Spanish host families often visit the camps, buying local products or leaving similar cash gifts. The relationships established during the program often endure beyond the summer months, as strong proto-familial relationships form between the children and their Spanish host families, and return trips reinforce such cross-border bonds (2,3,6).

The aims of this study are to examine anthropometric measurements and to evaluate the daily energy and nutrient intakes of Saharawi children of Tindouf (Algeria) hosted in Spain during the summer. To date, it is the first report about energy and nutrient intakes in these hosted children.

Methods

Study location and subjects

Research was conducted in Spain in collaboration with a local nongovernmental organization (NGO) for a two-month period during the summer in 2007 according to the "Holidays in Peace" program. This study was approved by the Human Subjects Committee of the University of Valencia (Spain), and informed consent was obtained from parents. The sample was 270 Saharawi children (130 boys and 140 girls), which were grouped from 4 to 8 years and from 9 to 13 years. These ranges were used according to the Dietary Reference Intakes (DRIs), Recommended Dietary Allowances (RDAs) or Adequate Intakes (AIs) of the Institute of Medicine (7-12). The study protocol was approved by the Ethical Committee of University of Valencia and each head of household gave their verbal consent after the study had been fully explained to them.

Anthropometric measures

All the anthropometric measurements were performed in triplicate accordingly to the Anthropometric Standardization Reference Manual (13) with the subjects wearing light clothing and barefoot, by the same trained anthropometrist. A Plenna scale (model MEA 07 400, USA; accuracy of 100 g) was used to determine weight and a Seca stadiometer (model 208, Germany; accuracy of 0.5 cm) was used to determine height. Body mass index (BMI) was calculated as body weight divided by the square of the height (kg/m2).

Dietary intake

Several dieticians recorded from food preparer daily dietary intake for a 7-day periods using the weighed food intake method (14), being the method that provides the most accurate estimation of usual individual intake (15). Furthermore, data about all foods and beverages consumed since the previous day, including methods of food preparation, description of ingredients and condiments consumed were compiled from the food preparer. The study was carried out from the stayed third week in Spain because these children in the first two weeks eat little. The daily average quantities are converted into energy and nutrient through the DIAL program, version 1.02 for Windows XP (Alceingenieria, Madrid, Spain). Dietary intakes of nutrients were compared with reference values reported by the DRIs, RDAs or AIs of the IOM (7-12).

Statistical analysis

Anthropometric, energy and nutrient intake values are presented as means and standard deviations (SD) grouped by group of age and by sex. A Kolmogorov–Smirnov test was used to test for normality. To compare the means of boys and girls, the Independent-Samples T-

Test was used in case of a normal distribution, otherwise the Mann–Whitney U test was used. Statistical significance was established at a P-value<0.05. All statistical analyses were performed using the SPSS Statistics 19.0 (SPSS Inc., Chicago, IL, USA).

Results

Table 1 shows the mean physical characteristics of the studied Saharawi children hosted in Spain. No significant differences were found in studied children in mean of height, weight and BMI. The highest value of BMI is obtained for girls aged from 9 to 13 (20.2 kg m-2). For the study of energy and nutrient intakes, dates are shown in Table 2, 3 and 4. Mean energy intake was 8.3, 8.0, 9.0 and 8.9 MJ day-1 for boys and girls aged from 4 to 8, and for boys and girls aged from 9 and 13, respectively. The highest value of the carbohydrate and fat intakes were for Saharawi boys aged from 9 to 13, but the highest value of protein intake were Saharawi girls aged from 9 to 13. No significant differences in profile of fat intake were detected among studied Saharawi children (Table 2). The PUFA/SFA ratio is lower than 0.5 and the (PUFA+MUFA)/SFA values are <2 for studied Saharawi children. The highest value of daily cholesterol intake is obtained for boys aged from 9 to 13 (352.5 mg day-1). No significant differences were found in studied children in mean dietary fibre. The intake of water was significantly higher in boys aged from 9 to 13 than boys aged from 4 to 8.

Table 1. Mean values and standard deviations of the physical characteristics of the Saharawi children hosted in Spain

	4-8 years (n=140)		9-13 years (n=130)	
	Boys (n=70)	Girls (n=70)	Boys (n=60)	Girls (n=70)
Age (years)	8.9±0.9	9.0±0.7	12.4±1.4	12.9±2.1
Height (cm)	135.0±10.1	136.1±14.1	144.0±10.8	141.2±23.1
Weight (kg)	31.5±4.8	26.7±3.1	39.4±7.2	40.2±8.9
BMI (kg m^{-2})	17.3±3.1	14.4±2.8	19.1±1.2	20.2±3.1

Table 2. Mean values and standard deviations of the daily energy, macronutrients, fibre, water and profile of fat intake of the Saharawi children hosted in Spain

	4-8 years (n=140)		9-13 years (n=130)	
	Boys (n=70)	Girls (n=70)	Boys (n=60)	Girls (n=70)
Energy (MJ)	8.3±2.2	8.0±3.4	9.0±2.9	8.9±2.8
Protein (g)	60.9±10.8	60.7±8.9	73.2±25.5	74.1±34.2
Carbohydrate (g)	222.1±48.3	212.4±87.9	251.4±84.1	248.4±98.7
Fat (g)	79.9±14.4	78.9±23.4	89.9±29.9	88.8±21.4
MUFA (g)	39.7±6.6	36.5±5.8	40.5±15.4	42.9±23.4
PUFA (g)	9.9±1.6	9.1±2.3	8.7±3.4	8.1±4.5
SFA (g)	23.4±3.6	20.2±2.4	24.6±9.2	25.4±11.1
PUFA/SFA	0.42±0.05	0.45±0.07	0.35±0.09	0.31±0.04
(PUFA+MUFA)/SFA	2.11±0.14	2.26±0.20	2.00±0.15	2.00±0.16
Cholesterol (mg)	248.0±114.2	238.7±108.1	352.5±130.5	324.2±110.1
Dietary fibre (g)	20.8±5.2	23.2±5.4	22.9±8.5	22.5±9.1
Water (g)	1322.4±144.7	1345.4±234.0	1564.1±477.5	1687.2±267.1

Table 3 reflects the values of vitamin intakes being the intake of thiamin was higher in girls aged from 9 to 13 than boys aged from 4 to 8. Vitamin B6 intake is higher in girls than boys aged from 4 to 8. Furthermore, non-significant differences in panthotenic acid were found between boys aged from 4 to 8 and the remainder of the children. The mineral intake is demonstrated in the Table 4 and potassium was found significant differences between boys and girls aged from 4 to 8 ($p < 0.05$). Furthermore, significantly differences between the iron intake of boys aged from 4 to 8 and girls from 9 to 13.

Discussion

In our study, the lowest and highest values of energy intake are obtained by the girls aged from 4 to 8 and boys aged from 9 to 13, respectively (Table 2). Compared to DRIs (12), energy intakes appeared to be generally satisfactory. The DRIs (12) recommended 10-30% of daily energy intake for protein being this value obtained in all studied groups. However, our values of carbohydrate and lipids are lower (44.4-46.7%) and higher (36.2-37.6%) than DRIs (12), which 45-65% and 25-35% of daily energy intake, respectively. For the cholesterol, the DRIs (12) suggest a range from 205 to 259 mg/day being these values exceed for children aged from 4 to 13 (Table 2). In the other hand, a deficiency in total fiber and water intakes is reflected in our study in comparison with AIs (12); 1.7, 2.1 and 2.4 litre of water/day and 25, 26 and 31 g of fiber /day from children (4-8 y), males (9-13 y) and females (9-13 y), respectively. The intake of water was significantly higher in boys aged from 9 to 13 than boys aged from 4 to 8 ($p < 0.05$).

Tables 3 and 4 reflected the analyzed micronutrients. Vitamin values are adequate, except in boys aged from 9 to 13 which have a quantity ingested for vitamin E (8.9 mg day-1) lower than the DRIs (9 mg day-1) (9). Furthermore, the intake of vitamin D is below for all studied children (Table 3) according to the AIs (7) (5 µg day-1 for all studied children).

Table 3. Mean values and standard deviations of vitamin intake of the Saharawi children hosted in Spain

	4-8 years (n=140)		9-13 years (n=130)	
	Boys (n=70)	Girls (n=70)	Boys (n=60)	Girls (n=70)
Thiamin (mg)	2.2±0.6	2.4±1.4	2.2±0.8	3.1±1.1
Riboflavin (mg)	1.4±1.1	1.2±1.0	1.9±0.9	2.1±0.7
Niacin (mg)	22.6±7.2	23.4±8.9	27.8±11.1	30.1±10.8
Panthotenic acid (mg)	4.1±0.5	5.1±0.8	4.9±1.6	4.9±1.3
Vitamin B6 (mg)	2.2±0.7	3.1±1.8	2.5±0.9	3.2±1.2
Biotin (µg)	24.6±8.6	22.7±9.1	32.5±11.5	33.4±21.3
Folate (µg)	294.2±88.5	280.5±78.5	311.1±143.7	333.4±190.2
Vitamin B12 (µg)	4.7±4.1	4.1±3.8	4.2±2.8	4.6±3.6
Vitamin C (mg)	150.3±17.5	160.8±28.2	177.9±67.8	176.4±56.7
Vitamin A (µg)	1148.0±368.7	1054.2±468.7	970.5±489.1	1111.4±678.3
Vitamin D (µg)	3.4±2.1	2.8±2.2	2.9±2.6	3.3±3.0
Vitamin E (mg)	10.2±1.1	10.5±2.4	8.9±3.5	11.3±5.6
Vitamin K (µg)	121.4±86.5	130.4±90.1	111.1±104.5	143.6±88.9

The intake of calcium is inadequate for all studied children (800 and 1300 mg day-1 for children aged from 4 to 8 and from 9 to 13, respecti vely) except for females aged from 4 to 8 (Table 4) according to the AIs (7) being the calcium/phosphorus ratio ranged between 1 and 0.5. It is due to the increased intake of beverages like colas and other soft drinks, especially those that use phosphoric acid as acidifier, among the studied children. In our study, they have iodine intakes (Table 4) below than the RDAs (10) (90 and 120 µg day-1 for children aged from 4 to 8 and from 9 to 13, respectively).

Table 4. Mean values and standard deviations of mineral intake of the Saharawi children hosted in Spain

	4-8 years		9-13 years	
	Boys (n=70)	Girls (n=70)	Boys (n=60)	Girls (n=70)
Sodium (mg)	3385.4±747.3	3200.5±890.5	3496.0±1311.3	3679.7±1777.7
Potassium (mg)	3045.6±469.9[*]	2300.2±540.6[*]	2349.5±1224.3	2567.8±1165.8
Calcium (mg)	785.4±178.7	810.4±156.4	844.2±290.3	898.5±313.2
Fluoride (mg)	2.2±0.6	2.0±0.9	2.4±1.0	2.6±1.1
Magnesium (mg)	267.4±33.6	288.9±43.6	302.3±107.4	319.2±110.8
Phosphorus (mg)	1200.1±225.4	1122.4±333.3	1357.2±491.4	1209.5±651.3
Iron (mg)	14.1±3.2	14.5±6.5	16.7±5.8	17.2±4.1
Zinc (mg)	6.8±2.9	5.3±2.2	9.0±3.4	8.8±4.5
Selenium (µg)	55.3±26.7	51.2±36.5	55.1±29.9	56.7±31.1
Iodine (µg)	53.6±23.1	54.1±34.3	64.3±25.5	62.4±33.3

[*] Mean value was significantly different between boys and girls.

In our view, this last micronutrient is very important in the Saharawi children because several studies (5, 16-18) reflected a high urinary iodine levels (965±348 µg/l) and high iodine concentration (180-400 µg/l) in drinking water in refugee camps in Tindouf (Algeria), which is related with clinical observation of goitre. Goitre is common around the world because many regions have inadequate iodine intake; however the situation is "slightly" different because in Saharawi refugee camps, there is an excessive intake of iodine (19), this situation has been cited in other places in the world; Central China (20) and Hokkaido (Japan) (21) that have an endemic goitre caused by excessive iodine intake. Díaz-Cadórniga et al. (16) reflected that the goiter was found in 58.1% of the school children placed in Tindouf (Algeria).

Our recommendation2 for host families is not given iodized salt from these children during the summer holidays. In the other hand, our values reflected that the iron is adequately intake in all groups being this date important due to that iron deficiency anaemia can lead to several health consequences, including impaired cognitive and physical development. According to the World Health Organization (22), these children have iron deficiency anaemia, according to the rutinary analysis carried out when they arrived to Spain, reflected in low iron values in conjunction with elevated iron-binding capacity values, yielding less than 16 percent transferrin saturation. Lopriere et al. (23) suggested in a personal communication of one of authors indicated a 70% of Saharawi children were anaemic.

In conclusion, our study reflected in some nutrients an inadequately intakes for these hosted children, although it should be better, with nutritional counselling from dietitians, to increase the nutritional and health benefits when these children returning to their refugee camps.

Acknowledgments

We are especially grateful to hosted families, Federació d´Associacions de Solidaritat amb el Poble Saharaui Pais Valencià and Conselleria de Inmigración y Ciudadanía of the Generalitat Valenciana (3014/2007). J.M. Soriano thanks to the European Union for the grant Long Life Learning Programme.

References

[1]   Spiegel PB. Forgotten refugees and other displaced populations. Lancet 2003;362:72-4.

[2]   Soriano JM. Niños y niñas Saharauis: Guía alimentaria para las familias de acogida. Servei de Publicacions. Universitat de València. 2008.

[3]   United Nations High Commissioner for Refugees (UNHCR)/World Food Programme (WFP)/Institute of Child Health (ICH). Anthropometric and micronutrient nutrition survey. Saharawi Refugee Camps. Tindouf. Geneva: United Nations High Commissioner for Refugees; 2007. Accessed 2012 Jan 12. URL: www.unhcr.org/publ/PUBL/45fa67bf2.pdf.

[4]   Dukic N, Thierry A. Saharawi refugees: life after the camps. Forced Migration Rev 1998;2:18-21.

[5]   Soriano JM, Domènech G, Mañes J, Catalá-Gregori AI, Barikmo IE. Disorders of malnutrition among the Saharawi children. Rev Esp Nutr Hum Diet 2011;15:10-9.

[6]   Refugee Studies Centre. The transnationalisation of care: Sahrawi refugee children in a Spanish host programme. Lessons Learned Report. Oxford: University of Oxford, 2005.

[7]   Institute of Medicine. Dietary Reference Intakes for calcium, phosphorus, magnesium, vitamin D and fluoride. Washington DC: National Academies Press, 1997.

[8]   Institute of Medicine. Dietary Reference Intakes for thiamin, riboflavin, niacin, vitamin B6, folate, vitamin B12, pantothenic acid, biotin, and choline. Washington DC: National Academies Press, 1998.

[9]   Institute of Medicine. Dietary Reference Intakes for vitamin C, vitamin E, selenium, and carotenoids. Washington DC: National Academies Press, 2000.

[10]   Institute of Medicine. Dietary Reference Intakes for vitamin A, vitamin K, arsenic, boron, chromium, copper, iodine, iron, manganese, molybdenum, nickel, silicon, vanadium, and zinc. Washington DC: National Academies Press, 2001.

[11]   Institute of Medicine. Dietary Reference Intakes for water, potassium, sodium, chloride, and sulfate. Washington DC: National Academies Press, 2004.

[12]   Institute of Medicine Dietary Reference Intakes for energy, carbohydrate, fiber, fat, fatty acids, cholesterol, protein, and amino acids (macronutrients). Washington DC: National Academies Press, 2005.

[13]   Lohman TG, Roche AF, Martorell R. Anthropometric Standardization Reference Manual. Champaign, IL: Human Kinetics Publishers, 1988.

[14]   Bingham SA. The dietary assessment of individuals; methods, accuracy, new techniques and recommendations. Nutr Abstr Rev (Series A) 1987;57: 705-42.

[15]   Buzzard M. 24-hour recall and food record methods. In: Willett, WC, ed. Nutritional Epidemiology. New York: Oxford University Press, 1998:50-73.

[16]   Díaz-Cadórniga FJ, Delgado E, Tartón T. Endemic goitre associated with high iodine intake in primary school children in the Saharawi Arab Democratic Republic. Endocrinol Nutr 2003;50:357-62.

[17]   Domènech G, Escortell S, Gilabert R, Lara M, Martínez MªC, Soriano, JM. Dietary intake and food pattern of Saharawi refugee children in Tindouf (Algeria). Proc Nutr Soc 2008; 67:E174.

[18]   Paricio Talayero JM, Santos Serrano L, Fernández Feijoo A. Health examination of children from the Democratic Sahara Republic (North West Africa) on vacation in Spain. An Esp Pediatr 1998;49:33-8.

[19]   Pezzino V, Padova G, Vigneri R. Iodine-independent endemic goiter in Saharawi refugee camps in Southwestern Algeria. IDD Newsletter 1998;14:1-3.

[20]   Li M, Liu DR, Qu CY Endemic goitre in Central China caused by excessive iodine intake. Lancet 1987;2:257-9.

[21]   Suzuki H, Higuchi T, Sawa K. Endemic coast goitre in Hokkaido, Japan. Acta Endocrinol (Copenh) 1965;50:161-76.

[22]   World Health Organization (WHO). Iron deficiency anaemia–Assessment, prevention, and control. A guide for programme managers. Geneva: World Health Organization; 2001. Accessed 2012 Jan 12. URL: www.who.int/nutrition/publications/en/ida_assessment_prevention_control.pdf

[23]   Lopriore C, Guidom Y, Briend A. Spread fortified with vitamins and minerals induces catch-up growth and eradicates severe anemia in stunted refugee children aged 3-6 y. Am J Clin Nutr 2004;80:973-80.

Submitted: January 24, 2012. *Revised:* April 03, 2012. *Accepted:* April 21, 2012.

In: Child Health and Human Development Yearbook 2013   ISBN: 978-1-63117-939-6
Editor: Joav Merrick   © 2014 Nova Science Publishers, Inc.

Chapter 17

Family size transition and its implication over child care in Andhra Pradesh, India

Ritwika Mukherjee, MA[*]

Centre for the study of Regional Development, School of Social Sciences,
Jawaharlal Nehru University, New Delhi, India

Abstract

The present study seeks to highlight the family size transition in Andhra Pradesh as a mechanism of twin process of fertility decline and nuclearisation of families impacting the levels and quality of child care through a longitudinal analysis from NFHS I, II and III unit level data. Appropriate bivariate and multivariate analysis such as binary logistic regression models have been worked to show the net effect of the selected demographic and socio-economic predictor variables impacting the probability of the betterment of children's post natal care. The summary results of the analysis points out that the small family norms which has been incepted in Andhra as an exception to the usual discourse of socio-economic development, have not seen to intensify the discrimination in child care to a greater level like its north Indian counterparts, rather portrays significant differential in quality and nature of child care. Small or nuclear households are reported to have performed better in terms of medical care like immunization whereas non-medical care such as breastfeeding is higher among non-nuclear households. The other proximate determinants of child care like mothers' occupational structure or their educational attainment are also seen to have similar effects where mothers' having lower level of education or those who are employed in agriculture are reported to perform better in terms of the time- intensive care of the child such as breastfeeding. However, in the nuclear families, lack of baby care owing to rising opportunity costs of the working and educated women are responsible for it. Hence the differential effect of the modernization factors is needed to be handled judiciously.

---

[*] Correspondence: Ritwika Mukherjee, Research Scholar, Room No: 222, Lohit Hostel (Girl's Wing), JNU, New Delhi 110067. Email: ritwika88@gmail.com or rattikaaa@gmail.com.

Keywords: Small Families, Socio-economic Development, Nuclearisation, Multivariate model, Child Post-natal Care

Introduction

The size of the family is of great importance not only for the country as a whole but also for the welfare and health of the individual. India adopted the goal of universalizing the 'two child family norm' lately by the end of this century, which has consequences both at the micro (individual) as well as the macro (community) level. A norm in relation to family size, according to sociologists, implies a pattern which sets limits for any community's fertility behavior. The size of the family affects greatly the quality of life of human beings. Recently, the decline in family size in most parts of India is controlled not only by the family planning initiatives, such as contraceptive use and sterilization of young fetus, but also the disintegration of the joint family system assumes another important mechanism. In this context Atinson (1) pointed out the rural-urban differentials in child care and the importance attached to the non-familial care particularly in rural areas.

The selection of the study area requires judicious and careful examinations of the family size transition across India as well as the extent of decline in the recent period in order to enquire the impact arising out of this negative change. Two criteria have been chosen, 1) The mean household size should be at a considerably low level and 2) An appreciable decline in mean household size in the recent period (NFHS III). Among all the states of India, Andhra Pradesh has recorded the steepest decline in average household size amounting to -1.19 points (Table 1) between 1998-99 to 2005-06 as compared to the national average decline of -0.69. The mean household size in 2005-06 was 5.62 ranking third at the national level. Hence, the southern state of Andhra Pradesh has been taken under consideration for the further analysis of the mechanisms of such steep decline and impact on child care.

Table 1. Average Household (HH) Size of Andhra Pradesh and India

ROUNDS	Average HH Size		Changes	
	Andhra Pradesh	India	Andhra Pradesh	India
NFHS I (1992-93)	6.75	7.92	-	-
NFHS II (1998-99)	6.81	7.68	0.06	-0.24
NFHS III (2005-06)	5.62	6.99	-1.19	-0.69

Source: NFHS I, II and III Rounds, Unit Level Records.

Inequity in child care is a composite outcome of a number of social, economic, cultural and environmental factors. In most cases it is controlled by all these factors wherein the change in family size acts as a catalyst to differentiation in child care. The main research enquiry in the present study is therefore to examine how much and to what extent the change in family size have *intensified* the inequity in child care at intra state level of Andhra Pradesh.

The principle aims of the study conform to: to highlight the transition of family size and the twin process of family planning and disintegration of families conjointly operating to cause the decline in family size; to check the paradox of family size transition and the conventional measures of socio-economic development and finally trace out the implications of small families on child care both in terms of curative and non-curative child care across the socio-economic dimensions.

Methods

In the analytical framework (Figure 1) presented a linear association is sought to explain the underlying mechanisms of small families and its direct influences upon child care. In India, the recent National Family Health Survey depicts that 12 out of 29 states have achieved the replacement level or below replacement level of fertility.

The decline in fertility is often associated with the 'desire for small families'. This context becomes significant in the case of Andhra Pradesh which has recorded Total Fertility Rate as low as 1.8 in 2005-06 (NFHS III) as compared to 2.25 in 1998-99 (NFHS II). Such a dramatic decline in fertility calls for the underlying mechanisms operating for which contraceptive usage has been used to check the desired result.

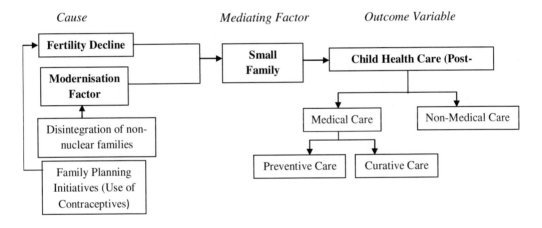

Figure 1. Schematic Representation of the Mechanism of Small Family Size over the Dimensions of Child Care.

One cannot merely overlook the modernisation factors possibly the increasing prevalence of nuclear families which often acts as a positive impetus on the overall development of the child. The above argument has been sought to check to bring out the relative variations of nuclear versus non-nuclear households at the intra-state level as well as according to place of residence in Andhra Pradesh.

Excluding endogenous genetic factors at the individual level, it is assumed that the chances of infant survival depend upon the degree of care in which the infant is brought up. Broadly visualized, care, starting from conception to the first birthday, i.e. during 21 months of life, is important for an understanding of the determinants of child's health status. The two dimensions of individual level factors which have a direct bearing on child care are:

- Timing
- Type of care

Timing may be divided into three categories namely,

- Pre-natal
- Peri-natal
- Post-natal

Type of care accrues to

- Medical
- Non-medical care.

Medical care includes immunization, treatment of illness and medical attention at birth. Non-medical care includes feeding practices, protection from environmental insults and general cleanliness. However, in the present analysis, only the post-natal care of the child has been considered since the aim is to enquire how family size affect child care after the child is born. Thus, the two main dimensions of care yield the following three main individual-level factors:

a. Post-natal non-medical child care- infant feeding practices, for example breastfeeding for at least six months.
b. Post-natal preventive medical child care- immunization.
c. Post-natal curative medical child care- incidence and treatment of illness and effectiveness of treatment.

These factors are not arranged in any order of priority. Their relative importance may vary from population to population and for the same population at different times.

But we put forward the hypothesis that household and community level factors would affect the chances of child care through one or more of these proximate determinants.

i. Selection of indicators for analyzing family size

The decline in family size can be sought as a joint mechanism for breakdown of joint families and fertility decline. Hence different indicators have been taken under these two broad heads for the overall analysis.

a. Indicators selected for modernization
The two basic indicators which depict the modern regime of small family size are of:

1. Mean Household Size (a proxy for small families)
2. Percentage of households by structure (nuclear/non-nuclear)

b. Indicators selected for family planning
Family Planning or conscious efforts of the family to limit its size are an important outcome of fertility decline. Indicators sought under it are

1. Percentage of families having two living children
2. Percentage of currently married women (aged 15-49) who have ever used any kind/method of contraceptives

ii. Selection of indicators to depict child care

As already mentioned Child Care includes both medical as well as non-medical care.

a. Indicators selected for child medical care

Post Natal Preventive Child Care: Percentage of children of 1-2 years who received universal immunization by birth order, sex of the child, place of residence and household structure.

Post Natal Curative Child Care: Percent of Children (0-2 years) who have received any kind of medical treatment in last two weeks (diarrhea, fever, cold or cough) according to background characteristics

b. Indicators selected for child non-medical care

Post Natal Non-Medical Care: Percentage of children below 1 years of age who are currently breastfed by household size and household structure and place of residence.

Appropriate Bi-Variate analyses are worked out to see the gross effect of different level factors over child care. However, the net or independent effects of all the factors have been captured by the binary logistic regression models. Two separate models have been used according to each of the dimensions of child care as described above, i.e. Medical care and Non-medical care.

Results

Family size transition in Andhra Pradesh: emerging trend of small families

The glaring decline in mean household size accompanied by the havoc decrease in the levels of fertility have ushered a wave of serious concerns of the socio-economic mechanisms and the demographic consequences of Andhra Pradesh. In this context, this subset of analysis gives a causative outline of the small family size by focusing on two important issues in the present context of development studies. As such the process of family transition in Andhra Pradesh has been faster than many other states of India, especially the North Indian states, the growing desire for small families in the emerging context of 'small family norms' and the breakdown of joint family system with modernization, the following analysis become more focused in emphasizing the two of the above issues.

Family planning initiatives

The recent 'revolution in family life' especially that of Southern India may not correspond to the classical theories of fertility where a decline in fertility is associated with changes in material conditions of the people. Recording a considerably higher birth rate than the other southern states, Andhra Pradesh has witnessed a steep decline in fertility rate in the recent periods. The small family norm which came out as an initiative on the Government front to reduce the Total Fertility Rate at the replacement level has been very much effective in Andhra Pradesh recording a much higher value of percent of families having two or less than two children than the all India level. At the national level, slightly more than half of the total households of the country have a tendency to adopt the two child family norm (Figure 2) whereas the corresponding figures for Andhra Pradesh almost constitute three fourths of the total households who desire for two children. More interestingly, the two child norm is more a recent phenomenon which have shown a dramatic increase from 1992-'93 to 1998-'99.

The possible decline in fertility rate and the progressive adoption of the two child family norm in Andhra Pradesh may be partially related to the use of contraceptives (any kind/method) of currently married women in the reproductive age group (Figure 3).

Unlike India, Andhra has shown a progressive increase in usage of any kinds of contraceptives across the three NFHS Rounds accompanied by a decline in total unmet need from 10.4% in 1992-'93 to 5.0% in 2005-'06. (NFHS III Report).

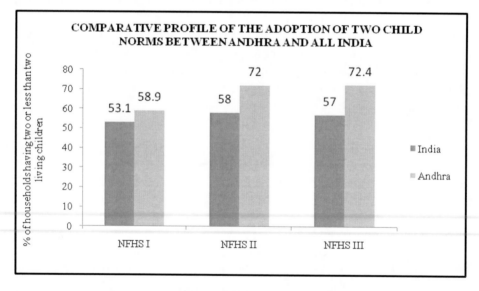

Figure 2.

The use of contraceptives among the currently married women within the reproductive age group at a more disaggregated level according to their educational levels and place of residence strikes some of the hidden facts more clearly.

Table 2 clearly depicts dissolution of the gaps in the levels of contraceptive use between rural and urban Andhra over the years (1992-'93 to 2005-'06) indicating a strong rural-urban convergence.

Not only the gap has lessened in terms of rural-urban differences, even in terms of differential levels of educational attainment among the currently married women (15-49 years), the gap in contraceptive use has narrowed down and women with no education who were the most vulnerable group in terms of contraceptive use in 1992-93 has in fact recorded the maximum usage of contraceptives in 2005-06 outnumbering those who have completed

10 or more years of education. Even though in this case a qualitative judgment based on the actual type/method of contraceptive use becomes important, but the alarming use of contraceptive among the rural and uneducated women clearly signify an equitable distribution for which the community level determinants and effective diffusion of the measures for controlling unmet needs become important.

Table 2. Percentage of currently married women (aged 15-49) who have ever used any kind/method of contraceptives according to Place of residence and Educational Levels

Periods	Place of Residence		Education Levels				Overall
	Rural	Urban	No Education	<8 years complete	8-9 years complete	10 years complete and above	
NFHS I (1992-93)	45.7	61	44.9	59.8	57.6	61.1	47.4
NFHS II (1998-99)	59.2	66.2	59.7	64	57.6	61.8	59.6
NFHS III (2005-06)	67.7	67.7	70.5	67.3	66.2	59.7	67.7

Source: NFHS I, II and III Rounds, Unit Level Records.

Role of modernization factors: Nuclearisation of families

Studies on the influence of modernity and industrialization on family structure has been a long-standing topic of discussion among sociologist, social anthropologists, etc their view been expressed that the joint family or extended family system typical of an agrarian, pre-industrial economy must inevitably give way to more smaller and adaptive nuclear families once the traits of modernization enters the society like urbanization, take-off for industrialization, etc.

With average household size amounting to 5.91 in 2005-06, Andhra clearly marks itself as one of the leading representative of small family size as far as the national scenario is concerned taking itself the third place. However, there appears a rural-urban variation in household size with the rural households once again performing much better in mean household size compared to the urban counterparts as the numbers which have been exemplified in Figure. 4. The actual mechanisms operating behind this deviation from the theoretical norm has been dealt in the later analysis.

The nuclear family which can be taken as a proxy of small families shows a contrasting picture between India and Andhra Pradesh (Figure 5), the latter recording more of nuclear households than the all-India picture essentially signifying the fact that the joint family system which often acts as an impediment to modernization is actually disintegrating among a small vocal class who have set the traits of modernization such that as the case of Andhra Pradesh reporting non-nuclear families less than the national average. This process of nuclearisation of families is essentially an urban phenomenon in Andhra as depicted in Figure 6 with the rural households exhibiting almost an equitable distribution in terms of family structure.

Size of the family according to socio-economic characteristics of the population

The size of family when cross-classified by wealth index (Table 3) shows an increasing trend of richest households to have higher family size rather than the poorer counterparts. Among all the household sizes the poorest households records the maximum proportion in the ideal family size, i.e 3-4 household members followed by 4-6 household size. This is essentially an interesting picture especially in the second and the third classes of the household sizes with the poorest recording the maximum proportion and richest the lowest.

Even in terms of rural-urban variation (Table 3), the poorest have shown the maximum concentration in small family clusters and the difference between the top 20 and bottom 20% is more pronounced in urban areas especially in the ideal family size, i.e. households constituting 3-4 members. However, in rural areas the larger family size (More than 6) has more of the middle classes (32.44%) as compared to the urban counterparts wherein the richest take the leading position in the largest family size (40.8%). One thing becomes quite clear from the above analyses is that the richer have a more tendency in making up larger families, which is more pronounced in the urban areas and the poorer, the most vulnerable group have gone towards smaller families irrespective of the place of residence.

Table 3. Percentage of households of different sizes by wealth index and place of residence (2005-'06)

Wealth Index	Rural				Urban			
	Less than or equal to 3	3-4	4-6	More than 6	Less than or equal to 3	3-4	4-6	More than 6
Poorest	6.56	39.34	40.98	13.11	9.4	34	28.3	28.3
Poorer	9.86	23.47	37.56	29.11	19.2	32.7	28.8	19.2
Middle	9.03	24.41	34.11	32.44	15.1	30.2	30.7	24.1
Richer	8.13	25.00	40.63	26.25	10.7	30.6	29.8	29
Richest	6.52	34.78	32.61	26.09	10.8	21.6	26.8	40.8

Source: NFHS III Round, Unit Level Records.

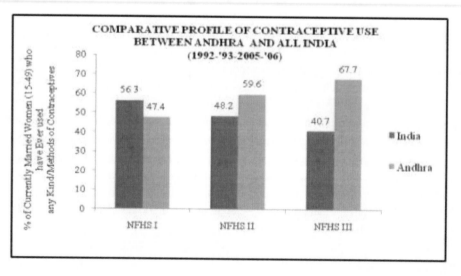

Figure 3.

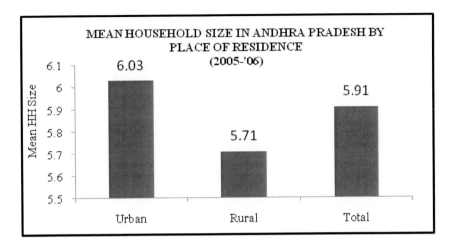

Figure 4.

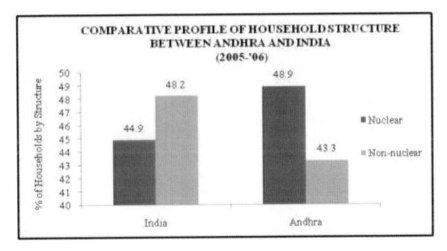

Figure 5.

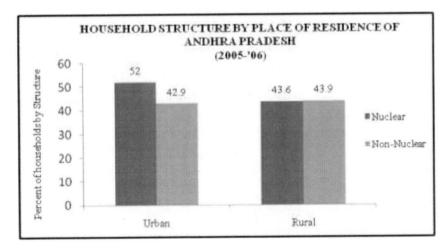

Figure 6.

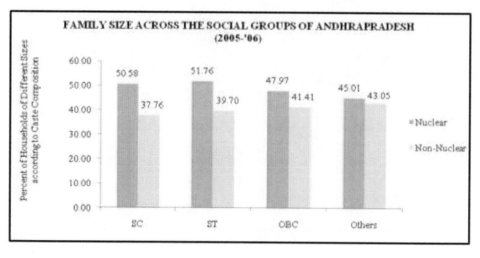

Figure 7.

Generally across all the social groups (Figure 7), the nuclear families show a higher proportion than the non-nuclear families but the highest concentration of such households could be observed across the marginalized groups i.e. the STs (Scheduled Tribes) and SCs (Scheduled Castes). The others castes comprising of the general community have only a marginal difference between nuclear and non-nuclear households.

Other Backward Class (OBC) constituting the half of the share of population in Andhra Pradesh (Table. 4) has 49% of the households living in nuclear families. The other half constitutes of one-fourth marginalized social groups (SC and ST) and about one-fourth General households. The marginalized groups have more than half of the households classified as nuclear families. The analysis again highlights the importance of nuclear families in the emerging household structure of Andhra Pradesh.

In terms of disaggregated household size, the difference between the social groups is not so prominent in the highest household size, however the gap becomes clearer towards the smaller household size such that of households with total number of members ranging from 3-4 and 4-6. For, the lowest class of household size (Table 5), here in fact the other castes have fared better than the SCs and STs in households less than or equal to 3 members. At a glance the maximum share of all the socio-economic groups could be recorded in households having 3-4 members.

Table 4. Share of Socio-economic Groups according to Place of Residence in Andhra Pradesh (2005-'06)

Place of Residence	Scheduled caste	Scheduled tribe	Other backward class	None of above
Urban	15.12	4.01	49.22	31.65
Rural	19.89	10.71	52.45	16.95
Total	17.50	7.36	50.84	24.30

Source: NFHS III, Unit Level Records.

Table 5. Percentage of Households of Different Sizes by Caste Groups

Type of Caste/Class	Household Size			
	Less than or equal to 3	3-4	4-6	More than 6
SC	5.90	33.49	36.08	24.53
ST	8.08	25.25	39.90	26.77
OBC	10.57	29.36	34.40	25.67
Others	12.65	26.88	31.03	29.45

Source: NFHS III, Unit Level Records.

The case of fertility decline in Andhra Pradesh: A paradox of socio-economic development

Rationale behind fertility decline

Among the factors other than private income that have a strong influence on fertility, basic education, especially *female education* is considered as one of the most powerful. According to Dreze and Sen (2) female education influences- 1) desired family size, 2) the relationship between desired family size and planned number of births, and 3) ability to achieve the planned number of births. Educated women are most likely to voice resentment at the burden of repeated pregnancies and to take action to lighten that burden. According to Dyson and Moore (3), this may occur because educated women have other sources of prestige and fulfillment besides reproductive performance, more control over household resources and personal behavior, and greater involvement in reproductive decisions. Further, opportunity cost of time tends to be comparatively high for educated women, and this creates an incentive to minimize such time-intensive activities such as child bearing and child rearing. Most importantly maternal education helps in achieving planned number of births by facilitating knowledge and command over contraceptives. *Female labour force participation* have a negative impact on fertility since the double burden of household work and gainful employment enhances the effectiveness of women's agency in society and repeated pregnancy quite stressful. The context of *urbanisation* becomes relevant and acts independently to control fertility on account of greater access to relevant information in urban areas and the breakdown of the socio-cultural hindrances to economic development such as joint family structure. The effect of *poverty* has significant impact upon fertility after controlling the other explanatory variables such as female work participation rate which is generally found to be higher in poor families.

Exemplification for the case of Andhra Pradesh

The discourse of fertility decline in India is mainly confined to the three southern states namely, Kerala, Tamil Nadu and Andhra Pradesh all having achieved fertility rates below the replacement level. James (4) held that the experience of Kerala led to the understanding that even without considerable improvement in the levels of industrialization, urbanization and material improvement in the standard of living of the population, fertility decline took place with social development. In case of Tamil Nadu, fertility decline almost paced as that of

Kerala even though with a somewhat lower level of social development. Of them female literacy assumes to be a very important determinant of social development governing the fertility decline. The massive decline in fertility in Kerala could be attributed to this indicator in spite of lower levels of urbanization and industrialization as already mentioned. Tamilnadu's story is not the magic female literacy as so much as that of Kerala, but more of the modernization factors like urbanization, etc. So the present analysis tends to draw an exploratory note on the socio-economic development versus fertility decline in Andhra Pradesh keeping in mind the contexts of Kerala and Tamil Nadu where the fertility decline has been achieved at a much early period.

With Total Fertility Rate much lower than the National Average and female literacy and urbanization slightly below the All India level, not mentioning the Head-Count Ratio which is 10% less compared to India (1999-00 and 2004-05), the fertility transition in Andhra Pradesh draws several questions to the mind of the researcher. The fast decline in fertility rate without any significant improvement in the conventional indicators of socio-economic development is mysterious and the nature and extent of this transition leading to the small family size calls for serious investigation.

Table 6 clearly suggest that there is a poor correspondence between female literacy rate and total fertility rate in Andhra Pradesh. Hence, from the experience of Andhra Pradesh it is difficult to prescribe any threshold level of female literacy for fertility transition.

Table 6. Socio-economic Indicators of Development of Andhra Pradesh and India for different Periods

Indicators	Years	Andhra Pradesh	India
Female Literacy (%)	1991	27.32	32.17
	2001	43.76	45.13
	2011	53.8	56.99
Female Work Participation Rate (%)	1991	30.05	15.93
	2001	35.11	25.6
Urbanisation (%)	1991	26.89	25.73
	2001	27.3	27.81
	2011	33.49	31.16
Head Count Ratio (%)	1999-00	15.77	26.1
	2004-05	15.8	27.5
Total Fertility Rate	1992-'93	2.6	3.4
	1998-'99	2.3	2.9
	2005-'06	1.8	2.7

Source: Primary Census Abstract, Census of India, 1991, 2001 and 2011; Planning Commission, Poverty Estimates, 1999-00 and 2004-05; NFHS I, II and III Reports.

Even though female work force participation is higher than the national average, but it often do not signify gainful employment as being a predominantly agricultural economy the majority of women work as agricultural labourers associated with low cultural rigidities of women work. Urbanization which is a proxy for economic development has been at a lower level even though the percent population below poverty line is much low than the national average. With the concentration of larger sized households (as well as non-nuclear) among the richer classes which have been empirically established in the previous section calls for a dichotomous situation between the levels of economic development and its implications on family size. The economically most vulnerable sections have in fact performed much better in relation to controlled family size and planned number of births which has been often supported from the Government interventions in the form of active interventions for the spread of the use of contraceptives among the rural poor.

Implications of small families on child health care

Child's medical care (post natal)
As mentioned earlier, medical care of the child is broadly categorized under two heads, namely, Preventive and Curative Care. The following subsections tries to establish causal links between the two types of medical care and its relationship with family size, here used as the explanatory variable.

The present subset attempts to analyze the effects of some selected demographic and socio-economic variables on the levels of immunization of a child for six vaccine preventable diseases such as tuberculosis, diphtheria, peruses, tetanus, poliomyelitis, and measles. According to the guidelines developed by WHO children (1-2 years) who received BCG, measles, and three doses each of DPT and polio, excluding polio0 (Polio 0 is administered at birth along with BCG) are considered to be fully vaccinated. The analysis tries to explore the status of immunization coverage from the demand-side with a simplifying assumption of ceteris paribus supply side constraint on account of a long history of Government negligence in health spending.

Post natal medical preventive care
Children are the unit of the present analysis which uses the children's recoded file (1-2 years) with an overall sample size of 1,214. The analysis of immunization coverage uses a number of demographic and socio-economic variables. The dependent variable is full immunization that says whether a particular child is fully immunized or not. The selected predictor variables are household structure, disaggregated household size, place of residence (rural, urban), wealth index, type of caste or tribe of household head, mother's employment status and sex specific birth order.

Children belonging from smaller household size find themselves to be better fully immunized than the largest household size. However, not much variation could be observed among the last three classes, in fact the ideal family size (3-4 members) tend to have a marginally less value than households with more than 6 members with respect to the immunization coverage. The nuclear and urban households which have less of non-nuclear families have in fact reported a better situation in immunization coverage. The rural-urban disparity in immunization is not due to demographic factors but due to socio-economic correlates. The likelihood of immunization increases with mother's employment status and wealth index. There appears a mixed situation of immunization coverage and the birth order of children. As in many cases boys of 4th order and girls of 5th order or higher seemed to have higher values than the 1st or 2nd birth order. A plausible explanation could be that of very few children existing in 4th or above birth order in Andhra Pradesh, its values thereby being inflated by getting a higher weightage. But boys are likely to be more immunized than girls in the 1ˢᵗ, 2ⁿᵈ even in the 3ʳᵈ birth order. There appears a considerable gap between the girl and boy in 3ʳᵈ birth order, with 13.4% girls receiving full immunization as compared to 32.4% boys (Table 7). The result depicts a greater apathy on part of the parents to immunize a higher order female child.

Table 7. Percent of children (1-2 years) who have received universal immunization according to Background Characteristics

Background Variables	Percentage of children of 1-2 years of age who have received universal immunisation
Household structure	
Nuclear	32
Non-nuclear	27.4
Family Size	
Less than or equal to 3	34.1
3-4	21.9
4-6	23.1
More than 6	23.1
Type of place of residence	
Urban	33.3
Rural	23.4
Wealth Index	
Poorest	14.6
Poorer	21.7
Middle	26.5
Richer	28.1
Richest	42.8
Mother's Employment	
Not Worked	25.2
Worked Last Year	14.3
Currently Working	31.1
Type of caste or tribe of the household head	
Scheduled caste	16.9
Scheduled tribe	16.3
Other backward class	28.9
None of above	33.6
Sex-Specific Birth Order	

Birth Order	Percentage of boys of 1-2 years of age who have received universal immunisation
1	36.7
2	25.1
3	32.2
4	44.1
5+	15
Birth Order	**Percentage of girls of 1-2 years of age who have received universal immunisation**
1	26.2
2	20.4
3	13.4
4	33.3
5+	35

Source: Computed from NFHS III, Unit Level Records.

Post natal medical curative care

The exercise for curative medical care for children aged 0-2 years who have been medically treated had they been suffering from diarrhea, fever, cold or cough within two weeks of occurrence, the analysis show a clear daughter disadvantage in treatment (Table. 8).

Table 8. Percent of Children (0-2 years) who have received any kind of medical treatment in last two weeks (diarrhoea, fever, cold or cough) according to background characteristics

Background Variables	Percentage of children (0-2 years) who received any kind of medical treatment in last 2 weeks while suffering in diarrhoea, fever, cold or cough
Household Structure	
Nuclear	81.5
Non-Nuclear	88.9
Household Size	
Less than or equal to 3	85.7
3-4	83.3
4-6	78.6
More than 6	100
Place of Residence	
Rural	85.7
Urban	83.3
Type of Caste or Tribe of the Household Head	
SC	84.6
ST	100
OBC	82.4
Others	86.7
Sex Specific Birth Order	
Boys	
1	92.3
2	100
3	83.3
4	80
5+	72.1
Girls	
1	60
2	52
3	50
4	48
5+	43
Wealth Index	
Poorest	85.7
Poorer	100

Table 8. (Continued)

Background Variables	Percentage of children (0-2 years) who received any kind of medical treatment in last 2 weeks while suffering in diarrhoea, fever, cold or cough
Middle	77.8
Richer	88.9
Richest	88.9
Employment Status of Mothers	
Not Employed	88.9
Employed in last year	100
Currently working	81.2

Source: Computed from NFHS III, Unit level Records.

Children of higher birth order are less likely to be medically treated which shows that the negligence effect more than offsets the learning effect. Unlike universal immunization, curative medical treatment functions well in non-nuclear households (a proxy for large families) with 100% coverage in households more than 6 members. Accordingly, the rural families which have a higher share of non-nuclear families report marginally higher value than the urban counterparts. This could be partially related to the employment status of the mother. Child preventive care is higher for unemployed and those who have been employed in the previous year signifying that the exclusive care of the child varies with the levels of preoccupation of mother's work. The tribal households generally involved in community living tends to impart some time for taking care of the diseases of their children, even if they believe in the more traditional forms of medication unlike the other castes. The analysis clearly indicates that the level of awareness captured by universal immunization of the child may not signify a comprehensive child care when the day to day child illness like diarrhea, cold, cough, etc enter as an obstacle to the healthy growth of the child which is highly dependent on the potential time devoted by the parents in taking care of their children. In joint families, the child is not left alone when its mother is working outside and here in comes the importance of traditional extended families in imparting care to the child which in most cases performed by the native kin relatives.

Post natal non-medical care

Breastfeeding constitutes an important component of the intensive care of the child. Table 9 provide a bivariate association between breastfeeding cross classified by the socio-economic and demographic predictive indicators for child care. It becomes clear that breastfeeding is more a common phenomenon among the non-nuclear households and families of larger size.

In support of this argument it could be said that parents alone do not have to bear the entire domestic burden in joint families, henceforth the double burden faced by working women is often offset by the helping hands provided by the members of an extended family. Contrary to the nuclear households, even if the woman is not employed, the entire burden of domestic chores rests upon her which tends to happen at the cost of sometimes feeding the child. However, there is not much discrimination in breastfeeding between a boy and girl infant so also across the birth orders as could be observed in other dimensions of child care.

Table 9. Percent children less than 1 year who are currently breastfed according to background characteristics

Background Variables	Percentage of children below 1 years of age who are currently breastfed
Household Structure	
Nuclear	81.6
Non-Nuclear	84.9
Household Size	
Less than or equal to 3	75.9
3-4	83.3
4-6	84.5
More than 6	87.3
Place of Residence	
Rural	76.4
Urban	88.2
Type of Caste or Tribe of the Household Head	
SC	91.7
ST	91.9
OBC	88.4
Others	65.5
Sex Specific Birth Order	
Boys	
1	82.5
2	86.4
3	90
4	100
5+	88.9
Girls	
1	80.1
2	79.8
3	88.9
4	90.5
5+	90
Wealth Index	
Poorest	91.1
Poorer	93.5
Middle	89.1
Richer	82.4
Richest	59.5
Employment Status of Mothers	
Not Employed	81.4
Employed in last year	100
Currently working	90.7

Source: Computed from NFHS III, Unit level Records.

However, significant discrepancy exist among the socio-economic groups, especially among communities at the lower end of the social ladder the practice of breastfeeding is widespread which have gone to the extent of around 91% of the households in which children are breastfed irrespective of the sex of the child as well as birth order.

The multivariate model

In order to trace out the differentials in child care in terms of the desired family size and a number of socio-demographic factors, a binary logistic regression analysis has been attempted. Two separate models have been worked out to show differentials in child care in terms of medical and non-medical terms. The dependent variable in the case of medical care is the percentage of children below 2 years who have received universal immunization, whereas in the other case, it is the percentage of children below 1 year who are currently breastfed. The main objective of this exercise to show the differences in probable outcomes in terms of child care according to different family sizes and household structure as well as to identify the other proximate determinants that in turn affect the quality of child care other than family size. It is notable that a number of these factors also have significant relation with changes in family size itself; therefore, the differential probabilities that may occur in response to these factors can be interpreted as the indirect effects of family size, or more specifically, the modernization factor itself.

Results of the two separate models has shown different outcomes in terms of medical and non-medical care that needs to be explained in terms of different effects of socio-demographic factors. It can be observed that for the preventive medical care like immunization, where the proportion of households, whether belonging to any category, shows significantly slower progress, have shown better responses from the nuclear or urban households and vice versa. However, the story is different in case of non-medical care like breastfeeding, where the conventional factors of modernization have not seen to have any significant effects.

Table 10 summarize the result, where it can be seen that the chances to universally immunize the child is lower in non-nuclear families, which is statistically significant. Opposite outcome can be observed for the same factor in the case of breastfeeding, where the odds ratio in favor of being breastfed declines in the case of nuclear families, although it's not statistically significant. Almost same kind of result can be found when we enquire the effects in terms of family size, where the smaller families that have less than or equal to four members have more chances to the child to be immunized rather than the families having more members than four.

The result is statistically significant for smaller families, although found to be insignificant in the case of breastfeeding, where the families having 4-6 members have the highest chances to the child below 1 year to be breastfed by his or her mother. It is notable that in this case, the odds ratios are significant in the case of larger families (4-6 members), which is just opposite to the case of immunization, where the smaller families have a significant result, thereby making the differentiation more concrete.

Apart from family size, the other proximate determinants of child care have shown significant observations.

Table 10. Summary of Binary Logistic Regression

INDEPENDENT VARIABLE	Percentage of children 1-2 years of age who have received universal immunization	Percentage of children below 1 year of age who are currently breastfed
	Odds Ratio	Odds Ratio
Household Structure (Ref. Nuclear)		
Non-Nuclear	0.939***	1.616
Household Size (Ref. More than 6)		
Less than or equal to 3	1.416**	0.966
3-4	0.926	1.169
4-6	1.139	1.723***
Place of Residence (Ref. Urban)		
Rural	0.746**	0.980
Caste of the Household Head (Ref. General)		
SC	0.497*	4.744*
ST	0.376*	3.668**
OBC	0.969	2.524*
Sex of the Child (Ref. Male)		
Female	0.582*	0.647***
Birth Order (Ref. 5+)		
1	1.669***	0.053**
2	1.004	0.082***
3	1.038	0.189
4	0.503*	0.230
Desire for more children (Ref. Don't Want)		
Want Child	0.902***	2.425*
Undecided	1.586***	1.263
Wealth Index (Ref. Richest)		
Poorest	0.284*	1.868
Poorer	0.419*	5.392*
Middle	0.613**	2.466*
Richer	0.493*	1.807***
Mother's Employment (Ref. Currently Working)		
Not Working	0.626***	0.557
Worked in Last Year	0.397***	6.298
Nature of Mother's Employment (Ref. No Work)		
Agriculture Self-Employed	2.717**	2.071***
Agriculture employee	1.194	1.679***
Skilled Worker	0.308**	0.678***
Unpaid HH worker	1.112	1.009
Mother's Educational Attainment (Ref. Higher than Secondary Education)		
No Education	0.235*	1.827
Incomplete Primary	0.431*	1.487
Complete Primary	0.504**	4.255*
Incomplete Secondary	0.644***	1.303***
Complete Secondary	0.380*	0.545***
Constant	1.325	9.555
-2 Log Likelihood	1523.174	462.774

Significance Levels: *1%, **5%, ***10%.

Households inhabiting in the rural areas are reported to have lower chances to universally immunize or breastfed their children than the urban counterparts, although the difference is quite marginal in the case of breastfeeding, whereas it is much higher in the case of immunization (both the results are statistically significant).

In other words, the difference in chances of being breastfed between the rural and urban areas is only 2% in favor of urban, whereas it is about 25.4% in the case of universal immunization. Such a factor again confirms the inverse effect of modernization factor over quality child care, especially in terms of non-medical purposes, where the factors like efficient management of children by providing enough time in care matters much than the factors like awareness about diseases or economic worth of the family. This hypothesis is clearly supported by the outcomes traced out by the factors like wealth index where the chances of immunizing the child is more or less uniform among the poorer, middle and richer classes in comparison to the richest class (all the results are statistically significant); whereas in the case of breastfeeding, the odds ratio of the poorer class seems to be much higher in favor of being breastfed in comparison to the richest class, which is statistically significant. Same kind of results can be found if the mother's level of education and occupational structure is taken into account. It can be seen that in the case of universal immunization, the chance of those mothers' who have no education is significantly lower to immunize her child than the mothers' who have higher education but in the case of breastfeeding the opposite result can be seen. The odds ratio in favour of breastfeeding in the case of mothers having no education is reported to be 1.827, which is 0.545 in the case of those mothers who have completed their secondary education, which is statistically significant. In other words, in comparison to the mothers who have higher than secondary level of education, the odds in favour of breastfeeding the child is reported to be 82.7% higher in the case of to the mothers who have no education, but 45.5% lower to the mothers who have completed their secondary education. Mothers worked in the last year are reported to have higher chances to breastfed their babies than the mothers who are currently working, although the result is statistically insignificant. However, further disaggregation according to the occupational structure of the mothers reveals the fact that in comparison to the women who do not work, women engaged in the agricultural workforce, whether self-employed or as labourers, are reported to have higher odds in favour of breastfeeding than the skilled workers engaged in tertiary sectors. The nuclear families or the smaller households, which are the most proximate outcomes of modernization and are reported to be centred in urban areas; mainly constituted by highly educated working couples and mostly by two or single child; are therefore, inevitably manifested their indirect effect over the levels of child care through these determinants.

The caste of the household, that have shown significantly higher concentration of nuclear and small size families among the scheduled caste and scheduled tribe households, also reported to have higher odds ratio in favour of breastfeeding in comparison to general households, which is statistically significant. In the case of universal immunization, the chances to immunize the children are seen to be lower in all castes in comparison to generals. The result is statistically significant and perhaps ascribed to the lower socio-economic status and social opportunities granted to these marginalized groups in comparison to non-scheduled castes. Another episode of discrimination, which deals with the gender differential in child care, clearly portrays the lower status granted to the girl child in case of both medical and non-medical care. However, a detailed analysis with respect to sex specific birth order in the previous sections has shown that boys in the first or second birth orders are subjected to immunized more than their female counterparts and vice versa. The same is in the case of breastfeeding, where the proportion of breastfed girls is much higher in high birth order than the boys. The odds ratios with respect to birth order have not shown any significant observations in the case of breastfeeding, although in the case of universal immunization, children in the first birth order are reported to have higher chances to be immunized than the children in the lower counterparts, which is statistically significant. Desire for more children in this respect plays an important role which more specifies the tendency of a family to provide quality care to its existing child and also to the future child. It is interesting to observe that in comparison to the families who do not want child, families that want child used to have lower chances to immunize their existing child, which is statistically significant. This factor, however, have no effect on breastfeeding, as existing children are reported to have fairly high odds in favour of breastfeeding in the families that want more child, which is also statistically insignificant. This factor partially explains the children in the upper birth order to be more immunized in the context of those families that want no more children.

In summary, it can be opined that the factors of modernization are reported to have significant effects over the levels and quality of child care in different terms. The curative and medical care that needs appropriate knowledge, sense and ability about hygiene and disease prevention is reportedly found in nuclear or small size families who have overcome unmet needs in medical care. On the other hand, the factors of non-medical care that demands efficient involvement of mothers with the child are found to be lower in smaller families, thereby resulting discrepancies in child care across different family size.

Discussion

- The family size transition in Andhra Pradesh evokes out of the desire for small families operating jointly through the mechanism of fertility decline and increasing trend of nuclearisation of families which could be taken as a proxy for small families.
- The process of nuclearisation is more an urban phenomenon. The richest set of households in terms of access to resources has higher non-nuclear families than the poorest.
- The process of fertility decline in Andhra Pradesh is unaccompanied by appreciable social development. Female Literacy which is one of the most important explanatory variables impacting fertility decline is well below the national average. The higher use of contraceptives is responsible for this.
- The integrative care of the child captured by post natal child health care shows differentiation in care according to family size when care is disaggregated into protective efforts, including curative and preventive care and the non-medical care signifying the intensive care of the child.
- The factors of modernization have different effects in terms of levels and quality of child care. Small or nuclear households are reported to have performed better in terms of medical care like immunization whereas non-medical care like breastfeeding are reported to have higher among non-nuclear households.
- The other proximate determinants of child care like mothers' occupational structure or their educational attainment are also seen to have similar effects where mothers'

having lower level of education or those who are employed in agriculture are reported to be perform better in terms of non-medical care like breastfeeding. However, in the nuclear families, lack of baby care owing to rising opportunity costs of the working women is responsible for it.

- A strong evidence of rural-urban dilution is observed in the levels of child care, where the rural families are seen to be attempting small family norms and also showing the tendency of quality child care like their urban counterparts.

The summary results of the analysis points out the key fact that the small family norms, that has been incepted in Andhra as an exception to the usual discourse of socio-economic development, have not seen to intensify the discrimination in child care to a greater level like its north Indian counterparts, rather than portrays significant differential in quality and levels of child care. Dissections across the characteristics of the family size, namely the place of residence or mothers' occupational structure or mothers' level of education has pointed out that the levels of child care differs not only according to the levels of education or income profile of the households but also the quality time or involvement of the parents to the child irrespective of income and educational level of the households. It is the differential effect of the modernization factors that is needed to be handled judiciously.

Acknowledgments

I am grateful to Dr. A Basu, Dr. PM Kulkarni and Dr. B Das for their valuable comments on an earlier draft. This would have been an incomplete work without the moral and academic supports of my parents, niece, beloved and sister. All remaining errors, if any, will solely be my responsibility.

References

[1]   Atinson MN. Rural and urban families' use of child care. Fam Coord 1994;43(1):16-22.
[2]   Dreze J, Sen A. India: Economic development and social opportunity. Delhi: Oxford University Press, 1995.
[3]   Dyson T, Moore M. On kinship structure, female autonomy, and demographic behavior in India. Popul Dev Rev 1983;9(1):35-59.
[4]   James KS. Fertility decline in Andhra Pradesh: A search for alternative hypotheses. Econ Polit Wkly 1999;(8):491-9.

Submitted: January 10, 2012. *Revised:* April 02, 2012. *Accepted:* April 24, 2012.

In: Child Health and Human Development Yearbook 2013   ISBN: 978-1-63117-939-6
Editor: Joav Merrick   © 2014 Nova Science Publishers, Inc.

Chapter 18

Schoolchildren's familiarization with the meaning of loss and death: The role of theatrical games

Angeliki Nikolakopoulou, BSc, PhD,
Fotini Garagouni-Areou, BSc, PhD,
Christina Roussi-Vergou, BSc, PhD,
and Maria Zafiropoulou, BSc, PhD[*]
Laboratory of Developmental Psychology and Psychopathology,
Department of Preschool Education, University of Thessaly, Volos, Greece

Abstract

Death and loss are undoubtedly some of the most emotionally painful events in a child's life. The research questions dealt with in this study are a) whether familiarisation with loss and death differs between children from urban and rural regions and b) whether theatrical games dealing with loss of a loved one could facilitate familiarisation with the meaning of death. One hundred and ninety one 3rd grade school students from Greek urban and rural regions participated in the study. Children were divided in four groups (2 experimental and 2 control groups). Children in the experimental groups participated in a theatrical game with death as a subject, while control groups engaged themselves with artistic and sports activities. All participants were appropriately interviewed before and after the intervention. According to results children's knowledge and familiarisation with death improved after implementation of the theatrical game.

Keywords: Child, loss, emotional state, theatre game

---

[*] Correspondence: Professor Maria Zafiropoulou, PhD, Department of Pre-School Education, University of Thessaly, Argonafton and Filellinon Street, Volos 38221, Greece. E-mail: mzafirop@ece.uth.gr.

Introduction

Death is a matter of grievous concern for children of all ages, except for those in very early childhood. It fills them with numerous questions about its nature and effects, and often causes them awe and fear. Relative literature describes death as the hidden cause of any pain (1), or as most predictable, though sad and unexpected (2). Usually, looking for answers about death emerges during the stormy years of adolescence (2).

The way each child perceives death depends on its cognitive, emotional and physical developmental stage. The three main aspects of death, namely universality, irreversibility and non-functionality, are understood as children grow older. Speece and Brent (3) in their in-depth literature review found many differences among researchers dealing with this issue. However, they concluded that, by the age of 7, most children have come to understand the above mentioned three concepts.

According to many researchers, learning about loss, death and lament can help students prepare themselves to actually face such an experience. They can also understand that grief is normal, and therefore they are not out of their minds, when grieving. Furthermore, learning about death and loss helps children understand the feelings of other classmates who experience the death of a loved one or other significant losses and can sympathize with them. (4). Moreover, emotional development during childhood enables children to understand the complexity of emotions and to show empathy for others' feelings (5, 6), while they show volatility of their emotions (7).

Theatrical games increase children's ability to communicate, since they see and are being seen, listen and answer, understand and are being understood, and all these are accomplished on many different levels, depending on the topics selected, each time (8).

Theatrical games, in the context of applied psychology, give children the opportunity for externalisation of thoughts and emotions. At the same time, drama acts as a regulator of any emotional burden, tension, aggression, etc. A theatrical game relaxes, releases children's creativity and facilitates internal balance (9).

Objectives

Two tragic road accidents which affected the whole of the Greek school community and caused extreme, but justifiable, psychological shock, launched the present study. Moreover, the awkwardness that teachers of all grades feel, when they face such problems within school communities, show that dealing with death in a way which indicates deliberate ignorance or even aversion should be seriously reconsidered within education.

There is a special protocol with guidelines for teachers and headmasters on how to manage death in school and to deal with such events. This protocol has been adopted by the U.S., Canada and many European countries (10), but not by Greece. A research study conducted nationally by the University of Athens, in which 1792 teachers participated, revealed that Greek schools have no organized intervention programs which could provide appropriate guidance to support a grieving student (11). Although school psychologists could provide assistance in this area, yet, such an institution does not exist within Greek schools unlike other European countries. It appears, therefore, that integration of the concepts of loss and death in the school curriculum is sine qua non. It is essential that students familiarize themselves with these concepts with the implementation of suitable psycho-educational techniques, depending on their age level. The objectives of the study were:

- to record elementary school children's level of knowledge, familiarity, and attitude towards the concept of death, in relation to their origin (urban or rural environment)
- to determine whether the above-mentioned parameters could alter after implementation of an appropriate intervention.

Methods

The sample consisted of 191 3rd grade students (147 students from urban and 44 from rural areas of Central Greece), who were divided into 4 research groups (2 experimental and 2 control groups) as follows:

- The urban sample was divided into two groups [Urban A (UA) and Urban B (UB)]. The students in UA participated in a theatrical game which referred to death. The students in UB, the control group, engaged themselves with artistic and sports activities and participated only in the initial interview.
- The rural sample was also divided into two groups [Rural A (RA) and Rural B (RB)]. As in the previous case, students in RA participated in a theatrical game dealing with death, while students in RB, the control group, engaged themselves with artistic and sports activities taking part only in the interview.

Research tools

The following methodological tools were used for the purpose of the study:

- A questionnaire recording the health and social background of the participants was used, in order for children with emotional disorders, children suffering from malignant disease, those who had recently experienced loss or had seriously ill parents, etc. to be excluded from the study.
- A theatrical game dealing with the death of a loved one (an imaginary grandmother) was created especially for the purpose of the study.
- An interview was also especially designed for the purpose of the study. The questions posed to the children were grouped so as to examine: a) children's perception of death, and b) level of their knowledge and familiarity with the concept of death.

More specifically,

- *Children's perception* was examined with questions based on the three main parameters of the death concept which, according to Childers & Wimmer (12),

Beauchamp (13) and Speece & Brent (3), are universality, irreversibility and non-functionality. (i.e. "Do you think death of an individual is temporary or permanent?", or "Do all people die?" etc).

- *Children's knowledge of death* was examined with questions concerning knowledge of the rituals of death (i.e. "Can you mention some customs that take place during a funeral?") and, finally,

- *Children's familiarity with death* was examined with questions related to children's experiences with death and their attitudes towards death (i.e. "Have you ever attended a funeral?", "Would you like to hear a story that refers to death?").

Process

The research process consisted of three sessions. During the first meeting the researcher met the students, drew their consent to participate in the study, and, finally, recorded information regarding their health and social background. During the second meeting students in both experimental groups participated in the theatrical game, whilst students in both control groups spent their time (the same length of time as the experimental groups) engaging with activities such as painting, free play and sports in the company of the researcher. Finally, the interviews were conducted.

The theatrical game referred to the death of an imaginary grandmother and was developed in the following stages:

Stage A: Liberation and acquaintance
Participants made a circle and were instructed to release themselves from any inhibitions. Each child said its name and interests.

In the middle of the circle a chair was placed and on the top of that chair a shawl was placed symbolizing an old woman (the grandmother). Students were asked to identify the symbol (shawl) to the image of real granny and to get to know her.

Stage B: Role playing game
In this stage children chose and played roles, and improvised short dialogues. They described how they thought the features and character of the grandmother were, and, at the same time, their "experiences' with the imaginary grandmother were recorded. More precisely, each child mentioned a pleasant or an unpleasant experience s/he had with granny i.e. a story or an adventure they had in the park, at home, at sea, etc. Students also described how they spend their spare time with her, what games they play together, or what tales and stories she tells them.

Stage C: Stage improvisation
Once the scenic area was formed, the stage of development and implementation of the thematic axis (death) began. That is, the grandmother's symbol (shawl) leaves the chair, because granny was taken to hospital. Students were asked to say:

- How they were feeling about granny being ill.
- If they went to visit her in the hospital.
- What granny's illness is and if she will manage to live.
- What they would like to happen regarding the progress of granny's health.

Then the animator, who pretended to be a doctor, gave children little envelopes and asked that each child wrote a wish for granny.

When grandmother's death was announced to the children, they were asked to relax and stop thinking about the grandmother's hospitalisation.

Finally, each child was given a little envelope, where the following phrase was written: *"I did not leave you. I'm in heaven now and I will be watching you from up there ".*

Stage D: Analysis-discussion

Children were asked, once again, to make a circle. Each child was, then, given about 30 seconds to say goodbye to granny in its own way. Finally, a discussion took place and the theme of the theatrical game was analysed. Children expressed their views, emotions and concerns about granny's "journey". They also proposed solutions and displayed ideas.

Results

Statistical analyses were performed using SPSS 13.0, Chi-square (x^2) and Fisher's exact tests.

As already mentioned, children's perception, knowledge and familiarization with death according to their origin (urban or rural) were investigated through interviews. Furthermore, the possibility of diversification in some of these parameters after the intervention was assessed. Comparisons among children in urban and rural areas were initially done and, then, the differences before and after the intervention were tested. Chi-square (x^2) *two-sample test* was used with our frequency data, with the following results.

Regarding children's perception, no differences were observed between children in the two communities. In fact, children in both groups were equally aware of the irreversibility of death.

On the other hand, in the case of knowledge and familiarity with death, results appeared to be statistically different. Namely, it was found that children in rural areas have significantly better knowledge and greater familiarity with the concept of death ($p <0.005$). More precisely, children in rural areas knew most of the funeral rituals ($x^2= 3,56$, df= 1, $p= 0,042$), they reported attending more funeral ceremonies ($x^2= 14,420$, df= 1, $p <0.001$) and, finally, a higher percentage of them would like to hear a story about death ($x^2= 4,620$, df= 1, $p= 0,039$).

A comparison was carried out among the above mentioned variables before and after intervention. The following findings came up: As far as perception is concerned, children seemed to have become more aware of the irreversibility of death after the intervention, but Fisher's exact test results did not show any statistically significant difference ($x^2= 3,103$, df= 1, $p= 0,092$). However, as far as familiarity is concerned, it was found that a greater number of children wanted to hear a story about death ($x^2= 3,294$, df= 1, $p= 0,048$).

Discussion

According to the results of the present study, children from rural areas have better knowledge and exhibit greater familiarity with the concept of death. In an attempt to interpret this finding one could argue that in small communities, as those in rural areas, death is close to their daily lives (14). Children of rural origin seem to actually participate during the process and rituals of mourning. On the contrary, the lack of familiarity recorded in children from urban areas is consistent with almost all the literature referred to death. According to Benoliel (15), in the new urban environment, death and mortality are experiences and situations which take place more and more away from the average person. As a result, the separation of the dying from the living deprives youngsters from the social 'assistance' to familiarize themselves with the reality of death. Thus, a so-called society that declines death has been created (16). Taking care of the sick in the last stages of their life and making relevant decisions are no longer "a family issue", but it belongs to the experts, i.e. complex and impersonal settings such as hospitals, clinics, nursing homes, mainly in cities (17, 18). Young persons' lack of familiarity with death leads them to a situation where even the idea of their own death or death in general, fills them with great anxiety (14).

Special attention should also be given to the fact that familiarity with the concept of death was improved in the students of both communities, after the intervention. Similar results were demonstrated by an experimental method of teaching about familiarization and management of dying people, through dramatization followed by discussion, which was applied to first-year nurses, which seemed to work effectively in the education of nurses (19).

Therefore, the positive effect of expressing and experiencing emotions, negative ones in particular, through art is obvious. Yet, other kinds of art, apart from story-telling and theatrical games, could be used so that the child is encouraged to "narrate" a powerful emotional experience. Drawing and painting are considered basic methods for either preventive or therapeutic intervention programs for children (20, 21, 22). As a result, many counselling psychology programs for children use drawing and painting as therapeutic means which serve many objectives (23, 24).

A particularly delicate issue is the one related to the methods that should be used in teaching about death. The subject of death should be treated with utmost sensitivity and be dealt with in a realistic and at the same time optimistic manner. Many researchers believe that learning about death should take place gradually through "small mourning" (25-27). The debate about death lies within small events or small deaths that occur in children's lives i.e. a dead bird found in the school yard, a tale that refers to the illness or death of the hero, etc (28). The discussion about death could even start via art lessons, history, mathematics or science (29,30).

In the light of the above findings, we believe that schools can play an important role in children's familiarization with the concept of death, by instructing students how to manage loss and grief experiences.

Finally, the present research study indicates that children's familiarity with the concept of loss is feasible and can occur in specific social contexts, where children have the opportunity to gain expertise and experiences. Yet, this indication certainly requires further investigation.

More specifically, it would be useful to further investigate whether the improved knowledge and familiarity observed after the intervention, are maintained over time with new interviews taken after two to six months in a follow-up process.

The familiarisation sessions should be more in number extending over a period of two-three months at least. This would allow for students' better understanding of the concept of death, through its three fundamental characteristics namely, universality, irreversibility and non-functionality. Finally, further attention should be given in the assessment of children's comprehension of the parameters of death. This is because the irreversibility and non-functionality of death might come into conflict with their already established religious beliefs, according to which soul is immortal.

References

[1]   Campbell J. The power of myth. London: Doubleday, 1988.

[2]   Gersie A. And life goes on. Athens: Kedros, 2002. [Greek]

[3]   Speece MN, Brent SB. Children's understanding of death: A Review of three components of death concept. Child Dev 1984;55:1671-86.

[4]   Glass J, Conrad Jr. Death, loss, and grief among middle school children. Element Sch Guidance Couns 1991;26:139-48.

[5]   Fabes R, Eisenberg N, Eisenbud L. Behavioural and psychological correlates of children's reactions to other in distress. Dev Psychol 1993;29:655-63.

[6]   Strayer J. Children's concordant emotions and cognitions in response to observed emotions. Child Dev 1993;64:188–201.

[7]   Zerman J. Emotional development. The Gale encyclopedia of childhood and adolescence. Detroit, MI: Gale Research, 1998.

[8]   Faure G, Lascar S. The theatrical play. Athens: Gutenberg, 2001. [Greek].

[9]   Kouretzis L. The theatrical play (Educational theory, practical and theatrological approach). Athens: Kastaniotis, 2001. [Greek]

[10]   Stevenson RG, Powers HL. How to handle death in the school. Educ Digest 1987; 199-215.

[11]   Papadatou D, Metallinou O, Xatzichristou C, Pavlidi L. Supporting the bereaved child: teacher's perception and experience in Greece. Mortality 2002;7(3):324-337.

[12]   Childers P, Wimmer M. The concept of death in early childhood. Child Dev 1971; 42:1299-1301.

[13]   Beauchamp NW. The young child's perception of death. (Doctoral dissertation Purdue University, 1974). Dissert Abstr Int 1974;35:3288A-3289A.

[14]   Benoliel JQ, Denger LF. Institutional dying: A convergence of cultural values, technology, and social organization. In: Wass H, Neimeyer R, eds. Dying: Facing the facts, 3rd ed. Washington, DC: Taylor Francis, 1995:117-41.

[15]   Benoliel JQ. Developments in thanatology. In: Nielsen M, Papadatou D, eds. Grief in our lives. Athens: Merimna, 1998:12-29. [Greek]

[16]   Nielsen M, Papadatou D. Grief in our lives. Athens: Merimna, 1998 [Greek].

[17]   Engel GL. The need for a new medical model: A challenge for Biomedicine. Science New Series 1977;196(4286):129-36.

[18]   Møller DW. On dying without dignity: The human impact of technological dying. Amityville, NY: Baywood, 1990.

[19]   Deeny P, Johnson A, Boore JRP, Leyden C, McCaughan EM. Drama as an experiential technique in learning how to cope with dying patients and their families. Teaching Higher Educ 2001;6(1):99-112.

[20]   Barrett P, Wedser-Lowry H, Turner C. Friends for children workbook. Queensland: Australian Academic Press, 2000.

[21]   Heegaard ME. Saying goodbye to your pet. Minneapolis, MN: Fairview Press, 2001.

[22]   Stallard P. Think Good-Feel Good. Chichester: Wiley, 2002.

[23]   Ronen T. Cognitive-developmental therapy with children. Chichester: Wiley, 1997.

[24]   Geldard K, Geldard D. Counselling psychology with children. Theory-applications. Athens: Ellinika Grammata, 2004. [Greek]

[25]   Kane B. Children's concepts of death. J Genet Psychol 1979;134:141-5.

[26]   Stevenson RG. Death and school environment. In: Nielsen M, Papadatou D, eds. Grief in our lives. Athens: Merimna, 1998:97-106. [Greek]

[27]   Bacque MF. Mourning and health then and now Athens: Thymari, 2001.[Greek]

[28]   Papadatou D. The Child in front of illness and death. In: When sickness and death touched school life. Athens: Ministry of Education, 1999:15-25. [Greek]

[29]   Stevenson RG. The role of the school to support children who are experiencing grief and mourning. In: Nielsen M, Papadatou D. When illness and death touched the school life Athens: Merimna, 1999:119-39. [Greek]

[30]   Jackson M, Colwell J. Talking to children about death. Mortality 2001;6(3):321-5.

In: Child Health and Human Development Yearbook 2013
Editor: Joav Merrick

ISBN: 978-1-63117-939-6
© 2014 Nova Science Publishers, Inc.

Chapter 19

Teaching young mothers to identify developmental milestones

Katelyn M Guastaferro, John R Lutzker*, Julie J Jabaley,
Jenelle R Shanley and Daniel B Crimmins
Center for Healthy Development, Georgia State University, Atlanta, Georgia,
United States of America

Abstract

Early identification of a developmental delay may allow early intervention which has been shown to improve child outcomes. Often, pediatricians rely on parent observations to share concerns about development. The purpose of this research was to examine whether a combination of line-art drawings and discussion framed within SafeCare® increases a mothers' identification of developmental milestones. Thus, we examined the tDevelop, a tool designed to increase parent identification of developmental milestones and age-appropriate activities. Two high-risk families with children approximately 24-months of age were recruited from a residential program for young mothers. The mothers were presented with the tDevelop along with standard SafeCare®Parent-Child Interaction (PCI) information, including Planned Activities Training and age-appropriate activities. Data from a multiple-probe, single-case experimental design, suggest that mothers are able to recognize developmental milestones with increased accuracy upon intervention with the Develop. The enhanced PCI protocol may enhance parental identification of developmental milestones and may have significant implications for the early identification of developmental delays.

Keywords: Child development, developmental milestones, early intervention

---

* Correspondence: Professor John R. Lutzker, PhD, Director, Center for Healthy Development, College of Health and Human Sciences, Georgia State University, POBox 3995, Atlanta, GA 30302-3995 United States. E-mail: jlutzker@gsu.edu.

Introduction

Developmental milestones are used to monitor social and behavioral growth in multiple aspects of child development: language and communication, motor skills, cognitive processing, and social/emotional skills. Proper stimulation and interactions in early childhood are critical in promoting optimal brain development. Disadvantaged parents may not have the resources or knowledge to provide the stimulation to foster this optimal brain development in their children (1). Mothers at high risk, especially teen parents, typically wane in providing developmental stimulation as their children age, specifically after the first six months of life (2).

Identification, intervention and surveillance

Developmental milestones are typically separated into four categories to capture the spectrum of child development. Language and communication milestones deal with the child's understanding and response to language stimulation in addition to progress toward independent communication. Milestones relating to motor skills, or physical movement, include gross motor and fine motor control. Cognitive processing milestones deal with problem-solving abilities. For infants, this might include learning to self- soothe, whereas with young, ambulatory children, it could mean finding a hidden toy during a game of hide and seek. Finally, milestones in the social- emotional category concern socialization of children, including their temperament development.

Early identification of delays in these four developmental areas can lead to early intervention to optimize development and minimize delays (3). It is estimated that early intervention yields positive effect sizes of nearly one-half to three-quarters of a standard deviation (4). The earlier a delay is identified, the greater the likelihood a disability is prevented, or minimized, and thus minimizing the negative impact on the child and family (5). Mild developmental delays can be identified by age two(6). However, despite the utility of early detection, it is estimated that in the global west, fewer than 30% of children with developmental and behavioral problems are identified prior to the child entering school (7).

Developmental surveillance is a continual process during which a health professional performs skilled observations of the child during routine well-child visits. Thus, pediatricians are often involved in early identification (8). Developmental surveillance is not a means of diagnosis; rather, it is a tool to identify children who need to be evaluated further. Continued surveillance is also essential as a child's risk factors may change or develop over time. The emphasis placed on parent-reported concerns has been controversial, and while parents should not be the sole screening source, research indicates that parental observations and concerns about language, fine motor, and cognitive and emotional-behavior development are highly predictive of a subsequent diagnosed delay (9). While parental concerns have been shown to be as accurate as professional screening, varying levels of parents' literacy and accessibility, in addition to motivation for screening need be considered. The lack of parental concern does not confirm the absence of a developmental delay (10). Thus, parents must be educated and provided with the tools to detect and assess developmental milestones, and must be enabled to discuss concerns with physicians.

Development and child maltreatment

Parents' unrealistic understanding of developmentally appropriate behaviors increases a child's risk for maltreatment (11). The US National Child Abuse and Neglect Data System (NCANDS) estimated that 3.6 million referrals of alleged maltreatment were received by Child Protective Services (CPS) in 2010, of which 78.3% experienced neglect (12). Sequelae of child maltreatment include impaired physical health, impeded emotional/mental health, social difficulties, cognitive dysfunction, high-risk behaviors, and behavioral problems (13).

Child maltreatment is viewed as an "extreme traumatic insult" to a child's developmental trajectory (14) with direct impact on neurodevelopment and lasting effects on the structure and functioning of the brain (15). Continual exposure to stress alters the neurophysiology and neuro-anatomy of the brain through the persistent activation of the hypothalamic-pituitary-adrenal (HPA) axis and the catecholamine stress system.

Intervention for child maltreatment

Evidence-based home visiting models, such as SafeCare (16), prevent incidences of child maltreatment with high-risk parents and prevent recidivism by parents with substantiated child maltreatment and have been determined effective by the by the United States Task Force on Community Preventative Services and the American Academy of Pediatrics (AAP). Early participation in primary prevention programs help parents to manage stress and create an optimal development environment before negative behavior patterns emerge (1). SafeCare is conducted with parents with children between 0-5 and targets three areas associated with child physical abuse and neglect: 1) parent-child interaction, 2) child health, and 3) home safety. The curriculum is particularly well suited to address neglect, the most common form of child maltreatment. In a statewide, seven-year randomized controlled trial in Oklahoma, SafeCare was shown to be effective in lowering risk for both physical abuse and neglect (17).

The participants of this study received only the Parent-Child Interactions (PCI) module of SafeCare. A core component of PCI is Planned Activities Training, which involves teaching parents strategies for structuring daily activities to prevent challenging behaviors. The curriculum encourages age-appropriate behaviors and activities so that the child understands what is expected and acceptable. It presents developmental milestones in a checklist format to parents intended as a screener, but no research has examined mothers' acquisition of the material.

Because of the increased prevalence of developmental disabilities, the Centers for Disease Control and Prevention (CDC) developed the Learn the Signs. Act Early. (LTSAE) campaign, which was launched nationally in 2004, by dissemination through social media. The LTSAE campaign provides parents with information on developmental milestones from birth through age five, activities to encourage development, and indicators of when to speak with the child's pediatrician. The materials are presented in a high text format at a 10th grade reading level. The multi-stage, audience-centered campaign was targeted for parents, healthcare educators, and early childhood educators (18). However, the primary target is parents of children under four-years-old because children under age four are at the highest risk for child maltreatment and developmental disabilities such as Autism Spectrum Disorder can be diagnosed under age three (19). Parents at risk for child maltreatment often have low literacy skills, so reduction of the literacy level of the LTSAE material could be beneficial for them.

Thus, to address these issues, our research question was: "Can a combination of line-art drawings and discussion increase mothers' identification of developmental milestones?" It was believed that the introduction of these milestones in a pictoral format would facilitate the mother's identification of developmental milestones for their 24-month-old child. A multiple-probe, single-case research design across two mothers was used to assess the efficacy of a tool created to enhance parental recognition of developmental milestones. The goal was to enhance the mothers' ability to detect milestones, detect delays, and to be alert to developmentally appropriate activities from her child while encouraging montoringmonitoring of her child's development, knowing when to contract the child's physician.

Method

The research presented here received approval from the Georgia State University Institutional Review Board. Participants were recruited with the help of the Georgia Parents as Teachers state leader. Mothers recruited met the following eligibility criteria: consented to participation; had a child between 19 and 30-months-old so that by the final follow-up session, the child would be at a minimum of 2-years-old, or would not have yet reached the next stage of developmental milestones (36-months); and, had an interest in enhancing their parent-child interactions.

The state leader connected the researcher (hereafter referred to as Home Visitor) to parent educators at an affiliate organization who had received basic information regarding the research and the eligibility criteria. Families A and B were recruited from this affiliate program aimed at empowering families and also provides rent-free housing to mothers between the ages of 13 to 26 with children under pre-school age. The mothers attend parenting classes and complete their education with the goal of becoming self-sufficient.

A residence coordinator initiated recruitment by screening participants using the eligibility criteria and introducing the study those eligible. The coordinator then invited the Home Visitor (HV) to attend an individual meeting with the families where the HV introduced herself, the SafeCare program, and briefly reviewed what being a participant would entail. A copy of the informed consent was given to the mothers to review before their first individual sessions. At the start of the first session, the HV reviewed the informed consent with the participant and the forms were signed. A copy of the informed consent was given to the mother. The mothers received $10 at the end of each session (six intervention sessions and first follow-up) and $30 at the end of the second follow-up (the total compensation was $100).

Demographic information for each family is presented in Figure 1. Family A, a 20-year-old mother and her 25-month-old daughter, had lived at the facility since the child was 7-months-old. The mother was enrolled in vocational classes, but was otherwise unemployed, earning an annual income under $10,000. The mother came from the foster care system due to a history of violence in her family of origin and a personal history in the criminal justice system. Family B, a 17-year-old mother and her 29-month-old daughter, were new to the facility. The mother found the program through Internet searches as a means of avoiding a turbulent home environment and the foster care system. Prior to moving into the residence, she was living in another state while her daughter stayed with a family friend. The day they moved into the facility was the first time they had seen each other in two months. She worked part-time as an administrative support and teachers' aide in the daycare that her daughter attended.

Family	Marital Status	Age of Child	Highest Level of Education	Employment Status	Average Annual Income
A	Single, Never Married	25 month (daughter)	Some College	Unemployed	Under $10K
B	Single, Never Married	29 month (daughter)	Some High School	Part-Time Employment/ Looking	Under $10K

Figure 1. Demographic Description of Participants.

Setting

All training and observations were conducted at the participants' residence at the facility. SafeCare sessions are typically conducted in the parent's home environment to maximize generalization of skills. Because these two families resided in a residential center, sessions were conducted in convenient locations within the center and often involved role-playing daily routine activities, such as bath time and bedtime, as proxies to real-life situations. Sessions for Family A were conducted in the facility conference room or the caseworker's office. Initially, the HV met Family B in the conference room, but after seeking approval from the facility staff, the Family B mother invited the HV to conduct sessions 3-6 in her room.

Materials

Demographic form. A deidentified demographic survey was delivered to the mothers at the conclusion of the sixth visit. The demographic form was presented to the mother as a useful tool when discussing the relevance of the findings to a wider population.

Consumer satisfaction survey. Using a utilizing a Likert Scale, the mother rated the program and the HV so that improvements and modifications could be made for future participants.

Intervention materials. Throughout the course of training the mothers were provided with traditional PCI materials. As this research utilized an adaptation of the curriculum, please note that the 't' in material titles was used to indicate a toddler age. The mothers received 'tCards,' handouts emphasizing the skills taught by the HV including the PCI specific Planned Activities Training. Additionally, the mother was provided with the Daily Activities Checklist used to identify challenging parent-child interactions. This checklist is completed prior to training and after training to measure improvement in the ease of interactions. As an enhancement specific to this study, the mothers were presented with the tDevelop that the HV added to throughout the intervention. The tDevelop consisted of a series of 8.5" x 5.5" cards, with milestones segmented into the four categories delineated in the Learn the Signs. Act Early. (LTSAE) campaign. It is based closely on this campaign and was designed as a parent aide to integrate developmental milestones and corresponding developmentally appropriate activities into the SafeCare curriculum. Prior to this development, SafeCare materials presented participants with developmental milestones and age-appropriate activities separately.

The materials reflected an average of an 8th grade reading level. As the tDevelop was based closely on the LTSAE campaign, we sought to make the materials more accessible. The reading level was lowered, utilizing the Flesch-Kincaid Grade Level readability function of Microsoft Word®. Representational pictures, those that have a close physical resemblance to the concept the picture is conveying, guided modifications and were created for each individual milestone (20). Line drawings, a more abstract, highly detailed version of representational pictures that rely on realism in visualization were the most effective and helpful to adult learners (20).

The front side of each card contained a verbal description of two to three developmental milestones, such as "Gets excited with other children," and a line art scenario depicting each developmental milestone, such as a girl smiling and raising her arms when she sees children her age. On the backside of each card were activities that support corresponding development through interaction between child and parent. Additionally, the cards provided guidance and recommendations should the mother be concerned about missed developmental milestones. The tDevelop cards were designed to be given to the mother one at a time, so as to control the amount of materials and information. Each session, the HV added more cards to the tDevelop until all 27 milestones specific to 2-years-old were represented. The order of cards presented to the mothers was randomized and the number of cards presented to each mother during a given session varied due to individual learning levels.

Home visitor materials. The HV created a score sheet to assess progress in the mothers' identification of developmental milestones. Each score sheet consisted of 10 sections, each for one of the randomly pre-selected milestones on which the mother would be assessed each session. In these sections, the HV had space to document the milestone asked, the mothers' verbal response, and any gestures accompanying her answer. There was a space where the HV would designate if the mother was correct or incorrect. An unscored copy of assessments was provided to the reliability observer (RO).

Observation system

Data Collection. Data were collected by the HV using the score sheet. The milestones for the assessments were randomized with replacement. Thus, the families were likely to have the same prompts repeated any number of times during the course of all the sessions. The HV documented the mothers' response verbatim on the score sheet as well as any gestures or movements that accompanied their responses. For each response reflecting an example of a child behavior that corresponded to the milestone prompt, a check mark was placed in the score box on the score sheet. Answers that did not provide an example of a child behavior corresponding to the milestone prompt were recorded with an 'X'. The mothers were given the assessment at the beginning of each session.

Data were collected during Condition A, during which the HV prompted the mother to provide an example of a child behavior that corresponded to a milestone prior to any intervention and without any reference materials. For example, if the milestone read: "Says sentences with 2 to 4 words," the mother needed to supply an answer such as, "More milk!" for a correct score to be recorded. An incorrect answer might have been "I'd like to go to the zoo tomorrow and wear my new dress" or "mmmmm milk" or "I don't know."

During condition B, the mother responded to the prompt after having received training with the tDevelop. The mother responded to the same prompt from the HV, but was able to consult the tDevelop that was received and reviewed with the HV during a prior session. When prompted by the HV, the mother had to provide a novel behavior, meaning one different from that was depicted in the line art scenarios, in order to receive a correct score. If the milestone read: "Says sentences with 2 to 4 words," and the line art scenario depicted a child saying "More milk!" the mother had to supply a different response indicating a novel concept such as "Let's go!" for a checkmark to be recorded. If an example extremely similar to that depicted in the line drawing is supplied, such as "More Water!", an '(X') was recorded. Mastery criteria were specified as correctly identifying 8 out 10 correct responses during a given session.

Reliability

The RO, a graduate research assistant, repeatedly reviewed the materials with the HV using a bank of sample responses to the probes provided in advance by a sample of students, staff, and faculty. The RO completed the score sheet with the HV to create operational definitions and guidelines that were used as a guide for reliability scoring. The HV and RO practiced scoring until reliability agreement consistently reached a minimum of 80%. Reliability was calculated by the following equation: agreements over agreements plus disagreements multiplied by 100. Reliability observations were conducted a minimum of 25% of each condition for each mother. The HV provided the unscored completed score sheet electronically to the RO. Gestures and all verbal responses were recorded on the score sheet.

Experimental procedure

Design. Multiple probe designs are used to validate the functional relationship between an intervention and outcomes, and in doing so, establish internal validity of the intervention (21). A multiple probe design across mothers was employed to evaluate the effects of the tDevelop intervention on parents' acquisition of milestones. Milestone training was introduced sequentially such that after two probes showing the lack of requisite knowledge (baseline), tDevelop cards were introduced. The staggered introduction of the interventions between mothers indicates that mastery of milestones occurs upon the introduction of the tDevelop and not other external factors, thus establishing internal validity. Not only are these designs robust, but they are clinically relevant in that parents do not become overwhelmed with lengthy baselines.

Dependent variables. Mothers were prompted by the HV to provide examples of behaviors corresponding to developmental milestones for the referent child during baseline and training conditions. Intervention implementation, the introduction of the tDevelop, taught the mothers developmental milestones using line art scenarios to facilitate comprehension and generalization. The HV prompted mothers the same way in each condition: "One milestone for a two- year old is _____. Can you give me an example of a 2-year old _____?" For example, "One milestone for a 2-year-old is copying others. Can you give me an example of a 2-year old copying others?"

Intervention

In order to contextualize the milestones, the HV integrated the milestone discussion into the planned activities training of PCI. First, the mother would read the milestone with the HV, pointing out important components of the accompanying line-art scenario, for instance, noting the smile and arms raised for the "Gets excited when with other children" milestone. The HV and mother then selected the related activity on the opposite side of the tDevelop card and asked the mother to go through the planned activities training steps as applicable to the specified milestone. Milestones were discussed in a random order.

Baseline. The mother's existing knowledge regarding behaviors that depict developmental milestones was assessed during baseline in which the mother was provided no instruction, materials or feedback from the HV.

Training. If the data showed a descending or stable baseline trend for Mother A, training was implemented, and when the data then showed skill increases with Mother A and baseline showed stability with Mother B, the intervention was implemented with Mother B. The Mothers were presented with a two to five tDevelop cards and the HV reviewed the critical components of the milestone with the mother. The HV presented possible ways of considering the milestone, emphasizing what elements were important following the example provided in the line art scenario. The Mother was then asked to choose corresponding activities to practice for homework. At the beginning of each training session, the HV prompted the mother for responses to the 10 pre-selected milestones. The HV assessed the responses quickly in situ and then modeled with the mother considerations for how to identify the milestones, if necessary, while introducing the subsequent round of milestones.

The mother was permitted to refer to the cards she had previously received during subsequent assessments. Assessment questions were randomly pre-selected as were the tDevelop cards the mother received during each session. Thus, the mothers may or may not have had the tDevelop card specifically addressed in the assessment at her disposal even though she was allowed to refer to her cards at any time. The tDevelop cards were left with the mother to review and practice corresponding age-appropriate activities for homework at the conclusion of every session.

Follow-up. At one month and two month postintervention, the HV returned to the residential facility to assess the mothers' retention of 24-month developmental milestones. The mothers were permitted to refer to the tDevelop cards if they wanted to do so; however, neither mother referred to the cards during either follow-up session.

Results

Figure 2 shows that there was a considerable improvement after introduction of the discussion of developmental milestones with the tDevelop cards. Each mother received six sessions and two follow-up sessions at one and two months post intervention. The duration of visits ranged from 30 .5 to 1.5 hoursrs.

Outcomes for both mothers during baseline sessions were below the identified mastery criterion (8 correct responses). Mother A's data indicated a decreasing trend. Mother B's data remained stable at 3 correct answers during her first two sessions. Intervention began with Mother A at the conclusion of the session 2 because the descending baseline trend. She was given several tDevelop cards to review and practice corresponding activities until the next home visit. Upon receiving training, which included a subset of tDevelop cards and discussion with the HV, Mother A's scores increased to 9 correct answers. Thus, intervention began with Mother B who then displayed 10 out of 10 correct responses. Both mothers subsequently showed 100% mastery. The duration of sessions for each mother is presented in Table 2. Session duration was not longer than typical PCI sessions without the tDevelop enhancement.

At one-month post intervention, Mothers A and B showed a high level of retention. At the two-month post intervention follow-up, Mother A again showed a high level of retention, correctly identifying 8 out of 10 milestones. Mother B's scored 7 out of 10 correct.

Reliability

Reliability sessions were conducted in three of the six sessions with each mother. Two reliability sessions occurred for each family during baseline and once during intervention. Reliability observation means for the two families were 90% and 93.3%, respectively. Given the high level of reliability during intervention, reliability was not conducted during follow-up sessions.

Consumer Satisfaction Results

The mothers completed a consumer satisfaction survey during the sixth session. Overall, the mothers' responses showed a general satisfaction with the HV and SafeCare, including the tDevelop. Both mothers indicated they had learned new or useful skills and that they believed the training and materials would be useful to other parents. When asked about providing age-appropriate activities to their children following the PCI training, both mothers 'strongly agreed' that they had more ideas and felt comfortable in engaging in the activities. Both mothers agreed that the pictures on the tDevelop were clear; however, they disagreed on whether they actually made it easier to understand the milestones. Each mother was positive in response to her use of the cards to follow her child's development. There was a discrepancy with regard to the use of the cards to decide to speak to the child's pediatrician; one mother indicated 'neutral' and the other 'agree'.

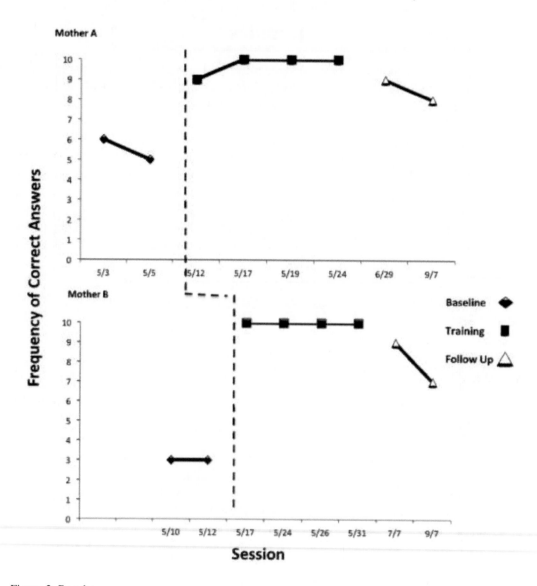

Figure 2. Results.

Discussion

The purpose of the present study was to increase a mothers' ability to identify developmental milestones, observe delays, and provide developmentally appropriate activities to her child. The introduction of the tDevelop and discussion to the SafeCare PCI module yielded an increase in each mother's identification of developmental milestones for her two-year-old child. The multiple probe design demonstrated that it was the intervention that caused the improvement in identification rather than extraneous factors. The findings confirm that these mothers were able to identify developmental milestones and generalize milestones to their own child's behaviors once trained. This finding has the potential to inform modifications to the SafeCare curriculum and future research endeavors.

Prior to intervention, neither mother was able to translate a standard milestone to her own child's development. Mother A scored moderately well during baseline, indicating some familiarity with the material. Mother B displayed less ability during baseline. Upon introduction of the tDevelop tool, a marked increase in correctly identified developmental behaviors indicates that when provided proper training, mothers can be successful in this task. Both mothers surpassed the mastery criterion immediately and sustained it throughout the intervention. The one-month post intervention follow-up data showed a slight decrease in correct responses, although remaining above mastery criteria. At the follow-up two-months post intervention, both mothers dropped below mastery criterion. The decreases in correctly identified responses may be indicative of a loss of retention of the materials or other factors. During the second follow-up session, both mothers commented to the HV that the task was challenging given their child's progression towards milestones more typical of a 36-month-old. They stated it was challenging to give an example of a milestone that their child had passed. Additionally, the HV observed the mothers appeared to face challenges in providing abstract examples of a milestone; that is, their remarks focused exclusively on their own children's development.

The tDevelop tool utilized the findings of prior research in an effective manner. Turner and colleagues (22) showed that pediatricians use simple language, repetition and the limiting of materials presented per session and Parker's (23) finding that health educators "teach back" was a successful strategy employed by the HV in having the mothers discuss the important aspects of the milestones. The success of the line drawings confirms Dwyer's research showing these pictures that relied on realism in visualization were the most helpful to adult learners (20).

The mothers were told that they were allowed to refer to the milestone cards as they needed during assessments, however, the HV observed Mother A do this only once and Mother B did not actively refer to her cards during assessment, although they were in a visible location each time the HV was in the family's room. This speaks to their level of comprehension of the material, but may also suggest that it was the discussion played a critical role in retention. Additionally, the randomization of the milestones during each assessment supports this speculation.

The consumer satisfaction survey results indicated an affinity for the program, materials, and home visitor. The mothers were generally positive in their perception of the tDevelop material. However, one mother suggested the cards be 'updated'. Although she did not elaborate, her feedback is useful when considering making large-scale modifications to the SafeCare curriculum. The overall positive attitude toward the tDevelop is evident in its positive effect on assessment outcomes.

Parents should be provided the opportunity to learn developmental milestones, recognize them in their children, and receive guidance on when to seek medical opinion. Additionally, these findings also indicate that particularly high-risk mothers succeed when provided individual support and modeling.

Given what is known about the barriers high-risk parents face while raising their children, it could not have been predicted that these mothers would do so well. These young mothers are atypical given the structured, parent-centered environment in which they reside, however, the mother's age, education level, income, and marital status highly represent a typical child welfare parent sample. The success of the tDevelop in this population bodes well for other mothers at varying degrees of risk.

The introduction of the tDevelop into standard PCI sessions did not prolong session duration. The variation in session duration is perhaps attributable to information overload as the longest sessions for the Mothers included the most amount of new material. Additionally, varied session duration could be attributable to the child being in the same room during the session and occasionally requiring a shift in the mothers attention. To be a sustainable, effective intervention, the more concrete and succinct the material is, the better suited it is for dissemination (24).

While these findings are promising, several limitations are apparent. Only two high-risk young mothers with low incomes and levels of education limit the generalizability of these findings to other populations at risk. It would be beneficial to see how the materials are received and interpreted by a wider range of participants. Additionally, the present research does not examine whether typical SafeCare Home Visitors can produce similar results. Also, we did not assess whether or not these parents would follow-through with seeking medical consultation when a delay or missed milestone is detected. Thus, another limitation assessing whether the intervention translates into action by the parent. For Mother B, changing the setting from baseline (conference room) and intervention (her room) sessions may have introduced or eliminated distractions. By design, the present research sought to evaluate the effects of discussion supported by the tDevelop. It is thus not possible to determine whether it was the discussion alone, the tDevelop aide alone, or the pairing of the two that had the positive effect on identification of developmental milestones.

In future research, it would be beneficial to include a broader range of milestones to examine the validity of the materials with other ages. Also, putting the tDevelop in an electronic format, such as a Smartphone App, would be of interest as prior research has indicated the introduction of technology increase adherence to treatment in physical and mental health interventions (25).

Despite the recognized limitations, the present research suggests that the integration of developmental milestones and age appropriate activities in the SafeCare curriculum is effective in increasing parental identification of developmental milestones. Moreover, this research shows that high-risk mothers can be taught to utilize the tDevelop tool. This may be beneficial in the long-term in preventing instances of child maltreatment, and aiding parents in making early decisions to seek intervention for a child whom they determine may have a developmental delay.

Acknowledgments

The publication is funded in part by the Centers for Disease Control and Prevention (CDC), National Center on Birth Defects and Developmental Disabilities (NCBDDD) under Cooperative Agreement U01DD000231 to the Association of University Centers on Disabilities (AUCD). The content of this material does not necessarily reflect the views and policies of CDC, NCBDDD nor AUCD.

References

[1]   Hawley T, Gunner M. Starting smart: How early experienesexperiences affect brain development. Washington: Zero To Three, Ounce Prevention Fund, 2000.

[2]   Pomerleau A, Scuccimarri C, Malcuit G. Mother-infant behavioral interactions in teenage and adult mothers during the first six months postpartum: Relations with infant development. Infant Ment Health J 2003;24(5):495-509.

[3]   Majnemer A. Benefits of early intervention for children with developmental disabilities. Semin Pediatr Neurol 1998;5(1):62-9.

[4]   Sonnander K. Early identification of children with developmental disabilities. Acta Paediatr Suppl 2000;434:17-23.

[5]   Geeraert L, Van den Noortgate W, Grietens H, Onghena P. The effects of early prevention programs for families with young children at risk for physical child abuse and neglect: A meta-analysis. Child Maltreat 2004; 9(3):277-91.

[6]   Glascoe FP. Screening for developentaldevelopmental and behavioral problems. Dev Disabil Res Rev 2005;11:173-9.

[7]   Williams N, Mughal S, Blair M. 'Is my child developing normally?': A critical review of web-based resources for parents. Dev Med Child Neurol 2008;50:893-7.

[8]   Committee on Children with Disabilities. Developmental surveillance and screening of infants and young children. Pediatr 2001;108(1): 192-5.

[9]   Committee on Children with Disabilities. Role of pediatrician in family-centered early intervention service. Pediatrics 2001;107(5): 1155-7.

[10]   American Academy of Pediatrics, Council on Children With Disabilities, Section on Developmental Behavioral Pediatrics, Bright Futures Steering Committee, Medical Home Initiatives for Children with Special Needs Project Committee (AAP). Identifying infants and young children with developmental disorders in the medical home: An algorithm for developmental surveillance and screening. Pediatrics 2006;118(1): 405-20.

[11]   Azar ST, Weinzierl KM. Child maltreatment and childhood injury research: A cognitive behavioral approach. J Pediatr Psychol 2005;30(7): 598-614.

[12]   US Department of Health and Human Services, Administration for Children and Families, Administra¬tion on Children, Youth and Families, Children's Bureau. Child maltreatment 2010. Accessed 2012 Apr 02. URL: http://www.acf.hhs.gov/programs/cb/stats_research/index.htm#can.

[13]   Chapman DP, Dube SR, Anda RF. Adverse childhood events as risk factors for negative mental health outcomes. Psychiatr Ann 2007;37(5): 359-64.

[14]   Hagele DM. The impact of maltreatment on the developing child. NC Med J 2005;66(5):356-9.

[15]   Cicchetti D, Rogosch FA. Adaptive coping uderunder conditions of extreme stress: Multilevel influences on the determinants of resilience in maltreated childernchildren. In: EA Skinner, MJ Zimmer-Gembeck, eds. Coping and the development of regulation. New directions for child and adolescent development. San Francisco: Jossey-Bass, 2009:47-59.

[16]   Edwards-Gaura AE, Whitaker DJ, Lutzker JR, Self-Brown S, Lewis E. SafeCare: Application of an evidence-based program to prevent child maltreatment. In: Rubin A, ed. A clinician's guide to evidence-based practice. Hoboken, NJ: John Wiley, 2011:259-72.

[17]   Chaffin M, Hecht D, Bard D, Silovsky JF, Beasley WH. A statewide trial of the SafeCare home-based serviced model with parents in child Child pProtectives Services. Pediatrics; 129(3):509-515., in press.

[18]   Daniel KL, Prue C, Taylor MK, Scales TM. Learn the signs. Act early: A campaign to help every child reach his or her full potential. Public Health 2009;123:e11-6.

[19]   Corsello CM. Early intervention in autism. Infants Young Child 2005; 18(2):74-85.

[20]   Alesandrini KL. Pictures and adult learning. Instr Sci 1984;13:63-77.

[21]   Barlow DH, Nock MK, Hersen M. Single-case experimental design: Strategies for studying behavior change. Boston, MA: Pearson Allyn Bacon, 2009.

[22]   Turner T, Cull WL, Bayldon B, Klass P, Sanders LM, Frinter MP, et al. Pediatricians and health literacy: Descriptive results from a national survey. Pediatrics 2009;124(Supp 3):S299-S305.

[23] Parker R. Health literacy: a challenge for American patients and their health care providers. Health Promot Int 2000;15(4):277-83.

[24] Fixsen DL, Naoom SF, Blase KA, Friedman RM, Wallace F. Implementation research: A synthesis of the literature. Tampa, FL: University of South Florida, Louis de la Parte Florida Mental Health Institute, The National Implementation Research Network (FMHI Publication #231), 2005.

[25] Kazdin AE. Evidence-based treatments and delivery of psychological services: Shifting our emphases to increase impact. Psychol Serv 2008;5(3):201-15.

In: Child Health and Human Development Yearbook 2013   ISBN: 978-1-63117-939-6
Editor: Joav Merrick   © 2014 Nova Science Publishers, Inc.

Chapter 20

Reproductive wastage in carrier couples of hemoglobinopathies: Experiences from a retrospective study in Madhya Pradesh, India

Ranbir S Balgir, MSc Hons, PhD[*]

Department of Biochemistry, Regional Medical Research Centre for Tribals, Indian Council of Medical Research, Jabalpur, Madhya Pradesh, India

Abstract

The β-thalassemia syndrome and sickle cell disorders are the major genetic and public health challenges in Central India. In view of credit for the 2nd highest infant mortality rate (IMR) in Madhya Pradesh (70 per thousand live-births in 2011), it was presumed that carriers of hemoglobinopathies might be one of the contributing factors for the high IMR. Couples including their offspring with at least one affected/suspected case of hemoglobinopathies, referred to us from NSCB Medical College and Hospital, Jabalpur were consecutively studied as matched case controls. A total of 333 couples were referred during the period from March 2010 to March 2012. Out of 333 couples, 138 were found normal and 195 couples had different hemoglobin disorders. It was observed that the number of conceptions (2.456 vs 1.522), live-births (2.246 vs 1.319), surviving offspring (2.005 vs 1.406), stillbirths (0.082 vs 0.051), and deaths under 10 year (0.236 vs 0.145) were higher and neonatal deaths (0.103 vs 0.116), and deaths under one year (0.118 vs 0.123) per couple at the time of investigations were lower in couples with hemoglobinopathies in comparison to normal controls. It was observed that the frequency of couples with combinations: HbAS x HbAS, HbAS x HbSS, and β-Thalassemia Trait x β-Thalassemia Trait, was considerably higher in the under-privileged communities such as scheduled castes (SC) and scheduled tribes (ST), and in Other Backward Castes (OBC) of the state of Madhya Pradesh. Affected families were imparted genetic/marriage

---

[*] Correspondence: Ranbir S Balgir, Ph D, Scientist-F/Deputy Director (Senior Grade) and Head, Department of Biochemistry, Regional Medical Research Centre for Tribals (ICMR), Nagpur Road, PO: Garha, Jabalpur-482 003, Madhya Pradesh, India. E-mail: balgirrs@yahoo.co.in.

counseling. This study indicated that afflicted couples with these hereditary disorders were increasing the affected/carrier offspring. This increased production of defective offspring leads to increased morbidity and mortality and may be contributing towards increased neonatal/infant mortality or fetal wastage in the state of Madhya Pradesh, India.

Keywords: Hemoglobinopathies, carrier couples, reproductive wastage, neonatal mortality, infant mortality, retrospective study, Madhya Pradesh, India

Introduction

The hemoglobinopathies are a group of heterogeneous single gene disorders that includes the structural hemoglobin variants and the thalassemias. More than 270 million people worldwide are heterozygous carriers of hereditary disorders of hemoglobin, and at least 300,000 affected homozygotes or compound heterozygotes are born each year (1). It has also been estimated that about 45 million are carriers and about 15,000 infants born each year with hemoglobinopathies in India (2). Of the several abnormal hemoglobins so far identified in India, there are three variants – sickle cell (Hb S), hemoglobin E (Hb E) and hemoglobin D (Hb D), which are predominantly prevalent (3). There are regional variations for the distribution of these structural variants of hemoglobin. The cumulative allele frequency in different parts of India for these variants has been found to be 5.35% (3). The average allele frequency of sickle cell and hemoglobin D has been observed to be 4.3% and 0.86%, respectively with hemoglobin E constituting 10.9% in North Eastern region of India (3). The sickle cell disease is wide spread in tribal as well as in nontribal communities especially in the Central-Eastern region of India. With a prevalence range of 3-17% (average 4.2%), the β-thalassemia syndrome is prevalent throughout India (2). Thus, hemoglobinopathies are a huge genetic burden and pose a major clinical health care challenge in India.

The sickle cell hemoglobinopathy and β-thalassemia syndrome are a major genetic and community health care challenge in Central India. The victims include the infants, growing children, adolescent girls, pregnant women and a large number of ignorant and vulnerable people. Inherited disorders of hemoglobin cause high degree of hemolytic anemia, clinical jaundice, frequent infections, painful crises, splenomegaly, development and growth retardation (4-6) and are responsible for high infant morbidity, mortality and fetal wastage in India (7-10). In sickle cell disease, the distorted red cells lead to increased viscosity, hemolysis, and anemia and a further decrease in oxygenation. When sickling occurs within small blood vessels, it can cause logjams (clogging) that can interrupt blood supply to vital organs (vasoocclusive crisis). Repeated vasoocclusive crises result in widespread microvascular obstruction with interruption of normal perfusion and function of several organs, including the spleen, lungs, kidneys, heart, and brain. Adults with sickle cell disease are functionally asplenic, having undergone auto-splenectomy and contribute to the increased incidence of severity of infection. A great deal of literature is available in India regarding the clinical and hematological aspects of these disorders, but the details regarding the reproductive outcome in affected couples are scanty (8,11).

The neonatal (NMR) and infant mortality rate (IMR) are the most important indicators of socio-economic status of a community/country. After the failure of achieving the target goal of "Health for All by the year 2000" the emphasis and thrust of Indian government has shifted to qualitative improvement in the health services through strengthening of physical facilities like provision of essential equipment, supply of essential drugs and consumables, construction of buildings and staff quarters, filling up of vacant posts of medical and paramedical staff and ongoing in-service training of staff to enhance their knowledge in the latest medical development and technology. The stress, however, remained on the provision of preventive, promotive and rehabilitative health services to the people, thus, representing a shift from medical care to health care and from urban to rural population of India. For developing vast human resources of the country, accelerating the socio-economic development and attaining improved quality of life, Primary Health Care has been accepted as one of the main instruments of action.

Early detection and effective clinical management of anemia in pregnancy may contribute substantially to the reduction in under-nutrition in childhood, adolescence and improvement in maternal health and reduction in maternal mortality. Maternal anemia is associated with poor intrauterine growth and increased risk of preterm births and low birth weight babies. This in turn results in higher perinatal morbidity and mortality, and higher infant mortality rate (8, 9). A doubling of low birth weight rate and 2 to 3 fold increase in the perinatal mortality rates is seen when the hemoglobin is less than 8g/dl (12). Intrauterine growth retardation and low birth weight inevitably lead to poor growth trajectory in infancy, childhood and adolescence and contribute to low adult height (12). Parental height and maternal weight are determinants of intrauterine growth and birth weight (13). Thus maternal anemia contributes to intergenerational cycle of poor growth in the offspring (12).

In view of credit of the 2nd highest infant mortality rate (IMR) in the state of Madhya Pradesh (70 per thousand live-births in 2011) in comparison to other states and in India (53) and the high prevalence of hemoglobin disorders, it was presumed that β-thalassemia syndrome and hemoglobinopathies might be one of the significantly contributing factors for the infant/neonatal mortality or fetal wastage in carrier couples of hemoglobinopathies in the state of Madhya Pradesh, India.

Methods

In the present study, a total of 333 native couples (families) were screened for β-thalassemia and other hemoglobinopathies during the period between March 2010 to March 2012, irrespective of age, sex, religion, caste, and community. Detailed reproductive history of each couple was recorded like total number of conceptions, abortions, miscarriages or stillbirths, live-births, surviving children, infant or neonatal deaths, cause of death, etc. A couple was asked the detailed reproductive history only once to avoid duplication. Matched couples who were free from any kind of β-thalassemia syndrome and hemoglobinopathies served as case controls for the present study.

The couples (parents) including their offspring with at least one suspected/confirmed case of homozygous β-thalassemia/HbE/Sickle cell anemia or compound heterozygosity routinely referred to us from Netaji Subhash Chandra Bose Medical College & Hospital, Jabalpur were included in the study. Those cases with only iron deficiency anemia, induced abortion or accidental deaths were excluded from the study.

For the present study, the neonatal mortality rate (NMR) is defined as the number of deaths within 28 days of life per thousand live-births in a particular area, whereas, the infant mortality rate (IMR) is defined as the number of deaths within one year per thousand live-births in a particular area.

There are several relevant co-confounding and concomitant non-genetic variables that are known to affect reproductive outcome in terms of neonatal and infant mortality and enhance reproductive wastage in both normal controls and carrier cases of hemoglobinopathies (8). For inclusion criteria, the factors like lack of tetanus toxoid immunization, malnutrition (nutritional deficiencies), neonatal infection, prematurity (low birth weight), acute respiratory infection, abnormal condition of placenta and cord, anemia and jaundice, hand and foot syndrome, retarded growth and development, diarrhea, malaria, lack of basic health care, prevalent unhygienic conditions, poverty, illogical socio-cultural traditions and taboos, single parenthood, were covered.

The neonatal period constitutes almost two-third of the deaths of IMR. The causes of death during neonatal period are: sepsis, birth asphyxia (when a baby does not breathe or cry immediately after birth), prematurity (born before 37 weeks of gestation) and low birth weight (less than 2.5 Kg), birth injury and congenital anomaly (cleft lip and cleft palate, heart disease) including genetic defects (hemolytic anemia or jaundice). The post neonatal period (29 to 365 days) accounts for deaths due to acute respiratory tract infection, diarrhea, hemolytic anemia, malnutrition, measles, malaria or genetic abnormalities. Among the chief causes of neonatal mortality, neonatal infections (pneumonia, septicemia, meningitis and diarrhea) are the most common accounting for almost 50% of all deaths. Exclusion criteria for this study include birth asphyxia, birth injury, HIV infection, sexually transmitted diseases (syphilis, etc.), aplastic anemia and other hematological disorders, congenital anomalies, measles, accidental death, etc.

Intravenous 2ml. of blood was taken under aseptical conditions from each individual after taking informed/written consent for screening of hemoglobinopathies and β-thalassemia syndrome. Blood so collected was transported to our laboratory under wet-cold conditions for investigations. All the adopted techniques and procedures standardized in the laboratory were followed as described elsewhere (8, 10). For quality control, results were cross-checked periodically.

Out of 333 couples, 138 were found normal and 195 couples had different hemoglobin disorders. Results of investigations were given to parents for treatment and further clinical management by the concerned referring doctor. It was envisaged to bring awareness among these couples through genetic counseling about the genetic disorders and their causal effects on health. Their eradication is necessary because they are not curable but preventable through carrier detection, education and genetic counseling, prenatal diagnosis.

Results

It is emphasized that both normal controls and abnormal subgroups (combined hemoglobinopathies) had similar characteristics with respect to the concomitant factors and the present observations of reproductive outcome are attributable to different genotypes of hemoglobinopathies in the state of Madhya Pradesh from Central India.

The reproductive history of normal controls as well as different combinations of genotypes of hemoglobinopathies in carrier couples is presented in Table 1. It is interesting to note that the number of conceptions (2.456 vs 1.522), live-births (2.246 vs 1.319), surviving offspring (2.005 vs 1.406), stillbirths (0.082 vs 0.051), and deaths under 10 year (0.236 vs 0.145) were higher and neonatal deaths (0.103 vs 0.116), and deaths under one year (0.118 vs 0.123) per couple at the time of investigations were lower in couples with hemoglobinopathies as compared to normal controls.

It was also observed that the frequency of couples with combinations: HbAS x HbAS, HbAS x HbSS, and β-Thalassemia Trait x β-Thalassemia Trait, was considerably higher in the scheduled castes (SC), scheduled tribes (ST), and in Other Backward Castes (OBC) in the state of Madhya Pradesh.

Further, it is noteworthy that the fertility or the number of conceptions per defective (combined hemoglobinopathies) couple is higher than in the normal controls (Table 1). This implies that the carrier couples produce more children than the normal couples to ensure the survival of at least some of them.

Table 2 presents the surviving offspring with hemoglobinopathies per couple as well as per 1000 live-births in different diagnostic categories.

Discussion

This study strongly supports the contention that hereditary hemoglobin disorders including β-thalassemia syndrome and sickle cell disease contribute significantly to the reproductive wastage and high neonatal, infant and childhood morbidity and mortality in the state of Madhya Pradesh in Central India. There are several high risk vulnerable communities that practice territorial endogamy and marriage among blood relatives because of economic/property benefits leading to inbreeding due to small effective community size. There have emerged several independent breeding isolates of a community with the passage of time which had a common stock in the distant past. Historically, the written records are not available and only the verbal instructions are followed generation after generation but these genetic characteristics indicate their common origin. Moreover, the increased frequency of homozygous hemoglobinopathies (in surviving offspring) of autosomal recessive disorders (Table 2) either testifies the occurrence of inbreeding or high prevalence of hereditary hemolytic disorders (β-thalassemia syndrome and hemoglobinopathies) in the vulnerable communities leading to high morbidity, neonatal and infant/childhood mortality and fetal wastage in Madhya Pradesh. These findings are in agreement with our previous similar studies carried out in the state of Orissa (8).

This study has revealed that hereditary causes, apart from other concomitant non-genetic factors, could also be responsible for the high neonatal/infant mortality in Madhya Pradesh. It is apparent that the reproductive wastage (stillbirths, neonatal deaths, and childhood deaths) per couple with hemoglobinopathies is higher, compared to normal couples (Table 1 and 2). These results are consistent with our previous findings (8, 9). Moreover, the number of deaths of offspring below 1 year of age (infant mortality) and below 10 years of age (childhood mortality) in such couples is also higher than in normal couples.

Ranbir S Balgir

These findings show that the progeny of sickle-cell trait, β-thalassemia, and sickle cell/β-thalassemia, etc. couples contribute disproportionately to the high neonatal/infant mortality in the state of Madhya Pradesh. Similar findings are also expected from the adjacent state of Chhattisgarh, being earlier the part of undivided state of Madhya Pradesh.

Table 1. A comparative study of reproductive wastage in couples with different hemoglobinopathies and normal controls

Diagnosis (Genotypes of Couples)	No. of Couples		Conceptions	Abor-tions	Still-births	Neonatal Deaths●	< 1 year Deaths■	< 10 years Deaths
Hb AA X Hb AS	44		89	6	6	4	4	4
		Per Couple	2.023*	0.136	0.136*	0.091	0.091	0.091
Hb AA X Hb SS	13		24	2	4	1	1	1
		Per Couple	1.846*	0.154*	0.308*	0.077	0.077	0.077
Hb AS X Hb AS	57		176	11	2	7	8	24
		Per Couple	3.087*	0.193*	0.035	0.123*	0.140*	0.421*
Hb AS X Hb SS	8		14	0	0	3	3	6
		Per Couple	1.750*	0.000	0.000	0.375*	0.375*	0.750*
Hb AS X Hb AE	1		3	1	0	0	0	0
Hb SE X β-Thal. Trait	1		4	0	0	0	0	0
Hb AE X β-Thal. Trait	1		7	0	0	0	0	0
Hb AS X β-Thal. Trait	13		45	1	0	0	1	3
		Per Couple	3.461*	0.077	0.000	0.000	0.077	0.231*
Hb AA X S-β-Thal.	2		2	0	0	0	0	0
		Per Couple	1.000	0.000	0.000	0.000	0.000	0.000
Hb AS X S-□β-Thal.	5		11	0	1	1	1	1
		Per Couple	2.200*	0.000	0.200*	0.200*	0.200*	0.200*
β -Thal. Trait X S-β-Thal.	2		3	0	0	0	0	0
		Per Couple	1.500	0.000	0.000	0.000	0.000	0.000
Hb AA X β-Thal. Trait	17		27	0	3	3	3	3
		Per Couple	1.588*	0.000	0.176*	0.176*	0.176*	0.176*
β-Thal.TraitXβ-Thal.Trait	31		74	4	0	1	2	4
		Per Couple	2.387*	0.129	0.000	0.032	0.064	0.129
Hemoglobinopathies (Combined)	**195**		**479**	**25**	**16**	**20**	**23**	**46**
		Per Couple	**2.456***	**0.128**	**0.082***	**0.103**	**0.118**	**0.236***
Hb AA X Hb AA (Normal)	138		210	21	7	16	17	20
		Per Couple	1.522	0.152	0.051	0.116	0.123	0.145

●Birth to 28 days. ■Birth to 365 days or within 1 year. *Higher values than the controls.

Further, it is intriguing in the state of Madhya Pradesh, the number of conceptions (fertility) per defective poor couple is higher (combined hemoglobinopathies) than in the normal controls (Table 1).

This implies that the carrier and poverty-stricken couples produce more children than the normal couples to overcome the non-survival of some of them. These results are consistent with our previous similar findings reported from the state of Orissa (8, 14).

Fetal wastage from abortions, stillbirths, and neonatal deaths is increased in mothers with homozygous sickle-cell disease (15). Spontaneous abortions occurred in 19.2% of pregnancies of sickle-cell disease mothers (16). An increased rate of stillbirths (11.5%) in pregnant women with sickle cell disease (16) and 5% was observed in pregnant women in Baltimore (17). Overall perinatal mortality (stillbirths and neonatal deaths) was 8.1%, four-fifths attributable to stillbirths and one-fifth to neonatal deaths (16).

Table 2. Surviving children (offspring) with hemoglobinopathies

Diagnosis (Genotypes of Couples)	No. of Couples	Conceptions	Total Surviving	Hb AA		Hb AS		Hb SS		S-β Thal.		β-Thal. T		β Thal. Major		Hb SE		Hb E-Thal		Hb AE	
				M	F	M	F	M	F	M	F	M	F	M	F	M	F	M	F	M	F
Hb AA X Hb AS	44	89	73	33	21	8	11														
Hb AA X Hb SS	13	24	17			10	7														
Hb AS X Hb AS	57	176	140	30	26	0	16	35	23												
Hb AS X Hb SS	8	14	8			2	4	0	2												
Hb AS X Hb AE	1	3	2	0	1											1	0				
Hb SE X β-Thal. Trait	1	4	3			0	2													0	1
Hb AS X β-Thal. Trait	13	45	41	2	3	4	5			11	2	6	8								
Hb AS X S-β-Thal.	5	11	9			1	1	1	1	2	1	0	2								
Hb AA X S-β-Thal.	2	2	2	0	1							0	1								
Hb AA X β-Thal. Trait	17	27	20	6	11							0	3								
β-Thal. Trait X β-Thal. Trait	31	74	66	8	17							6	9	10	16						
β-Thal. Trait X S-β-Thal.	2	3	3			2	0			1	0										
Hb AE X β-Thal. Trait	1	7	7	1	4							1	0					0	1		

Table 2. (Continued)

Diagnosis (Genotypes of Couples)	No. of Couples	Concep-tions	Total Surviing	Hb AA		Hb AS		Hb SS		S-β Thal.		β-Thal. T		β Thal. Major		Hb SE		Hb E-Thal		Hb AE	
				M	F	M	F	M	F	M	F	M	F	M	F	M	F	M	F	M	F
Hemoglobinopathies (Combined)	195	479	391	80	84	37	46	36	26	14	3	13	23	10	16	1	0	0	1	0	1
Per Couple* Per 1000 Live-births*		2.456	2.005 893	0.841 375		0.426 190		0.318 142		0.087 39		0.185 82		0.133 59		0.0005 2		0.0005 2		0.0005 2	
Hb AA X Hb AA (Normal)	138	210	194	82	112																
Per Couple* Per 1000 Live-births*		1.522	1.405 924	1.405 867																	

* Sexes combined.

In the present study comparatively lower number of abortions, stillbirths, neonatal mortality, infant mortality, and mortality below 10 years per 100 live-births have been observed to be 5.7%, 3.7%, 4.6%, 5.3%, and 10.5%, respectively in couples with carrier of hemoglobinopathies (combined) in the state of Madhya Pradesh. These findings show comparatively improvement in medical health care in India with the passage of time.

It is emphasized that there is an urgent need to take up intervention and prevention program at least in affected couples at grass root level in the state of Madhya Pradesh to mitigate the sufferings of poverty stricken underprivileged, innocent, and vulnerable people.

The quality of child health care in Madhya Pradesh (India) is hampered by various factors and some of these are listed here:

1. Pregnant women have unequal access to health care, before, during and after birth and newborns suffer as a consequent of it. Almost two-third of pregnant women deliver at home and only half of them receive care from skilled birth attendants. Similarly, less than 50% have 3 or more antenatal checkups during gestational period and one-third do not get two doses of tetanus toxoid vaccine indicating poor antenatal care. This leads to complicated deliveries resulting in maternal and neonatal morbidity and mortality.

2. Families in rural areas generally consult a primary health care provider close to their home for their sick baby and only visit a hospital or a specialist in a situation where irreversible damage has already been done.

3. Poverty stricken people from the villages and urban slums do not avail the referral system out of fear for loss of daily wages.

4. Recognition of illness by parents in a newborn is always delayed due to the subtle signs and symptoms. In addition, disease often progresses rapidly in newborns and allow little time for parents to take a decision.

5. Care seeking is influenced by traditional customs more in neonatal period than afterwards. In many areas/communities the newborns are not taken out of the house during the first 12 days or so even though the baby falls sick. In some communities, the belief is to give a complete bath on certain day only. These harmful practices contribute to higher number of deaths.

6. Female babies (daughters) are neglected more often than the sons when they fall sick.

7. Poor communication and transport facilities are other hurdles.

8. Over 80% of qualified doctors work in urban areas and private sectors. Poor people living in villages have no other option but to go to local practitioners, out of whom many are unqualified or herbal/witchcraft/magic healers.

9. There is a scarcity of trained nursing personnel who form the backbone of perinatal-neonatal and child care at all levels of care. The system itself lacks resources for training and capacity building to fulfill the gap thus arisen.

10. Discrimination being practiced against a particular community/individual further mars the health seeking attitude/behavior. Misbehavior by the greedy staff of the health facility. No incentive is given to any good health performing individual doctor/paramedical staff by the concerned authority or the government.

Conclusion

To sum up it is stated that the sickle cell disease and β-thalassemia syndrome are the major genetic and public health challenges in Central India. In view of credit of the 2nd highest infant mortality rate (IMR) in Madhya Pradesh (70 per thousand live-births in 2011) it was presumed that the hemoglobinopathies might be one of the contributing factors in the carrier couples of hemoglobinopathies for IMR. Couples (parents) including their offspring with at least one affected/suspected case of hemoglobinopathies referred to us from NSCB Medical College & Hospital, Jabalpur were consecutively studied as matched case controls.

A total of 333 couples were referred during the period from March 2010 to March 2012. Out 333 couples, 138 were found normal and 195 couples had different hemoglobin disorders. It was observed that the number of conceptions (2.456 vs 1.522), live-births (2.246 vs 1.319), surviving offspring (2.005 vs 1.406), stillbirths (0.082 vs 0.051), and deaths under 10 year (0.236 vs 0.145) were higher and neonatal deaths (0.103 vs 0.116), and deaths under one year (0.118 vs 0.123), per couple at the time of investigations were lower in couples with hemoglobinopathies as compared to normal controls.

The frequency of couples with HbAS x HbAS, HbAS x HbSS and β-Thal.T x β-Thal.T combinations was considerably higher in the scheduled castes, scheduled tribes, and in Other Backward Castes. Affected families were imparted genetic/marriage counseling. This study indicated that afflicted couples of these hereditary disorders were increasing the defective offspring (surviving: 58%). This increased production of defective offspring (surviving: 58.06%) leads to increased morbidity and mortality and may be contributing towards increased neonatal/infant mortality or fetal wastage in Madhya Pradesh, India.

Acknowledgments

Author is grateful to Dr. V. M. Katoch, Secretary, Department of Health Research, Government of India, and Director General, Indian Council of Medical Research, New Delhi for the permission and providing the necessary research facilities. Author gratefully acknowledges Dr. Shashi Khare, Dr. Monika Lajras, and Dr. Sharad Jain of NSCB Medical College & Hospital, Jabalpur for referring the patients for investigations to us. Technical help of Mr. V. K. Kachhi and Mr. P. Patel, Laboratory Technicians is thankfully acknowledged. Thanks are due to all the couples for their kind cooperation during the study.

References

[1]   Angastiniotis M, Modell B. Global epidemiology of hemoglobin disorders. Ann New York Acad Sci 1998;850:251-69.

[2]   Balgir RS. The burden of hemoglobinopathies in India and the challenges ahead. Curr Sci 2000;79:1536-47.

[3]   Balgir RS. Genetic epidemiology of the three predominant abnormal hemoglobins in India. J Assoc Phys India 1996;44:25-8.

[4]   Balgir RS. The clinical and hematological profile of sickle cell disease cases in India. Indian Practr 1995;48:423-32.

[5]   Balgir RS. Clinical genetics and hematological profile of sickle cell cases in twenty families of Orissa. Indian J Hemat Blood Transfus 2006;22:45-52.

[6]   Balgir RS. Epidemiology, population health genetics and phenotypic diversity of sickle cell disease in India. Internet J Biol Anthropol 2007;1:1-26.

[7]   Balgir RS, Dash BP, Das RK. Fetal outcome and childhood mortality in offspring of mothers with sickle cell trait and disease. Indian J Pediatr 1997;64:79-84.

[8]   Balgir RS. Infant mortality and reproductive wastage associated with different genotypes of hemoglobinopathies in Orissa, India. Ann Hum Biol 2007;34:16-25.

[9]   Balgir RS. Detrimental intrinsic factors contain population explosion for sustainable development in 18 indigenous communities of Orissa, India. In: Pati RN, Jain Atul Kumar, eds. Biodiversity and sustainable development. New Delhi: Sarup Book Publishers Private Limited, 2010:507-16.

[10]   Balgir RS. Hematological profile of pregnant women with carrier status of hemoglobin disorders in coastal Odisha, India. Int J Child Health Hum Dev 2011;4:325-32.

[11]   Balgir RS. Reproductive profile of mothers in relation to hemoglobin E genotypes. Indian J Pediatr 1992;59: 449-54.

[12]   Kalaivani K. Prevalence and consequences of anemia in pregnancy. Indian J Med Res 2009;130:627-33.

[13]   Prema K, Neela Kumari S, Ramalakshmi BA. Anemia and adverse obstetric outcome. Nutr Rep Int 1981;23:637-43.

[14]   Balgir RS. Birth control necessary to limit family size in tribal couples with aberrant heterosis of G6PD deficiency and sickle cell disorders in India: an urgency of creating awareness and imparting genetic counseling. J Assoc Phys India 2010;58:357-62.

[15]   Serjeant GR, Serjeant BE. Sickle cell disease, 3rd ed. New York: Oxford University Press, 2001.

[16]   Milner PF, Jones BR, Dobler J. Outcome of pregnancy in sickle cell anemia and sickle cell-hemoglobin C disease. Am J Obstet Gynecol 1980;138:239–45.

[17]   Charache S, Scott J, Niebyl J, Bonds D. Management of sickle cell disease in pregnant patients. Obstet Gynecol 1980;5:407-10.

In: Child Health and Human Development Yearbook 2013   ISBN: 978-1-63117-939-6
Editor: Joav Merrick   © 2014 Nova Science Publishers, Inc.

Chapter 21

Don't tag me as mentally retarded, as I am normal: A case study to understand the emotional development, dreams and insecurities of mentally challenged people

Munir Moosa Sadruddin*, PhD Scholar,
and Zaira Wahab, PhD
Hamdard Institute of Education and Social Sciences (HIESS), Hamdard University,
Karachi, Pakistan and Faculty of Education and Learning Sciences and Faculty of
Business Administration, Iqra University, Karachi, Pakistan

Abstract

The purpose of this paper is to understand the emotional development of mild mentally challenged people. The researchers are primarily interested in understanding the feelings, emotions and fears of mild mentally challenged people and how they perceive social relations. This paper also deals with social and emotional problems faced by mild mentally challenged people. In this case study, single descriptive (providing narrative accounts) case study methodology is carried out. A mild mentally challenged man was selected for the case study. The data is collected through multiple sources: in-depth interviews and direct observation. The case is narrated followed by detailed perspectives about few incidents. The researcher finds that the selected mild mentally challenged person was expressive, cooperative, supportive, kind- hearted, intelligent and understandable. He was peace loving and express same kind of emotions and fears which a normal person have; however his wishes could be of different nature. The respondent for this particular case was not socially active due to fears and anxiety. He has minor communication and physical movement problems, but his expressions were mature. The

---
* Correspondence: Munir Sadruddin, Hamdard University, Institute of Education and Social Sciences, Pakistan. E-mail: munirmoosa@yahoo.com.

respondent was emotionally disturbed, insecure about his future and exhibit mild behavior problem mainly because of being rejected by society. The respondent had negative feelings for this world and for their own lives. The barrier of society norms and family attitude towards the respondent construct negative feelings for people and life. The respondent needs courage and moral support to face the realities. Finally, the respondent wants people to stop tagging him mental. Based on the findings, valuable learning's are provided at the end.

Keywords: Mental retardation, intellectual disability, mentally challenged emotional development, dreams, insecurities

Introduction

We, the humans, have unique nature, traits and types of personalities. We consider ourselves as an important part of society and mostly interact with socially active people; but we often look down upon those people, who are unable to adapt basic social skills or have some kind of cognitive/mental disabilities. People with mental retardation or intellectual disability are mostly found wrestling with society to make people understand their feelings and emotions. These challenging people are often tagged as 'mental', which is inhumane to mankind.

According to AAMR (1), mental retardation (MR) or intellectual disability (ID) refers to limitations in intellectual functioning and in two or more adaptive skills areas from the following: communication: self-care, home living, social skills, community use, self-direction, health and safety, functional academics, leisure, and work. Manjunatha et al (2) defined mental retardation (MR) as sub-average general intellectual functioning, associated with disability in adaptive behavior. Mental retardation may occur as part of a syndrome or broader disorder (3), while Arizona Revised Statutes as cited in Smith and Strick (4) defined mental retardation as a disability associated with development rather than a mental disease. Multiple factors contribute for mental retardation which includes genetics, infections during pregnancy, infectious illness during infancy or drug abuse by mother during pregnancy.

Pelegano and Healy (5) categorize mental retardation into five general categories: borderline, mild, moderate, severe and profound. The categorical divisions are based on the scores obtained though standardized tests of cognitive ability. The IQ of mild retarded is between 50- 70. They show no unusual physical signs, but are slow in all developmental areas. They can integrate themselves in society but need practical and vocational skills. Moderate retardation shows noticeable delay, particularly physically or in speech. Their IQ is between 35-49. They learn simple skills like communication, self-care, safety habits etc., and perform simple tasks easily. Severe retardation shows marked delay in physical development. Their IQ is between 20-34. They have communication barriers and require supervision to learn simple tasks such as self-care, daily routines, etc., while profound retardation shows mark delay in all the areas of development. Their IQ is below 20 and can only perform physical tasks under close supervision.

According to Daily et al (6) both children and adults with mental retardation may also exhibit some or all of the following characteristics like delay in the development of adaptive behaviors and oral language development; difficulty in learning basic skills; problem solving skills and social rules.

People with intellectual disability have same emotional illness as people with normal intellectual abilities. Full range of personality disorders, behavior disorders that are noted in the normal population are also noticeable in people with intellectual disability (7).

According to the diagnostic studies of Webster (8), it was revealed that mental retardation includes an impairment in emotional as well as intellectual development. Children with mental retardation are less proficient in recognizing emotions, in responding to others' emotions, and in pro-social behaviors. Longitudinal studies on retarded children below 12 years reported a 20% to 35% frequency of emotional disturbances (9-11).

In the views of Scheerenberger (12), mild mental retardation is one of the classifications of mental disability. Daily et al (13) defined mild mental retardation are those with intelligence test scores between 70 and 85. They are capable of improving their mathematics and reading skills to the level of a typical child aged 9 to 12 and they can learn basic skills besides performing basic tasks easily.

People with intellectual disability have difficulty in communication. They find it difficult to communicate besides learning skills at a slower pace. However those with mild/borderline mental retardation are often able to lead independent lives as adults and learn adaptive behaviors through peers. http://www.humanillnesses.com/Behavioral-Health-Fe-Mu/Mental-Retardation.html (14).

But unfortunately, children with mild intellectual disability are mostly rejected by peers (15). According to Zigler et al (16) and Eaton et al (17) since people with intellectual disability have greater sensitivity and fewer interpersonal coping skills, such rejection greatly hampers their mental and social development.

According to Reynolds and Dombeck (18), individuals with mild intellectual disability are less emotionally immature. Contrary to that Olley (19) suggested that people with intellectual disability know love, anger, fear and joy and feel the same emotions as the other feels.

According to Kumar et al (20), due to low intellectual growth and limited functions, the mentally challenged people are less socially active. These children vary greatly in their social skills. The nature and degree of social impairment may vary depending on the diagnostic condition associated with mental retardation (21).

This case study is concerned with the aspects of exploring the emotional development, dreams and insecurities of mild mentally retarded people. The research questions arising from the case-study are as follows:

- Are people with mild intellectual disability emotional? Do they think in a similar pattern as we do?
- Are people with mind intellectual disability socially active?
- What are the dreams and insecurities?
- How do they perceive people?
- How do they react at different situations?

Methods

Case study research holds rich history across many disciplines. Hamel (22) traced the origin of modern social science case studies through anthropology and sociology. Merriam (23) advocated a general approach to qualitative case studies in the field of education, while Stake (24) used systematic procedures for case study research.

Feagin et al (25) viewed case study as an ideal methodology when an in-depth investigation is required. Clifford (26) considered it as a method which gives reflection of reality and provides 'thick description' of participants' lived experiences of thoughts about and feeling for a situation.

According to Yin (27) one of the reasons to consider case study design is when the focus of the study is to answer "how" and "why" questions. In case- study method, Crabtree and Miller (28) believed that there is a close bonding between the researcher and the participant, while enabling participants to tell their stories (29,30) and they believed that through these stories the participants are able to describe their opinions, close to reality.

In this research, holistic single qualitative case study, Yin (31) methodology is carried out. According to Alvarez et al (32), the descriptive type of case study is used to develop critical thinking and to describe an intervention or phenomenon and the real-life context in which it occurred.

Since the researcher wanted to understand the multi-layered emotions and feelings of mild mentally retarded people, a single mild mental retarded man was selected for the study.

The potential participant was informed about the nature and purpose of the research and about the expected benefits to the society. The purpose of the study was also shared to the participant. An informed consent was signed by the respondent on voluntary basis. Field and Morse (33) and Munhall (34) referred consent as a negotiation of trust, and it requires continuous renegotiation. The name was kept confidential throughout the research paper and the final outcomes were also shared to the respondent for which the respondent agreed to share it to the researchers.

The data is collected through multiple sources: in-depth interviews and direct observation. The case is narrated followed by detailed perspectives about few incidents. In the final interpretative phase, the researcher reports, as Lincoln and Guba (35) mention, the lesson learned from the case.

A case study

Joseph is tall, fair and handsome man with presentable personality. He is 30 years of age and has mature attitude. He thinks, analyze and observe each situation before expressing his opinions. It's hard for anyone to recognize that he is tagged as "mental" by the people. Though, medical sciences have proved that he has mild mental retardation but the tagged stigma has disturbed him emotionally.

This case study is unique because a person with mild intellectual disability never inquires God about his problems associated with communication and movement. He only blames people for treating him bad and for recalling his disabilities. He has few joyous memories like us, and he dreams to achieve his goals. He worries about his future like we do. He is intelligent and no one can beat him in counting. His cognitive abilities are very sharp. He wants to get pleasure from life to the fullest, but he is emotionally disturbed. He thinks hundreds of time before expressing his emotions and often curses his fate as he believes that no one give importance to him. He wants to socialize, but has many fears in mind as the community people often treat him like a kid and at times, people ignore him. He thinks that he is living in a cage and considers himself as a robot, operated by the owners of remote control. He wants the world to avoid calling him "mental". According to him

> "I am living a miserable life because I can't express my feelings to others. Most of the people consider my comments as unripe dialogues; but I want the world to understand and worth my views and opinions."

He was informed to meet me at the mosque regularly after the religious congregation. He was punctual and excited throughout the sessions. One the very first meeting he inquired

> "I am very much excited. You want to take my interview right? Please publish it around the world to let other know that I am a NORMAL human being. I want others to know that I am not mental. I walk, speak, talk, and think like others. Though I have minor physical disability and can't communicate clearly; that doesn't mean that I am abnormal. … don't forget to publish about my decorated handmade bottles, as I really want to boost my business."

No one would believe that the above mentioned comments were communicated by a person with mild intellectual disability. When asked to give a brief introduction, he told me that he is 30 years of age and has three siblings. Routinely, he wakes up early in the morning, brushes teeth, eats breakfast and then goes to vocational centre with a social worker. He returns back home at 1 pm, eats lunch and then rest for two hours. Later, he attends religious congregation. After returning home, he eats dinner and before going to bed, he routinely watches TV. He makes decorative bottles on weekends and also spends some time rendering community services. He loves to play bocce and wish to travel by plane. He wants to earn in order to support his family and wants to be independent in his life.

He lives with his family, but his social activities are very limited. He is not allowed to go anywhere alone, except of religious place. Though he visited several places with vocational centre volunteers and students, but he was not liberal to enjoy the beauty of nature as he experienced sympathy and mercy of social workers towards him.

At times, it was difficult to understand his speech. He stooped his head when he was unable to speak few words clearly, but he was given morale support to speak-up with confidence without thinking of communication barriers.

Spradlin (36) found that individuals with intellectual disability have more speech-related problems. Dunn (37) noted that as they mature, language differences between normal and mildly retarded learners become more pronounced. Kirk and Gallagher (38) reported that persons with mild intellectual disability encounter problems communicating effectively. In this case, Joseph was facing some articulation and speech problems however his thoughts and ideas were clear.

Joseph was unable to recall his childhood clearly, but he informed that he was enrolled in rehabilitation centre for disabled children by one of the family members. When the news echoed his ears, he was shocked and wept a lot. He inquired one of his family members to

know the reasons behind enrolling him to a rehabilitation center. He was informed that since
he is uneducated and has communication problems, he has to attend classes at rehabilitation
centre. During conversation, he looked really disappointed and his voice was very cold. For
few minutes he was quiet and refused to give further comments. Later he informed that he
cried a lot because he wanted to learn with normal children, and that it was difficult for him to
adjust in new environment. He said

> "I wish I could attend a main stream school... I have to live my whole life like a
> mental person because I am of no worth for any one. No one values my opinion. Why
> people call me scary? Am I really scary?"

Life of mentally challenged people has not been as easy as we think. Joseph's personality
was underdeveloped, because he faced many critical incidents and challenges in his life, but
was unable to share it to others. His thinking was a bit constructed in a negative way, as the
society made him realize that he is alien on this earth. His mood also swung multiple times
during interview sessions.

Mood disorders are also common amongst individuals with intellectual disability. This
view was further strengthened by Marston, Perry, & Roy (39) by revealing the facts of several
studies that found very high rates of depression ranging from 44 percent in individuals with
mental disabilities. When asked about his three most demanding wishes, he thought and
replied

> "I want to travel by bus and want to experience a journey by plane and want to earn
> lots of money."

When asked about the places he travelled so far, his eyes sparkled with tears. I found him
upset and felt as if something was going on in his mind. For few minutes, he looked here and
there and was quiet, but later he broke the ice to inform me about the false promises and tall
talks made by the management of the rehabilitation centre to take him to Islamabad (Capital
of Pakistan) via plane to participate in games, but that day has not yet arrived. Once he asked
his parents to go for outing, but he was totally de-motivated. Moreover, a social worker
wanted to take him for outing, also faced rudeness and slur from his family side. He shared

> "I am a controlled robot. I can't go anywhere. I heard and learnt about the places
> through TV because I can't go anywhere alone; I'm bounded. I only go to attend religious
> congregations at my own, but people overlook me. I am confined not to travel without
> permission. My siblings went to international destinations during holidays, but I was
> never offered to accompany them. I want to experience the thrill, but I know, this would
> always remain a dream because I am MENTAL. The rehabilitation centre lied to take me
> to Islamabad by plane but I was very much disappointed when I realized that it was
> nothing more than a tall talk."

Something was going on in Joseph's mind. He later asked about my experience of
travelling by public bus and airplane. While sharing my experience, he listened me with
anticipation, though interrupted multiple times due to excitement, and also expressed his wish
to experience the same. Mikkelsen (40) believed that people with intellectual disability

experience the full range of human emotions. In this case study, the same was observed by the researcher as Joseph shared both happy and gloomy emotions during detailed interviews.

Turkington and Harris (41) wrote that many people with mild intellectual disability are able to live and work independently. When asked, what sort of work he wants to do, he informed that he is already earning by selling decorative handmade bottles and earns around 10- 15$ per month. He shared that he always wanted to earn but was discouraged by XYZ during his adolescence; however at the age of 21, he started selling rosary at public places through the support of a social worker but was highly discouraged by the volunteers of rehabilitation centre. When his family was informed, he was disregarded. He informed that he was also threatened that if he works at public places, he would face severe consequences. Things changed for him at the age of 27 when a team of social worker supported him to make decorative bottles.

He was dissatisfied with the reaction of society. According to him, few people buy decorative bottles because they consider him mental. Few even offer him money and eatables without buying bottles because they feel pity over his condition, while there are some people, who keep distance from him as they consider him insane. At times, Joseph was frustrated and aggressive by recalling his past, but his behavior and aggression was under control. The only reason behind such aggressive behavior was an immature attitude of society towards him.

Aggressive behavior is commonly found among people with intellectual disability. Crocker and Hodgins (42) mentioned that number of researches documented high rates of aggressive behavior and violence. A model was developed by Gardner and Graeber (43) that suggested that aggressive behavior is determined by a number of factors including genetic disorders, personality traits, anti- social personality disorder or depression. When asked whether his family is happy to know about his work, he gave a positive gesture. He believed that his siblings are now giving him importance. He said

> "...I know XYZ consider me mental but I have to adjust else XYZ might take me out of the house and I have nowhere to go. I earn very less but my family has now started giving me some importance and encourages me to sell and earn more."

According to Bedrosian and Prutting (44), a research was conducted with four adults with intellectual disability to analyze the communicative performances and social interactions. The results indicated that they were capable of expressing the same types of control as normal adults. In this particular case study, it was observed and realized that the social interaction of the respondent was limited; however the respondent was capable to express his views to trustworthy people.

He informed that he fears in sharing his ideas to many people because several times, he tried to ask people to help in getting a job, but the people just calmed him and made false promises. Once he approached a shop to sell his bottle, but the owner called names, which abandoned him to further express his views.

The respondent was closed to his father. He cried a lot when his father expired because he felt all alone. Since the day his father departed from this world, he is insecure and lives a life full of fears and worries. In his opinion, although he has a family but no one can fill that alien feeling within him. He shared

"…though I have my mother and siblings, but dad is dad. No one can fill that gap. I feel insecure that what would happen after my mother dies? Who will take care of me? I can do things on my own but I can't."

According to Blodgett (45), people with intellectual disability do have feelings and emotions but they do not develop their emotional capacity to the same degree or with the same differentiation as do normal children. Throughout the discussions, I found him emotionally disturbed. His facial gestures were clear and supported him conversations, but at times, he was drowned in perplexity.

Begun (46) found that there was less bonding in the sibling relationship when one had a disability. When inquired about his relations with siblings, he informed that he is close to his sister; however he is often ignored by his brothers. He also added that since his brothers are educated, they are given more privileges and favor from family side.

He asked me several flabbergast questions like, if a person can't read or write, should we tag them mental? If a person has speech problem, does that mean that he is mental? Why people keep distance from me in society? Is it possible that I can earn more to become rich? His questions were mature enough to ponder, why he constructed such questions in his mind? Does that really mean that he is still confused about his status in society or is he dissatisfied with the kind of reaction he is getting from the people?

All moral support was provided to him throughout the interviews. We also cherished happy moments. He informed about the most unfavorable incident that XYZ always calls him mental in front of others and his relatives also taunt him the same, that's why he keep himself detach from society as he fears of experiencing the same from others.

The mentally challenged people face the same emotional challenges which other adults face but don't always receive the same levels of attention and understanding from family members and caregivers. Their emotions and feelings are often overlooked. He said

"I have emotions but when others call me MENTAL, it sometimes force me to commit suicide because I can't tolerate such comments. It is more of an allegation than a gesture. No one cares for me. My feelings are baseless for everyone."

He attempted to commit suicide thrice in his life. The reason he gave me for taking such step was due to the pressure of society and restrictions from the family side. Once he tried to cut his hand; the second time he wanted to eat tablets but was unable to eat, while for third time, he tried to run away from home but was caught red-handed.

Mulick et al (47) mentioned that many researches indicate that intellectual disability frequently is accompanied by personality disorder, notably problems of aggression. In this particular case anxiety, aggressive attitude and fear were observable during interactions with the respondent. I found him gloomy when he told me that he has not achieved anything in his life which he wanted to achieve, that's why he had negative feelings about his life.

According to American Academy of Child and Adolescent Psychiatry [AACAP] (48), adolescents and young adults with intellectual disabilities may become depressed. They might not have enough language skills to express their feelings. In this case study, it was revealed that mild retarded people do have language skills to talk about their feelings but are limited to share their views to everyone.

He was interested in knowing about my hobbies and education. When he learnt about my interest in playing piano and singing, he informed about his similar interest. He also sang a song for me. He loves to play piano and he is crazy about computers. Unfortunately, he can't touch computer at home as he is disallowed to do so. He shared that he used computer for the very first time at the age of 27, when the rehabilitation centre provided him a platform to learn it for few days. He wants to learn computers to prove others that he is not illiterate. Moreover, he wants to market his decorative bottles worldwide though net.

When asked about his social interaction with friends and community members, he informed me that no one is close to him in community. He loves to live in isolation because he has observed people keeping distance with him. He shared that once he visited the Office of National Identity Card with his family members, where he was asked for the signature. The man on the counter rejected his signature and suggested him to print thumb on the paper and tagged him mental in front of others. This discrimination led him to think about his identity in this world.

Gresham and MacMillan (49) conducted an empirical research examined the social competence (social skills, adaptive behavior, peer relationship) and affective functioning of children with mild disabilities. The review showed that children with mild disabilities had poorer social skills, exhibited more interfering problem behaviors, and were poorly accepted or rejected by peers.

Sigafoos et al (50) view mentally challenged people as those with poorly socialized behavior that is expressed in a variety of ways, including aggression, conduct disorders, etc. In this case, the respondent lacked social interactions and also exhibited mild behavior problem mainly because of being rejected by society.

Joseph heard people calling him mental. He has seen parents keeping their children away from him. Moreover, he has observed and heard negative comments about his personality. Sometimes, children also make fun of him. He feels bad when people reject him. He sits alone in religious congregation and keeps distance from the people. Joseph informed that since he is tagged mental due to difficulties in physical and oral speech, he feels shame to face people because people sometimes find it difficult to understand him.

A study was conducted by Institute of Psychiatry (51), where adolescents and young adults with intellectual disability, together with non-retarded children individually matched for verbal mental age, were given tasks to understand their understanding about emotions The results suggest that individuals with intellectual disability may have specific deficits in recognizing how bodily expressions of emotion are coordinated with each other. This case study proofs that people with mild intellectual disability are emotionally expressive. The similar pattern of activity was conducted. Throughout the activity, he performed well and there was no specific deficit in recognizing bodily expressions of emotions.

He informed me that his future plan is to sell more decorative bottles and wants to earn his living by starting his business on national and International platform. He repeatedly asked for the moral support.

Several questions were asked to assess the feelings and emotions, situation tackling capabilities, intelligence, besides knowing how mild mentally challenge people respond at different situations. The gathered answers were quiet mature. He shared that he feels happy when he earns but wants people not call him mental. He considers world as a place of living for rude people, but he never hates human beings. He is willing to help his family members in the future but he wants to demagnetize himself from the other people. He keeps his savings in bank as he is well aware about the risk of keeping money at home. He provides financial support to his mother and also buys dress from his own earning. He doesn't want to begin his family because people consider him mental and that tag has emotionally disturbed him beside other social barriers. He expressed his wish to travel by plane. He expressed his insecurity as he has fears that no one would keep him after the death of his mother. Whenever he feels loneliness, he watches TV. Once he fought with someone as he was unable to control his temper over intolerable situation. He knows basics of first aid and knows how to tackle different situations. He considers his life as a precious gift of god but often curse his fate. He keeps himself up-to-date about world affairs and replied all general IQ answers correctly. He also understands the sensitive terms like terrorism. He recalls all the phone numbers, date, time and performed well in calculation test. Few general knowledge questions were also asked like: who the current President of Obama and what is the capital of India? He replied correct to most of the questions. Many objects were exposed to him and he successfully identified objects through names. When a task was given to compare things, he chose respect over disrespect, love over scold, family over world, love over hate, peace over war, sister over brothers, money over poverty, money over friendship, and opted airplane over bus ride.

Conclusion

The case concludes that the selected case with mild intellectual disability was expressive, cooperative, supportive, kind- hearted, intelligent and understandable. He was peace loving and evaluate things closely. He had no specific deficit in recognizing bodily expressions of emotions; however, he was some way or the other way emotionally disturbed, insecure about the future and life. He lacked social interactions and also exhibited mild behavior problem mainly because of being rejected by society. Anxiety, mood swing and fear were observable. He had minor communication and physical movement problems, but his expressions were mature.

He wants to lead a liberal life and want to experience different moments of joys. He had positive views about their families but negative feelings for this world and for his own life. He dreams like us but with some limitations. He wants motivation and support from society and want the world to accept him with an open arm. This case study taught us to correct our behavior towards all mentally challenged people. To change their views about us, we must socialize with them and value their opinions. Parents should never underestimate their emotions. Parents should love and provide them support to follow their dreams. At the same time, we must avoid rude remarks and stop tagging them mental. They are like any other human being and nothing is different about them. They need courage and moral support to face the world with realities. They are willing to share their experiences with us but the only need of time is to correct our attitudes towards them. They should get opportunities to turn their dreams into realities for which awareness is the most powerful tool to integrate them with us.

References

[1]   Luckasson R, Coulter DL, Polloway EA, Reiss S, Schalock RL, Snell, ME, et al. Mental retardation: Definition, classification, and systems of supports, 9th ed. Washington, DC: American Association Mental Retardation, 1992.

[2]   *Manjunatha KR, Chetan GK, Arathi R*, Bhaskara GV, Latha P, Padma S, et al. Frequency, association and genetic implications of chromosomal fragile sites in mental retardation. Int J Health Geogr 2002;2:33-9.

[3]   Donna K, Holly H, Grace E. Identification and evaluation of mental retardation. Am Fam Physician 2000;61(4):1059-67.

[4]   Smith C, Strick L, eds. Learning disabilities: A to Z: A parent's complete guide to learning disabilities from preschool to adulthood. New York: Simon Schuster, 1999.

[5]   Pelegano JP, Healy A. Mental retardation Part II- Seeing the child within. Fam Pract Recertification 1992;14:58-71.

[6]   Daily DK, Ardinger HH, Holmes GE. Identification and evaluation of mental retardation. Am Fam Physician 2000;61(4):1059-67.

[7]   Bertelli M, Scuticchio D, Ferrandi A, Lassi S, Mango F, Ciavatta C, et al.

[8]   Reliability and validity of the SPAID-G checklist for detecting psychiatric disorders in adults with intellectual disability. Res Dev Disabil 2012;33(2):382-90.

[9]   Webster TG. Problems of emotional development in young retarded children. Am J Psychiatry 1963;20(1):37-43.

[10]   Chess S. Emotional problems in mentally retarded children. In: Menolascino FJ, ed. Psychiatric approaches to mental retardation. New York: Basic Books, 1970:55–67.

[11]   Menolascino FJ, Bernstein NR. Psychiatric assessment of the mentally retarded child. In: Bernstein NR, ed. Diminished people. Boston: Little Brown, 1970:201-22.

[12]   Phillips I, Williams N. Psychopathology: A study of 100 children. Am J Psychiatr 1975;132:1265-73.

[13]   Scheerenberger RC. A history of mental retardation: A quarter century of promise. Baltimore: Paul Brookes, 1987.

[14]   Daily DK, Ardinger HH, Holmes GE. Identification and evaluation of mental retardation. Am Fam Physician 2000;61(4):1059-67.

[15]   Mental retardation. Human diseases and conditions. Accessed 2012 Jan 01. URL: http://www.humanillnesses.com/Behavioral-Health-Fe-Mu/Mental-Retardation.html

[16]   Taylor AR, Asher SR, Williams GA. The social adaptation of mainstreamed mildly retarded children. Child Dev 1987;58:1321-34.

[17]   Zigler E, Burack JA. Personality development and the dually diagnosed person. Res Dev Disabil 1989;10:225-40.

[18]   Eaton LF, Menolascino FJ. Psychiatric disorders in the mentally retarded: types, problems, and challenges. Am J Psychiatry 1982;139: 1297-1303.

[19]   Reynolds T, Dombeck M. Mental retardation (intellectual disabilities). Accessed 2012 Jan 01. URL: http://www.mentalhelp.net/poc/view_doc

[20]   Olley JG. Mental retardation. Nature, cause and development. Philadelphia, PA: Brunner Mazel, 1999.

[21]   Kumar I, Singh AR, Akhtar S. Social development of children with mental retardation. Ind Psychiatry J 2009;18:56-59.

[22]   Kasari C, Bauminger N. Social and emotional development in children with mental retardation. In: Burack JA, Hodapp RM, Zigler E, eds. Handbook of mental retardation and development. Cambridge: University of Cambridge, 1998.

[23]   Hamel J, Dufour S, Fortin D. Case study methods. Newbury Park, CA: Sage, 1993.

[24]   Merriam SB. Qualitative research and case study applications in education. San Francisco: Jossey-Bass, 1998.

[25]   Stake R. The art of case research. Thousand Oaks, CA: Sage, 1995.

[26]   Feagin J, Orum A, Sjoberg G, eds. A case for case study. Chapel Hill, NC: University North Carolina Press, 1991.

[27]   Clifford G. Thick description: Toward an interpretive theory of culture. In: Clifford G, ed. The interpretation of cultures: Selected essays. New York: Basic Books, 1973:3-30.

[28]   Yin RK. Case study research: Design and methods. Newbury Park, CA: Sage, 1984.

[29]   Crabtree BF, Miller WL. Doing qualitative research, 2nd ed. Thousand Oaks, CA: Sage, 1999.

[30]   Lather P. Critical frames in educational research: Feminist and post-structural perspectives. Theory Pract 1992;31(2):87-99.

[31]   Robottom I, Hart P. Research in environmental education: Engaging the debate. Australia: Deakin University Press, 1993.

[32]   Yin RK. Case study research: Design and methods, 3rd ed. Thousand Oaks, CA: Sage, 2003.

[33]   Alvarez M, Binkley E, Bivens J, Highers P, Poole C, Walker P. Case-based instruction and learning: An interdisciplinary project. Proceedings 34th Annual Conference, College Reading Association, 1990:2-18.

[34]   Field PA, Morse JM. Nursing research. The application of qualitative approaches. London: Chapman Hall, 1992.

[35]   Munhall P. Ethical considerations in qualitative research. Western J Nurs Res 1988;10(2):150-62.

[36]   Lincoln YS, Guba EG. Naturalistic inquiry. Newbury Park, CA: Sage, 1985.

[37]   Spradlin JE. (1963). Language and communication of mental defectives. In Ellis, N. R. (Ed.) Handbook of mental deficiency. New York: McGraw-Hill, 1963.

[38]   Dunn LM. Exceptional children in the schools: Special education in transition. New York: Holt Rinehart Winston, 1973.

[39]   Krik SA, Gallagher JJ. Educating exceptional children, 3rd ed. Boston: Houghton Mifflin, 1979.

[40]   Marston GM, Perry DW, Roy A. Manifestations of depression in people with intellectual disability. J Intellect Disabil Res 1997;41:476–80.

[41]   Mikkelsen E. Is psychotherapy useful for the mentally retarded? Harvard Mental Health Letter 1994;11(2):8.

[42]   Turkington C, Harris J. The encyclopedia of the brain and brain disorders, 3rd ed. New York: Infobase, 2002.

[43]   Crocker AG, Hodgins S. The criminality of noninstitutionalized mentally retarded persons. Evidence from a birth cohort followed to age 30. Criminal Justice Behav 1997;24(4):432-54.

[44]   Gardner WI, Graeber JL. Treatment of severe behavioral disorders in persons with mental retardation: A multimodal behavioral treatment model. In: Fletcher R, Dosen A, eds. Mental health aspects of mental retardation. New York: Lexington Books, 1993.

[45]   Bedrosian JL, Prutting C. Communicative performance of mentally retarded adults in four conversational settings. J Speech Hearing Res 1978;21:79-95.

[46]   Blodgett HE. Mentally retarded children. What parents and others should know. Minnesota: University Minnesota, 1971.

[47]   Begun AL. Sibling relationships involving developmentally disabled people. Am J Ment Retard 1989;93: 566–574.

[48]   Mulick JA, Hammer D, Dura JR. Assessment and management of antisocial and hyperactive behavior. In: Matson JL, Mulick JA, eds. Handbook of mental retardation. New York: Pergamon Press, 1991.

[49]   AACAP. Children who are mentally retarded. Washington, DC: American Academy Child Adolescent Psychiatry, 2004.

[50]   Gresham FM, MacMillan DL. Social competence and affective characteristics of students with mild disabilities. Rev Educ Res 1997;67(4):377-415.

[51]   Sigafoos J, Elkins J, Kerr M, Attwood T. A survey of aggressive behaviour among a population of persons with intellectual disability in Queensland. J Intellect Disabil Res 1994;38(4):369-81.

[52]   Hobson RP, Ouston J, Lee A. Recognition of emotion by mentally retarded adolescents and young adults. Am J Ment Retard 1989;93(4): 434-43.

In: Child Health and Human Development Yearbook 2013   ISBN: 978-1-63117-939-6
Editor: Joav Merrick   © 2014 Nova Science Publishers, Inc.

Chapter 22

Using VML (Verbal Motor Learning) method techniques in treatment of prosody disorder due to childhood apraxia of speech: A case study

*Elad Vashdi**
Yael Center, Aloney Aba, Israel

Abstract

Childhood apraxia of speech (CAS) is a motor deficit phenomenon that affects the child's ability to communicate verbally with his environment and has a wide spectrum of classifications. One of these classifications is a prosody deficit which has a pragmatic manifestation. In this case study we examine the influence of manual VML techniques on prosody. The subject is a 14 years old teenager diagnosed with severe CAS and limb apraxia. The subject was treated for years for prosody with no success. We applied a new manual technique as an experiment for a month involving daily sessions. Results showed reduced volume, differentiation between high and low pitch and improved control over word lengths. This is one step in creating a wide inventory of manual techniques to treat prosody among CAS patients.

Keywords: CAS, apraxia, child development, speech, prosody, intonation, pitch

Introduction

Communication among people can be expressed in several ways such as through written correspondence, body language picture exchange or visual signals. However, the most powerful communication tool is speech which is unique to humans. Speech is built from

---

* Corresponding author: Elad Vashdi, BPT, MPE, DPT, Yael Center, POBox 197, Aloney Aba, Israel. E-mail: Center@yaelcenter.com.

verbal structures such as words and sentences and from nonverbal structures. A non-verbal communicative element of speech is the intonation which is produced by a combination of Vocal cord frequency, duration and intensity (1). Intonation is an ability that a child starts to control and develop in the first year of his life. This case study will describe the absence of intonation control in a child with childhood apraxia of speech (CAS) and a VML intervention for intonation control and prosody.

The origin of CAS is debated. Researchers have several approaches to CAS that lead to different treatment approaches (2). There are the motor control models and the psycholinguistic theories (3) that try to define the disorder. The ASHA committee (4) defines CAS as "A neurological childhood (pediatric) speech sound disorder in which the precision and consistency of movements underlying speech are impaired in the absence of neuromuscular deficits (e.g., abnormal reflexes, abnormal tone)". CAS may occur as a result of a known neurological impairment, in association with complex neurobehavioral disorders of known or unknown origin, or as an idiopathic neurogenic speech sound disorder. The core impairment in planning and/or programming spatiotemporal parameters of movement sequences results in errors in speech sound production and prosody.

One of the diagnostic markers for CAS examines the ability to imitate movements of the three basic systems of speech: articulators (oral imitation), breathing (blowing out a candle, blowing bubbles) and vocal cords (sound production of any kind). The ability to imitate speech means that there is an ability to imitate combined movements of each of these systems. Speech is both the combined and timed work of these three systems.

If there is a problem in imitating movements of one of these systems in the absence of muscle tone deficits, lack of muscle power or anatomic disorder, than the speech problem is probably due to CAS.

One of the deficits in CAS is the lack of intonation. The child has difficulties in delivering a non-verbal message through his speech. Verbal language without intonation becomes poor and robotic. The loss of intonation has been well demonstrated among people after a head injury (5). Without intonation, the non-verbal message is unclear just as reading would be if it was done without punctuation marks. Teaching intonation to a child who doesn't understand how to produce the sound is not an easy task. Very few articles have been written on this subject. Exceptions are Helfrich-Miller (6) who demonstrated the Melodic Intonation Therapy Method which used melody patterns in order to organize speech patterns and Boutsen and Christman (7) who described the prosody issues in apraxia of speech.

Prosody is the patterns of stress and intonation in a language. The term generally covers intonation, rhythm, and focus in speech (8). Acoustically, prosody describes changes in the syllable length, loudness, pitch (frequency of a sound), and certain details of the formant structure of speech sounds. From the speech articulator's perspective, prosody is a result of changes in the velocity and range of motion in articulators like the jaw and tongue, along with change in the air pressure in the trachea and a change in the tension of the laryngeal muscles. Phonologically, prosody is described by tone, intonation, rhythm, and lexical stress (9).

The VML method is a set of Manual techniques, motor learning principles and multi-disciplinary therapeutic guidelines that is aimed at treating apraxia of speech.

The method was developed via field work with children diagnosed with CAS. Based on theory and previous research, the practical techniques framework, and evaluation, analysis and treatment forms were created.

The method is being taught in Hebrew and English. The VML method includes hundreds of different techniques to treat CAS.

In this case study the influence of several manual techniques on prosody was examined. One of the techniques is the Distal Dynamic Stabilization Technique (DDST).

The basic principle of the DDST is to stabilize dynamically the distal end of the moving system in order to perform movement in the proximal end. The specific DDST in this case study relates to dynamic stabilization of the jaw movement in order to elicit movement around the vocal cords in order to influence intonation. For further information about the DDST see appendix 1. Other techniques were breathing control via diaphragmatic breathing and candle blowing control.

The main purpose of this study was to test the impact of DDST and breathing control techniques on prosody parameters.

More specifically, the goals of the intervention were to decrease the loudness of the child's voice, to achieve expressive differentiation between high and low pitch and to reduce word duration.

Case study

The subject was a 14 years old teenager, diagnosed with severe general motor apraxia and severe Apraxia of speech. A few years after this intervention took place the subject was diagnosed with OCD (obsessive compulsive disorder). He attended a small special class in a regular school together with 10 other children diagnosed with learning disabilities.

At birth the subject received high Apgar scores of 9 and 10 and there were no reported complications. He was very quiet as a baby and didn't babble during his first year of life. His motor development was unusual; at the age of a year and two months he stood up for the first time, sat down and then crawled. He was very clumsy as a child. He couldn't pronounce phonemes through imitation or spontaneously. The physician who saw him at the age of two years said that the child wasn't mentally retarded since he had "smart eyes" and that he wasn't autistic either.

As a child he used to cry a lot and would occasionally bang his head on the floor. His behavior and lack of speech caused his parents to send him to special kindergartens where the educational team didn't know exactly what to do with him. At the age of four, a speech language pathologist (SLP) was the first to diagnose him with Severe Apraxia of speech.

I started working with him using the VML method when he was 6 years old. At that age he still couldn't pronounce phonemes, syllables or words through imitation or spontaneously, he couldn't walk up stairs without support and would walk down stairs in a step to step manner (STS) with poor control. He couldn't stand on one leg or jump. However he could read. In the entrance to the kitchen in his home was a big board on which he posted written words in short sentences such as "I want to eat". He taught himself to read through working on the computer. His reading ability was the proof of his academic potential. He was in a special kindergarten just before entering the first grade and was supposed to go to a special-education school.

We worked primarily on speech for the first 6 months and then integrated gross motor skills into the program. He acquired all the syllables in Hebrew after six months and started forming words and using them. Thanks to that he entered a regular school the year after.

In the following nine years he acquired motor-speech abilities and could use his speech pragmatically though his pronunciation wasn't clear. The main problem with his speech was the prosody of speech. The child couldn't control the loudness of his speech nor did he have versatility of tones in his speech. These prosody problems prevented him from delivering non semantic messages via speech which is a very important element in pragmatic verbal interactions. Four years of treatment on prosody in different ways such as changing head position, practicing asking questions, playing the piano, singing and working on voice control didn't bring a change in intonation.

The DDST idea came to my mind and we decided to give it a chance while performing the therapy in a research paradigm.

Procedure

The child had a 30 minute professional VML treatment session once a week and 6 more similar sessions a week conducted by his mother. The mother was watching the professional session and performed the same during the week under the guidance of the VML therapist. Each session included four exercises: 1) Blowing on a candle without extinguishing the flame 15-20 times 2) Imitating words of two open syllables faster than usually with a focus on reducing the fragment of time it takes to pronounce the vowel in the syllable 3) DDST was used to teach high and low pitch differentiation 4) Imitating words while lying on the back and breathing diaphragmatically. For protocols of the intervention see appendix 1. The program was conducted for four weeks. Tests were taken at the beginning of the first session of the program and at the end of the last session.

Measurements

The child performed two tests: 1) producing the highest pitch using /I/ sound without and with DDST, 2) Imitation of 18 words at a regular pace. The child's voice was recorded using a microphone attached to professional headphones. The voice recording took place in the child's room in the pre and post intervention testing. The microphone was placed as near as possible to the child's mouth in order to prevent inaccuracy of sound recordings and to prevent inconsistency in voice recordings. We used the same headphones for both measurements. We used "speech analyzer version 1.5" software (10) for voice analysis.

The dependent variables that were examined are: 1) words length, 2) Maximum loudness of words, 3) Maximum frequency of words, 4) Maximum frequency of pitch with and without DDST, 5) Minimum frequency of pitch with and without DDST, 6) Maximum loudness of pitch with and without DDST, 7) length of pitch with and without DDST.

Variables one and seven were measured in seconds. Variables 2 and 6 were measured as the percentage of loudness relative to a level provided by the software. Variables 3-5 were measured in Hertz units.

Statistical analysis

Paired T tests were used to examine the statistical significance of the difference between the word lengths, loudness and frequencies before and after the intervention. In regards to the pitch, as only the best measures out of 10 attempts was recorded for each condition (i.e. before, after, with, without), no significance test was used. However, there was a substantial difference in few of the pitch variables.

Results

Tables 1 & 2 provide the results of the experiment. Word length decreased significantly ($p<0.001$). The average words length at the beginning of the experiment was 0.7 seconds while after the experiment it decreased to 0.52 seconds. The maximum loudness of the words also decreased significantly from 27.37% on average at the beginning of the experiment to 20.29% ($p<0.001$). The maximum frequency of the words also decreased significantly from 198.88 HZ on average at the beginning of the experiment to 158.62 HZ ($P<0.0001$) at the end.

The pitch tests were examined for tendency. Maximum pitch frequency tends to increase with the DDST in comparison to no DDST condition. No tendency for change was observed between beginning and end of intervention as for results of Minimum frequency of pitch with and without DDST. The length of pitch tends to be higher at the end of the intervention in comparison to the beginning. Maximum pitch loudness tends to be higher for the DDST condition in comparison to no DDST condition.

Table 1. Pitch results summary

	with support	without support	Time
max' pitch frequency (HZ)	280	243	Beginning
	276	232	End
Min' pitch frequency (HZ)	186	176	Beginning
	192	172	End
length of pitch (seconds)	0.68	0.61	Beginning
	2.24	1.15	End
max' pitch loudness (% of max	56.8	33.8	Beginning
	21.9	12.2	End

Table 2. Words results summary

	before		after				
Var	avg	std	avg	std	t test	df	Sig'
word loudness	27.37059	6.152211	20.29412	5.726088	3.719139	16	<0.0001
word frequency	198.8824	10.50525	158.6235	7.208114	12.43725	16	<0.0001
word length	0.709829	0.16586	0.526741	0.133803	5.30602	16	<0.0001

Discussion

The use of DDST support shows tendency for changes in maximum pitch frequency and in maximum pitch loudness. Usually, we can find proximal dynamic stabilization for an angular movement in the body's joints. For example, the shoulder muscles give proximal stabilization to the elbow movements; the muscles that surround the elbow stabilize the elbow joint in order to allow movement around the wrist joint etc. In this case; a distal dynamic stabilization was given through DDST technique since it encouraged proximal muscles to work. Using the distal dynamic stabilization technique was crucial in this case as there was no other apparent way to approach these deep muscles. There may be two possible explanations for the tendency using the distal dynamic stabilization mechanism. The first explanation is that the vocal cord muscles and the jaw retraction muscles work as a group in this specific task. In order to perform the task all the muscles that belong to the group must work together otherwise the task can't be performed. This group of muscles might have neuronal connections (similar to agonist-antagonist neuronal connections) thus, activating part of the group with intention to activate the other parts as well, might cause a neurological overflow from one part to the other.

The other explanation is simpler. A co-contraction of the jaw openers and the Masseter muscles creates a distal stabilization that performs a close kinematic chain. Stabilization of the distal part of the chain enables movement in the proximal part of the chain, just as when performing push up exercises the distal part (i.e. the wrists) are stabilized while the proximal parts (i.e. the elbow and shoulder joints) are moving.

The decrease in loudness between the baseline and end can be explained by the improved control in breathing in general and exhalation in particular. The control of breathing enables the child to exhale with more control while talking thus more accurately monitoring the air pressure in the vocal cords area. Increased loudness usually increases pitch frequency because of the increased air pressure beneath the vocal cords. An ability to decrease the air pressure beneath the vocal cords (decreased loudness) while increasing pitch frequency (rather than decreasing) shows movement discrimination.

The DDST was developed in order to increase tone. This explains the child's inability to decrease tone beyond the baseline measurements. The improved control over breathing was due to the candle blowing and diaphragmatic exercises while practicing speed pronunciation intensively. It brought a significant change in the words length. The change wasn't only numeric but was expressed functionally as the child became more understandable in interactions with unfamiliar people.

The results are even more impressive when taking into consideration the child's age, history of previous failures and the relatively little amount of practice (15 minutes a day for a month). Since this is only a case study and no statistical analysis was made for the pitch variables we should be very careful in generalizing the study findings. There might have been other factors that influenced the results such as maturation or intensity of practice (rather than the technique itself). The techniques should be employed in other treatment programs in bigger study designs in order to determine its efficacy on other children or adults. The influence of the techniques on prosody should be examined functionally in an objective study.

Acknowledgments

Many thanks to the child and his family for participation and commitment. Without the support and active participation of the family we wouldn't have been able to perform the study.

Appendix 1

Protocols of intervention

1. Blowing on a candle without extinguishing the flame – the therapist explains the exercise to the child. The child sits on a chair and the therapist faces him. The therapist lights the candle and puts it 40-50 cm in front of the child's face. The child is instructed to blow on the candle without extinguishing the flame. If he succeeds the therapist will put the candle closer and the child tries again. If he succeeds again then the candle is put closer to the child at approximately 15 cm. the child will blow 15-20 times in each session.

2. Imitating words of two open syllables faster than usual with special consideration of reducing the fragment of time it takes to pronounce the vowel in the syllable. The child is introduced to the same list of 20 words each session.

3. Distal Dynamic Stabilization Technique (DDST) was used to teach high and low pitch differentiation. The child is asked to say the sound /I/ in a regular tone and in a low tone without support and in a high tone with and without DDST. DDST technique is performed by putting the first fingers (left and right) under the chin while pressing caudally. Simultaneously the two indexes are placed above the zygomatic arc. The child is asked to open his mouth. When he presses his jaw down the therapist asks him to say /I/ in a high pitch. It can be performed also with the support of only the first fingers. The exercise is done 10-15 times each session.

4. Imitating list of 20 words while lying on the back and breathing diaphragmatically

References

[1]   Denes PB, Pinson EP. The speech chain. New York: WH Freeman,1993.

[2]   Ziegler W. Psycholinguistic and motor theories of apraxia of speech. Semin Speech Lang 2002; 23: 231-44

[3]   Ken RD. Research on speech motor control and its disorders: A review and prospective. J Commun Disord 2000; 33(5): 391-428.

[4]   Asha.org/policy [Internet]. Childhood apraxia of speech [Position Statement]. [cited 2011 Nov 10]. Available from http://www.asha.org/docs/html/PS2007-00277.html.

[5]   Toshniwal SS, Joshi NA. Residual speech impairment in patients with traumatic brain injury. Indian J Neurotrauma 2010; 7(1): 61-6.

[6]   Helfrich-Miller KR. A clinical perspective: melodic intonation therapy for developmental apraxia. Clin Commun Disord1994; 4(3): 175-82.

[7]   Boutsen, FR. Christman SS. Prosody in apraxia of peech. Semin Speech Lang 2002; 23: 245-56

[8]   Rom A, Segal M, Tchur B. [Child, what does he say?] Tel Aviv: Mofet Institute. 2003. [Hebrew].

[9]   http://en.wikipedia.org   [Internet].   Prosody.   [Cited   Oct   10,   2007].   Available   from
        http://en.wikipedia.org/wiki/Prosody_%28linguistics%29

[10]   http://www.sil.org   [Internet].   Speech   Tools.   [Cited   Oct   20,   2007].   Available   from
        http://www.sil.org/computing/speechtools/SATdownloads2.htm

Section three – International health

In: Child Health and Human Development Yearbook 2013   ISBN: 978-1-63117-939-6
Editor: Joav Merrick   © 2014 Nova Science Publishers, Inc.

Chapter 23

DIR®/Floortime™: Evidence-based practice towards the treatment of autism and sensory processing disorder in children and adolescents

*Esther B Hess**

Center for the Developing Mind, Los Angeles, California, United States of America

Abstract

Interventions for children/adolescents with developmental delays such as autism have often been limited to behavioral approaches that focus on the successful completion of a task rather than in the joyous reciprocal interaction of individuals relating to one and another. DIR/Floortime™ (Developmental, Individual Difference, Relationship-based) offers an alternative perspective to therapy that takes into account an individual's intrinsic level of interest and then expands on that initial level of motivation to incorporate mutual interest of others, all the while supporting various neurological differences that may be impeding the actual level of development in the first place. The result is a reciprocal interaction that results in an overall improvement in actual brain development processing. This article offers an overview of the theoretical, conceptual, and practical approach to the assessment, diagnosis and treatment of children/adolescents with developmental delays such as autism through the developmental relationship intervention known as DIR/Floortime™. Adaptation of play techniques will be examined for use with those impacted, in individual, and family therapy contexts as the primary area of focus.

Keywords: DIR®/Floortime™, developmental capacities, Individual neurological differences, relationship- based affective interactions

* Corresponding author: Esther B Hess, PhD, Center for the Developing Mind, 2990 South Sepulveda Blvd, #308, Los Angeles, CA 90064 United States. E-mail: Drhess@centerforthedevelopingmind.com.

Introduction

Play is a complex phenomenon that occurs naturally for most children; they move through the various stages of play development and are able to add complexity, imagination, and creativity to their thought processes and action. However, for many children with autism spectrum disorder (ASD), the various stages of play are difficult to achieve. Challenges in motor planning, expressive and receptive communication, imitation and fine and gross motor movements are just some of the many obstacles that children with ASD encounter during play (1). The Developmental, Individual Difference, Relationship-based model (DIR®)Floortime™ model is an interdisciplinary framework that enables play clinicians, parents and educators the ability to construct a holistic assessment and intervention program that comprehensively incorporates the child's and family's unique developmental profile that addresses these core deficits (2).

Floortime™ is the heart of the DIR® Floortime™ model and it is the play component of a comprehensive program for infants, children, adolescents and their families with a variety of developmental challenges including autism spectrum disorders. This comprehensive program includes working on all elements of the DIR® Floortime™ model, the functional emotional developmental levels and the underlying, individual, neurological differences in processing capacities, thus creating those learning relationships that will help the child move ahead in their development.

These relationships in turn are tailored to the child's individual differences that move them up the developmental ladder, mastering each and every functional emotional developmental capacity that they are capable of (3). The DIR® Floortime™ model involves often not just Floortime™, but different therapies like speech and language therapy, occupational therapy, physical therapy, educational programs, counseling support for parents, and home programs as well as school programs. For the purposes of this article though, I will focus on the Floortime™ component, which is the heart of both the home and the school component. This paper includes a summary of evidence based research that lends support to this developmental/relational based play intervention for children impacted by autism and their families.

The DIR Floortime™ model

Floortime™ is a particular technique where the play partner gets down on the floor and works with the child to master each of their developmental capacities. But to represent this model fairly, you will need to think about Floortime™ in two ways (4):

- A specific technique where for 20 or more minutes at a time a parent gets down on the floor to play with their child.
- A general philosophy that characterizes all of the interactions with the child. All of the interactions have to incorporate the features of Floortime™ as well as the particular goals of that interaction including understanding the child's emotional, social and intellectual differences in motor, sensory, and language functioning, and the existing caregiver, child and family functioning and interaction patterns.

At the heart of the definition of Floortime™ are two of what could be called emphases that sometimes work together very easily and other times may appear to be at opposite ends of a continuum:

- Following the child's lead.
- Joining a child in his world and then pulling them into a shared world to help them master each of his functional emotional developmental capacities (2).

It is critical to be aware of both of these polarities, tendencies or dimensions of Floortime™.

Following the child's lead

The most widely known dimension of Floortime™ is following the child's lead- in other words, harnessing the child's natural interests. But what exactly does that mean? By following a child's interests, or their lead, we are taking the first steps in making what I call a great date with a child, in other words a validating emotional experience. What are the elements of a great date? For most of us, it includes being in the company of someone who is attentive, available, fun. And when we are with a person who incorporates all of these emotionally affirming elements, we obviously want the date to go on forever. Conversely, if we are on a bad date, with someone who does not make us feel good about ourselves or our experience, most of us would attempt to escape that encounter as soon as possible. Following a child's lead, taking the germ of their idea and making that the basis of the experience that you are about to share with the child, actually encourages the child to allow you into their emotional life. Through the child's interests; through the child's natural desires, we get a picture of what is enjoyable for the child. Consequently the child stays regulated and engaged longer is able to learn within the experience and ultimately moves forward developmentally (5).

Case example

A child appears not to be able to leave their home without holding onto a stick. This seems like something inappropriate and something we might want to discourage. But yet something about this object has meaning for this child. So we first have to start off asking ourselves, what is it about this activity that is so meaningful for the child? It is minimizing to simply attribute what we assume to be aberrant behavior to the fact that a child has a developmental delay like autism. Not only is this short sighted, but it does little to help us understand the underlying causes that are potentially fueling the odd behavior. The key to understanding the child is to follow their lead as an entry point into their world, create an emotional connection, a relationship that allows us to pull that child into a shared emotional experience. This might mean that the adult facilitator picks up his own stick and attempts to mimic the gestures of the original item. Then it is up to the adult to expand the initial gesture into something socially appropriate and mutual, say taking the two sticks and gently pretending to fence with them and/or helping the child with developmental delays enter the world of symbolism by pretending that the stick is actually the body of an airplane, the play facilitator guiding by making the appropriate sounds and gestures of a gliding plane.

Here the two philosophies behind DIR® Floortime™ are at work. We are accepting the child and their beloved object knowing that there is something intrinsically valuable in the relationship that that child has with the object and we are also encouraging a child to leave their preferred world of isolation in favor of an experience where his original idea of holding onto a stick has magically emerged into a shared play experience.

Joining the child's world

Following the child's lead is only one half of the equation; one half of this dynamic that we call Floortime™. There is another half; joining the child in their world and pulling them into a shared emotional experience in order to help them master each of their Functional Emotional Developmental Capacities. These are the fundamentals of emotional, social, language and intellectual development. When we talk about Functional Emotional Capacities, we're talking about the fundamentals of relating, communicating and thinking (3).

The larger goal is joining the child in their world. We want to then pull them into our shared world to teach them and help them learn how to focus and attend, how to relate with real warmth, how to be purposeful and take initiative, and have a back-and-forth set of communications with us through non-verbal gestures, and eventually through words. We want to teach them how to problem solve and sequence and get them involved in a continuing interaction with the environment and the people in their environment. We want to teach them to use ideas creatively and then we want to teach them to use ideas logically and then progress up the developmental ladder until they are not only using ideas logically but actually showing high degrees of reflective thinking and high degrees of empathy and high degrees of understanding the world so that they can evaluate their own thoughts and feelings. Not every child is capable of achieving the highest level of reflective thinking, but almost all children are capable of moving up the developmental ladder, mastering their own Functional Emotional Developmental Capacities in regards to optimum social, emotional, and intellectual, linguistic and academic growth (6). Some concerns expressed by play clinicians is whether or not DIR® Floortime™ is applicable to children who have moderate to severe forms of developmental delays. The direct answer is yes, even with children who are severely impacted with developmental delays, with the right kind of support, you can move that child forward and upward.

Case example

Jane is five years old chronologically, although her current developmental age is about 6 months old. She has no functional language and does not appear to have the interest or the capacity to play with toys. In addition to the diagnosis of severe autism, the child also has a co-morbid diagnosis of moderate to severe mental retardation. She enters the playroom mostly aimless, not able to stay engaged with anything or any person for any length of time.

Characteristic of the disorder, the child flaps her arms in a self-stimulatory gesture in a continuous horizontal pattern.

The difficulty that play clinicians often face with severely impacted children is the confusion of how to follow a child's lead when the child appears to not be able to offer any lead to follow. This is the art of Floortime™. You cannot do Floortime™, the play therapy portion of this intervention, unless you understand the child's DIR® (the developmental capacity, the underlying, neurological, processing differences and how to use the child's relationship in the world to woo that child into a shared experience). By knowing a child's DIR®, the interventionist knows how and where to enter the child's world in such a way as to create a validating experience- in other words, the great date. To move a child forward developmentally, to become a more complex thinker, despite overt cognitive delays, we need to make sure they possess the basic capacity to be regulated and stay engaged.

Since Jane is only offering her hand movements as "the lead", this is where the clinician must enter. Playfully, the therapist puts her own hands within the child's self-stimulatory hand and arm movements. Notice, that the clinician is not entering the play encounter thinking that she is with a 5 year old child; rather the therapist joins Jane at the little girl's developmental capacity. In other words, in the clinician's mind, she is now playing with a child who is 6 months old and must drop her intervention and her level of expectation to that level, while she uses her relationship to support the child's underlying processing challenges. Consequently, the therapist slows the child's flapping gesture down, creating a regular opening and closing rhythm to what was a moment before, a chaotic gesture. As the interventionist slows and regulates to the beat of the activity, the clinician also uses her voice and her facial gestures to create a high affective encounter. The clinician begins to sing a classic child's song, "Open shut them, open shut them, give a little clap". Suddenly, Jane, who up until this time appeared not to be able to focus and attend, looks with curiosity into the face of her play partner. She appears intrigued and curious. The clinician has just taught this child the first fundamental game of play, pat-a-cake. The developmental age of this child and subsequently her ability to be a more complex thinker, has improved within one play session from 6 month of age to 9 months of age.

Progressing from following a child's lead to mastery

How do we use "following the child's lead" to actually mobilize and help the child master these critical developmental milestones? To help children master the first stage of shared attention, when they are, for example, wandering away from our interaction with them, we may play a game that places the play partner in front of the child essentially blocking the child's exit from the interaction. The blocking gesture necessitates the child creating some kind of engagement with their play partner, even if it's a gesture of annoyance. This will form the foundation of the first act of shared attention that they are providing. The play partner is encouraged to continue to up the ante by creating more playful obstructions (like asking for a ticket or a token from the child to assure passage). These types of maneuvers create multiple opportunities for shared attention as well as sustained engagement, because the child is otherwise involved with the therapist. Interestingly, this is also the beginning of purposeful action because the child is trying to move the obstruction (in this case the therapist) out of the way. As they continue to attempt to maneuver the obstacle out of the way, the therapist "plays dumb," forcing the children to solve their way out of the current obstacle. These strategies are called playfully obstructive strategies and they are for the most aimless of children or the most avoidant child.

Case example

A 5-year-old boy named Ian, impacted with a moderate degree of autism, enters the play room and appears to absent mindedly pick up a piece of chalk, before dropping the drawing material randomly on the floor. Previously, his mother has expressed concern that her son is not showing any age- appropriate interest in drawing, coloring, or cutting, and she fears that the child is progressively falling further and further behind his classmates. The clinician, keeping in mind the parent's concern, decides to take the play activity out of the playroom and into an outdoor play area. She follows Ian's lead by attempting to incorporate the child's fleeting interest in the chalk and then attempting to expand that germ of an idea into a sustained play encounter by doing some chalk drawing on the sidewalk. Once outside, she places Ian in her lap, both to prevent flight and also to help the child become more regulated and engaged by providing proprioceptive input (deep pressure) around which he can organize and reduce the anxiety that is potentially fueling his resistance to the play activity. She hands the child a piece of chalk, while mimicking hand- over-hand gestures in its use. Ian completely rejects the activity and withdraws his hand from any attempt to handle the chalk.

One of the basic principles of Floortime™ is "never take no for an answer." In other words, try not to back away from the resistance that is going to be presented when you try to initially move a child forward developmentally. The first step in this case, is to clarifying the child's actual capacities to see if he has the physical ability to hold a piece of chalk in his hand. Using occupational therapy strategies, the therapist explores whether or not the child has an adequate pincher grasp (the ability to pinch together the thumb and the forefinger) by seeing if the child is capable of handing the clinician's therapy dog a dog biscuit. The thinking is that the child's resistance to drawing can be overcome by his greater love for the clinician's dog. Ian is readily able to feed the dog with the appropriate grasp. This encourages the clinician to further expand the interaction by having the child draw the letters of the dog's name in chalk and then having him use his pincher grasp to again dot the letters of the dog's name with muffin (left over from a previous social skills baking activity) while instructing the dog to "eat up her name" on command. This time around, the request to draw with the chalk is met with absolutely no resistance as Ian delights in the use of this "living puppet" to playfully overcome his resistance to the task and ultimately move him forward developmentally.

The goal of playfully obstructive strategies is to follow the child's lead on the one hand but then create opportunities and challenges that help the child master each of his functional emotional developmental goals on the other. That is the dialectic, the two opposite polarities of Floortime™: joining the child in his rhythms while creating systematic challenges that creates opportunities to master new developmental milestones. It is in those systematic challenges that many of the specific techniques and strategies of Floortime™ come into play.

In conclusion, DIR® Floortime™ requires clinicians, and the parent or caregiver whom they are training to appreciate the polarity between following the child's lead and entering their world. Only then can children be "pulled" into a shared world, by finding their pleasure and joys while continually challenging them to master each of the functional developmental capacities. That means paying attention to the child's underlying neurological differences in the way that they processes sound and sights and movements and modulates sensations. It also means paying attention to the family patterns and to your own reactions as play clinician. This encourages both self-awareness and improved techniques as one enters a child's world and tailors interactions to the child's specific nervous system.

Evidence base for the DIR® Floortime™ approach

Evidence-base practice integrates the best available scientifically rigorous research, clinical expertise, and the therapist's characteristics to ensure the quality of clinical judgments and delivery of the most cost-effective care (7). A starting point to measure effectiveness of intervention is to determine the factors to be measured. Developmental programs like DIR® Floortime™, in contrast to behavioral approaches that tend to measure specific targeted behaviors, target underlying capacities, or "core deficits" as the focus of intervention, with progress evident in a complex array of changes in interactive behavioral patterns.

Developmental capacities seek to measure changes in an individual's capacity for shared attention, the ability to form warm intimate and have trusting relationships and the ability to initiate using intentioned actions and social engagement that leads to spontaneous communication. Additionally, developmental capacities look at problem- solving strategies by assessing the ability to have co-regulation and consequently being able to adapt to the feelings of others. Developmental capacities also determines individual's ability to be creative as well as the capacity to have logical and analytic thought while developing a sense of self or core values (8).

Developmental models emphasize individual processing differences and the need to tailor intervention to the unique biological profile of children as well as the characteristics of the relationship between parent and child. Because both the factors being measured are complex and because the wide range of individual neurological processes in the population, research on the effectiveness of a developmental framework has progressed by examining the subcomponents of the overall approach. The subcomponents can be summarized by looking at the three major aspects of the DIR® Floortime™ approach:

- D for developmental framework
- I for the underlying, neurological, processing differences of a child
- R for relationship and subsequent affective interactions

D: The developmental framework

A developmental approach considers behavior and learning in the greater context of a developmental or changing process. In 1997, evidence first showed the promise of the DIR® Floortime™ approach when 200 charts of children who were initially diagnosed with autistic spectrum disorder were reviewed. The goal of the review was to reveal patterns in presenting symptoms, underlying processing difficulties, early development and response to intervention in order to generate hypotheses for future studies. The chart review suggested that a number of children with autistic spectrum diagnoses were, with appropriate intervention, capable of empathy, affective reciprocity, creative thinking, and healthy peer relationships (2). The results of the 200 case series led Greenspan and Wieder to publish in 2000 the full description of the DIR® Floortime™ Model (4,9). In 2005, Greenspan and Wieder published a 10-to 15-year follow up study of 16 children diagnosed with ASD that were part of the first 200 case series. The authors described that 10 to 15 years after receiving DIR® Floortime™ as a treatment method, these children had become significantly more empathetic, creative and reflective adolescents with healthy peer relationships and solid academic skills (10).

The DIR® Floortime™ Model has provided a developmental framework that has been studied and found to be accurate in understanding behavior. A common pediatric assessment tool, The Bayley Scale of Infant Development, has adopted the DIR® milestones, specifically configured as the Greenspan Social-Emotional Growth Chart (SEGC) as the measure by which social and emotional development is measured (9Greenspan, 2004). In 2007, Solomon et al., published an evaluation of the Play Project Home Consultation (PPHC), an in-home based version of the DIR® Floortime™ model that trains parents of children with autism spectrum disorder in the DIR® Floortime™ model. The results showed significant increase in the child subscale scored on another pediatric assessment tool the Functional Emotional Assessment Scale (11) after an 8- to 12-month program using DIR® Floortime™ (12).

I: Individual underlying neurological processing differences

In 1979, occupational therapist Jean Ayres, pioneered discoveries about the way in which a child's sensory processing capacities could impact the way in which children learned and integrated themselves into their worlds (13). This revolutionary idea provided a new way to understand the importance of movement and regulatory behaviors in children and began to offer explanations for some of the more worrisome behaviors impacting children with developmental concerns like autism. Over the last 40 years, a large body of research has further illuminated the impact of biologically based differences in regards to both sensorimotor processing and the impact on emotional regulation. In 2001, the National Research Council of the National Academy of Sciences published a report titled, "Educating Children with Autism," which called for the tailoring of treatment approaches to fit the unique biological profile of the individual child (14). Lillas and Turnball (15), in their published text, described how all behavior is influenced by the sensory systems in the brain. They indicated that an infant's sensory capacities are genetically prepared to respond to human interaction and are shifting in direct relationship to the parent's touch, facial, vocal and movement expressions. Child-parent interactions and sensory activities create nerve cell networks and neural pathways in the development of the child's brain. The exchange of that takes place during child-parent play interactions are seen as an ongoing loop of sensorimotor transformations (15).

R: Relationship and affect

Developmental models have evolved from many years of discovery in the field of infant mental health. Beginning in the 1950s, there was a new understanding of the importance of parent-child interaction (16). Building on these years of research in developmental psychology that underscores the importance of early relationships and family functioning, Dr. Stanley Greenspan and his partner, Dr. Serena Wieder, began their work together studying the interaction of mothers and their babies in the context of infants who were at high risk for attachment problems (17). Subsequently, there have been numerous research studies confirming the importance of parent-child interaction and the value of intervention programs that focus on supporting the parent-child relationship, particularly in the areas of joint attention and emotional attunement (18). In 2006, Gernsbacher published a paper that showed how intervention itself between a parent and child could change the way in which parents interact, in turn increasing reciprocity, and that these changes correlated to positive changes in social engagement and language. And in 2008, Connie Kasari and colleagues at the University of California-Los Angeles (19) used a randomized controlled trial to look at joint attention and symbolic play with 58 children with autism. Results indicated that expressive language gains were greater for treatment groups where a developmental model was utilized as compared with a control group that was based on exclusive behavioral principles.

Discussion

Autism is now recognized as a disorder of integration among various distinct brain functions. Research investigation is currently focused on understanding deficits in neuronal communication as a basis of the wide array of behavioral manifestations of the disorder (8). Developmental intervention has advanced to incorporate the use of affect to enhance integration of sensory-regulatory, communication and motor systems. With that in mind, neuro-imaging research is beginning to provide a deeper understanding as to how emotional experiences are actually impacting developing brain growth. Siegel (20) showed how attuned relationships in infancy change brain structure in ways that later impact social and emotional development, and recently, a research study by Casenhiser, Stieben and Shanker (21) at the York University in Canada, investigated the behavioral and neuro-physiological outcomes of intensive DIR® Floortime™ intervention, using both event-related potential (ERP) and electroencephalography (EEG) measurements. Discussion is also continuing on ways to apply the basic principles of DIR® Floortime™ towards an adult developmentally delayed population (22).

Efforts continue to deepen our understanding of the complexities of autism. The alarming increase in the diagnosis of autism worldwide (23), as well as the lack of specific information about etiology of the disorder demands that play therapists increase their knowledge and understanding of how a child's development is impacted by the individual, underlying, neurological processing differences and the interaction of the relationships that the child has in the world (10). In September 2009, Zero to Three focused an issue on the importance of play, specifically on the role of spontaneous, child-led, social play experiences that support social, emotional, and cognitive growth (24). Although research continues, it is imperative that developmental approaches like DIR® Floortime™ remain a viable option for intervention for children and adolescents with developmental delays and their families.

References

[1]   Mastrangelo S. Harnessing the power of play: Opportunities for children with autism spectrum disorders. Teach Excep Child 2009; 42(1): 34-44.

[2]   Greenspan SI, Wieder S. A functional developmental approach to autism spectrum disorders. JAS 1999; 24: 147-61.

[3]   Greenspan SI. Floor Time™: What it really is, and what it isn't. Accessed 2012 Aug 20. URL http://www.icdl.com/dirFloortime/newsletter/FloortimeWhatitReally isandisnt.shtml.

[4]   Interdisciplinary Council on Developmental and Learning Disorders. Clinical practice guidelines: Redefining the standards of care for infants, children and families with special needs. Bethesda, MD: ICDL, 2000.

[5]   Hess E. DIR®/Floor Time™: A developmental/ relational approach towards the treatment of autism and sensory processing disorder. Presented at the American Psychological Association Annual Conference, Toronto: CN, 2009.

[6]   Greenspan SI. The affect diatheses hypothesis: the role of emotions in the core deficit. In autism and the development of intelligence and social skill. J Dev Learning Dis 2001; 5: 1-46.

[7]   Weisz J, Gray JS. Evidence-based psychotherapy for children and adolescents: Data from the present and a model for the future. ACAMH 2007; 27: 7-22.

[8]   Cullinane, D. Evidence base for the DIR®/Floortime approach. Accessed 2012 Aug 20 URL: http://www.drhessautism.com/img/news/EvidenceBasefortheDIR®Model Cullinane0901

[9]   Greenspan SI. The Greenspan Social Emotional Growth Chart: A screening questionnaire infants and young children. San Antonio, TX: Harcourt Assessment, 2004.

[10]   Greenspan SI, Wieder S. Can children with autism master the core deficits and become empathic, creative and reflective? A ten to fifteen year follow-up of a subgroup of children with autism spectrum disorders (ASD) who received a comprehensive developmental. individual-difference, relationship-based (DIR®) approach. J Dev Learning Dis 2005; 9: 39-61.

[11]   Greenspan SI, DeGangi G. Research on the FEAS: Test development, reliability, and validity studies. In: Greenspan S, DeGangi G, Wieder S, eds. The functional emotional assessment scale (FEAS) for infancy and early childhood. Clinical and research applications. Bethesda, MD: ICDL, 2001: 167-247.

[12]   Solomon RS, Necheles J, Ferch C, Bruckman D. Pilot study of a parent training program for young children with autism: The P.L.A.Y. project home consultation program. Autism 2007; 11(3): 205-24.

[13]   Ayres JA. Sensory integration and the child. Los Angeles, CA: Western Psychological Services, 1979.

[14]   Lord C, McGee JP, eds. Committee on educational intervention for children with autism. Educating children with autism. Washington, DC: Nat Acad Press , 2001.

[15]   Lillas C, Turnball J. Infant/child mental health, early intervention and relationship-based therapists: A neuro-relationship framework for interdisciplinary practice. New York: Norton, 2009.

[16]   Bowlby J. Maternal care and mental health. Geneva: WHO, 1951; 51.

[17]   Greenspan SI, Wieder S. Developmental patterns of outcome in infants and children with disorders in relating and communicating: A chart review of 200 cases of children with autistic spectrum diagnoses. J Dev Learning Dis 1987; 1: 87-141.

[18]   Mahoney G, Perales F. Relationship-focused in early intervention with children with pervasive developmental disorders and other disabilities: a comparative study, J Dev Behav Ped 2004; 26: 77-85.

[19]   Kasari C, Paparella T, Freeman S, Jahromi LB. Language outcome in autism: randomized comparison of joint attention and play interventions, J Consult Clin Psychol 2008; 76(1): 125-37.

[20]   Siegel D. Toward an interpersonal neurobiology of the developing mind: attachment relationships, "mindsight," and neural integration. Infant Ment Health J 2001; 22: 67-94.

[21] Casenhiser D, Stieben J, Shanker S. Learning through Interaction. Accessed 2012 Aug 20. URL: http: //research.news.yorku.ca/2010/08/11/ontarios-lieutenant-governor-visits-yorks-

[22] Samson A. Applying DIR®/Floor Time™ principles to a developmental disabled adult population. Presented at California Association for Disabilities, Los Angeles, 2010.

[23] Kogan MD, Blumberg SJ, Schieve LA, Boyle CA, Perrin JM, Ghandour RM, et al. Prevalence of parent-reported diagnosis of autism spectrum disorder among children in the US. Pediatrics 2009; 10: 1522-42.

[24] Hirschland D. Addressing social, emotional, and behavioral challenges through play, Zero to Three 2009; 30: 12-7.

In: Child Health and Human Development Yearbook 2013   ISBN: 978-1-63117-939-6
Editor: Joav Merrick   © 2014 Nova Science Publishers, Inc.

Chapter 24

Do inequalities in child health get wider as countries develop?

Nayan Chakravarty and Sanghamitra Pati*
Indian Institute of Public Health (PHFI), Bhubaneswar, India

Abstract

The future of any nation hinges on the health and nutrition status of its children. Over the last few decades, despite the reduction in infant mortality rate and improvement of child health in general, it is largely debated whether there has been gross inequity in this achievement. As a country develops it is expected that its development would have a rippling effect across the entire population. This paper would consider different arguments and counter arguments regarding the causes of inequality in child health. Methods: Extensive review of literature during 1976-2011 was conducted. Results: There seems to be no clear cut relationship between the development of a country and inequalities in child health due to the complexity in measuring both these areas. Any relationship is complicated by context and this can be seen in the literature which is at many times contradictory. Determinates that influence child health and mortality discussed are not only complex but are also overlapping and it is often a combination of contextual factors that influence a child health. Conclusion: Overall, critical child health indicators, particularly child survival, have improved globally but improvements in some countries or particular regions of countries have not been seen. The absolute differences have come down but the relative difference still remains the same. It is evident that people who have the greatest need are often the ones that receive the least as stated in the 'inverse care law'.

Keywords: Child health, inequality, determinants, equity

* Corresponding author: Nayan Chakravarty, MPH, PGDRM, Assistant Professor, Indian Institute of Public Health (PHFI), Bhubaneswar, Odisha, JSS Software Technology Park, E1/1, Infocity Road, Patia, Bhubaneswar, India 751024. E-mail: nayan.chakravarty@iiphb.org.

Introduction

The future of any nation hinges on the health and nutrition status of its children. Over the last few decades, despite the reduction in infant mortality rate (IMR) and improvement of child health in general, it is largely debated whether there has been gross inequity in this achievement. One could argue, this inequity is evident when the huge disparity in child mortality between countries is observed. This is demonstrated by the fact that every day as many as 25,000 children die and the vast majority are from developing countries (1). Disparities within countries are also largely debated among researchers. Large variations have been recorded among different sub-groups (2). Whatever the situation may be, it is often the poor people who find themselves in disadvantageous bargaining positions and are the most susceptible to ill health. Often with poor immune systems, resulting from perennial under-nutrition, thus they are more susceptible to infectious diseases (3). In worst case scenario this contributes to death in early childhood.

Health, is defined by the WHO as "A state of complete physical, mental and social well-being and not merely the absence of diseases or infirmity" (4). This paper will consider this broad definition of health in reference to child health. There are multiple determinants which influence the health of a child that can be broadly classified as social, cultural, economic and political determinants. These cover all aspects of physical, psychological and mental health. Mother's literacy levels were recorded as being the strongest determinant in societies where services were not widely available and dispersed (5). Educated mothers were thought to have been able to seek better health care for their children. Other determinants which need consideration are water and sanitation, access to health services, gender and environmental factors which includes housing (6).

As defined by Braveman (7), "Equity in health is the absence of systemic disparities in health (or in the major social determinants of health) between groups with differential levels of underlying social advantage/disadvantage- that is, wealth, power or prestige". Inequity can be looked at as absence of equity. The issue of inequalities in child health has often been an area of keen interest, not only among researchers but also among policy makers. As a country develops it is expected that its development would have a rippling effect across the entire population. However, whether or not the economic development has contributed to improvement of health indicators in general and more importantly if the bread of development has been shared equally is often debated.

The gap that exists between rich and poor countries is wide and some researchers argue that the gap is increasing (8). Inequality, with respect to child mortality, in different ethnic groups has also been studied in the past (9) where child health status in Africa was seen to vary between different ethnic groups.

There seems to be no clear cut relationship between the development of a country and inequalities in child health due to the complexity in measuring both these areas.

Any relationship is complicated by context and this can be seen in the literature which is at many times contradictory. This essay will look at the different arguments and counter arguments regarding the causes of inequality in child health that have been presented by different scholars. It will discuss some of the determinants of health and explore how context is important. Furthermore, the "inverse equity hypothesis" will be discussed which proposes an explanation for why some public health interventions contribute, decrease, or have no effect on child inequalities (10). The influence policy can have on these inequalities will also be considered.

Methods

A systematic review methodology was adopted to identify published evidence of the inequalities in child health in the global context. While the search was international, inclusion criteria limited the material to a period of thirty five years (1975 to 2011) and only evidence that was relevant to children up to 6 years were included.

The key areas of search are the combination of key words i.e. Child Health; Inequality; Determinants; Equity. Majority Search has been done using Pub-Med and Web of Science while additional report and papers were extracted from London School of Hygiene And Tropical Medicine and Senate House library, London. From an initial pool of 78 full text articles, a total of 30 articles published, met the inclusion criteria. The systematic review process is shown in each paper was read by three reviewers with articles included on the basis of relevance to the study. The inclusion and exclusion criteria for the search are shown in table 1.

Discussion

Child mortality is often considered to be one of the prime and sensitive indicators of child health globally. Technological advancement has brought down the level of child death, particularly during the second half of 20th Century. The median under five mortality has reduced from 150 per 1000 live births during 1950s to about 40 per 1000 live births during 1990s (11). However, there has been an increasing international concern because child-health inequalities are growing. The gap is widening between the richer and poorer countries (10). This give rises to a vital question; are the socioeconomic differences between countries, with respect to child health, widening or narrowing? Often, issues relating to child health are set aside due to the lack of comparable data which can be analyzed (12). There are conflicting views in favour and against common arguments. The study conducted by Whitehead and Drever "Narrowing social inequalities in health?" provides some evidence that the reduction in inequalities was achievable especially in developed countries (13). However, existing evidence by Minujin and Delamonica in "understanding socio-economic inequalities in mortality and health in developing world" (12) highlighted that child mortality disparity remained constant in developed countries and worsened in most of the developing countries.

Forty years ago, Hart stated (14) the "inverse care law" in his pioneering work. He highlighted the inverse relationship between need of medical care and its availability. This law still holds true in many of the developing as well as some developed countries where invariably the heath model is centered around places where it has a lesser demand/need. As a corollary to the "Inverse Care Law" the "inverse equity hypothesis" was framed by Victora and her team. (10). This explains the inequalities between the rich and the poor and how the rich and the poor respond differently to public health programs. Their work further explained how it is the rich who benefit first, before the poor. Any intervention first reaches the higher socioeconomic society before reaching the poor. It is only when the rich receive a particular level of care from an intervention that the poor tend to benefit the same intervention. Interpreting inequalities is often a complex process and people in this process have been cautioned by Razzaque (15): "Before interpreting results, the following points should be kept in mind. Measuring the impact of (a) health intervention on time trend data is complex because some interventions might reach the poor after a certain period and can reduce the poor-rich differences while at the same time a new intervention that might be used more by rich than the poor and might have increased the poor-rich differences".

When considering the determinants of child health, maternal education has been found to be a more decisive determinant compared to the husband's occupation when child survival is considered (16). Multiple studies have highlighted that a mother's education plays a very important role in determining their child's health and survival. During 1985 the United Nations analyzed data from 15 countries and noticed a linear relationship between maternal education and childhood mortality. With each extra year of education a mother has, child mortality came down by an average of 7-9% (17). However, Cladwell (16) pointed out that the influence of education should not be considered in isolation from the wider context. Cooksey and colleagues (18) argued that the effect of maternal education has been exaggerated. Nevertheless, equalizing education obliterates inequality. Understanding and applying the "inverse care law" (14) is particularly difficult. Resources often struggle to reach the places where they are needed the most, that is, in areas with poor child health. If an appropriate program focusing on elementary or primary education can be designed, this could benefit the poor. The rich would have already achieved this level education; therefore solely the poor would be targeted. Considering the present level of low education among the poor they would utilize this opportunity, which in turn, would influence child morbidity and mortality while decreasing the inequalities that exist between the rich and the poor. Better education has often been found to have created am increased demand for (health) services and hence influence the service delivery mechanism (19).

Water, sanitation and environment are already considered some of the most important determinants of child health universally. Preston and Van (20) during 1978, pointed out that the improvement in urban environment appeared to have played a major role in the decline of mortality in many European cities during the 19th century. The relationship is complex and depends on a wide range of other contextual factors. A child's health may vary from one child to another with respect to sanitation level, immunity (21), maternal education (5), feeding practices (22) and maternal attitudes (23). Ian and Lush argued the importance of housing on child health. They argued that the reason for better child health in Thailand than Brazil was attributed to better housing. Children in Egypt who shared toilets with other children and families were found to have been 60% more likely to suffer from diarrhea than children whose families had their own toilet (24).

Socioeconomic status is yet another well-known determinant of child health. Last three decades has witnessed substantial reduction in child mortality in most developing nations. Despite this reduction analysis of Demographic Health survey (DHS) and World Fertility Survey (WFS) shows that socioeconomic inequality in child survival chances have not narrowed between 1970s data and 1980s, in some cases it has actually widened (25).

Table 1. Inclusion and exclusion criteria

Criteria	Inclusion	Exclusion
Time Period	Within the time period 1975–2011	Any text out of this period
Language	English	Non-English
Place of study	Global Context	No exclusion
Geographical dimensions	No limitations	No limitation
Study population	Children up to 6 years	Any participants out of the inclusion criteria
Aspects to be covered in the study	Child health inequity and equality	

Brockerhoff argued that there is a link between ethnicity and child health in his paper on child survival among different ethnic groups in African countries (9). His study further stated how child mortality is directly linked with economic inequalities, differential use of health services and less directly linked with intergroup variations in geographical settings and cultural status of women.

A rural-urban inequality is also seen, with respect to child health. Before the sanitation revolution the urban child mortality rate was slightly higher than rural. This was understood to be due to the overcrowding living conditions and poor sanitation. Reduction in child mortality happened after the 1st world war when access to clean water, sanitation facilities and child nutrition improved (26). In general, in developing countries it was not until after World War II that the urban child mortality rate dropped below the rural rate. However, in some major cities in developing countries have witnessed increases in urban child mortality, which have been linked to extreme poverty, family disintegration, lack of hygiene and infectious diseases such as HIV (26).

As a country develops, urbanization seems to be an unavoidable factor, which leads to increasing rural to urban migration. In some countries rural to urban migration has detrimental effects on child health and mortality. As Antai pointed out, children of rural non-migrant mothers were at lower risk of child mortality when compared to children of rural-urban migrant mothers in Nigeria (27). Disruption of family and community ties, low socioeconomic status and vulnerability were found to be the reasons contributing to increased child mortality.

Social determinates influencing child health are highly contextual and vary from region to region and between countries. Moisi (28) in her paper, highlighted that geographical access to health care is not a determinant of child mortality in rural Kenyan settings with good health care facilities. DeFriese (29) contradicted Moisi and believed that poor access to health care is associated with poor child health.

Determinates that influence child health and mortality discussed are not only complex but are also overlapping and it is often a combination of contextual factors that influence a child health. The huge complexity of the issue therefore merits more understanding before formulation of a response. Inappropriate policy formulation and implementation without much understanding of the issues runs the risk of targeting the wrong people, such as those who are already better off in the community and leaving behind those who are relatively more needy.

To transform a plan into action, right kind of approaches is key. Cesar and his colleges (8) stated that there are two basic approaches which can raise coverage in poor population groups. The first one approach is the targeted approach, to focus on particular programs or interventions that are mainly targeted towards the poor. The other approach is to aim for universal coverage, which covers all segment of the society (both poor and the rich). However while universal programming, emphasis would be to address conditions important for disadvantaged groups. Alongside these approaches politics has a role to play. Strong political will that advocates for more egalitarian policies, including the strengthening of health care services, cannot be avoided. This should also be regarded as important in not only improving but also maintaining a nation's health (30).

Conclusion

Overall, critical child health indicators, particularly child survival, have improved globally but improvements in some countries or particular regions of countries have not been seen. The absolute differences have come down but the relative difference still remains the same. There are multiple determinates that influence child health. These vary depending on the context and often overlap. Maternal education has been the most widely discussed determinant and was seen to have a direct negative linear effect on child health. As no single program can be effective for all contexts, there is a large need to evolve individual policies to attend to the desired goal of, not only improving child health, but also to bridge down the gap, the gap of inequality that exists in different forms. Inappropriate understanding of the origin of inequality may result in the creation of a program that benefits the better in society rather than the poor. This can therefore widen the gap of inequalities. As a country develops, the best approach is one that benefits the poor and marginalized members of communities, benefited out of different health care programs. Right targeting towards the poor or designing programs which reaches universal coverage quickly benefiting all segments of the society seem to increase the success of interventions. It is evident that people who have the greatest need are often the ones that receive the least as stated in the 'inverse care law'. However, it must be remembered that reaching out to this segment of the society can be challenging. It becomes challenging, because there is often no demand for service from this segment of the society. Therefore, reaching out to these individuals can be costly. Caldwell, in his paper, (16) argues powerfully, "the key to low mortality at the societal level may be a synergy between mass education and egalitarian politics which lead to demands for a health service that caters to the needs of all".

References

[1]   Denburg A, Daneman D. The link between social inequality and child health outcomes. Healthc Q 2010; 14(1): 21-31.
[2]   Feachem RG. Poverty and inequality: A proper focus for new century. Bull World Health Organ. 2000; 78(1): 1-2.
[3]   Salomon JB, Mata LJ, Gordon JE. Malnutrition and the common communicable diseases of childhood in rural Guatemala. Am J Public Health Nations Health 1968; 58(3): 505-16.

[4]   World Health Organization. Preamble to the Constitution of the World Health Organization as adopted by the International Health Conference. New York: WHO, 1946.

[5]   Cleland JG, Van Ginneken JK. Maternal education and child survival in developing countries: the search for pathways of influence. Soc Sci Med 1988; 27(12): 1357-1368.

[6]   Wang L. Determinants of child mortality in LDCs: empirical findings from demographic and health surveys. Health Policy 2003; 65(3): 277-99.

[7]   Braveman P, Gruskin S.Defining equity in health. J Epidemiol Community Health 2003; 57(4): 254-8.

[8]   Cesar JA, Matijasevich A. The use of maternal and child health services in three population-based cohorts in Southern Brazil, 1982-2004. Cad Saude Publica 2008; 24(Suppl 3): S427-36.

[9]   Brockerhoff M, Hewett P. Inequality of child mortality among ethnic groups in sub-Saharan Africa. Bull World Health Organ 2000; 78(1): 30-41.

[10]   Victora CG, Vaughan JP. Explaining trends in inequities: evidence from Brazilian child health studies. Lancet 2000; 356(9235): 1093-8.

[11]   Omar B, Lopez AD, Inoue M. The decline in child mortality: A reappraisal. Bull World Health Organ 2000; 78(10): 1175-91.

[12]   Delamonica AME. Socio-economic inequalities in mortality and health in the developing world. Demographic Res Spec Collect 2004; 2(article 13): 331-54.

[13]   Whitehead MDF. Narrowing social inequalities in health? BMJ 1999; 318: 908-12.

[14]   Tudor Hart J. Inverse Care Law. Lancet 1971; 1(7696): 405-12.

[15]   Razzaque A, Streatfield PK. Does health intervention improve socioeconomic inequalities of neonatal, infant and child mortality? Evidence from Matlab, Bangladesh. Int J Equity Health 2007; 6: 4.

[16]   Caldwell JC. Route to low mortality in poor countries. Populat Dev Rev 1986; 12(2): 171-220.

[17]   UN department of Social and Economic Affairs. Socio-economic differentials in child mortality in develeoping countries. New York: United Nations, 1985.

[18]   Cooksey ER. Annual meeting of Population Association of America. San Francisco, 1986.

[19]   Ensor T, Cooper S. Overcoming barriers to health service access: influencing the demand side. Health Policy Plan 2004; 19(2): 69-79.

[20]   Johnson G. Health Condition in rural and urban areas of developing countries. Populat Stud 1964; 17: 293-309.

[21]   Maggini S, Wenzlaff S. Essential role of vitamin C and zinc in child immunity and health. J Intern Med Res 2010; 38(2): 386-414.

[22]   Senarath U, Dibley MJ. Determinants of infant and young child feeding practices in Sri Lanka: secondary data analysis of Demographic and Health Survey 2000. Food Nutr Bull 2010; 31(2): 352-365.

[23]   Mulder C, Kain J. Maternal attitudes and child-feeding practices: relationship with the BMI of Chilean children. Nutr J 2009; 8: 37.

[24]   Timaeus IM, Lush L. Intra-urban differentials in child health. Center for population studies. Health Transit Rev 1995; 5(2): 163-90.

[25]   Cleland J, Bicego G, Fegan G. Socioeconomic inequalities in Childhood mortality: the 1970s to the 1980s. Health Transit Rev 1992; 2(1): 1-18.

[26]   Garenne M. Urbanisation and child health in resource poor settings with special reference to under-five mortality in Africa. Arch Dis Child 2010; 95(6): 464-8.

[27]   Antai D,Wedren S, Bellocco R, Moradi T. Migration and child health inequities in Nigeria: a multilevel analysis of contextual- and individual-level factors. Trop Med Int Health 2010; 15: 1464-74.

[28]   Moisi JC, Gatakaa H. Geographic access to care is not a determinant of child mortality in a rural Kenyan setting with high health facility density. BMC Public Health 2010; 10: 142.

[29]   DeFriese GH, Hetherington JS. Child health and the problem of access to care. Fam Commun Health 1982; 4(4): 71-83.

[30]   Chung H, Muntaner C. Political and welfare state determinants of infant and child health indicators: an analysis of wealthy countries. Soc Sci Med 2006; 63, 829-42.

In: Child Health and Human Development Yearbook 2013   ISBN: 978-1-63117-939-6
Editor: Joav Merrick   © 2014 Nova Science Publishers, Inc.

Chapter 25

Low-fat, no-fat and sugar free: An examination of children's knowledge of nutrition, food preferences and television use

*Kim Bissell**

Department of Journalism, University of Alabama, Tuscaloosa, Alabama,
United States of America

Abstract

The prevalence of childhood obesity remains a critical issue as the number of children being diagnosed as overweight or obese is continuing to rise. This study examined 602 3rd-6th grade children's time spent viewing television, their nutritional knowledge, their nutritional reasoning, their food preferences, and their dietary behavior at home and at school to determine which factors were stronger predictors of children's nutritional knowledge. Using a survey, students were presented with food pairs increasing in difficulty and asked to select the food they thought was most capable of helping them grow up to be healthy and strong. A nutritional knowledge scale was constructed and then compared with other predictor variables to identify the factors related to higher or lower knowledge scores. Regression analysis indicates that television viewing was related to increased levels of nutritional knowledge. Television viewing was also related to a stronger preference for unhealthy foods across the sample. Children in the sample further perceived the food they consumed at school to be significantly healthier than the food they consumed at home. Demographic variables proved to be strong predictors of students' nutritional knowledge and also proved to be a significant predictor of students' preferences toward healthy food. Children across demographic groups believed the foods they received in school lunch and breakfast programs were healthy and high in nutritional value even though the actual food consumed was similar to what was consumed at home.

* Corresponding author: Professor Kim Bissell, Ph.D., Associate Dean for Research, College of Communication and Information Sciences, University of Alabama, Box 870172, Tuscaloosa, AL 35487 United States. E-mail: kbissell@ua.edu.

Keywords: Nutritional knowledge, television, food preferences, adolescents, nutritional reasoning

Introduction

Recent reports from the International Obesity Task Force indicated that in 2006, 22 million children worldwide under the age of five years were classified as obese or overweight. Furthermore, results from the 2003-2004 National Health and Nutrition Examination Survey indicated that an estimated 17% of children in the US between 2-19 years were overweight. What is known from empirical studies across disciplines is that multiple factors may be related to the likelihood of a child to be overweight or obese: genetics, lack of physical activity, and increased consumption of high-calorie, low-nutrition foods and beverages (1). Of importance here are factors that children cannot control—access or encouragement to participate in physical activities, access to healthy or unhealthy foods at home or at school, and a social or home environment that either promotes or discourages healthy eating and exercise. Along these lines, children and adolescents may presume that their parents are making responsible and healthy choices for them as it relates to food and physical activity (2), and probably will not spend a great deal of time analyzing the nutritional attributes of a specific food item (3). Children will either rely on parents to make good choices for them, or respond to terms on the products such as "low fat" or "low sugar", and they may not examine the actual nutritional content of the products themselves. A recent study published by the Institute of Medicine of the National Academies (IOM report) indicated that the current practices for food marketing put children at a health risk because dietary patterns begin early in childhood and are shaped by social, cultural and mediated factors, including television advertising. Furthermore, children may presume that the foods they receive at school in lunch or breakfast programs are also healthy and may not critically consider the nutritional attributes of the foods being served. Accordingly, this study examined 3rd-6th graders' television use, their knowledge of nutrition, their food preferences, and their food intake at home and at school in order to better assess which factors may prove more influential in shaping their overall knowledge about nutrition and health.

Even though parents are responsible for the food children consume at home, many researchers suggest the media, especially advertising, influence children's purchasing behavior and food purchase requests (4). Certainly, as studies over the last decade have illustrated, food ads targeted toward children have often emphasized unhealthy options versus healthy options (5). They further report that in the ads targeted toward children, few health-related messages were found, but of the ones with some mention of health, the message was related to the food containing natural ingredients or that the food was low in calories.

Studies more recently have examined the nutritional value of food served in public schools, suggesting that the school environment may be one source of a child's higher calorie diet. With the introduction of vending machines in schools and the shift to cheaper foods in bulk, the nutritional value of food served during the school day is questionable at best. Children, however, may not recognize the poor nutritional value of the foods they are consuming, especially if the food is coming from home or school. Children may further lack the awareness or understanding related to nutritional guidelines and may simply assume what they are eating is healthy. More sedentary lifestyles and changes in the home environment have also contributed to a shift in eating habits and behavior in the last few decades, especially in the foods children eat on a daily basis and their daily media diet.

Roberts and Foehr report that the average child spends up to five hours a day with various media (6), and as reported in a more recent study, elementary aged children spent several hours a day watching television programs on the Disney Channel, Nickelodeon, and the Cartoon Network and spent additional time on the websites associated with those channels as well as websites targeted toward children (webkins.com, neopets.com, and playhousedisney.com) (7). Harrison (8) and Peterson, Jeffrey, Bridgewater, and Dawson (9) argue that the way food products are advertised on television does affect children's understanding of nutrition and further influences the choices they make about food and the amount of food they consume. Brownell and Horgen (10) further suggest that food products that are associated with a media tie-in and that have a corresponding "toy" make resisting the food even more difficult.

Empirical studies examining children's overall knowledge of nutrition are scant at best, but a few studies have examined nutritional knowledge as it relates to media exposure. Signorielli and Staples (11) found that children who spent more time watching television were more likely to select a food that was unhealthy and this was found across gender, race, or reading ability.

Table 1. Independent t-tests for television exposure and Internet use by gender

	Boys Mean SD	Girls Mean SD			
Minutes during the day	N	N	F	df	p value
TV before school	36.46 (28.27)	39.00 (32.96)			
	246	300	6.07	544	n.s.
TV after school	40.24 (27.46)	45.67 (28.59)			
	246	305	.28	549	*p<.05*
TV before bed	48.10	51.74			
	(26.16)	(29.54)	2.10	550	n.s.
Weekly minutes viewing	874.17 (450.89)	955.03 (482.14)			
	246	300	.45	544	*p<.05*
Internet usage*	3.68 (1.59)	3.58 (1.66)			
	244	302	1.85	500	n.s.

*Internet usage was measured using the following responses (0=never, 1=once a week, 2=a few days a week, 3=almost every day of the week, 4=every day of the week, 5=an hour or more each day).

In a similar study, Harrison (12) examined adolescents' television viewing with their knowledge of nutrition using similar measures for the dependent variable. Harrison also examined nutritional reasoning, which was defined as the child's rationale for selecting the specific food from the food pairing as being the healthier or more nutritionally sound choice.

Harrison found that heavier television viewing was related to lower levels of nutritional knowledge and nutritional reasoning, but this relationship was only found for food that were marketed as weight-loss products.

The media are often blamed for the increases in childhood obesity, but beyond articulating that children spend too much time with the media, very little is known about how the specific content children are exposed to may influence their thoughts and decisions about the foods they consume. Lowry, Wechsler, Galuska, Fulton, and Kann (13) report in their study of high school students' media use and their rates of sedentary lifestyles and obesity that one in three White students, one in two Hispanic students, and three in four Black students watched more television per day than what is recommended by the American Academy of Pediatrics (two hours per day). Most importantly, the authors report that in their sample, television viewing was found to be positively related to the consumption of high-fat foods and those participants who were overweight were also more likely to spend more time with television.

The general conclusion from these studies is that television viewing may be negatively related to children's food preferences, food intake and nutritional knowledge because it may not only shape what they view to be healthy and good for them, but it may also shape their preferences for specific foods and affect how much food they eat while watching television.

Hammermeister, Brock, Winterstein, and Page (14) found in their analysis of psychosocial health characteristics in television-free and television-viewing individuals that those who viewed moderate amounts of television were more likely to display a negative psychosocial health profile compared to their non-viewing counterparts. Based on the literature reviewed, the following research questions were posed:

- RQ1: How is television viewing related to children's nutritional knowledge?
- RQ2: How is television viewing related to children's food preferences?
- RQ3: How do food preferences and the home dieting environment relate to nutritional knowledge?

Methods

In order to examine the relationship between media consumption, food preferences, knowledge of nutrition, and the home and social eating environment, a survey was administered to children in grades 3-6th in several counties in a state in the South. Of the 601 participants, 45% were boys and 55% were girls with ethnic representation that was closely matched to that of the counties where data was collected: Eighty percent of the sample was Caucasian, 16% was African American, and the remaining 4% reported to be Hispanic, Asian or "other."

Instruments

Independent variables

Children were asked to list the television shows they watched "yesterday before school," "yesterday after school but before dinner," and "yesterday after dinner but before bed." This measure of television viewing was used in place of the traditional items that ask participants to report the average number of minutes per day spent viewing television and has been validated in studies using similar samples (16).

Throughout the instrument, children in this sample were shown pictures of three different foods and were asked the following question: Which of the foods above would you most like to eat right now? This item was not designed to measure purchase intent nor was it designed as a measure of nutritional knowledge; rather, it was designed to measure the preferences toward specific types of foods and potentially tap into participants' gut-reactions or instinctual responses to food preferences. Options for the food choices were as follows: Reese's Peanut Butter Cup, Doritos, carrots; McDonald's French Fries, M&Ms, grapes; Subway sandwich, Pizza Hut pizza, watermelon. For each of the three questions, responses were recoded as healthy or unhealthy, resulting in a recoded, additive scale representing food preferences. For this scale, unhealthy food choices (Reese's, Doritos, fries, M&Ms, pizza) were recoded as a 0 and healthy food choices (carrots, grapes, sandwich, and watermelon) were recoded as a 1. Results from responses to all three items were combined with a mean score of 1.27 (sd=.97). The scale ranged from a low of 0, meaning a participant chose all unhealthy foods to a high of 3, meaning a participant chose all healthy food options. In the sample of 601 3rd-6th graders, 24% had a score of 0, 37% had a score of 1, 25% had a score of 2, and 13% had a score of 3. The scale used to measure food preferences simply represents an additive scale of responses recoded as either healthy or non-healthy choices on food preferences. Cronbach's alpha on this scale was .70.

Finally, children were asked a series of questions about their eating habits and patterns, the source of the foods they consumed, and how nutritious they felt their food was. Participants were asked to indicate their frequency of consuming a long list of food items ranging from healthy to unhealthy choices each day at home and at school. Responses to these items were used to create a daily food intake index, which had secondary component to it related to the child's perceived nutritional value of his/her daily diet. As expected, daily food intake varied across the sample, but the following patterns were observed. When asked about the frequency of consuming foods such as fruits, vegetables, milk, or other dairy products, children indicated consuming these foods an average 3.67 (sd=1.78) days per week at school and 2.78 days per week at home (sd=2.01). When asked about the consumption of eating foods such as potato chips, candy, or soda, participants reported eating these foods an average of .91 (sd=1.32) days per week at school and 5.74 (sd=1.79) days per week at home. Participants perceived the food they consumed at school, including food brought in a lunch box, to be significantly more healthy than the foods they consumed at home (school mean=3.79, sd=2.21, home mean=2.24, sd=1.89, on a scale ranging from 1-5 with 5 representing the most nutritious).

Dependent variables

To measure knowledge of nutrition, participants were shown four pairs of foods (fat-free ice cream/yogurt, orange juice/Diet Coke, white bread/wheat bread, fruit snack/granola bar) and were asked the following question: which of the two items above is better to help you grow up healthy and strong? Respondents could only select one answer. These specific food pairings were selected because they represented a range of foods and because they represented varying degrees of difficulty in terms of assessing which would be more nutritional. All responses were recoded as being correct or incorrect. Each response option was recoded as a healthy or unhealthy choice and those four responses were added together for the final nutritional knowledge scale with a Cronbach's alpha of .64. Participants' responses were added together to create a final scale ranging from 0 (all incorrect answers) to 4 (all correct answers). The mean nutritional knowledge score was 2.62 (sd=1.09, N=560).

Participants were also asked about their reasoning behind making the above choices. After indicating which food they thought was better to help them grow up healthy and strong, they were then asked why. Responses for this item were as follows: it is good for you, it tastes good, it will keep you healthy, my mom says it is good for me, it is nutritious. Answers were then recoded in terms of whether the child's response reflected nutritional reasoning (it is good for you, it will keep you healthy, my mom says it is good for me, it is nutritious) or non-nutritional reasoning (it tastes good). Responses for all four items were then combined to create a single score representing each child's nutritional reasoning. Each non-nutritional reasoning response was recoded as 0, and each nutritional reasoning response was recoded as 1, and when the responses for all four items were added together, the nutritional reasoning scale had a mean score of 2.92 (sd=1.19, N=554). Reliability analysis on the 4-item scale was .69 using Cronbach's alpha.

Results

The first research question addressed the relationship between television viewing and participants' knowledge of nutrition. Regression analysis indicated a significant relationship between television viewing and knowledge of nutrition; however, the results indicate that children who watched more television had higher scores on the nutritional knowledge scale than those who watched less television. When the television viewing variable was recoded into low, medium and high groups, one-way ANOVA tests indicated that those in the high viewing group had a mean nutritional knowledge score of 2.80 (sd=1.06, on a scale ranging from 0-4, with 4 representing the greatest nutritional knowledge) compared to those in the low viewing group who had a mean nutritional knowledge score of 2.56 (sd=1.02). Post-hoc Tukey's tests indicate differences between the high and low viewing groups were significant.

The second research question examined the relationship between television viewing and food preferences. As reported in findings from earlier studies, it was projected that children who spent more time watching television would be more inclined to prefer food that had less nutritional value than children who spent less time with television. While regression analysis indicated a significant relationship between the variables, the beta was very low, (.13), so additional tests were run to examine this relationship. One-way ANOVA tests were run again to examine the food preferences of high, medium and low television viewers, and in this case, those watching the most television were also the most likely to prefer non-nutritional foods. For example, those in the high viewing group (N=157) had a mean food preference score of 1.06 (sd=.95, on a scale of 0-3 with 0 representing the least nutritional choices of the food groups) whereas those in the low viewing group (N=182) had a mean food preference score of 1.34 (sd=.98). Participants in the medium viewing group (N=213) had a mean nutritional food preference score of 1.21 (sd=.97). Post-hoc Tukey's LSD tests indicated significant differences between the low and high television viewing groups. Thus, findings from this statistical test parallel what's been reported in other studies—television viewing was related to children's preferences for foods that have less nutritional value.

The third research question examined the relationship between food preferences, the home dieting environment, and nutritional knowledge. In this case, it was predicted that children who tended to prefer foods that were less nutritious would also exhibit an inability to make accurate choices about what foods would be healthier options for them. While preferences for specific foods could be related to a variety of social, environmental and media factors, as indicated from the descriptives reported earlier, only 13% of the sample of 601 children chose healthy options in all three cases and 24% chose the unhealthy option in all three cases. Regression analysis indicated a significant relationship between the two variables (β=.36, p<.001). One-way analysis of variance tests using the recoded food preference score (0-3 with 3 representing a stronger preference for healthier foods) indicated similar patterns in a very linear fashion. Children who preferred healthier foods (N=73) had the highest nutritional knowledge scores with a mean of 3.19 (sd=.81) compared to those who preferred the non-healthy foods (N=130) who had a mean nutritional knowledge score of 2.30 (sd=1.27). Post-hoc Tukey's tests indicated significant differences between all groups except the group scoring a 0 on the food preference score, meaning they chose no nutritional foods, and those scoring a 1, meaning 1 healthy food choice was made. When age, gender and race were considered as predictors in the regression model, the significant relationship held except for race. Regression analysis using age, gender, and food preferences as a predictor of nutritional knowledge resulted in a beta of .43 (p<.001), and regression tests using TV exposure, age, gender and food preferences also resulted in a significant, positive beta of .57 (p<.001, see Table 2).

Table 2. Summary of multiple hierarchical regression analyses regressing overall nutritional knowledge on television viewing, age, gender, and food preferences

Predictor Variable	β	R2	F	df
Dependent Variable:				
Nutritional Knowledge Index				
Step 1				
Television Viewing	.07	.01	.37	458
Step 2				
Age	-.06	.05	2.15	456
Gender	.43***			
Step 3				
Food Preferences	.57***	.11	12.58	455

***p<.001.

Table 3. Exploratory factor analysis of four food choices with varimax rotation

	Rotated loadings		
	Factor 1	**Factor 2**	**Factor 3**
Food choices			
Choice 1 (orange juice vs. diet coke)	.74	.03	.03
Choice 2 (fat-free ice cream vs. yogurt)	.58	.24	.24
Choice 3 (white break vs. wheat bread)	.70	.06	.21
Choice 4 (fruit snack vs. granola bar)	.09	.16	.90

*The three factors reported in this table were those with eigenvalues over 1.00. Factor 1 explained 27% of the variance; Factor 2 explained 14% of the variance; Factor 3 explained 13% of the variance. Food choices that were considered the more nutritious of the two are noted in italics.

A child's home and social eating environment was significantly related to food preferences and nutritional knowledge. Children who reported eating unhealthy foods at home tended to select unhealthy foods as their preference and had significantly lower nutritional knowledge scores (β=.42, p<.001). When asked to indicate how healthy their food choices were in terms of their daily food intake, participants acknowledged that many of the foods they consumed at home (friend chicken, fast food, candy, and soda) were not the most healthy for them. When asked about the nutritional value of the foods consumed at school, participants were more likely to associate their school-consumed foods as healthy. When each index was compared with nutritional knowledge, the home eating index was a significant predictor of lower nutritional knowledge scores (r=.42, p<.01), but the school eating index was not statistically related to nutritional knowledge or nutritional reasoning.

Discussion

This study of 601 3rd-6th grade boys and girls in a Southern state examined their time spent viewing television along with their knowledge of nutrition, their nutritional reasoning, their food preferences, and their home and school food intake. Results indicate that television viewing was not a strong predictor of decreased levels of nutritional knowledge but rather that television viewing was related to increased levels of nutritional knowledge. However, television viewing was also related to a stronger preference for unhealthy foods across the sample.

When television viewing was examined with the individual nutritional knowledge items, results indicate that as the nutritional knowledge items became more difficult, television viewing was a stronger predictor of participants making an incorrect choice. For example, when television viewing was grouped into high, medium and low groups, participants across the groups had roughly equal numbers of correct or incorrect answers when asked to select between fat free ice cream or yogurt. When participants were asked to choose between orange juice and Diet Coke, children in the low and medium viewing groups were more likely to get the answer correct when compared to those in the high viewing group. But, when examining responses to the question related to fruit snacks or granola bars, the number of children getting the answer correct was roughly the same across viewing groups. Analysis of television viewing with the individual food preference items also proved interesting. For the first item

(Reese's Peanut Butter Cup, Doritos, carrots), 38% of the sample chose Doritos, followed by 36% of the sample choosing the Reese's, and 26% choosing carrots. Children who spent the most time watching television were the least likely to select carrots as the food they would like to eat right now but were the most likely to select Doritos. Children who watched the least amount of television were also more likely to select Doritos, but a significantly higher number of them selected carrots than those in the high viewing category. While the role of television in this sample's decision-making with regard to food preferences and nutritional knowledge is still largely unclear, other variables examined remain important considerations.

One interesting finding from the study was participants' perceptions of the nutritional value of the foods they consumed at home and at school. Participants readily admitted some of the foods they consumed at home were unhealthy, and this could simply be because of the packaging of the food (frozen dinners or pre-packaged meals) or because they know the food came from a fast food restaurant. However, even though the actual food consumed (fried chicken or French fries) might have been the same at home and at school, the perceived nutritional value of it was higher when consumed at school. As Harrison (12) reported in an earlier study, the way foods are presented in a mediated context will influence the way they subsequently think about the nutritional value of food.

Limitations

Even though the findings of this study contribute to knowledge in the area of health communication and media, this study is not without its limitations. One important limitation was the exclusion of exposure to media other than television. It is possible that children learn about food and nutrition from media sources other than television, but given the large amount of evidence documenting the frequency of food ads on television, it was thought appropriate to only include television exposure in this study. These other possible predictor variables include measures related to the child's social and home environment. An important missing variable from this study was a measure of each child's daily dietary intake and the environment in which food is consumed.

Findings from this study suggest that it is quite possible the media may serve a role in educating children about diet, nutrition, and overall health. The key to this is in finding a way to get children's attention in this area so they can start playing a role in decision-making as it relates to their own health.

Acknowledgments

An earlier version of this paper was presented to the Science Communication Interest Group at the annual meeting of AEJMC in Boston, MA, 2009.

References

[1]   Warren R, Wicks RH, Wicks JL, Fosu I, Chung D. Food and beverage advertising on U.S. television: A comparison of child-targeted versus general audience commercials. J Broadcasting Electronic Media 2008; 52: 231-46.

[2]   Campbell KJ, Crawford DA, Ball K. Family food environment and dietary behaviors likely to promote fatness in 5-6 year-old children. Int J Obesity 2006; 30: 1272-1280.

[3]   Gibson EL, Wardle J, Watts CJ. Fruit and vegetable consumption, nutritional knowledge and beliefs in mothers and children. Appetite 1998; 31: 205-228.

[4]   Donkin AJ, Neale RJ, Tilston C. Children's food purchase requests. Appetite 1993; 21: 291-294.

[5]   Strasburger VC. Children and TV advertising: Nowhere to run, nowhere to hide. J Dev Behav Pediatr 2001; 22: 185-7.

[6]   Roberts DF, Foehr UG. Kids and media in America. New York: Cambridge University Press, 2004.

[7]   Bissell K, Hays H. Understanding anti-fat bias in children: Television exposure and demographic variables in 3rd-6th graders' implicit and explicit attitudes toward obesity. Mass Commun Society 2011; 14(1): 113-40.

[8]   Harrison K. Fast and sweet: Nutritional attributes of television food advertisements with and without Black characters. Howard J Commun 2006; 17: 249-64.

[9]   Peterson PE, Jeffrey DB, Bridgwater CA, Dawson, B. How pro-nutritional television programming affects children's dietary habits. Dev Psychol 1984; 20: 55-63.

[10] Brownell KD, Horgen KB. Food fight: The inside story of the food industry, America's obesity crisis, and what we can do about it. New York: McGraw-Hill, 2004.

[11] Signorielli N, Staples J. Television and children's conceptions of nutrition. Health Commun 1997; 9: 289-301.

[12] Harrison K. Is "fat free" good for me? A panel study of television viewing and children's nutritional knowledge and reasoning. Health Commun 2005; 17: 117-32.

[13] Lowry R, Wechsler H, Galuska DA, Fulton JE, Kann L. Television viewing and its association with overweight, sedentary lifestyle, and insufficient consumption of fruits and vegetables among US high school students: Differences by race, ethnicity and gender. J Sch Health 2002; 72: 413-21.

[14] Hammermeister J, Brock B, Winterstein D, Page R. Life without TV? Cultivation theory and psychosocial health characteristics of television-free individuals and their television-viewing counterparts. Health Commun 2005; 17: 253-64.

In: Child Health and Human Development Yearbook 2013   ISBN: 978-1-63117-939-6
Editor: Joav Merrick   © 2014 Nova Science Publishers, Inc.

Chapter 26

Memorable stories: A qualitative study of mothers' experiences with breastfeeding

Cecilia S Obeng[*] and Adrienne Shivers

Applied Health Science Department, Indiana University, Bloomington, Indiana,
United States of America

Abstract

Purpose. This study explores mothers' experiences with breastfeeding and the impact of breastfeeding on the health of their infants. Design/methodology/approach. This study was conducted using grounded theory approach. The research was conducted in the state of Indiana in the United States. Data were collected by the authors and a research assistant. A total of 26 mothers were included in this study.

Findings Five themes emerged from the data: 1) Breast feeding education should be part of initial doctor's visits; 2) mothers and their infants falling asleep together while nursing; 3) mothers and doctors should be able to watch the children grow free of health problems; 4) breast pumps and other incentives should be provided to encourage mothers to breastfeed and 5) there is a general lack of information on breastfeeding to which mothers are exposed. The majority of the mothers in this study reported a positive response to breastfeeding their babies. Participants, especially African-Americans, reported that breastfeeding was not encouraged as an option at the time when they had their babies.

Conclusions: The findings of this study show that giving incentives to breastfeed, providing breastfeeding education, and encouragement from health professionals all are crucial toward increasing the likelihood that mothers will breastfeed their children.

Keywords: Breastfeeding, health, maternal health, child health, public health

---

[*] Corresponding author: Associate professor Cecilia Obeng, PhD, Department of Applied Health Science, Indiana University, 1025 E 7th Street, HPER 116, Room 296-I, Bloomington, IN 47405 United States. E-mail: cobeng@indiana.edu.

Introduction

The number of infants who die before their first birthday worldwide is astronomical. In the developed world, the United States was ranked 30th in infant mortality in 2005 (1). The United States also ranked much higher than most European countries in infant mortality rates for infants born at 37 or more weeks of gestation. In 2005, it was discovered that one in eight births in the United States was preterm (1).

The preliminary infant mortality rate for 2010 in the United States was 6.06 infant deaths per 1000 live births. In Indiana, where this breastfeeding research was conducted, although statistics indicate that the number of infant deaths declined between 1996 and 2006, the state's infant mortality rate is unnecessarily high. The average infant death in Indiana is 7.87 deaths in 1000 births; the above-stated figure most certainly puts Indiana's mortality rate higher than the national average.

According to United States Center for Disease Control and Prevention (CDC) (2), the four leading causes of infant death in the United States are congenital malformation, disorders related to short gestation, low birth weight, and sudden infant death syndrome (SIDS). Concerning the health of infants and young children, the America Academy of Pediatrics' policy statement document on Breastfeeding and the Use of Human Milk and the World Health Organization document, Infant and Young Child Feeding, note that a mother's milk is best for all infants. Babies of low birth weight are at risk for mortality, and feeding a child with the mother's milk is the best strategy to ensure their survival and wellbeing (3,4). A mother's milk, can adapt to the nutritional needs of babies. Incidence of SIDS, also, is lower in babies who are breastfed (4,5).

Regarding breastfeeding in the United States, the CDC's (2) Breastfeeding Report Card indicates the achievement of the 75% target set by Healthy People 2010 for mothers to initiate breastfeeding upon giving birth. Targets as set by Health People 2010 for breastfeeding at six months and twelve months, and for exclusive breastfeeding (i.e., no water, human milk only) at three months and six months, however, were not met by mothers in the United States (2). In addition, the Breastfeeding Report Card stated that although there has been great improvement in babies being born at Baby-Friendly facilities in the United States, the 4% rate attained is considered to be extremely low (2). According to Bartick and Reinhold (5), "if 90% of US families could comply with medical recommendations to breastfeed exclusively for 6 months, the United States would save $13 billion per year and prevent an excess 911 deaths" (3).

Convincing a majority of mothers to practice exclusive breastfeeding will be challenging for healthcare professionals. The World Health Organization document, Infant and Young Child Feeding, indicates that infant feeding is often neglected in the basic training of healthcare professionals such as doctors, nurses, and allied health professionals. Lack of knowledge about breastfeeding among healthcare professionals may lead to a situation where mothers are either not given advice at all or are given advice that may not ensure the child's optimal health. In order to reduce the infant mortality rate, it would be beneficial to improve breastfeeding education, especially among healthcare professionals. Research indicates that breastfeeding helps to prevent many childhood diseases, including obesity (5). The capacity for breast milk to help curb childhood obesity will more likely, then, help to prevent other health-related problems such as asthma, fatty liver disease, and sleep apnea in children (6,7).

The purpose of this paper, therefore, is to: (a) highlight possible attributes that make breastfeeding possible for mothers and the problems that mothers encounter; and (b) provide recommendations that will encourage breastfeeding among mothers.

Method

The study took place in Indianapolis (Indiana State's capital) and surrounding towns in 2011, after approval from an Institutional Review Board of Indiana University. Participants were recruited through snowballing and purposeful sampling. To qualify to participate in the study, a participant ought to have had at least one child. There were 40 questionnaires distributed to mothers, and 26 took part in the study, with a response rate of 65%. Some potential participants for this study were contacted through e-mail and, where possible, were met in person. Others also participated through snowballing research approach.

Study design and analysis

The instrument used in this study contained six questions and consisted of both closed- and open-ended questions. The closed-ended questions dealt with demographic information of the participants. The open-ended questions were used as the primary questions of this study. The questions were developed by the lead author after several years of having taught children's health courses in which breastfeeding was a major component. The instrument for this study was pilot tested with 15 participants. This was done in order to make sure the wording and the content of the information were appropriate for mothers who were breastfeeding. None of the mothers who took part in the pilot study participated in the main study. This was done in order to prevent participants from having the advantage of previous knowledge about the questions. The demographic information asked participants their ethnicity/race and the number of children they had. The primary questions asked participants whether they breastfeed their child/children and their best and worst experiences while breastfeeding their child/children. All of the questions used in the pilot study were used in the main study, with the addition of another question that asked what mothers would need to make breastfeeding possible. Participation was voluntary.

To verify whether the information collected from the participants was what they actually said or wrote, the researchers went back to the participants after one week for verification. This study also employed the grounded theory approach (8). Because the study used grounded theory approach, the data was closely examined and placed into various categories (e.g., participants were categorized by demographic details, and the responses were categorized into specific analytical categories or themes). Comparisons were made to determine differences and similarities in participants' responses.

Results

There were 12 African-Americans, 11 Caucasians, 2 Hispanics, and 1 Native American in the study. Five themes emerged from the data, and there were three responses that did not fit in any of the five themes. The five themes were: (a) the need for breast pumps and other incentives to encourage mothers to breastfeed; (b) the need for breastfeeding education to be part of the initial doctor's visit; (c) mother and infant falling asleep together while nursing; (d) the desire to watch children grow free of health problems; and (e) the need for more information on breastfeeding. Table 1 below illustrates a thematic summary of the participants' responses about breastfeeding.

Responses that did not fit into the five themes include: "When she was almost one year she will like to stand up and nurse"; "He will put his hand on my chest while nursing"; and "When he was older he would nurse on one breast and put his hand on the other breast."

Table 1. Thematic summary of the participants' responses about breastfeeding

Theme	Group Summary	Individual Quotes
Breast pumps and other incentives to encourage mothers to breastfeed	Participants in this group believed that families being given incentives would encourage breastfeeding.	*"I have no breast pump and I think if I can afford one it will help me a lot to breast feed my child."*
Breastfeeding education should be part of the initial doctor's visit	Participants in this group believed that they were not given advice from the start when they visited their healthcare professional.	*"If I was advice right from day one I would have breastfed my baby up to two years or beyond. I nursed my baby for only one month"*
Mother and infant falling asleep together while nursing	The mothers in this group reported positive experience with breastfeeding when they awoke to see they had fallen asleep with their infants during the nursing period. Three of the mothers said they wished their families had taken a picture of them.	*"Both of us will fall asleep together in the rocking chair."*
Desire to watch children grow free of health problems	Participants reported that they barely reported any health problems when they nursed their children	*"Although she was born almost 11 pounds by nursing my baby her weight stabilized and she grow up perfect in weight and in height"*
Lack of information on breastfeeding	More than one-third of the African-American participants reported that they did not receive the needed information that would have encouraged them to breastfeed.	*"I was not informed enough about breastfeeding otherwise I would have definitely breastfed my child for months. I did two weeks of breastfeeding""*

Discussion

This study adopted a strength-based approach that encouraged expectant mothers to nurse their children to enhance their children's health. For instance, six mothers reported that insurance companies covering the purchase of a breast pump would go a long way toward encouraging mothers who return to work after their baby is born to breastfeed. Some mothers suggested that the breast pumps would not only help mothers who work outside the home but also mothers with such problems as small nipples; they noted that mothers with large nipples will also find breast pumps useful. Engorgement mothers, they noted, would also benefit from the breast pump. In addition, participants indicated that including breastfeeding information in prenatal education and teaching mothers the differences between human milk and milk substitutes for infants would go a long way toward helping mothers decide whether or not to breastfeed. We inferred from the many positive responses from participants that a majority of the mothers enjoyed breastfeeding. Some mothers even reported that the best way to avert the obesity pandemic is for mothers to nurse their children.

Although some mothers indicated that falling asleep together with their child while nursing in a chair made them happy, caution should be taken because this could lead to a baby falling out of the mother's arms while both mother and baby are asleep and possibly hurting herself/himself.

Additionally, our data indicate that some African-American mothers indicated that breastfeeding was not encouraged enough at the time of having their babies. This lack of information thus contributed, in part, to the situation whereby some of them did not consider breastfeeding as an option. The findings of this study show how crucial it is for healthcare professionals to inform mothers and families about breastfeeding and about the differences between breast milk and milk substitutes for infants.

The findings in this study offer information about the positive attributes of breastfeeding and incentives that might encourage mothers to breastfeed their children. The kinds of incentives that mothers need to encourage them to breastfeed should be investigated along with how these incentives will reach mothers. This study could also be replicated, using equal number of mothers from diverse backgrounds and ethnicities to enable a better understanding of the situation and to subsequently learn about the positive attributes of breastfeeding. A quantitative and qualitative study to examine mothers' knowledge of nutrition and their views on the differences between breast milk, cow's milk, and formula could also be done.

Limitations

The fact that there were only 26 participants in this study and that the study was done in only one state in the United States prevents the study from being a true representation of the whole country. In addition, there were not many participants from the Hispanic and Native American communities. Having participants from different states and more participants from the Hispanic and Native American communities will be needed in order to reveal the more accurate nature and extent of positive attributes that encourage mothers to nurse. Based on the findings in this study, the following recommendations are made:

- Healthcare professionals should teach mothers the differences between breast milk and other infant foods right from the beginning at their first visit to doctor's office and when their babies are born.
- Insurance companies should be encouraged (or even required) to pay for breast pumps and to give incentives (e.g., provide diapers, reduce insurance premiums) to encourage mothers to breastfeed, given the fact that research shows that breastfeeding helps to reduce the incidence of many childhood diseases and consequently helps to reduce healthcare costs.

References

[1]   MacDorman MF, Mathews TJ. Behind international rankings of infant mortality: how the United States compares with Europe. Int J Health Serv 2010;40(4):577-88.
[2]   Center for Disease Control and Prevention. Accessed 2012 Apr 15. URL: http://www.cdc.gov/mmwr /preview/mmwrhtml/mm5642a8.htm
[3]   American Academy of Pediatrics (AAP). Policy statement. Accessed 2012 Apr 15. URL: http://pediatrics.aappublications.org/content/early/2012/02/22/peds.2011-3552
[4]   World Health Organization. Infant and young child feeding. Accessed 2012 Apr 15. URL: http://www.who.int/child_adolescent_health/documents/9789241597494/ en/I ndex.html
[5]   Bartick M, Reinhold A. The burden of suboptimal breastfeeding in the United States: A pediatric cost analysis. Pediatrics 2010;125(5):1048–56.
[6]   Williams JD. Early childhood obesity: A call for early surveillance and preventive measures. Can Med Assoc J 2004;171:243-4.
[7]   Lobstein T, Baur L, Uauy R. Obesity in children and young people: A crisis in public health. Report to the World Health Organization by the International Obesity Task Force. Obes Rev 2004;5(1):5–104.
[8]   Strauss AL, Corbin J. Grounded theory research: Procedures, canons and evaluative criteria. J Sociol1990;19:418-32.

In: Child Health and Human Development Yearbook 2013   ISBN: 978-1-63117-939-6
Editor: Joav Merrick   © 2014 Nova Science Publishers, Inc.

Chapter 27

Factors associated with accidental burn injuries in children twelve years and below admitted at Chitungwiza and Harare Central Hospitals in Zimbabwe

Theodora M Chikwanha*, Tamisayi Chinhengo
and Addmore Chadambuka
Departments of Rehabilitation and Community Medicine, University of Zimbabwe,
Harare, Zimbabwe

Abstract

Chitungwiza and Harare Central hospitals experienced increases in paediatric burn injuries occurring at home from 35% and 31% in 2008 to 41% and 38% in 2009 respectively. A study was carried out to determine factors associated with these accidental burn injuries occurring at home. Methods: A matched 1:1 case control study was carried out at Chitungwiza and Harare Central Hospitals. A case was a child twelve years and below admitted with accidental burn injuries occurring at home between 1st May 2010 and 31st July 2010 residing in Chitungwiza and Harare. A control was a child twelve years and below admitted for other medical conditions at the two institutions during the same period and residing in the same neighbourhood as the case. Interviewer administered questionnaires were administered to consenting caregivers of cases and controls within the wards. Results: 131 cases and 131 controls were interviewed. Independent risk factors for accidental burn injuries were child unattended at home AOR=2.88 (1.10-7.55), using same room for cooking and sleeping AOR= 5.08 (2.29-11.27), not taking precaution when cooking AOR =4.86 (1.73-13.65) and not taking precautions when serving food AOR =7.85 (2.18 -28.25). Previous health education on burn prevention AOR =0.39 (0.26-0.71) was protective. Conclusion: Most of the

* Corresponding author: Theodora M Chikwanha, Department of Rehabilitation, University of Zimbabwe, PO Box A178, Harare, Zimbabwe. E-mail: middychiky@yahoo.co.uk or tchikwanha@medsch.uz.ac.zw.

identified risk factors for burn injuries were within the home environment yet most caregivers reported taking precautions. There is need to educate the community on methods of modifying the home environment in order to reduce occurrence of burn injuries at home.

Keywords: Accident, burn, injury, risk factor, protective factor, children

Introduction

Burn injuries are emerging as an important largely preventable, growing public health problem in developing countries, gradually climbing the ranking list of causes of mortality and morbidity. Every year over 300 000 people die from burns. In addition, millions of people are disabled and disfigured by severe burns (1).

Globally paediatric burn injuries occurring within the home are the third most frequent cause of injury and death among all children from birth up to the age of nineteen years. Statistics on burn injuries are often fragmented when available as many burn injuries often go unreported if they are considered minor. This underestimates the severity of the problem. Despite global acknowledgement of burn injuries as a major public health problem, many Countries have given it limited attention. This is due to limited resources and co-existence of other competing health problems e.g. HIV/AIDS (2,3).

Thousand survivors have to live with permanent disabilities. This is experienced even more by children as they grow into adolescents and adults with permanent physical and sometimes psychological scarring caused by an accident that occurred in childhood (4).

In Africa approximately 99% of the burn injuries in children occur within the home (4). In Zimbabwe burn injuries account for an estimated 37.5% of hospital admissions and contribute 15% of the total deaths annually in children fourteen years and under (5). However relatively little policy formulation and intervention work on burn injuries has been reported (6,7). Much of the intervention strategies on burn prevention in Zimbabwe have been on provision of health information and education material to public health institutions.

Since 2005 paediatric burns continued to account for over a quarter of accidents occurring at home, leading to hospital admissions at Harare and Chitungwiza Central Hospitals (see table 1). In 2008 burn injuries accounted for 35% of injuries occurring at home leading to hospital admissions in the paediatric ward at Chitungwiza Hospital and 31% at Harare Central Hospital. In 2009 paediatric burn injuries accounted for 41% of injuries occurring at home leading to hospital admissions at Chitungwiza Hospital and 38% at Harare Central Hospital.

A study was carried out to determine factors associated with burn injuries in children aged 12 years old and below. Specific Objectives were to describe occurrence of burns by time, place and person, to determine causes of burns among admitted children, to assess severity of paediatric burns, to assess burn prevention measures taken within the home, to determine risk factors for burn injuries.

Table 1. Paediatric burns admissions at Chitungwiza and
Harare Central Hospitals 2005-2009

Year	Total Paediatric burns admissions Chitungwiza Central Hospital	Total paediatric admissions Harare Central Hospital
2005	194(29%)	469(30%)
2006	157(26%)	693(39%)
2007	295(37%)	572(28%)
2008	308(35%)	740(31%)
2009	306(41%)	807(38%)

Methods

A matched 1:1 case control study was conducted at Chitungwiza and Harare Central Hospitals. Cases and controls were frequency matched for place of residence. A case was a child twelve years and below admitted with burn injuries occurring at home between 1st May 2010 and 31st July 2010 at Harare and Chitungwiza Central Hospitals residing in Chitungwiza and Harare. A control was a child twelve years and below admitted for other medical conditions at the same institutions during the study period residing in the same neighbourhood as the case.

Assuming overcrowding was the most significant risk factor in burn injuries occurring in children twelve years and below with an odds ratio of 2.2 (8) and that 61% of burns in Zimbabwe occur in children twelve years and below (9), using a case to control ratio of 1:1 at the 95% confidence interval and 80% power, a sample 134 cases and 134 controls was computed.

Cases were recruited prospectively upon consent as they reported to the paediatric wards at Chitungwiza and Harare Central Hospitals for treatment. Controls were selected prospectively from children twelve years and below admitted for other medical conditions and staying in the same neighbourhood as the cases.

An interviewer-administered questionnaire was administered to consenting caregivers of cases. Patient case files were reviewed to obtain demographic information, diagnosis and severity of injury. The same questionnaire was administered to caregivers of controls within the wards at the two institutions.

Data was entered, cleaned and analysed using Epi Info statistical software. Odds ratios were calculated as measures of associations between identified risk factors. Logistic regression was performed to identify independent risk factors and simultaneously control for various confounding factors.

Approval to conduct study was sought from the Clinical Directors of Harare Central Hospital and Chitungwiza Central Hospital and from the Health studies office.

Ethical approval was sought and obtained from the Medical Research Council of Zimbabwe. Confidentiality was maintained and information obtained from participants was only used to identify risk factors for burn injuries. Purpose and benefits of the study were explained to participants and informed consent was sought from all caregivers.

Results

A sample size of 134 cases and 134 controls had been calculated for the study; however 131cases and 131 controls were enrolled during the study period. Eighty one (62%) of the cases were males, fifty (38%) were females. Seventy of the controls (54%) were males, 61 (46%) were females. Five (4%) of the cases and one (1%) of the controls had epilepsy. Three of the cases (2%) and four of the controls (3%) had previous burn injuries. Median age of cases was 3 years (Q1=1, Q3=6) and for controls was 3 years (Q_1=1, Q_3=5).

Causes and time of occurrence of burn injuries

Eighty one (62%) of the burn injuries were caused by hot liquid, twenty two (17%) by hot porridge, seven (5%) by hot oil. The rest were caused by candles, hot ash, electricity, paraffin and hot plastic. Fifty eight (44%) of the burn injuries occurred in the evening, forty one (32%) in the morning and thirty two (24%) in the afternoon.

Place of burn occurrence

Fifty three (41%) of the injuries occurred in the kitchen, thirty (24%) occurred outdoors. Twenty seven (21%) occurred in a room used both as a kitchen and bedroom, thirteen (10%) occurred in the other tenants rooms as some households had two or more tenants sharing the same house and five (4%) in the bathroom.

Severity of burn injuries

Forty (31%) of the children had less than 5% total body surface area injured, Fifty four (41%) had between 5% and 9% total body surface area injured and 37 (28%) had 10% and more body surface area injured. One hundred and fifteen children (87%) had first degree burns and sixteen (13%) second degree burns.

Socio-demographic characteristics for caregivers

One hundred and twenty nine (98%) of caregivers for the cases were female and two (2%) were males. All the caregivers for the controls were female. One hundred and ten (84%) of the cases and one hundred and fifteen (88%) of the controls were cared for by their parents. Ninety percent of the caregivers for the cases and 87% of the caregivers for controls had secondary education. Eighty eight (67%) of the caregivers for the case and one hundred (76%) of the caregivers for the controls were unemployed.

Socio-economic factors associated with burn injuries

Median number of rooms used by the family for cases was 2 (Q_1=1, Q_3=3) and for controls was 3 (Q_1=1, Q_3=3). Average number of people per household for both cases and controls was 4 people. Forty four (34%) of the cases families and seventeen (13%) of the controls families had average monthly incomes of equal to or less than US$100. Ninety four (72%) of the cases and eighty nine (68%) of the controls cooked indoors when there was no electricity. Ninety (69%) of the cases used paraffin, thirty three (25%) used open fire and the rest used gas and gel for cooking when there was no electricity. Seventy three (56%) of the controls used paraffin, thirty seven (28%) used open fire, sixteen (12%) used gel and five (4%) used gas when there was a power cut.

Burn prevention measures practised by caregivers

Seventy eight (60%) of the caregivers for cases and ninety nine (75%) of the caregivers for controls took burn prevention precautions within their homes. Precautions taken by caregivers for both cases and controls included not leaving children unattended near the cooking area (68%), putting pot handles away from children's reach when cooking (6%), sitting children away from cooker (28%), not saving children with hot beverages (20%) and hot food (62%), putting cold water first when bathing (54%), not boiling bathing water (13%) and not leaving children unattended in the bathroom (10%).

Table 2a. Factors associated with burn injuries burns in children twelve years and below admitted at Chitungwiza and Harare Central Hospitals 2010

Factor	Cases n=131	Controls n=131	mOR	95% CI
Child unattended at home				
Y	25	9	3.20*	1.43-7.15
N	106	122		
Using Same room for cooking and sleeping				
Y	68	19	6.36*	3.51-11.54
N	63	112		
Average monthly income (US$)				
<100	44	17	3.39*	1.82-6.34
>100	87	114		
>4 people Y	36	14	2.82*	1.45-5.47
Per room N	95	117		
Taking precautions when cooking				
Y	27	6	5.41*	2.15-13.60
N	104	125		
Taking precautions when serving food				
Y	32	3	13.79*	4.10-46.35
N	99	128		
Indoor use of paraffin stove				
Y	94	89	1.20	0.71-2.03
N	37	42		

Table 2b. Risk factors associated with burn injuries in children twelve years and below admitted at Chitungwiza Central Hospital, 2010

Factor	Cases	Controls	mOR	95%CI
Precaution when bathing child				
Y	63	89	1.75	0.93-3.30
N	68	42		
Health education on burns				
Y	21	43	0.39*	0.22-0.71
N	110	88		
Previous burn injury requiring medical care?				
Y	3	8	0.36	0.09-1.39
N	128	127		
Child's Sex				
F	50	61	0.71	0.43-1.16
M	81	70		
Staying with parent				
Y	110	115	0.729	0.362-1.469
N	21	16		

Table 3. Independent risk factors associated with burn injuries in children admitted at Chitungwiza and Harare Central Hospitals 2010

Term	AOR	95%CI	Coeff	SE	Z-stats	P-Value
Caregiver age LR	2.27	1.18-4.44	0.82	0.33	2.46	0.01
Child unattended	2.88	1.10-7.55	1.06	0.49	2.15	0.03
Same room cooking and sleeping	5.08	2.29-11.27	1.63	0.41	3.10	0.001
No precautions when cooking	4.86	1.73-13.65	1.58	0.52	3.01	0.03
No precautions when serving food	7.85	2.18-28.25	2.06	0.65	3.16	0.002

Factors associated with sustaining burn injuries

Risk factors for burn injuries (Table 2a,2b) were child remaining unattended at home [mOR 3.20 CI 1.43-7.15] ,using the same room for cooking and sleeping [mOR 6.36 CI 3.51-11.54], crowding [mOR 2.82 CI 1.45-5.47] ,having a monthly income of less than or equal to US$100 [mOR 3.39 CI 1.82-6.34] having a caregiver who is less than 18 years old [mOR 1.79 CI 1.05-3.05], not taking precautions when cooking [mOR 5.41 CI 2.15-13.60] and no precautions when serving food [mOR 13.79 CI 4.10-46.35].

Other risk factors not statistically significant were indoor use of a paraffin stove [mOR 1.92 CI 0.71-2.03] and being cared for by a caregiver who had only completed primary school (grade 7) [mOR 1.31 CI 0.42-3.62]. The only statistically significant protective factor was having had health education on burn prevention [mOR 0.39 CI 0.26-0.71]. Health education was given in form of lectures at some clinics in Harare and Chitungwiza.

Independent risk factors for burn injuries

Independent risk factors identified using logistic regression (see table 3) were caregivers age less than 18 years [AOR 2.27 CI 1.18-4.35], child remaining unattended at home [AOR 2.88 CI 1.10-7.55], using same room for cooking and sleeping [AOR 5.08 CI 2.29-11.27], not taking precaution when cooking [AOR 4.86 CI 1.73-13.65] and not taking precautions when saving food [AOR 7.85 CI 2.18- 28.25].

Discussion

Low income affected the type of accommodation that the children and their families stayed. Staying in a single room that was used for both cooking and sleeping put the children at a greater risk of sustaining a burn injury. Given that the average size of a room in the high density suburbs were most participants stayed was six square metres, a single room used for cooking and sleeping was more likely to have been overcrowded. Arrangement of furniture and other possessions within this room might not have left enough room for both children and adults to walk freely far away from the cooking area and hence the increased risk for children to sustain burn injuries as they are less likely to always remember to take necessary precautions.

Leaving a child alone at home was a risk factor for burn injuries. While this was consistent with findings in Ghana (10) and Brazil (11) where risk of burns was higher for children who were sometimes left unattended, reasons why children were often left unattended in this study were different. Children were left alone as parents mostly mothers went to their informal work places, to the market, or as parents visited friends in the neighbourhood. Some children were left just for a few minutes as their mothers hurried to the nearest shop (tuckshop) to buy bread for breakfast. In Zimbabwe these are common practices as most mothers who either unemployed or not formally employed cannot afford baby minders even for short periods of time or on a part time basis.

It is important to note that when children are left alone, regardless of the time period that they are left unattended, they are always at risk of having an accidental injury either through playing or as they try to prepare a meal for themselves. Therefore caregiver education should be clear on the risks associated with leaving children alone at home and how accidental injuries occur even when children are left for short periods of time.

Indoor use of paraffin stoves though not statistically significant cannot be ignored as a risk factor for burn injuries. Study results show that most of the burn injuries occur when there are power cuts and many people resort to using paraffin stoves within their homes for cooking. Currently there are frequent power cuts in most parts of Zimbabwe and as such there is likely to be an increased use of alternative sources of cooking energy with paraffin being the mostly used. There is need therefore to educate the communities of the dangers of using paraffin stoves and the necessary precautions they can take to prevent burn injuries.

Having previous health education on burn injuries was found to be protective against burn injuries. This was consistent with findings by Delgado et al. (8) who found that history of previous accident and health education on burn injuries had a significant protective effect among children who lived in good environmental conditions. However health education was only being given at a few clinics in both Harare and Chitungwiza and not all mothers visit these health care facilities. Health education messages should disseminated in such a way that even those who do not visit the health care facilities access the information.

The majority of injuries occurred in the kitchen and were caused by hot liquids. Peak time for burn occurrence was during the evening when evening meals were being prepared. Unlike other meal times when children can play and wait to be called when the meal is ready, during evening meal times most children will be indoors and depending with the available space within the home they might go near the cooking area as they play or move within the room hence occurrence of more burns during this time.

Some of the injuries occurred in the neighbours' house. In Zimbabwe it is common practice to have more than three families sharing the same house with each family occupying one or two rooms. Therefore even if the caregivers of children take precautions within their own homes burn injuries may still occur because the neighbours might not take any precautions possibly because they might not have younger children in their homes. Those without young children in their homes must also be targeted when educating the communities about burn prevention within the homes.

Two thirds of the admissions for burn injuries were children less than five years with more boys being affected than girls. These findings were consistent with those by Mzezewa et al. (9) and Muguti et al. (12). Younger children are less likely to understand and follow burn prevention measures in the home than older ones hence more children less than five years being admitted for burn injuries. Boys are also naturally likely to be more adventurous and engage in play that would result in them sustaining more injuries than girls.

While majority of caregivers reported that they took precautions within their homes to prevent occurrence of burn injuries, not taking burn prevention precaution within the home when cooking and serving food wer seen to increase the likelihood of a child getting a burn injury. Also most of the injuries occurred during meal preparation times. It is essential to look at other precautions that the caregivers may take in the homes during meal preparations apart from the ones they are already taking as several measures may actually be required during meal preparation times to prevent burn injuries.

In conclusion, most burn injuries occurred in low income households. Burn injuries in children were associated with inadequate accommodation, leaving children unattended and not taking precautions when cooking and serving food. Children less than five years were mostly admitted for burn injuries.

Recommendations

Non-communicable diseases and health education and promotion departments

- To develop burn prevention programmes focusing on community education on:
  - how burn injuries occur within the homes
  - burn injury prevention methods that can be taken within homes

Health education and promotion department
- To involve the Media in broadcasting burn prevention programmes on local television and radio

Public health officers
- Public Health officers should periodically evaluate the effectiveness of burn prevention strategies in use so that they remain relevant to the communities.

Actions to date
- Study findings and recommendations submitted to Non-communicable diseases and health education and promotion departments within the Ministry of Health and Child welfare (Zimbabwe) for use in future development of burn prevention programmes.

Acknowledgments

Mrs T Chinhengo – Field supervisor, Mr A Chadambuka - Academic supervisor, Department of Community Medicine University of Zimbabwe, Zimbabwe Field Epidemiology and Training Programme, Chitungwiza Central Hospital, Harare Central Hospital, Statisticians. Sponsors: Mr M A Muchengi, Mrs AN Mudondo, Dr E Chikwanha and Dr IT Chikwanha

References

[1]   Mock C. World Health Organisation joins forces with international society for burn injuries to confront global burden of burns. Inj Prev 2007; 13(5): 303.

[2]   Dissanaike S. Epidemiology of burns injuries: Highlighting cultural and sociodemographic aspects. Int Rev Psychiatr 2009; 21(6): 505-11.

[3]   World Health Organization. The injury chart book. A graphical overview of the global burden of injuries. Geneva: WHO, 2009.

[4]   Celko AM, Grivna M, Barss P. Severe childhood burns in Czech Republic: risk factors and prevention. Bull World Health Organ 2009; 87: 384-381.

[5]   Ministry of health and child welfare Zimbabwe. Disability and rehabilitation report. Accessed 2009 November 13. URL: www.mohcw.gov.zw/index.php/disability-and-rehabilitation.

[6]   Forjour SN, Zwi B, Mock N. Injury control in Africa, getting governments to do more. Trop Med Int Health 1998; 3(5): 349-56.

[7]   Atiyer BS, Rubeiz M, Ghananimeh G, Nassor AN, Al Amm CA. Management of paediatric burns. Euro-Mediterranean Council Burns Fire Disasters 2000; 13(3): 1-3.

[8]   Delgado J, Ramirez-Cardich M, Gilman R, Lavareilo R, Dahodavala N, Bazou A. Risk factors for burns in children: crowding, poverty and poor maternal education. Inj Prev 2000; 8(11): 38-41.

[9]   Muzezewa SN, Johnsson K, Aberg M, Salemark L. A prospective study on the epidemiology of burns in patients admitted to the Harare burns units. Burns 1999; 25(6): 499-504.

[10] Fourjor SN, Guyer B, Smith GS. Childhood burns in Ghana. Epidemiological characteristics and home based treatment. Burns 1995; 21(1): 24-8.

[11] Werneck GL, Reichenhem ME. Paediatric burns and associated risk factors in Rio de Janeiro, Brazil. Burns 1997; 23(6): 478-83.

[12] Muguti GI, Mazabane BN. An analysis of factors contributing to mortality rates in burns patient's treatment at Mpilo Central Hospital, Zimbabwe. J R Coll Surg Edinb 1997; 42(4): 259-61.

In: Child Health and Human Development Yearbook 2013   ISBN: 978-1-63117-939-6
Editor: Joav Merrick   © 2014 Nova Science Publishers, Inc.

Chapter 28

Patterns and determinants of gender bias in child health in India

Nilanjan Patra[*]
Institute of Economic Growth, Delhi, India

Abstract

The study will make an attempt to identify patterns of gender gap in child health in India and their determinants, and examine the possible role of female education and women's agency in reducing the gap. With the help of 21 selected indicators of health-seeking behaviour and health outcome, it is shown that there is ample evidence of varying level of gender gap. It is found that the gender gap in various health outcomes are not much related to the gender gap in various indicators of health-seeking behaviour. However, for the girl children's health achievement, the indicators of health-seeking behaviour are significantly related to the indicators of health outcome. It is also shown that any consistently robust pattern of gender bias against girl children in child health is *not* present in India. But there is a consistent pattern of girl children's absolute health achievement. Hence we focus on the girl children exclusively and tried to identify the determinants of health achievements for girl children. Given the Rawlsian theory of justice, the same determinants will, in turn, be able to reduce gender bias. We analyse the effects of some selected demographic and socioeconomic variables on the chance of full immunisation, chance of medical treatment in diarrhoea and medical treatment in fever/cough, chance of breastfeeding, chance of malnutrition and chance of mortality for girl children. Except for a few cases, the results are consistently robust.

Keywords: Gender bias, child health, NFHS, female literacy, women's empowerment, India

[*]Corresponding author: NilanjanPatra, Institute of Economic Growth, University Enclave, University of Delhi, Delhi-110007, India. E-mail: nilanjanpatra@gmail.com.

Introduction

Provision of public health is a basic human right and a crucial *merit* good, defined as an activity with very high positive externalities. Universal access to health together with safe drinking water, sanitation, nutrition, basic education, information and employment are essential to a balanced development. If India is to glean the gains of a demographic dividend and become a major economic power by 2030, it will have to guarantee that her people are healthy, live long and generate wealth.

Ever since the Bhore Committee Report (1) and the Constitution of India, the Government of India (GoI) has reiterated many times its aim of advancing the average health of its citizens, reducing inequalities in health, and fostering financial access to health care, particularly for the most destitute.

In the Directive Principles of State Policy (2) of the Constitution of India, Articles 38-2 and 41 stress the need for equitable access and assistance to the sick and the underserved, along with the rights to employment and education, while Article 47 stresses improving nutrition, the standard of living and public health. Article 39 and Article 45 point to gender equality and the protection of children rights including education and Article 42 asks for just and humane work environment and maternity relief. Article 14 suggests that men and women have equal rights and opportunities in the political, economic and social spheres and Article 15-1 prohibits discrimination against any citizen on the grounds of religion, race, caste, sex, etc. Nevertheless, roughly by any benchmark, India's triumph in achieving these goals can at best be reckoned as varied (3).

Inequality between women and men can come out in many diverse forms—it has many faces, *e.g.*, survival inequality, natality inequality, unequal facilities, ownership inequality, unequal sharing of household benefits and chores and domestic violence and physical victimisation (4). Gender disparity is, in fact, not one hardship but a multitude of problems. Gender inequality of one type tends to encourage and sustain gender inequality of other kinds (4). In most nations women have failed to 'hold up half the sky'. There are extensive inequalities even in morbidity and mortality in substantial parts of Asia and North Africa (5). In family behaviour, inequalities between men and women (and between boys and girls) are often accepted as 'natural' or 'appropriate' (5). Gender inequality takes the brutal form of remarkably high mortality rates of women and a subsequent predominance of men in the total population (4). Gender inequality is evident not just in the old form of mortality asymmetry, but also in the new form of sex-selective abortions aimed at eliminating female foetuses as many parents want the newborn to be a boy rather than a girl (4). Given equal nutrition and health care, women live on average slightly longer than men, even allowing for a modest level of maternal mortality. However, discrimination against females in many parts of the world meant that there were more than 100 million 'missing women' in the world in 1986 (6,7). Daughters are likely to be put to work for the household at a very young age, are much less likely to be educated and to attain literacy than sons of the same households and, worst of all — being less valued than their brothers — they have less chance of staying alive, because they are more deprived of food or of healthcare (8-10). Women in both rich and poor countries also suffer from severe 'time poverty', since they are carrying the 'double burden' of domestic and breadwinning responsibilities (11). Along with these doubly burdened productive works women are also burdened with unpaid reproductive work.

Almost all over the world, cultural traditions pose obstacles to women's health and empowerment. Many traditions have portrayed women as less important than men, less deserving of basic life support, or of fundamental rights that are strongly correlated with quality of life, such as health, education, self-respect, right to work, social and political liberty and participation (4,6). According to the 1995 UN Human Development Report, there is no country in the world in which women's quality of life is equal to that of men, according to a complex measure that includes longevity, health status, educational opportunities, employment and political rights.

The Constitution of India promises women equal employment opportunities (as men) and equal pay for equal work. But still today there is a significant degree of gender inequality in work opportunities and remuneration, and an astonishing range of variation in female labour force participation (12). The social barriers on the lifestyles of women tend to become more rigid as one moves up in the caste hierarchy (13). Generally, there is more seclusion of females in North India than in the South and among upper castes and classes than among lower castes and classes (14).

There is a need to study gender as it deals with 'emancipation of women from their subordination, and their achievement of equality, equity and empowerment' (15). The United Nations Decade for Women (1976-85) played an essential role in highlighting the 'important but often previously invisible role of women in the social and economic development of Third World countries and communities, and the particular 'plight' of low-income women' (15). During this decade 'policy-makers began to shift their focus from a universal concern with welfare-oriented, family-centred programmes which assumed motherhood as the most important role for women in the development process, to a diversity of approaches emphasising the productive role of women' (15). Women are increasingly seen as active 'agents' of development from the earlier view of passive 'patients'.

Health policies are aimed at the betterment of all children—boys and girls. But, as we will see later, the persistent seemingly gender-blind health policies have resulted in a situation where boys' achievements outperform that of girls' in almost all indicators of health. Thus it is important to look at the extent by which girls are lagging behind boys in the indicators of health. It is not only the absolute level of achievement of girls but the relative achievement of girls to boys which is important to study. As reduction and removal of gender bias in health can go a long way in achieving gender parity in many other dimensions of human development, not only for the present generation but also over the generations, studying gender bias is of utmost importance.

Preference for sons is prominent in Asia and North Africa (16) and it is particularly strong in the Indian subcontinent (17). In India, son preference endured for centuries. Population sex ratios from censuses almost steadily stepped up, from 1030 males per 1000 females in 1901 to 1064 males per 1000 females in 2011 (18-23). Sex ratios for children under age 10 years became more masculine in India over 1961-1991 (19, 24-28). 'A strong preference for sons has been found to be pervasive in Indian society, affecting both attitudes and behaviour with respect to children and the choice regarding number and sex composition of children (29-37). Son preference is an obstructing factor for maternal and child health care utilisation (38,39).

Mortality rates of females often exceed than those of males (40-47). Gender discrimination prevails regardless of the realisation that prejudice in morbidity, nutritional status, or use of health care will probably contribute to greater gender bias in mortality (14, 30, 48-56).

Gender bias in India was traced as early as the 1901 Census, which notes 'there is no doubt that, as a rule, she (a girl) receives less attention than would be bestowed upon a son. She is less warmly clad, … she is probably not so well fed as a boy would be, and when ill, her parents are not likely to make the same strenuous efforts to ensure her recovery' (14). Due to unequal treatment of women, India now has the largest share of 'missing women' in the world (57). Female infanticide has been widely recorded in India, especially in North and North-western India (58,59). Such a practice has also been noted recently in South India, in Tamil Nadu (60,61). Also the advanced technology to determine sex of the foetus helps in female foeticide (16).

Gender bias, even when it is not disastrous, may still create greater debility among surviving girls and its effect may be perpetuated over generations (46,47,62-64). If the 'Barker thesis' (*i.e.*, foetal origin of adult diseases hypothesis) (65, 66) is true, there is a possibility of a causal connection 'that goes from nutritional neglect of women to maternal under-nourishment, and from there to foetal growth retardation and underweight babies, thence to greater child under-nourishment' and to a higher incidence of permanent disadvantages in health much later in adult life (4,67). 'What begins as a neglect of the interests of women ends up causing adversities in the health and survival of all—even at advanced ages' (4). Thus, gender bias not only hurts women, but inflicts a heavy economic cost on the society by harming the health of all, including that of men (67). Gender bias can be a blend of 'active' bias (*e.g.*, 'intentional choice to provide health care to a sick boy but not to a sick girl'), 'passive' neglect (*e.g.*, 'discovering that a girl is sick later than that would be the case for a boy, simply because girls may be more neglected in day-to-day interactions than are boys'), and 'selective favouritism' ('choices made by resource-constrained families that favour those children that the family can ill afford to lose') (46).

Women in India face discrimination in terms of social, economic and political opportunities because of their 'inferior' status. Gender bias prevails in terms of allocation of food, preventive and curative health care, education, work and wages and, fertility choice (68-71). A large body of literature suggests that son preference and the low status of women are the two important factors contributing to the gender bias against women. The patriarchal intra-familial economic structure coupled with the perceived cultural, religious and economic utility of boys over girls based on cultural norms have been suggested as the original determining factors behind the degree of son preference and the inferior status of women across the regions of India (16,46,68). Daughters are considered as a net drain on parental resources in patrilineal and patrilocal communities (72). Intra-household gender discrimination has primary origins not in parental preference for boys but in higher returns to parents from investment in sons (73).

Gender bias in child health prevails even today when India is *shining* in terms of aggregate economic growth indicators or *Bharat Nirman* (reconstruction of India) is going on. There are several conflicting findings in the literature on the issue of gender bias. For example, gender bias tends to diminish with higher female literacy (74) and lower female literacy (75); with higher levels of poverty (8,76,77) and lower levels of poverty (78); with higher levels of fertility (8,79) and lower levels of fertility (75,80). Other household opportunities (*e.g.*, urbanisation, higher household standard of living, better parental education, mother's empowerment, etc.) can also affect gender bias. Female household headship can also affect female disadvantage. The reasons behind women household headship may be economic, sociological, geographical or ecological (81).

It is found that enhanced employment opportunities for adult women tend to raise the relative survival chances of girls (82). Some studies also show that the relative survival chance of girls is positively related to female labour force participation (51,52). 'Higher levels of female literacy and (female) labour force participation are strongly associated with lower levels of relative female disadvantage in child survival' (4). Gender bias in child survival could also be affected by some other variables, *e.g.*, mortality, fertility, development indicators, geographical location, *etc*. It is evident that gender bias in child survival tends to be relatively low among poor households, among backward castes, and among households with high levels of female labour force participation (83).

Given that there is a strong preference for sons in India, there are significant variations in the extent of this preference within the country (16). Prevalence of 'female disadvantage' is evident in large parts of India, particularly in the large northern states rather than the southern states (16,41,51,80,83-88). There exists a 'Bermuda Triangle' for the female child in India in a zone of 24 districts consisting parts of Rajasthan, Haryana, western Uttar Pradesh and Madhya Pradesh (89). The country can be roughly divided into two by a line that resembles the contours of the Satpura hill range, extending eastward to join the Chota Nagpur hills of southern Bihar. To the north of this line sex ratios are high and to the south sex ratios are comparatively low (16,90). One study have explained the North-South demographic divide in terms of female autonomy, *i.e.*, decision-making ability regarding personal matters, with low female autonomy in the North compared to higher female autonomy in the South (90).

Boys are much more likely than girls to be taken to a health facility when sick in both north and south India (41,51,80,83-88). Again, girls are more likely to be malnourished than boys in both northern and southern states (30,41,67,80,91-94). 'The states with strong anti-female bias include rich ones (Punjab and Haryana) as well as poor (Madhya Pradesh and Uttar Pradesh), and fast-growing states (Gujarat and Maharashtra) as well as growth-failures (Bihar and Uttar Pradesh).

It is thus clear that we have to look beyond material prosperity or economic success or GNP growth into broadly cultural and social influences' (4). '... variables that relate to the general level of economic development and modernisation turn out, in these (83,95) statistical studies, to have no significant effect on gender bias in child survival, and can sometimes— when not accompanied by empowerment of women—even strengthen, rather than weaken, the gender bias in child survival. This applies *inter alia* to urbanisation, male literacy, the availability of medical facilities, and the level of poverty. In so far as a positive connection does exist in India between the level of development and reduced gender bias in (child) survival, it seems to work mainly through variables that are directly related to women's agency, such as female literacy and female labour force participation' (4).

Objective and research questions

The study will make an attempt to identify the pattern of gender gaps in child health in India, to find out its socioeconomic and demographic determinants and explore the possible role of female education and women's agency in reducing the gender gap. It will focus on selected indicators of health outcomes (*e.g.*, post-neonatal mortality, child mortality, prevalence of malnutrition) and health-seeking behaviour (*e.g.*, immunisation coverage [preventive health care], medical treatment in diarrhoea and medical treatment in fever/ cough [curative health care] and breastfeeding [feeding practice]). Here neonatal mortality is not considered because it is least affected by socioeconomic and demographic indicators and is mostly due to biological reasons. On the basis of exploratory data analysis, the study intends to address the following questions:

- Is there evidence of gender gap in various indicators of health-seeking behaviour (*e.g.*, immunisation coverage, medical treatment in diarrhoea, medical treatment in fever/cough and breastfeeding), and if so, how does the gender gap vary between different regions?
- Is there evidence of gender gap in various health outcomes (*e.g.*, post-neonatal mortality, child mortality, malnutrition), and if so, how does the gender bias vary between different regions?
- Can the gender gap (if any) in various health outcomes be related to a corresponding gender gap in various indicators of health-seeking behaviour?
- If gender gap exists, what is the regional pattern of gender gap in child health in India? How has this regional pattern of gender gap changed over the study period of almost one-and-a-half decades?
- What are the socio-economic and demographic determinants of gender gap in health outcomes and health-seeking behaviour?
- How does female education and women's agency affect the gender gap in health outcomes and health-seeking behaviour?
- Are the results of previous analyses robust?

Methods

The present study uses secondary data from National Family Health Survey (NFHS)-III (2005-06), NFHS-II (1998-99), and NFHS-I (1992-93) (37,45). These surveys provides state-level estimates of demographic and health parameters as well as data on various socioeconomic and demographic factors that are critical for bringing about desired changes in India's demographic and health situation. NFHS-I was a 'landmark in the history of collection of demographic data through surveys' (96). 'It is widely recognised that the NFHSs play a pivotal role in providing valuable conventional and non-conventional demographic and health information on India' (97). It is worth noting that the NFHS series is regarded as 'storehouse of demographic and health data in India' (97). The NFHS is 'unique' (or 'unprecedented') because of—uniformity of its questionnaires, sampling method, data collection, analysis of data; a representative sample in the north-eastern states for the first time; in-depth uniform training of interviewers and strict supervision (98,99). The NFHS sampling design followed a systematic, multi-stage stratified random sample of households, all over the country (98). A post-survey check (with five percent of samples) of NFHS-I also confirmed its 'high quality data' (100).

Children under age three years are the unit of the present analysis. A child data file is created by merging selected household and mother's characteristics from household and women's data files respectively. The predictor variables could be birth order of the child [1, 2, 3, 4 and above], residence (rural, urban), mother's education (illiterate, primary, secondary, higher), mother's age [19 or less, 20-24, 25-29, 30-49 years], antenatal care (no, yes), religion (Hindu, Muslim, Christian and other religious minorities), caste/ tribe (general, other backward class, scheduled caste, scheduled tribe), standard of living index (low, medium, high) or wealth index (poorest, poorer, middle, richer, richest), media exposure[1] (no, yes), sex of household head (female, male), mother's empowerment index[2] (low, medium, high), zone of states (Central, North, East, Northeast, West, South), electricity (no, yes).

The study identifies patterns of gender gap in post-neonatal mortality, child mortality, and prevalence of malnutrition, immunisation coverage, diarrhoea treatment, fever/ cough treatment, and breast-feeding. The gender gap is calculated as a relative gap between the achievement of boys and girls (first two questions). For the third question, state-level OLS regression is undertaken. The study uses the Borda rule and Principal Component Analysis to see the regional pattern in gender gap in child health for the fourth question. For the fifth question, binary bivariate and multivariate logit regression analyses are performed. Structural estimation of the full model is beyond the scope of the present study, which estimates a few reduced form models examining the magnitude of gender bias in child health after controlling for socioeconomic and demographic factors that could influence gender bias. Logistic regression results are presented in multiple classification analysis (MCA) form. This involves calculating unadjusted and adjusted values of the response variable for each category of every predictor variable. Unadjusted values are calculated from logit regressions incorporating only one predictor variable. Adjusted values are calculated from logit regressions incorporating all predictor variables simultaneously. When calculating the adjusted values for a particular predictor variable, all other predictor variables are controlled by setting them to their mean values in the underlying regression (101). The effectiveness of female education and women's empowerment (sixth question), can be seen from the adjusted effects of the logistic regression results. The robustness of the results is tested using the first and second round of the NFHS dataset.

Results

Gender gap in health-seeking behaviour for children in India

Here we will explore if there is any evidence of gender gap in the selected indicators of health-seeking behaviour for children in the states of India. The selected indicators of health-seeking behaviour are: childhood immunisation, childhood diarrhoea, childhood fever/ cough, and childhood breastfeeding. We will see the extent of gender gap in these indicators in the Indian states and how this gender gap changes over the study period of almost one-and-a-half decades.

The state-wise gender gap for all the indicators is calculated using the following relative gap formula: $\text{Gender Gap} = \dfrac{X_{Boy} - X_{Girl}}{X_{Girl}} \times 100$. This measure of gender gap is the relative gap between boy and girl minus one and then taken in per cent (6,46,68,83, 102-105). Some studies measure gender gap as the absolute gap (106,107) or as the relative gap (108—simple arithmetic average of relative gaps) or both (109,110). These studies use a particular gap (or more than one gap) without giving much rationale for the choice.

A relative gap measure captures both the levels of coverage and gender equality. The value of gender gap decreases as coverage rates increase for both boys and girls with same absolute gap between them and it decreases as coverage rates increases for both boys and girls with lower absolute gap between them. A gender-equity-sensitive indicator (GESI) would have been a better measure, though the choice of degree of inequality aversion equal to two is questionable.

This relative gap formula satisfies all the four principles of an inequality index, namely, *principle of population symmetry*, *principle of transfer*, *principle of scale invariance* and *principle of constant addition*. An absolute gap formula, however, does not satisfy *principle of scale invariance* and *principle of constant addition*. Moreover, the absolute gap formula is not unit-free but a relative gap formula is free of any units.

State-wise gender gap in full immunisation is shown in figure-1. There exists a positive gender gap in immunisation in India in all three rounds of NFHS (more than five percent). The states witnessing a reduction in gender gap over time are: Delhi, Haryana, Himachal Pradesh, Rajasthan, Uttarakhand, Uttar Pradesh, Orissa, Nagaland, Sikkim and Tamil Nadu. Bihar is the only state where gender gap remains almost stagnant at above 40 percent over the thirteen year period. Meghalaya is the only state that has a gender gap favourable to girl children in all three rounds of NFHS though its extent is decreasing over time. Maharashtra is the only state where gender gap consistently increased over time.

For all three indicators of childhood diarrhoea, state-wise gender gap in three rounds of NFHS is presented in figures 2-4. There exists a positive gender gap in all three indicators of childhood diarrhoea in India in favour of boys in all three rounds of NFHS.

In case of diarrhoea, girls received no treatment at least eight percent more than boys and boys received medical treatment at least five percent more than girls in India. Boys are also more likely receive ORS than girls.

Gender gaps in the two indicators of childhood fever/ cough across the states are presented in figures 5 and 6. There exists a positive gender gap in both the indicators of childhood fever/ cough in India in favour of boys in all three rounds of NFHS. In case of fever/ cough, girls received no treatment at least ten percent more than boys and boys received medical treatment at least six percent more than girls in India.

It clearly shows that in most of the states there is a decrease in medical treatment in public health facility over the years (figure 7)[3]. Gender gap in childhood fever/ cough treatment in public and private health facility across the states are presented in figures 8 and 9 respectively.

State-wise gender gaps in childhood breastfeeding for five indicators (never breastfed, less than six months breastfed, at least six months breastfed, currently breastfeeding and exclusively breastfed for first six months) are shown in figures 10-14.

So it is evident that there is strong evidence of gender gap in the selected thirteen indicators of health-seeking behaviour in immunisation, diarrhoea, fever/ cough and breastfeeding for children in all the states of India. For a particular state, it might so happen that for a particular variable, gender gap (and/or its sign) changes over time and the gender gap (and/or its sign) changes for different variables in a particular time period.

Gender gap in health outcome for children in India

Here we will explore if there is any evidence of gender gap in the selected indicators of health outcomes for children in the states of India. The selected indicators of health outcomes are childhood malnutrition and childhood mortality. Gender gap in childhood malnutrition is shown in figures 15-20.

Post-neonatal death rate is calculated as the percentage of children age 1-11 months who died among the children ever born for boy and girl children separately for each state. Gender gap in post-neonatal death is shown in figure 21. Child death rate is calculated as the percentage of children age 12-35 months who died among the children ever born for boy and girl children separately for each state. Gender gap in child death is shown in figure 22. From figures 21 and 22 one can argue that as children grow older, girl children receive more harshly biased treatment.

So it is evident that there is strong evidence of gender gap in the selected eight indicators of health outcome in malnutrition and mortality for children in the states of India. For a particular state it might so happen that for a particular variable gender gap (and/or its sign) changes over time and gender gap (and/or its sign) changes for different variables in a particular time period.

Impact of gender gap in health-seeking behaviour on gender gap in health outcome[4]

Here we will examine whether the gender gap in various health outcomes is related to a corresponding gender gap in various indicators of health-seeking behaviour. Ordinary least square (OLS) method will be used for state-level reduced-form regressions. The selected dependent variables are gender gap in post-neonatal survival, gender gap in childhood survival and gender gap in childhood nutrition. Independent variables are gender gap in full immunisation, gender gap in medical treatment in diarrhoea, gender gap in medical treatment in fever/ cough and gender gap in breastfeeding with at least six months breastfed. In addition we incorporate two dummy variables for major states and southern states. We run OLS regression for three separate statistical models for each round of NFHS as well as for the pooled data of all three rounds.

The study found that the gender gaps in various health outcomes are not much related to the gender gaps in various indicators of health-seeking behaviour. So the gender gap in health-seeking behaviour does not really transform into the gender gap in health outcome for the children in the states of India.

However for girl children's health achievement, the indicators of health-seeking behaviour are significantly related to the indicators of health outcome. Full immunisation rate for the girl children has a consistently significant impact on all the indicators of health outcome. An increase in full vaccination coverage rate for girl children reduces post-neonatal mortality, childhood mortality and childhood malnutrition rates for the girl children. Girl children's health outcome is worse in the major states compared to other non-major states.

Pattern of gender gap in child health in India

Here we will try to see if there is any pattern of gender gap in child health exists in India. Also we will try to explore whether this pattern of gender gap in child health remained consistent over the study period of almost one-and-a-half decades. If we can identify the consistent pattern of gender gap, it is possible to focus on those particular areas to reduce and remove gender gap.

State-wise pattern of gender gap in child health in India[5]

The selected 21 indicators of health-seeking behaviour and health outcome are: for childhood immunisation—A: childhood full vaccination; for diarrhoea—B: childhood diarrhoea with 'no treatment', C: childhood diarrhoea with 'medical treatment', D: childhood diarrhoea with 'given ORS'; for breastfeeding—E: childhood breastfeeding with 'never breastfed', F: childhood breastfeeding with 'less than six months breastfed', G: childhood breastfeeding with 'at least six months breastfed', H: childhood breastfeeding with 'currently breastfeeding', I: childhood breastfeeding with 'exclusively breastfed for first six months'; for malnutrition—J: severely stunted (height-for-age, -3 SD), K: stunted (height-for-age, -2 SD), L: severely underweight (weight-for-age, -3 SD), M: underweight (weight-for-age, -2 SD), N: severely wasted (weight-for-height, -3 SD), O: wasted (weight-for-height, -2 SD); for fever/ cough— P: childhood fever/ cough with 'received no treatment', Q: childhood fever/ cough with 'received medical treatment', R: childhood fever/ cough with 'received medical treatment in public health facility', S: childhood fever/ cough with 'received medical treatment in private health facility'; and for mortality—T: post-neonatal death, U: child death.

The 21 dimensions will be reduced by some ordinal measure. As an ordinal aggregator, the study used the well-known Borda rule (named after Jean-Charles de Borda who devised it in 1770). The rule gives a method of rank-order scoring, the method being to award each state a point equal to its rank in each indicator (A-U) of ranking, adding each state's scores to obtain its aggregate score, and then ranking states on the basis of their aggregate scores (111), separately for each round of NFHS.

Each state is ranked for each of the chosen indicators to capture the relative position of the Indian states in gender bias against girl children. A higher rank (number) indicates higher gender bias against girl children.

Ranking is done in ascending order (a higher value indicates higher gender bias against girls) for the following indicators—A, C, D, G, H, I, Q, R, and S. For the rest of the indicators, ranking is done in descending order (a lower value indicates higher gender bias against girls). Borda rank is calculated for each state on the basis of their aggregate scores for each round of NFHS. State-wise Borda rank in gender bias against girl children in child health is presented in table 1.

Again, a higher rank (number) signifies higher gender bias against girls. For any NFHS round, a Borda rank of one signifies lowest gender bias against girls in that state for that period.

From table 1, one can see that there are lot of ups and down in the state-wise rankings as we move from NFHS-I to NFHS-III. Over almost the one and a half decades of the study period, Gujarat, Himachal Pradesh, Uttarakhand, Jharkhand, Chhattisgarh and Meghalaya consistently improved their ranks, *i.e.*, gender bias against girl children has consistently reduced relative to the other states.

But the picture is just the reverse for Punjab and Mizoram where gender bias against girl children in child health has consistently increased over time relative to the other states. Table 2 provides the rank (Spearman) correlation coefficient for each pair of Borda rankings from the three rounds of NFHSs (given in table 1). The rank correlation coefficients are not significant even at 10 percent level, suggesting that the state-wise pattern of gender bias against girl children in child health is not consistent.

To check the robustness of the absence of a consistent state-wise pattern in gender bias in child health, the analysis needs further calibration. First, instead of all the 21 indicators we took only six indicators (A, C, G, L, Q and U) for all the 29 states. Doing the same exercise as above, the (Spearman) correlation coefficients for each pair of Borda rankings from the three rounds of NFHSs are not significant even at 10 percent level as before (table 3). Second, we do the same exercise for the major 19 states with the same six indicators (A, C, G, L, Q and U). Again the correlation coefficients are also not significant (see tables 4 and 5).

To check robustness of the results the study also uses Principal Component Analysis (PCA) technique as a second tool to reduce dimensions. PCA reduces a large set of variables to a much smaller set that still contains most of the information about the large set. It reduces the variation in a correlated multi-dimension to a set of uncorrelated components. Principal components (defined as a normalised linear combination of the original variables) are constructed from the 21 indicators.

The principal components with Eigen value greater than one are considered. Then a composite index is constructed as a weighted average of the principal components or factors, where the weights are (Eigen value of the corresponding principal component)/ (sum of all Eigen values) (112). On the basis of the values of the composite index all the states are ranked in ascending order separately for each round of NFHS.

For calculation of PCA, all the 21 indicators were made *unidirectional*. Say, for b, we used the B: childhood diarrhoea with 'no treatment'. We deducted the percentages of boys and girls who received 'no treatment' from 100 to get percentages of boys and girls who received 'any treatment'. Then the gender gap is calculated using the previously mentioned formula. The same method is applied for b, e, f, j, k, l, m, n, o, p, t, and u also. With the values of composite index, states are ranked in ascending order, separately for each round of NFHS. A higher rank (number) indicates higher gender bias against girls. With the values of composite index, states are ranked in ascending order, separately for each round of NFHS. A higher rank (number) indicates higher gender bias against girls.

Here we consider six principal factors with Eigen values greater than one in both NFHS-I and –II; and in NFHS-III, seven principal factors with Eigen values greater than one are considered. The cumulative variance explained by these principal factors is 83 percent for NFHS-I, 78 percent for NFHS-II and 82 percent for NFHS-III. With these principal factors, we construct a composite index and rank the states accordingly. Table 6 presents the state-wise composite index and the ranks of the states. From table 6 one can see that there are lot of ups and down in the state-wise rankings as we move from NFHS-I to NFHS-III. Over the study period of thirteen years, Gujarat, Himachal Pradesh, Rajasthan, Karnataka and to some extent Orissa, consistently improved their ranks, *i.e.*, gender bias against girl children has consistently reduced relative to the other states. But the picture is just reverse for Punjab, Bihar and Mizoram where gender bias against girl children in child health has consistently increased over time. For the entire picture of state-wise pattern of gender bias over the three rounds of NFHSs, we need table 7.

Table 7 provides the rank (Spearman) correlation coefficient for each pair of rankings from the three rounds of NFHSs (given in table 6). The correlation coefficients are not significant even at 10 percent level suggesting that there is no consistent state-wise pattern of gender bias against girl children in child health.

To check the robustness of the absence of a consistent state-wise pattern in gender bias in child health, the analysis is calibrated further. First, we consider only one principal component that explains the largest proportion of total variation in all the 21 indicators. The total variance explained by the first principal component is only 24 percent for NFHS-I, 23 percent for NFHS-II, and 20 percent for NFHS-III. But the rank (Spearman) correlation coefficients are not significant except for the correlation coefficient between the ranks in NFHS-I and NFHS-II (significant at five percent level). As the total explained variance is quite low, we should not place much weight on this solitary exception.

Secondly, we considered only the 19 major states. Now, we are considering only two principal factors with Eigen values greater than one in NFHS-I and three principal factors with Eigen values greater than one for both NFHS-II and -III. The cumulative variance explained by these principal factors is 57 percent for NFHS-I, 79 percent for NFHS-II and 76 percent for NFHS-III. With these principal factors, we construct a composite index and rank the states accordingly. Again, the correlation coefficients of the ranks are not significant as before.

The study found that any consistently robust state-wise pattern of gender bias against girl children in child health is *not* present among all the 29 Indian states over the three rounds of NFHSs. However, the absence of any consistent state-wise pattern in gender bias does not mean that there is no gender bias in child health in the Indian states. Among the 19 major states, overall, there is high gender bias in three Empowered Action Group of states (namely, Uttar Pradesh, Madhya Pradesh, and Bihar) and in Andhra Pradesh, Punjab, and Gujarat as well. The states which succeeded in reducing gender bias against girl children in child health over the years as compared to the other states are Gujarat, Himachal Pradesh, Rajasthan, West Bengal, Uttarakhand, Chhattisgarh, and Jharkhand. But for the states of Jammu and Kashmir, Punjab, Uttar Pradesh, Madhya Pradesh, Bihar, Maharashtra, Andhra Pradesh and Tamil Nadu gender bias against girl children has consistently increased over time relatively.

Along with the gender gap one should also look at the absolute level of health achievement for both boys and girls. There may be untoward cases of low gender gap with low absolute achievement level for both sexes. By the Rawlsian (113) theory of justice[6] which gives complete priority to the worst-off group's gain (116), one should focus on the health achievement by the girl children only with reduction in gender bias in child health being the ultimate motto.

An attempt has been made to see if there is any state-wise pattern in health status for girl children only over the three rounds of NFHSs. For this we selected only six indicators (A, C, G, L, Q and U) of health-seeking behaviour and health outcome for girl children only. Based on these six indicators, the Borda ranks of the states are presented in table 8 for three rounds of NFHSs. Table 9 shows that the (Spearman) rank correlations of the ranks of states for various NFHS rounds are strongly significant now. Thus there is a consistent state-wise pattern of girl children's health status. This finding may be interpreted as, overall, girl children's health achievement in different states moved more or less in the same direction, but girl children's relative achievement compared to boys in health has not moved in the same direction for all the states over the study period.

Concentrating on the consistent state-wise pattern of girl children's health achievement is fairly justified on the Rawlsian premise as in the social valuation function it assumes the degree of inequality aversion tending to infinity. As a policy measure, to reduce gender bias in child health, we need to focus on the states with low health achievement by girls (*i.e.*, lower Borda ranks in table-8), *viz.*, Rajasthan, Uttar Pradesh, Uttarakhand, Madhya Pradesh, Chhattisgarh, Bihar, Jharkhand, Orissa, Assam and Andhra Pradesh.

Regional pattern of gender gap in child health in India[7]

Here six indicators, one from each dimension, are chosen: health-seeking behaviour— childhood full vaccination, childhood diarrhoea with 'medical treatment', childhood breastfeeding with 'at least six months breastfed', childhood fever/ cough with 'received medical treatment'; health outcome— childhood nutrition (weight-for-age, above -2 SD), childhood survival.

For the variable region of states, *North* includes Delhi, Haryana, Himachal Pradesh, Jammu and Kashmir, Punjab and Rajasthan; *Central* includes Madhya Pradesh, Chhattisgarh, Uttar Pradesh, and Uttarakhand; *East* includes Bihar, Jharkhand, Orissa and West Bengal; *Northeast* includes Arunachal Pradesh, Assam, Manipur, Meghalaya, Mizoram, Nagaland, Sikkim and Tripura; *West* includes Goa, Gujarat and Maharashtra; *South* includes Andhra Pradesh, Karnataka, Kerala and Tamil Nadu.

A gender-equity-sensitive indicator (GESI) is used to measure gender inequality which is simply the Atkinson index. Lesser the value of the index, lesser will be the gender inequality, *i.e.*, a lower value implies better status (118). For robustness of the results, in addition to this, gender gap is also calculated using the previous relative gap formula. The six dimensions are reduced by the Borda rule and PCA technique.

The study found that any consistently robust region-wise pattern of gender bias against girl children in child health is *not* present among the six Indian regions of states over the three rounds of NFHSs. However, there is a consistent region-wise pattern of girl children's health status.

Pattern of gender gap in infant mortality in India: Evidence from NFHS and SRS Data[8]

Here infant mortality rate (IMR) is taken as a proxy for child health conditions. The causes of infant mortality are 'strongly correlated to those structural factors like economic development, general living conditions, social wellbeing, and the quality of the environment, that affect the health of entire population' (121). State-wise IMR is computed from the unit-level records for the major sixteen states of India for five-year period preceding the survey for both boys and girls separately as well as for all children for three NFHSs. For robustness, IMR data is also taken from the published Sample Registration System (SRS) data. Gender gap is calculated as a relative gap as before. From figures 23-28, it is evident that there is gender bias in IMR though its extent differs across surveys.

The study found that any consistently robust state-wise pattern of gender bias against girl children in IMR is *not* present among the sixteen major states. But, there is a consistent inter-temporal state-wise pattern in girl infants' mortality status. This result remains valid irrespective of the data we use.

Thus it is evident that any consistently robust pattern of gender bias against girl children in child health is *not* present in India. But there is a consistent pattern of girl children's health achievement. This is true irrespective of the number of indicators we use or the number of states we select or the measurement of gender bias or the method to reduce dimensions.

As a policy measure, to reduce gender bias in child health, we need to focus on the states with low health achievement by girls *viz.*, Rajasthan, Punjab, Haryana, Uttar Pradesh, Uttarakhand, Madhya Pradesh, Chhattisgarh, Bihar, Jharkhand, Orissa, Assam, Andhra Pradesh, Tamil Nadu and Gujarat.

Determinants of gender gap in child health in India

A consistently robust inter-temporal pattern of girl children's health achievement emphasises the need to focus exclusively on the girl children. If we can identify the factors which can improve girl children's health achievements, the same factors will, in turn, be able to reduce gender gap in child health on the Rawlsian premise. To find out the determinants of girl children's health achievement, the study will use logistic regression technique to examine only girl children's health achievements. Logistic regressions are performed (a) for all India level, (b) for rural areas in India, (c) for demographic factors only in India and (d) for socioeconomic factors only in India. The dependent variables[9] are—full immunisation, and malnutrition.

Determinants of full immunisation for girl children

The analysis of immunisation coverage focuses on living girl children age 12-23 months during the Survey. This age group is selected because full immunisation (BCG, three doses each of DPT and Polio and measles) is recommended for all children by the age of one year. Multicollinearity problem is not there as the correlation coefficients are much less than the threshold magnitude.

Table 10 shows the unadjusted and adjusted effects on full immunisation coverage in India for three rounds of NFHS. There is a consistently inverse relationship between immunisation coverage and birth order of a girl child in India. The majority of first-order births occur to younger women who are more likely to utilise maternal and child health care services than older women. One can think of two countervailing effects of increasing birth-order on likelihood of vaccination. The positive one could be some kind of *learning effect* about immunisation which almost does not vary with higher birth-order. The negative one could be some kind of *negligence effect* to the higher order births and this effect perhaps increasingly increases with higher birth order. Thus for higher order births, it seems that the *negligence effect* more than offset the *learning effect*.

The unadjusted likelihoods of residence suggest that it has a positive effect on the girl children from urban areas. After controlling for other variables the rural-urban disparity almost vanishes (except for NFHS-II). When we control for the demographic factors only, urban girl children are significantly more likely to be fully immunised in all three rounds of the data.

This implies that the unadjusted likelihoods for residence in baseline regressions capture mainly the effects of the selected socioeconomic variables. Hence it can be argued that the rural-urban disparity is not due to demographic factors but to socioeconomic factors. High immunisation coverage in urban areas is however supported by many researchers (122,123).

There is a strong positive relationship between mother's education and girl children's immunisation coverage. The adjusted effects are lower than unadjusted ones but still strongly significant. Such positive effect of maternal education is also hypothesised by many researchers (64,122-126) though some researchers find a spurious effect (127).

The chance of immunisation of girl children increases with the mother's age only up to the age group of 25-29 year and then decreases. A positive relationship is also noted by researchers (128). In the context of rural Bangladesh, researchers show that the likelihood of vaccination decreases for the mothers older than 28 years (125).

Antenatal care during pregnancy has a strong positive direct effect on vaccination. Antenatal care increases the possibility of meeting health-care personnel who help mothers to raise their awareness by disseminating information regarding immunisation. Such a positive relationship is also noted by researchers (125).

The likelihood of immunisation also varies with religion. Girl children from Muslim households are less likely to be fully vaccinated and girl children from Christian and other religious minority households are more likely to be fully vaccinated, compared to girl children from Hindu households. Caste/tribe also affects full immunisation. The chance of being fully vaccinated is consistent with the relative traditional social hierarchy of castes/ tribes. So girl children from the backward caste/ tribe households are less likely to be fully immunised even if vaccines are available to all for free.

The chance of immunisation increases with the standard of living index or wealth index of girl children's households (except for the adjusted ones in NFHS-II). Researchers also argue for household income as a proximate determinant of immunisation coverage (64,125). Though vaccines are freely available under UIP, household income (as measured by SLI or wealth index) does have a positive effect on childhood immunisation.

Girl children of mothers with some exposure to mass media are more likely to be fully vaccinated than their counterparts whose mothers do not have any exposure to mass media. This indicates that media exposure has a significantly positive effect on immunisation. However, some researchers do not find any significant effect of media (127).

After controlling for the other included variables, the sex of household head does not have any significant effect on full vaccination (except in NFHS-II). However, in the context of rural Orissa, studies show that children from male headed households are more likely to be immunised than those from female headed households (129). Moreover, he shows that the gender inequality (boys are more likely than girls) in preventive health care persists regardless of the gender of the household head.

Mother's empowerment index has a positive effect on full immunisation in NFHS-III but it does not have any significant effect in NFHS-II. The immunisation rate varies widely across different zones too. Girl children from northeast zone are the least likely to be fully vaccinated. Household electrification has also a significantly strong positive role on full immunisation in India. Such a positive effect possibly works through availability of electronic mass media, establishment of an institutional health facility in the vicinity, higher wealth index, *etc.* Some studies also noted such a positive relationship (125).

The effects of the variables remain same in case of rural India or for demographic factors only or for socioeconomic factors only as in the all-India regression model.

Determinants of malnutrition for girl children

The analysis of childhood malnutrition focuses on the living girl children age below 36 months. Here malnutrition refers to underweight. Children whose weight-for-age is below minus two standard deviations from the median of the international reference population are considered to be underweight. Multicollinearity problem is not there as the correlation coefficients are much less than the threshold magnitude.

Table 11 shows the unadjusted and adjusted effects on malnutrition in India for three rounds of NFHS. The unadjusted likelihoods suggest that as a girl child's birth order increases she will be more and more likely to be malnourished. After controlling for other variables, the effect of birth order almost vanishes. When we control for demographic factors only, birth order does have a positive effect on malnutrition. This implies that the unadjusted likelihoods for birth order in all-India regressions capture mainly the effects of the selected socioeconomic variables. Thus the effect of birth order is not due to the demographic factors but due to selected socioeconomic factors.

Adjusting for other variables girl children from urban areas are not less likely to be malnourished than their rural counterparts. When we control for demographic factors only, girl children from urban areas are strongly less likely to be malnourished than their rural counterparts in each round of NFHS. Hence the rural-urban gap is not due to the demographic factors but due to the socioeconomic factors.

Girl children of educated mothers are less likely to be malnourished than their counterparts of illiterate mothers. Girl children of more aged mothers are more likely to be malnourished than girl children of mothers' aged 19 years or less. Antenatal care during pregnancy reduces the likelihood of malnutrition for a girl child. Girl children from backward caste households are strictly more likely to be malnourished than girl children from general caste households.

The chance of being malnourished strongly decreases with the standard of living index or the wealth index of the girl children's household. Mothers' exposure to mass media also reduces the likelihood of malnutrition. The chance of being malnourished varies significantly across different zones too. Household electrification reduces the likelihood of malnutrition for girl children after controls.

The effects of the variables remain same in case of rural India or for demographic factors only or for socioeconomic factors only as in the all-India regression model.

Conclusion

Gender inequality is a far-reaching societal impairment, not merely a special deprivation of women (4: 250). Gender inequality of one type tends to encourage and sustain gender inequality of other kinds (4: 220). Health being one of the most basic capabilities, the reduction and removal of gender bias in child health can go a long way in achieving gender parity in many other dimensions of human development, not only for the present generation but also over the generations.

The study selected thirteen indicators of health-seeking behaviour in immunisation, diarrhoea, fever/ cough and breastfeeding and eight indicators of health outcome in malnutrition and mortality for children age less than three years. It was shown that there is ample evidence of varying levels of gender gap in all the states of India over almost one-and-a-half decades. For a particular state it might so happen that for a particular indicator, gender gap (and/ or its sign) changes over time and gender gap (and/ or its sign) changes for different indicators in a particular time period.

The gender gap in health-seeking behaviour does not transform much into the gender gap in health outcome for the children in the states of India. However for girl children's health achievement, the indicators of health-seeking behaviour are significantly related to the indicators of health outcome.

Full immunisation rate for the girl children has a consistently significant impact on all the indicators of health outcome. Increases in vaccination coverage rates for girl children will reduce post-neonatal mortality, childhood mortality and childhood malnutrition rates for girl children. Girl children's health outcome tends to be worse in the major states compared to other (non-major) states.

It was shown that any consistently robust pattern across states of gender bias against girl children in child health is *not* present. But there is a consistent pattern of girl children's absolute health achievement. This is true irrespective of the number of indicators we use or the number of states we select or the measurement of gender bias or the method to reduce dimensions.

The result remains valid even when it is performed at the regional level instead of state level. Assuming the Rawlsian theory of justice, which gives complete priority to the worst off group's gain, one should focus on the absolute health achievement by the girl children only, even when reduction in gender bias in child health is the ultimate motto. As a policy measure, to reduce gender bias in child health, we need to focus on the states with low health achievement by girls, *viz.*, Rajasthan, Punjab, Haryana, Uttar Pradesh, Uttarakhand, Madhya Pradesh, Chhattisgarh, Bihar, Jharkhand, Orissa, Assam, Andhra Pradesh, Tamil Nadu and Gujarat.

On the determinants of child health achievement, except for a few cases, the results were consistently robust across the different models as well as across different dependent variables.

Robust results

- Increase in birth order of a girl child reduces the likelihood of health achievement. It seems that the *negligence effect* more than offsets the *learning effect*. The result perhaps shows greater apathy on the part of parents to take care of subsequent children. Also higher order birth children are more and more constrained by household resources.
- The likelihood of health achievement is higher for girl children from urban areas. The rural-urban disparity in child health is not due to demographic factors but due to socioeconomic factors.
- The likelihood of health achievement for girl children increases with mother's education level, mother's empowerment index, mother's age and mother's exposure to mass media. These variables tend to enhance the mother's autonomy or agency within the household and raise the value ascribed to girl children, which in turn helps mothers to take greater care of girl children.

- Some antenatal care during pregnancy raises the chance of health achievement for girls significantly. Having antenatal care increases the possibility of meeting health personnel who help mothers to raise their awareness by disseminating information regarding child health. This information spill-over or learning-by-doing raises health care for girl children.
- Among the religious groups, Muslim girl children are the least likely to be fully immunised and the most likely to be malnourished, in comparison with girl children from Hindu households.
- The likelihood of health achievement is less for girl children from backward caste/ tribe households compared to girl children from general caste households.
- Household income measured either by the standard of living index or wealth index raises the likelihood of health achievement for girl children. With higher household income, parents are more likely to spend more money and time for girl children.
- The gender of the household head has no effect on the likelihood of health achievement for girl children.
- The likelihood of health achievement for girl children increases in households with electricity. Household electrification indirectly raises awareness about the value of girl children and helps parents to take greater care of them.

These findings support Sen's claim that 'we have to look beyond material prosperity or economic success or GNP growth...' (4). The non-existence of any consistent pattern of gender bias in child health implies that there are many pathways of gender injustice. However, the consistent pattern in girl children's health achievement calls for some policy interventions to reduce and hopefully to remove gender bias in child health on the Rawlsian premise.

The above results suggest that a synergistic effort incorporating a number of other sectors is needed to reduce the gender gap in child health. The need of the hour is an equitable, participatory and intersectoral approach to health and health care (130). Policies and programmes in other sectors such as education, welfare, industry, labour, information, environment, *etc.* have also to be informed and influenced by public health considerations (131). To bring gender justice, we need coordination and convergence in the programmes of various Ministries of the Government. The policy managers should also try the following means to reduce gender gap in child health in India:

- Focus on female education and raising the female literacy rate.
- Step up information, education and communication (IEC) to enhance media exposure of mothers.
- Generate enough gainful employment opportunities to raise household's standard of living. Also there is a need to create jobs for women to raise empowerment of mothers.
- Ensure quality antenatal care focusing on supply-side issues.
- Promote small family norm and discourage early marriage.
- Focus on girl children from Muslim households and backward castes.
- Provide electricity to every household particularly in rural areas.

- Provide basic facilities that are commonly available in urban areas universally in rural areas.

In the new millennium, nations are judged by the well-being of their people; by levels of health, nutrition and education; by the civil and political liberties enjoyed by their citizens; by the protection guaranteed to children and by provisions made for the vulnerable and the disadvantaged. Here we will discuss the extent of concern of Government policies about gender bias in child health and how they can remove it. In the various schemes and policies of Ministry of Health and Family Welfare and the Planning Commission of Government of India there is hardly any mention of gender bias in child health, leave alone the elaboration of policies to reduce and remove it.

The focus appears to be on mothers and children generally rather than specifically on girl children. In the 'shining' India, a Judge of Supreme Court of India has noted that 'the fact is that women's exploitation is a reality and gender justice a fragile myth' (132).

The persistent gender bias in an array of indicators of child health in almost all the states of India over one-and-a-half decades calls for devising a gender-aware child health policy. To reap the benefits of the demographic dividend, first we have to ensure that our children are healthy and capable of being healthy human capital. We need to ensure that girl children are effectively benefited by the government health schemes that would penetrate the problem that has roots in social behaviour and prejudices in large parts of the country. We need to raise awareness of the people to make them understand that women are no longer 'patients', but the 'agents' of growth and development of a country. Such an awareness campaign will help parents to demand healthcare facilities for their children; not only for their sons but for their daughters too. We have to ensure gender-justice in child health by ensuring that there is no discrimination on the basis of gender. Government as well as the civil society has to oversee the enforcement of gender justice in health schemes and also ensure that they effectively reach all children irrespective of their class, caste and religion. Removal of gender bias in child health is one of the early hurdles that the country needs to overcome. Universal access to the health schemes will hopefully put India on a double-digit growth path in a foreseeable future.

The study shows that it is high time that policy makers acknowledge gender bias in child health and act to curb this menace. It pleads the policy makers to design health policies by taking note of some of the way outs mentioned here to reduce gender bias in child health in India.

The policy makers must keep in mind that improvement in the lives of girl children will actually be able to improve lives of all—men, women and children. They should ensure that the girl children are not left unattended by the health policies so that in future they are able to 'hold up half the sky'.

Endnotes

1. It includes whether a child's mother reads newspaper/ magazine at least once a week or almost every day or listens to radio at least once a week or almost every day or watches TV at least once a week or almost every day or go to cinema hall/ theatre at least once a month.

2. It shows decision making power of mothers' within a family. The following recoded variables are chosen for its construction: permission to get medical help for self, who decides how to spend money, mother's type of earnings for work, final say on health care, final say on making large household purchases, final say on making household purchases for daily needs, final say on visits to family or relatives, final say on deciding what to do with money husband earns, allowed to go to market, allowed to go to health facility, allowed to go to places outside this village/ community, have bank or saving account, has money for her own use. The method of *unweighted aggregation* is followed by which the scores of the above-mentioned thirteen recoded variables are simply added to get the scores of MEI.

3. Percentage of the children (also for boy and girl children separately) who were sick and taken to any *public* health facility steadily declined over time from 27 percent in 1992-93 to 18 percent in 2005-06. But percentage of the children who were sick and taken to any *private* health facility steadily increased over the same time from 80 percent to 90 percent. This raises serious concern about the quality and acceptability of the public health facilities in India.

4. Tables will be provided on request.

5. For details, see (114).

6. Compared to the Utilitarian approach, the Rawlsian theory of 'justice as fairness' has many decisive advantages. The Rawlsian theory also has merits in terms of scope and reach over more relativist and less universalist approaches that have sometimes been proposed. The concern with equity in addition to efficiency as reflected in Rawl's principles of justice puts equity at the centre of disputes about justice in a way that utilitarianism (peripherally concerned with equity) fails to do (see 115).

7. For details, see (117).

8. For details, see (119, 120).

9. Logistic regression results for medical treatment in diarrhoea, medical treatment in fever/cough, at least six months breastfeeding and child death are almost similar and hence not shown in this paper.

Acknowledgments

An earlier version of this paper was presented at the 5th Doctoral Colloquium of Indian Institute of Management, Ahmedabad, India (7-8 Jan, 2012). The author is thankful for the comments received on the occasion. The author is grateful to Professor Jayati Ghosh. All remaining errors, if any, will solely be my responsibility.

Appendix

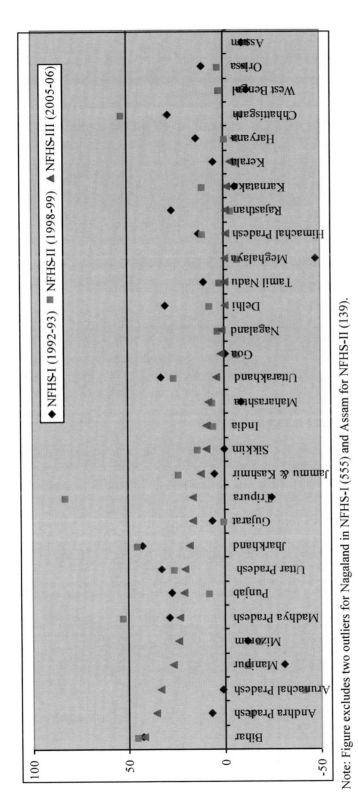

Note: Figure excludes two outliers for Nagaland in NFHS-I (555) and Assam for NFHS-II (139).

Figure 1. State-wise Gender Gap in Full Immunisation, Various NFHS Rounds.

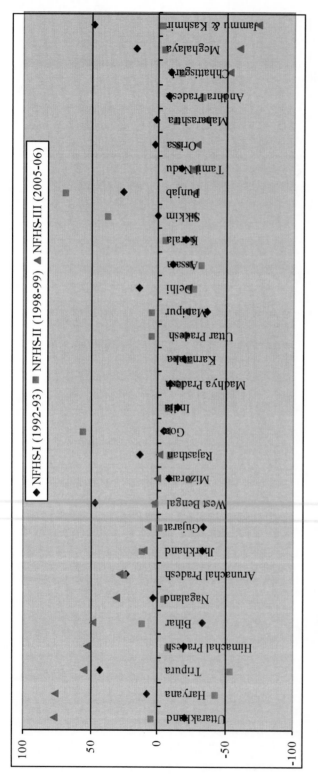

Figure 2. Gender Gap in Childhood Diarrhoea with 'No Treatment' by State.

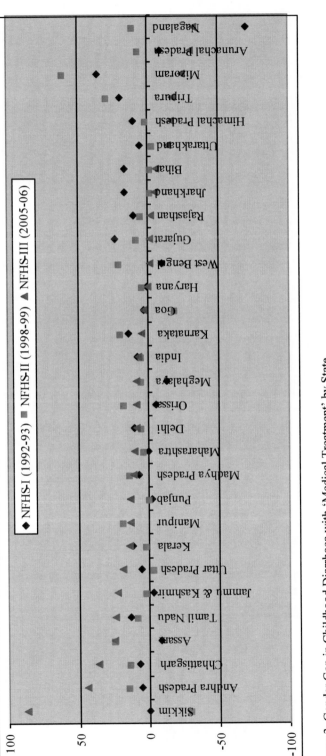

Figure 3. Gender Gap in Childhood Diarrhoea with 'Medical Treatment' by State.

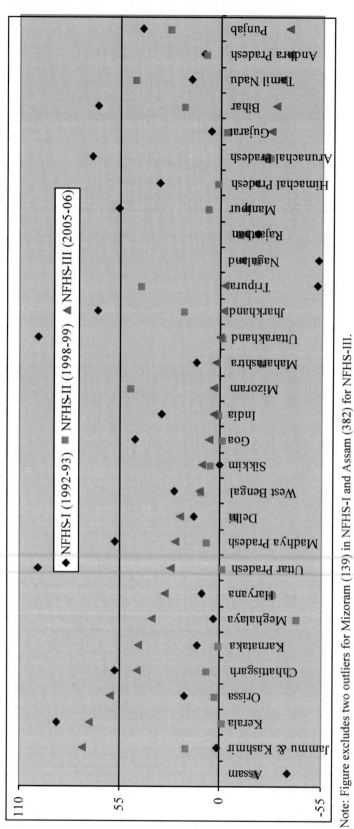

Note: Figure excludes two outliers for Mizoram (139) in NFHS-I and Assam (382) for NFHS-III.

Figure 4. Gender Gap in Childhood Diarrhoea with 'Given ORS' by State.

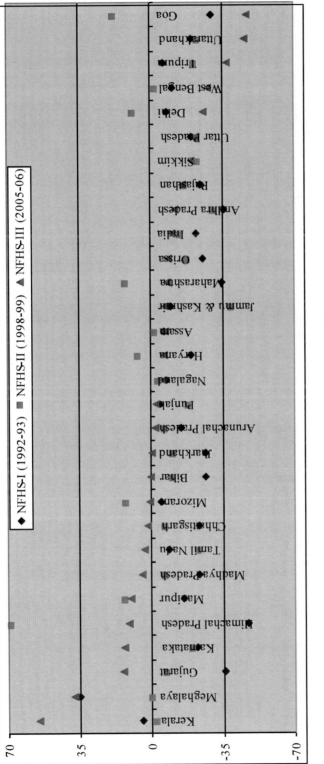

Figure 5. Gender Gap in Childhood Fever/ Cough with 'Received No Treatment'.

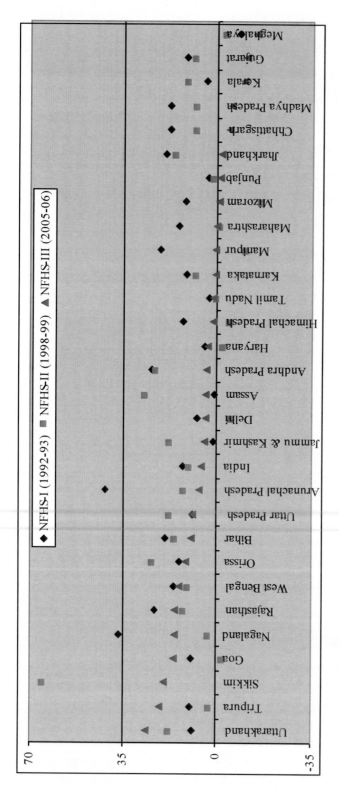

Figure 6. Gender Gap in Childhood Fever/ Cough with 'Received Medical Treatment'.

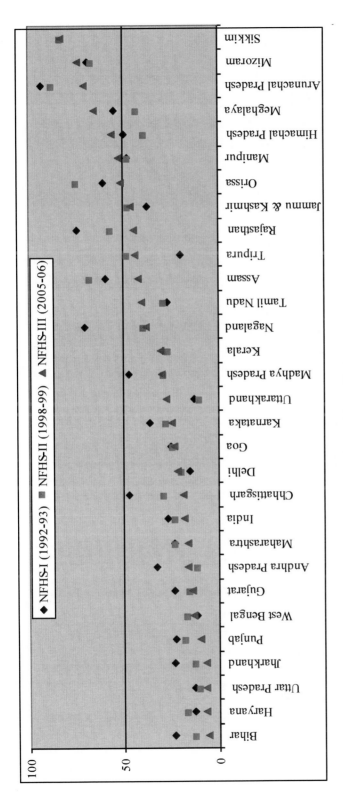

Figure 7. Fever/Cough with 'Received Medical Treatment in Public Health Facility'.

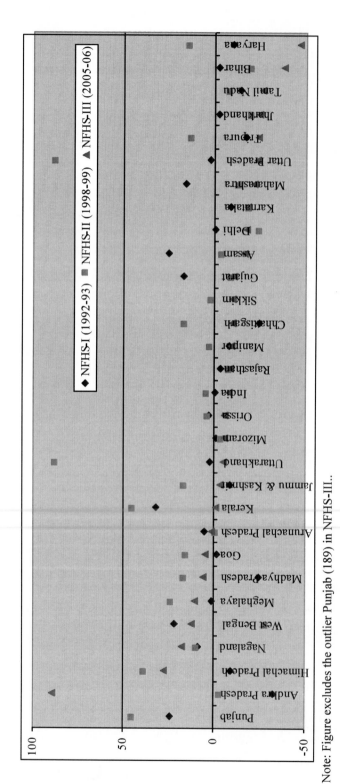

Note: Figure excludes the outlier Punjab (189) in NFHS-III..

Figure 8. Gender Gap in Childhood Fever/ Cough with 'Received Medical Treatment in Public Health Facility'

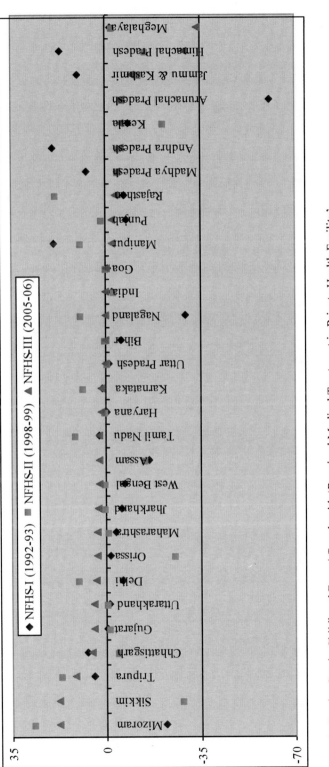

Figure 9. Gender Gap in Childhood Fever/ Cough with 'Received Medical Treatment in Private Health Facility'.

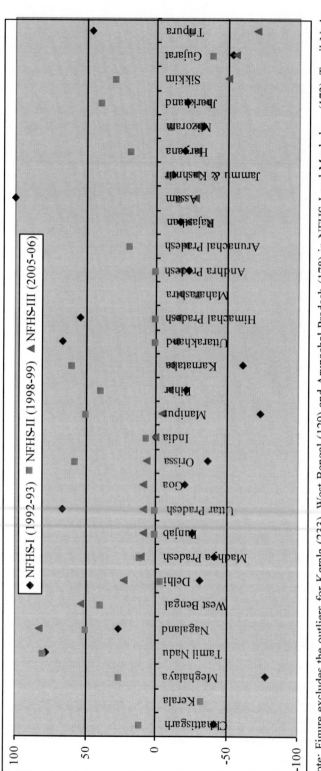

Note: Figure excludes the outliers for Kerala (233), West Bengal (129) and Arunachal Pradesh (178) in NFHS-I and Meghalaya (173), Tamil Nadu (160) for NFHS-III.

Figure 10. Gender Gap in Childhood Breastfeeding with 'Never Breastfed' by State.

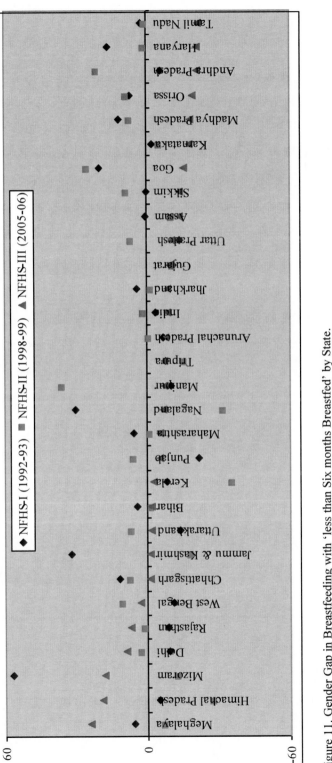

Figure 11. Gender Gap in Breastfeeding with 'less than Six months Breastfed' by State.

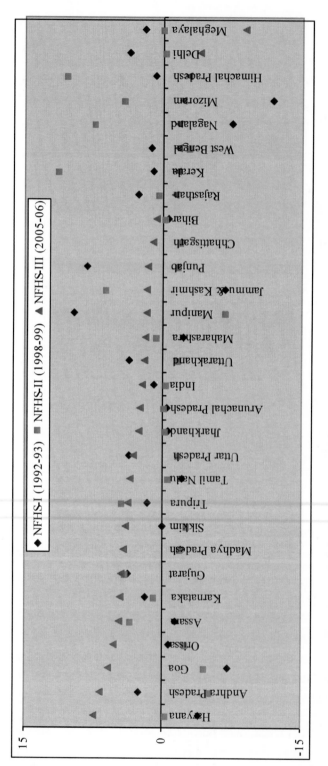

Figure 12. Gender Gap in Childhood Breastfeeding with 'at least six months Breastfed'.

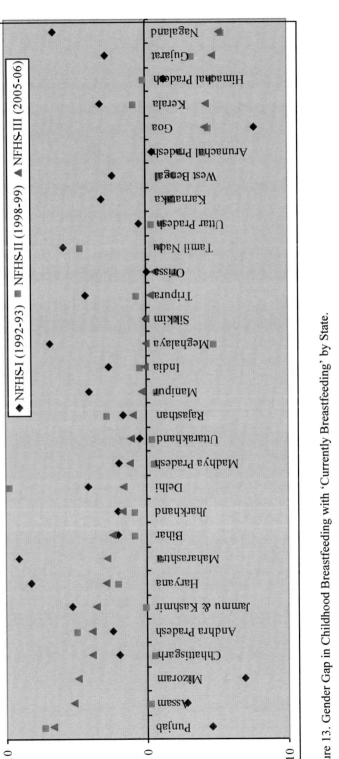

Figure 13. Gender Gap in Childhood Breastfeeding with 'Currently Breastfeeding' by State.

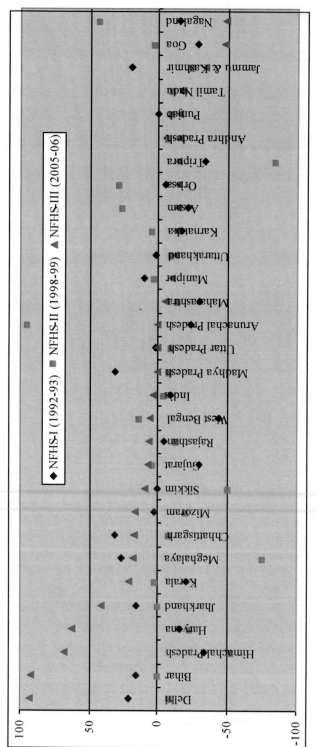

Figure 14. Gender Gap in Breastfeeding with 'Exclusively Breastfed for first Six months'.

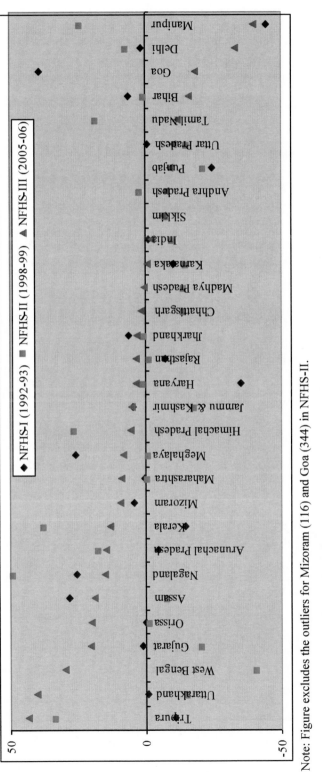

Note: Figure excludes the outliers for Mizoram (116) and Goa (344) in NFHS-II.

Figure 15. Gender Gap in Childhood Malnutrition (Severe Stunting).

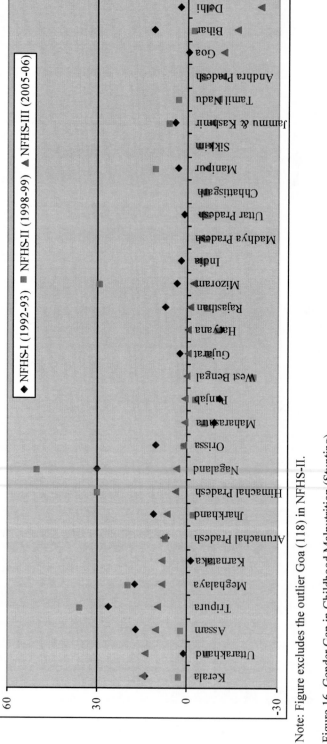

Note: Figure excludes the outlier Goa (118) in NFHS-II.

Figure 16. Gender Gap in Childhood Malnutrition (Stunting).

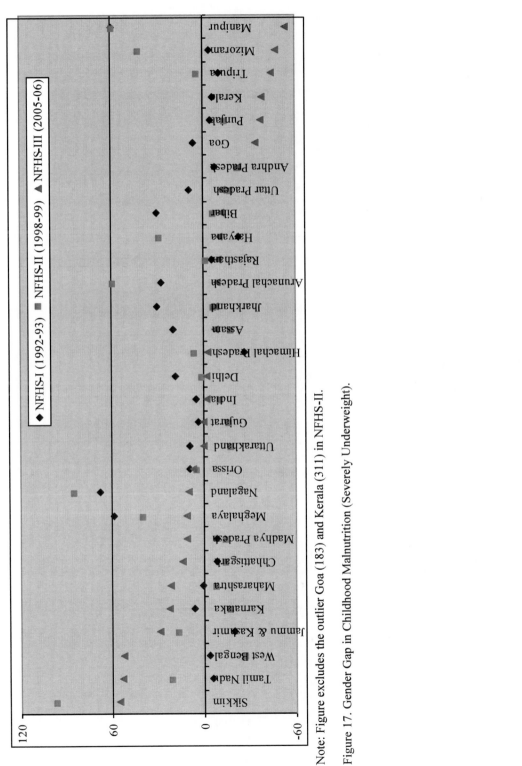

Note: Figure excludes the outlier Goa (183) and Kerala (311) in NFHS-II.

Figure 17. Gender Gap in Childhood Malnutrition (Severely Underweight).

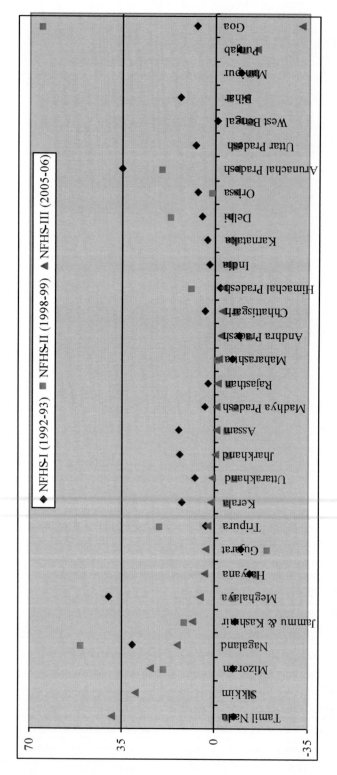

Figure 18. Gender Gap in Childhood Malnutrition (Underweight).

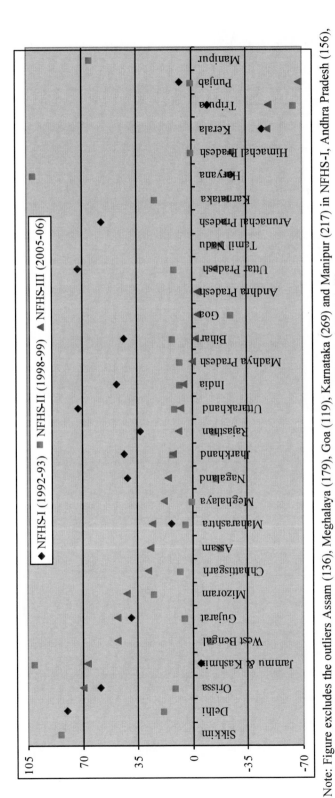

Note: Figure excludes the outliers Assam (136), Meghalaya (179), Goa (119), Karnataka (269) and Manipur (217) in NFHS-I, Andhra Pradesh (156), Arunachal Pradesh (433) and Kerala (150) in NFHS-II and Sikkim (125), Delhi (119) in NFHS-III.

Figure 19. Gender Gap in Childhood Malnutrition (Severe Wasting).

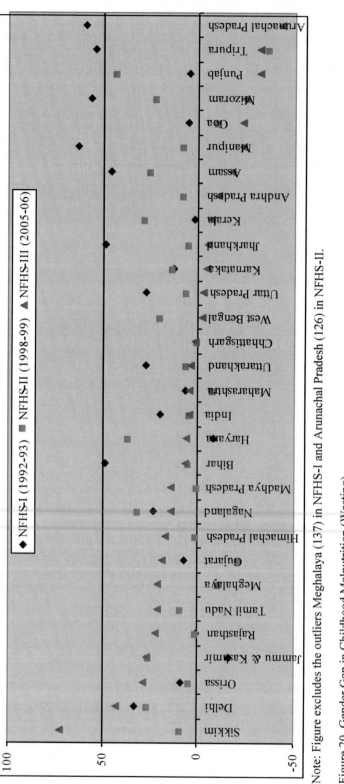

Note: Figure excludes the outliers Meghalaya (137) in NFHS-I and Arunachal Pradesh (126) in NFHS-II.

Figure 20. Gender Gap in Childhood Malnutrition (Wasting).

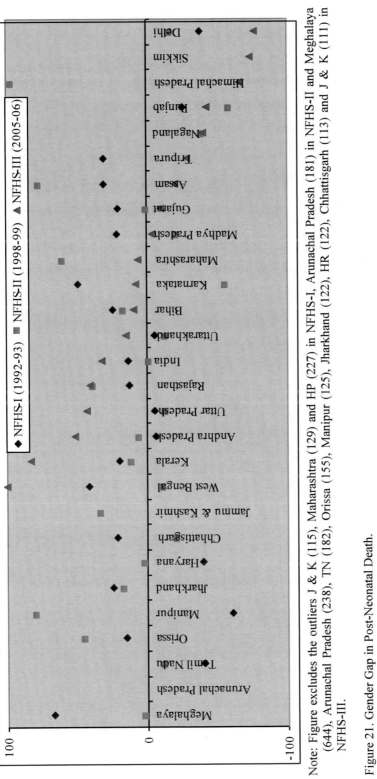

Note: Figure excludes the outliers J & K (115), Maharashtra (129) and HP (227) in NFHS-I, Arunachal Pradesh (181) in NFHS-II and Meghalaya (644), Arunachal Pradesh (644), TN (182), Orissa (155), Manipur (125), Jharkhand (122), HR (122), Chhattisgarh (113) and J & K (111) in NFHS-III.

Figure 21. Gender Gap in Post-Neonatal Death.

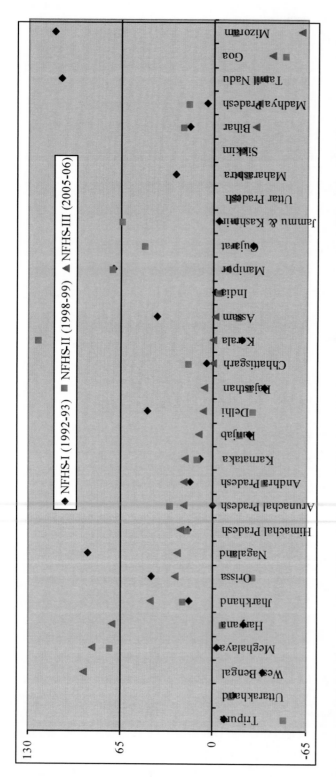

Note: Figure excludes the outliers Goa (457) and Mizoram (112) in NFHS-I, WB (139) and Kerala (122) in NFHS-II and Tripura (347) and Uttarakhand (217) in NFHS-III.

Figure 22. Gender Gap in Child Death.

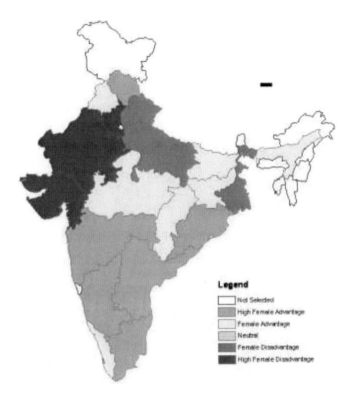

Figure 23. Gender Bias in IMR, NFHS-I (1988-92).

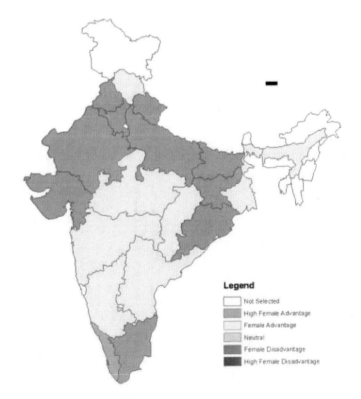

Figure 24. Gender Bias in IMR, SRS-1992.

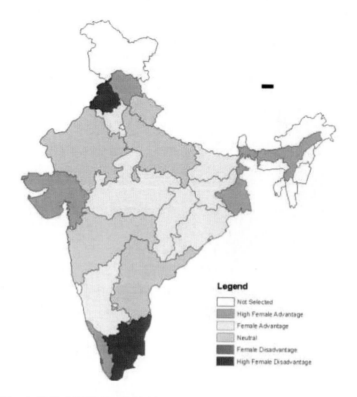

Figure 25. Gender Bias in IMR, NFHS-II (1994-98).

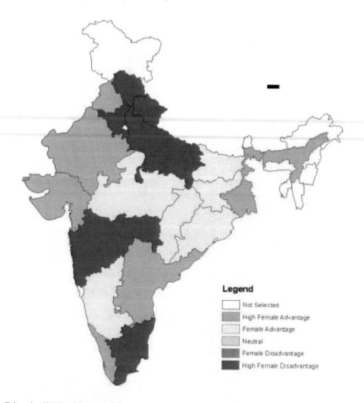

Figure 26. Gender Bias in IMR, SRS-1998.

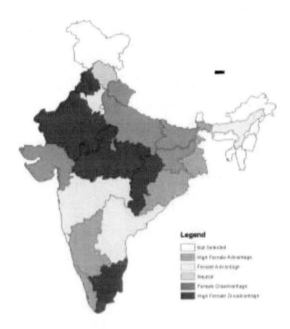

Figure 27. Gender Bias in IMR, NFHS-III (2001-05).

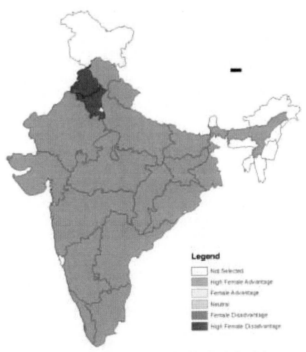

Legend key: x<=85: High Female Advantage, 85<x<=99: Female Advantage, x=100: No Female Advantage (neutral), 100<x<115: Female Disadvantage, 115=<x: High Female Disadvantage. Gender Gap (x) $= (X_g/X_b)*100$.

Figure 28. Gender Bias in IMR, SRS-2005.

Table 1. State-wise Borda rank in gender bias against girl children

	NFHS-I (1992-93)	NFHS-II (1998-99)	NFHS-III (2005-06)
Nagaland	2	10	1
Meghalaya	5	4	2
H.P.	17	8	3
Gujarat	28	26	4
W.B.	8	17	5
Uttarakhand	24	18	6
Rajasthan	21	25	7
Kerala	14	5	8
Jharkhand	19	13	9
Karnataka	18	27	10
Arunach.P.	4	1	11
Tamil Nadu	10	23	12
Tripura	8	29	13
J.& K.	7	16	14
Orissa	10	15	14
Maharashtra	12	11	16
Haryana	13	9	17
Mizoram	6	7	18
Delhi	15	11	19
Chhattisgarh	22	20	20
Assam	1	28	21
M.P.	22	20	22
Bihar	19	13	23
Sikkim	NA	6	24
Punjab	16	22	25
Manipur	27	3	26
U.P.	24	18	27
Andhra P.	26	24	28
Goa	3	2	29

Note: Total excludes the ranks obtained in the indicators—for NFHS-I: J, K, N, O, and T due to non-availability of data for some of the states other than Sikkim; for NFHS-II and III: E, and T due to non-availability of data for some of the states. States are ordered according to NFHS-III rankings.

Table 2. Rank-correlation (Spearman) matrix of Borda rankings

	NFHS-I	NFHS-II
NFHS-II	0.3	—
NFHS-III	0.2	-0.01

Note: none significant at 10% level (two tail).

Table 3. Rank-correlation (Spearman) matrix of Borda rankings

	NFHS-I	NFHS-II	NFHS-III
NFHS-I	—		
NFHS-II	0.26	—	
NFHS-III	0.10	0.04	—

Note: None significant at 10% level (two tail).

Table 4. Borda Rank in gender bias against girl children, major 19 states

	NFHS-I (1992-93)	NFHS-II (1998-99)	NFHS-III (2005-06)
W.B.	8	7	1
H.P.	15	4	2
Chhattisgarh	16	11	3
Kerala	5	3	4
Karnataka	5	19	4
Uttarakhand	9	16	6
Jharkhand	11	9	7
Rajasthan	19	14	8
Maharashtra	1	6	9
Orissa	1	18	10
Gujarat	18	8	11
Haryana	5	1	12
M.P.	16	11	13
Tamil Nadu	4	4	14
Punjab	13	2	15
J.& K.	1	11	16
Bihar	11	9	17
U.P.	9	16	18
Andhra P.	14	15	18

Note: States are ordered by NFHS-III rankings.

Table 5. Rank-correlation (Spearman) matrix of Borda rankings

	NFHS-I	NFHS-II	NFHS-III
NFHS-I	—		
NFHS-II	0.045	—	
NFHS-III	-0.059	0.084	—

Note: none significant at 10% level (two tail).

Table 6. State-wise composite index and rank in gender bias against girl children, various NFHS rounds

	Composite Index			Rank		
	NFHS-I	**NFHS-II**	**NFHS-III**	**NFHS-I**	**NFHS-II**	**NFHS-III**
Meghalaya	-0.54	-0.40	-1.18	3	5	1
H.P.	0.30	-0.06	-0.49	24	12	2
Nagaland	-0.48	-0.34	-0.41	4	6	3
Kerala	-0.39	-0.08	-0.33	7	10	4
Gujarat	0.37	0.33	-0.33	26	22	5
W.B.	-0.11	0.39	-0.33	11	23	6
Assam	-0.59	0.97	-0.16	1	29	7
Uttarakhand	-0.03	0.50	-0.16	16	27	8
Rajasthan	0.34	0.06	-0.15	25	15	9
J.& K.	-0.13	0.15	-0.14	8	21	10
Maharashtra	0.05	-0.13	-0.14	19	9	11
Orissa	-0.05	0.03	-0.14	14	14	12
Karnataka	0.16	0.11	-0.12	20	17	13
Tamil Nadu	-0.04	-0.08	-0.1	15	10	14
Jharkhand	-0.12	0.12	-0.08	9	18	15
Chhattisgarh	0.26	0.48	-0.08	22	25	16
Mizoram	-0.58	-0.44	-0.07	2	4	17
Haryana	0.03	-0.25	-0.01	16	8	18
M.P.	0.26	0.48	0.04	22	25	19
Delhi	-0.08	-0.34	0.06	12	6	20
Arunach.P.	-0.41	-0.99	0.08	6	1	21
Sikkim	NA	0.13	0.28	NA	20	22
Tripura	0.21	0.39	0.31	21	23	23
Manipur	1.51	-0.78	0.4	28	3	24
U.P.	-0.03	0.5	0.48	16	27	25
Goa	-0.45	-0.95	0.59	5	2	26
Punjab	-0.07	0.06	0.65	13	15	27
Bihar	-0.12	0.12	0.73	9	18	28
Andhra P.	0.77	0.02	0.77	27	13	29

Note: Total composition excludes the following indicators—NFHS-I: j, k, n, o, and t; NFHS-II & -III: e, and t —due to non-availability of data for some of the states. States are ordered according to NFHS-III rankings.

Table 7. Rank-correlation (Spearman) matrix of rankings in three rounds of NFHS

	NFHS-I	**NFHS-II**
NFHS-II	0.25	—
NFHS-III	0.18	-0.07

Note: none significant even at 10% level (two tail).

Table 8. Borda rank of health achievement for girl children

	NFHS-I	NFHS-II	NFHS-III
Kerala	27	28	29
W.B.	17	14	28
Goa	26	29	27
Haryana	23	25	26
H.P.	25	26	25
Maharashtra	21	27	24
Tamil Nadu	19	24	23
Delhi	22	22	22
Karnataka	18	20	21
Punjab	23	23	20
J.& K.	28	20	19
Sikkim	NA	12	18
Meghalaya	16	4	17
Tripura	7	18	16
Uttarakhand	2	9	15
Mizoram	20	13	14
Manipur	9	18	13
Gujarat	14	15	12
Orissa	8	6	11
Chhattisgarh	10	6	9
Nagaland	13	11	9
Andhra P.	12	17	8
M.P.	10	6	7
Bihar	2	1	6
Jharkhand	2	1	5
Rajasthan	1	5	4
Arunach.P.	15	16	3
U.P.	2	9	2
Assam	6	3	1

Note: The chosen indicators are A, C, G, L, Q and U. Ranking is done in ascending order (a higher value indicates better status of girls) for the following indicators— A, C, G, and Q. For L and U, ranking is done in descending order (a lower value indicates better status of girls). A higher rank (number) indicates better status of girl children. States are ordered according to NFHS-III rankings.

Table 9. Rank-correlation (Spearman) matrix of Borda rankings

	NFHS-I	NFHS-II	NFHS-III
NFHS-I	—		
NFHS-II	0.81[*]	—	
NFHS-III	0.79[*]	0.78[*]	—

Note: Level of significance (two tailed) — *: 1%.

Table 10. Summary of effects (P in %) on full immunisation coverage in India

Background Variables		NFHS-I (1992-93)		NFHS-II (1998-99)		NFHS-III (2005-06)	
		Unadj	Adj	Unadj	Adj	Unadj	Adj
Birth Order	1[#]	45*	36	53**	46	54*	48
	2	39*	31*	49**	42	48*	42*
	3	33*	28*	36*	30*	32*	33*
	4 & +	20*	22*	23*	28*	24*	31*
Residence	Rural[#]	29*	29	35*	36	37*	40
	Urban	52*	28	61*	40***	56*	39
Mother's Education	Illiterate[#]	22*	25	27*	32	24*	30
	Primary	42*	31*	51*	41*	45*	44*
	Secondary	62*	38*	63*	50*	61*	51*
	Higher	77*	49*	73*	49*	83*	63*
Mother's Age	19 or less[#]	35*	23	36*	25	38*	32
	20-24	36	26	43*	34*	43**	36***
	25-29	37	33*	46*	45*	44**	43*
	30-49	26*	32*	31**	43*	35	44*
Antenatal Care	No[#]	10*	15	17*	27	23*	30
	Yes	47*	39*	56*	45*	49*	44*
Religion	Hindu[#]	35*	30	41*	39	43*	42
	Muslim	25*	22*	31*	27*	34*	30*
	Christ &	50*	30	63*	53*	50**	38
Caste/ Tribe	General[#]	37*	30	46*	39	53**	44
	OBC	—	—	42**	36	39*	38*
	SC	26*	24*	39*	41	36*	38**
	ST	24*	29	24*	26*	32*	38***
Standard of Living Index	Low[#]	22*	25	31*	38	—	—
	Medium	34*	29**	41*	36	—	—
	High	60*	37*	63*	39	—	—
Wealth Index	Poorest[#]	—	—	—	—	23*	34
	Poorer	—	—	—	—	34*	39***
	Middle	—	—	—	—	45*	42*
	Richer	—	—	—	—	51*	38
	Richest	—	—	—	—	72*	49*
Media Exposure	No[#]	21*	26	24*	36	28*	37
	Yes	49*	32*	55*	39	54*	42*
Sex of HH-Head	Female[#]	43**	31	42*	32	40*	39
	Male	34*	29	41	38***	42	40
MEI	Low[#]	—	—	40*	39	37*	36
	Medium	—	—	41	36	43*	41*
	High	—	—	42	35	46*	44*

Background Variables		NFHS-I (1992-93)		NFHS-II (1998-99)		NFHS-III (2005-06)	
		Unadj	Adj	Unadj	Adj	Unadj	Adj
Zone	Central[#]	19*	20	19*	22	27*	31
	North	38*	32*	41*	34*	44*	39*
	East	22***	22	26*	29*	43*	53*
	Northeast	21	19	16	14***	34**	29
	West	61*	51*	70*	64*	51*	35***
	South	53*	40*	71*	60*	57*	42*
Electricity	No[#]	21*	27	22*	31	26*	35
	Yes	50*	31**	56*	42*	53*	44*

Note: Unadj: unadjusted, Adj: adjusted;
#: Reference category; Significance level (two tailed): ***10%, **5%, *1%.

Table 11. Summary of effects (P in %) on malnutrition in India

Background Variables		NFHS-I (1992-93)		NFHS-II (1998-99)		NFHS-III (2005-06)	
		Unadj	Adj	Unadj	Adj	Unadj	Adj
Birth Order	1[#]	48*	52	42*	47	40*	47
	2	51*	53	47*	50**	44*	48
	3	51*	50	51*	48	49*	47
	4 & +	57*	51	57*	50	58*	46
Residence	Rural[#]	54*	52	52*	49	50	47
	Urban	43*	51	40*	47	37*	48
Mother's Education	Illiterate[#]	58*	56	57*	52	57*	51
	Primary	51*	52*	46*	49*	48*	48**
	Secondary	36*	42*	38*	43*	37*	44*
	Higher	25*	32*	28*	37*	19*	30*
Mother's Age	19 or less[#]	49	47	46*	43	46*	43
	20-24	52***	52*	48***	50*	45	45
	25-29	51	53*	48	48*	47	48**
	30-49	54*	53*	53*	50*	53*	51*
Antenatal Care	No[#]	59*	53	58*	51	57*	52
	Yes	48*	51**	43*	47*	42*	45*
Religion	Hindu[#]	52*	52	50	49	48*	48
	Muslim	54	53	50	51	45**	44**
	Christ &	42*	50	33*	40*	39*	45
Caste/ Tribe	General[#]	51	52	43*	45	38*	44
	OBC	—	—	49*	49*	47*	46**
	SC	57*	54**	55*	51*	54*	50*
	ST	55*	50	57*	54*	57*	51*
Standard of Living Index	Low[#]	60*	56	58*	54	—	—
	Medium	52*	52*	48*	49*	—	—
	High	36*	44*	29*	37*	—	—

Table 11. (Continued)

Background Variables		NFHS-I (1992-93)		NFHS-II (1998-99)		NFHS-III (2005-06)	
		Unadj	Adj	Unadj	Adj	Unadj	Adj
Wealth Index	Poorest#	—	—	—	—	61*	53
	Poorer	—	—	—	—	54*	51
	Middle	—	—	—	—	45*	47*
	Richer	—	—	—	—	38*	44*
	Richest	—	—	—	—	25*	34*
Media Exposure	No#	59*	53	57*	49	56*	48
	Yes	45*	50**	42*	48	39*	46**
Sex of HH-Head	Female#	45*	49	47	49	48	47
	Male	52*	52***	49	49	47	47
MEI	Low#	—	—	48*	47	46	45
	Medium	—	—	50**	50**	48***	47**
	High	—	—	49	49	48***	49*
Zone	Central#	56*	54	55*	53	52*	49
	North	43*	44*	43*	46*	40*	43*
	East	57	55	54	50	55***	51
	Northeast	43*	42*	34*	31*	38*	33*
	West	52*	56	50*	54	43*	49
	South	46*	49*	39*	42*	35*	42*
Electricity	No#	58*	51	57*	50	58*	49
	Yes	46*	52	42*	48***	41*	45*

Note: Unadj: unadjusted, Adj: adjusted; (0: not malnourished, 1: malnourished).
#: Reference category; Significance level (two tailed): ***10%, **5%, *1%.

References

[1]   Govt. of India. Report of the health survey and development (Bhore) Committee. Delhi: GoI Press, 1946.
[2]   Bakshi, P. M. The constitution of India. 7th Ed. Delhi: Universal Law Pub, 2006.
[3]   Govt. of India. Investing in health for economic development, Background papers of report of national commission on macroeconomics and health. New Delhi: Min Health Fam Welfare, 2005.
[4]   Sen AK. The argumentative Indian. London: Penguin, 2005.
[5]   Sen AK. Gender inequality and theories of justice. In: Martha Nussbaum and Jonathan Glover, eds. Women, culture and development: A study of human capabilities. New Delhi: Oxford Univ Press, 1995.
[6]   Nussbaum MC. (1995): Introduction. In: Martha Nussbaum and Jonathan Glover, eds. Women, culture and development: A study of human capabilities. New Delhi: Oxford Univ Press, 1995.
[7]   Sen AK. More than 100 million women are missing. New York review of books, 20 Dec, 1990: 61-66.
[8]   Das Gupta M. Fertility decline in Punjab, India: Parallels with historical Europe. Mimeo. Center for PopulatDev Studies, Harvard University, 1993.
[9]   Drèze J, Sen AK. (eds). The political economy of hunger, Vol.-I: Entitlement and well-being. Oxford: Clarendon Press, 1990.

[10]   Papanek H. To each less than she needs, from each more than she can do: Allocations, entitlements, and value. In: Tinker I, ed. Persistent inequalities: Women and world development. Oxford: Oxford Univ Press, 1990.

[11]   Okin SM. Inequalities between the sexes in different cultural contexts. In: Martha Nussbaum and Jonathan Glover, eds. Women, culture and development: A study of human capabilities. New Delhi: Oxford Univ Press, 1995.

[12]   Chen M. A matter of survival: Women's right to employment in India and Bangladesh. In: Martha Nussbaum and Jonathan Glover, eds. Women, culture and development: A study of human capabilities. New Delhi: Oxford Univ Press, 1995.

[13]   Drèze J. Widows in rural India. DEP Paper No. 26, Dev Econ Res Programme. London: London Sch Econ, 1990.

[14]   Miller BD. The endangered sex: Neglect of female children in rural north India. Ithaca, New York: Cornell Univ Press, 1981.

[15]   Moser CON. Gender planning and development: Theory, practice and training. New York: Routledge, 1993.

[16]   Sinha B, Bhat PNM, Gulati SC. Son preference and gender bias in demographic behaviour: Jharkhand. Report No. 6, Packard Foundation funded project on Demographic Trends in Bihar and Jharkhand. Delhi: Populat Res Centre, Inst Econ Growth, 2005.

[17]   Arnold F. Gender preference for children. Demographic and Health Surveys Report No. 23, 1997.

[18]   Census of India. General population tables. New Delhi: Office of the Registrar General, Govt. of India, 2001.

[19]   Desai S. Gender inequalities and demographic behaviour: India. New York: Populat Council, 1994.

[20]   Visaria PM. The sex ratio of the population of India. Census of India 1961, Vol.-1, Monograph No. 10. New Delhi: Office of the Registrar General, India, Min Home Affairs, 1969.

[21]   Visaria PM. The sex ratio of the population of India and Pakistan and regional variations during 1901-1961. In: Bose A, ed. Patterns of population change in India 1951-61. Bombay: Allied Pub, 1967: 334-71.

[22]   Visaria L, Visaria P. India's population in transition. Populat Bull 1995; 50(3): 1-51.

[23]   Visaria L, Visaria P. Population (1757-1947). In: Kumar D, ed. The Cambridge economic history of India, Vol. 2. Cambridge: Cambridge Univ Press, 1983: 463-532.

[24]   Bhat PNM. Mortality and fertility in India, 1881-1961: A reassessment. In: Tim Dyson (ed). India's historical demography: Studies in famine, disease and society. London: Curzon, 1989: 73-118.

[25]   Das Gupta M, Bhat PNM. Fertility decline and increased manifestation of sex bias in India. Populat Stud 1997; 51: 307-15.

[26]   El-Badry MA. Higher female than male mortality in some countries of south Asia: A digest. Am Statistical Assoc J 1969; 64: 1234-44.

[27]   Miller BD. Changing patterns of juvenile sex ratios in rural India, 1961 to 1971. Econ Polit Weekly 1989; June 3: 1229-36.

[28]   Parasuraman S, Roy TK. Some observations of the 1991 census population of India. J Fam Welfare 1991; 37: 62-68.

[29]   Arnold F, Kishor S, Roy TK. Sex-selective abortions in India. PopulatDev Rev 2002; 28(4): 759-785.

[30]   Arnold F, Choe MK, Roy TK. Son preference, the family-building process and child mortality in India. Populat Stud 1998; 52: 301-15.

[31]   Arokiasamy P. Gender preference, contraceptive use and fertility in India: Regional and development influences. Intl J Populat Geography 2002; 8(1): 49-67.

[32]   Bhat PNM, Zavier AJF. Fertility decline and gender bias in northern India. Demography2003; 40(4): 637-57.

[33]   Clark S. Son preference and sex composition of children: Evidence from India. Demography 2000; 37(1): 95-108.

[34]   Das Gupta M, Zhenghua J, Bohua L, Zhenming X, Chung W, Hwa-Ok B. Why is son preference so persistent in east and south Asia? A cross-country study of China, India and the Republic of Korea. J Dev Stud2003; 40(2): 153-87.

[35] Mishra V, Roy TK, Retherford RD. Sex differentials in childhood feeding, health care and nutritional status in India. PopulatDev Rev 2004; 30(2): 269-95.

[36] Pande R, Astone N. Explaining son preference in rural India: The independent role of structural versus individual factors. Populat Res Pol Rev 2007; 26(1): 1-29.

[37] IIPS, Measure DHS+, ORC Macro. National family health survey (NFHS-3), 2005-06: India, Vol-1. Mumbai: Intl InstPopulatSci, 2007.

[38] Choi JY, Lee S-H. Does parental care increase access to child immunisation? Gender bias among children in India. SocSci Med 2006; 63: 107-17.

[39] Li J. Gender inequality, family planning, and maternal and child care in a rural Chinese county. SocSci Med 2004; 59: 695-708.

[40] Bairagi R. Food crisis, nutrition, and female children in rural Bangladesh. PopulatDev Rev 1986; 12: 307-15.

[41] Caldwell P, Caldwell JC. Gender implications for survival in south Asia. Health transition working paper No. 7. Canberra: National Centre Epidemiology Populat Health, Australian National Univ, 1990.

[42] D'Souza S, Chen LC. Sex differentials in mortality in Bangladesh. PopulatDev Rev 1980; 6: 257-70.

[43] Faisel A, Ahmed T, Kundi Z. Differentials in health-related variables among children at a diarrhoea training unit in Pakistan. J Diarrhoeal Dis Res 1993; 11: 19-24.

[44] Koenig MA, D'Souza S. Sex differences in childhood mortality in rural Bangladesh. SocSci Med 1986; 22: 15-22.

[45] IIPS, Measure DHS+, ORC Macro. National family health survey (NFHS-1), 1992-93: India. Mumbai: Intl InstPopulatSci, 1995.

[46] Pande RP. Selective gender differences in childhood nutrition and immunization in rural India: The role of siblings. Demography 2003; 40(3): 395-418.

[47] Sen AK. Mortality as an indicator of economic success and failure. The Econ J 1998; 108(446): 1-25.

[48] Bardhan PK. Little girls and death in India. Econ Polit Weekly 1982; Sep 4: 1448-50.

[49] Bardhan PK. On life and death questions. Econ Polit Weekly 1974; Aug: 1293-304.

[50] Doyal L. Gender, health and the millennium development goals (a briefing document and resource guide). Geneva, Switzerland: Global Forum Health Res, 2005.

[51] Kishor S. Gender differentials in child mortality in India: A review of evidence. In: M Das Gupta, TN Krishnan, L Chen, eds. Women's health in India: Risk and vulnerability. Mumbai: Oxford Univ Press, 1995.

[52] Kishor S. 'May god give sons to all': Gender and child mortality in India. Am Soc Rev 1993; 58(2): 247-65.

[53] Kurz KM, Johnson-Welch C. Gender differences among children 0-5 years: An opportunity for child survival interventions. A review paper prepared for the BASICS Project. Arlington, VA: BASICS, 1997.

[54] Makinson C. Discrimination against the female child. Intl J GynecolObstet 1994; 46: 119-25.

[55] Obermeyer CM, Cardenas R. Son preference and differential treatment in Morocco and Tunisia. Stud FamPlann 1997; 28: 235-44.

[56] Waldron I. Patterns and causes of excess female mortality among children in developing countries. World Health Stat Quart 1987; 40: 194-210.

[57] Klasen S, Wink C. A turning point in gender bias in mortality? An update on the number of 'missing women'. Discussion Paper 2001-13. Dept Econ, Univ Munich, 2001.

[58] Clark AW. Limitations on female life chance in rural central Gujarat. Indian Econ Soc History Rev 1983; 20: 1-25.

[59] Jeffery R, Jeffery P, Lyon A. Female infanticide and amniocentesis. SocSci Med 1984; 19(11): 1207-12.

[60] Chunkath SR, Athreya VB. Female infanticide in Tamil Nadu: Some evidence. Econ Polit Weekly 1997; 32(17): WS22-9.

[61] George S, Abel R, Miller BD. Female infanticide in rural south India. Econ Polit Weekly 1992; 27(22): 1153-6.

[62] Merchant KM, Kurz KM. Women's nutrition through the life cycle: Social and biological vulnerabilities. In: Koblinsky M, Timyan J, Gay JB, eds. The health of women: A global perspectives. Westview Press, 1992: 63-90.

[63] Mosley WH, Becker S. Demographic models for child survival and implications for health intervention programmes. Health Pol Plann 1991; 6: 218-33.

[64] Mosley WH, Chen LC. An analytical framework for the study of child survival in developing countries. PopulatDev Rev 1984; 10(Suppl): 25-45.

[65] Barker DJP. Fetal origins of coronary heart disease. BMJ 1995; 311: 171-4.

[66] Barker DJP. Intrauterine growth retardation and adult disease. CurrObstetGynaecol 1993; 3: 200-6.

[67] Osmani S, Sen AK. The hidden penalties of gender inequality: Fetal origins of ill-health. Econ Hum Biol 2003; 1: 105-21.

[68] Arokiasamy P. Regional patterns of sex bias and excess female child mortality in India. Population 2004; 59(6): 833-63.

[69] Miller BD. Social class, gender and intra-household food allocations to children in south Asia. SocSci Med 1997; 44(11): 1685-95.

[70] Pande RP, Yazbeck AS. What's in a country average? Wealth, gender, and regional inequalities in immunisation in India. SocSci Med 2003; 57: 2075-88.

[71] Pandey A et al. Gender differences in healthcare-seeking during common illnesses in a rural community of West Bengal, India. J Health PopulatNutr 2002; 20(4): 306-11.

[72] Dasgupta P. Population and resources: An exploration of reproductive and environmental externalities. PopulatDev Rev 2000; 26(4): 643-89.

[73] Hazarika G. Gender differences in children's nutrition and access to health care in Pakistan. J Dev Stud 2000; 37(1): 73-92.

[74] Bourne K, Walker GM. The differential effect of mothers' education on mortality of boys and girls in India. Populat Stud 1991; 45(2): 203-19.

[75] Basu AM. Culture, the status of women and demographic behaviour. Oxford: Clarendon Press, 1992.

[76] Krishnaji N. Poverty and sex ratio: Some data and speculations. Econ PolitWkly 1987; 6 June.

[77] Miller BD. On poverty, child survival and gender: Models and misperceptions. Third World Plann Rev 1993; 15(3): 3-8.

[78] Agarwal B. Women, poverty and agricultural growth in India. J Peasant Stud 1986; 13(4): 165-220.

[79] Das Gupta M. What motivates fertility decline? Lessons from a case study of Punjab, India. Mimeo. Centre for PopulatDev Studies, Harvard Univ, 1994.

[80] Das Gupta M. Selective discrimination against female children in rural Punjab, India. PopulatDev Rev 1987; 13(1): 77-100.

[81] Bose A. Where women prevail: 2001 census and female heads of households. Econ PolitWkly 2006; 41(22): 2192-4.

[82] Rosenzweig M, Schultz TP. Market opportunities, genetic endowments, and intrafamily resource distribution: Child survival in rural India. Am Econ Rev 1982; 72: 803-15.

[83] Murthi M, Guio A-C, Drèze J. Mortality, fertility, and gender bias in India: A district-level analysis. PopulatDev Rev 1995; 21(4): 745-82.

[84] Caldwell JC, Reddy PH, Caldwell P. The causes of demographic change in rural south India: A micro approach. PopulatDev Rev 1982; 8: 689-727.

[85] Ganatra B, Hirve S. Male bias in health care utilization for under-fives in a rural community in western India. Bull World Health Org 1994; 72: 101-4.

[86] Govindaswamy P, Ramesh BM. Maternal education and gender bias in child care practice in India. Paper presented at the Annual Meeting of the Populat Association America. New Orleans: 1996, May 9-11.

[87] Ravindran S. Health implications of sex discrimination in childhood: A review paper and an annotated bibliography. Geneva: WHO/ UNICEF, 1986.

[88] Visaria L. Level, trends, and determinants of infant mortality in India. In: Jain AK, Visaria P, eds. Infant mortality in India: Differentials and determinants. New Delhi: Sage, 1988: 67-126.

[89] Agnihotri S. Juvenile sex ratios in India. Econ PolitWkly 1996; 28: S3369-82.

[90]   Dyson T, Moore M. On kinship structure, female autonomy, and demographic behaviour in India.PopulatDev Rev 1983; 9(1): 35-60.

[91]   Basu AM. Is discrimination in food really necessary for explaining sex differential in childhood mortality?. Populat Stud 1989; 43: 193-210.

[92]   Pebley AR, Amin S. The impact of a public-health intervention on sex differentials in childhood mortality in rural Punjab, India. Health Transition Rev 1991; 1: 143-69.

[93]   Sen AK, Sengupta S. Malnutrition of children and the rural sex bias. Econ PolitWkly 1983; 18: 855-64.

[94]   Wadley SS. Family composition strategies in rural north India. SocSci Med 1993; 37: 1367-76.

[95]   Drèze J, Murthi M. Fertility, education, and development: Evidence from India. PopulatDev Rev 2001; 27(1): 33-63.

[96]   Visaria P, Rajan SI. National family health survey: A landmark in Indian surveys. Econ PolitWkly 1999; 34(42-43): 3002-07.

[97]   Rajan SI, James KS. Second national family health survey: Emerging issues. Econ PolitWkly 2004; 14: 647-51.

[98]   Kanitkar T. National family health survey: Some thoughts. Econ PolitWkly 1999; 16: 3081-83.

[99]   Bhat PNM, Zavier AJF. Findings of NFHS: Regional analysis. Econ PolitWkly 1999; 16: 3008-32.

[100]   Singh P. NFHS, 1992-93: Post-survey check. Econ PolitWkly 1999; 16: 3084-88.

[101]   Retherford RD, Minja KC. Statistical methods for causal analysis. New York: John Wiley, 1993.

[102]   Jatrana S. Explaining gender disparity in child health in Haryana state of India. Asian Meta Centre Research Paper Series No 16.

[103]   Macintyre S. Inequalities in health: Is research gender blind? In: D Leon, G Walt, eds. Poverty, inequality and health: An international perspective. Oxford: Oxford Univ Press, 2001.

[104]   Rajan SI, Sudha S, Mohanachandran P. Fertility decline and worsening gender bias in India: Is Kerala no longer an exception? Dev Change 2000; 31: 1085-92.

[105]   Yount KM. Gender bias in the allocation of curative health care in Minia, Egypt. Populat Res Pol Rev 2003; 22: 267-95.

[106]   Kimhi A. Gender differences in health and nutrition in southern Ethiopia. In: P Bharati, M Pal, eds. Gender disparity: Manifestation, causes and implication. New Delhi: Anmol Pub, 2006.

[107]   Nangia P, Roy TK. Gender disparity in child care in India: Findings from two NFHS. In: Manoranjan P, ed. Gender issues and empowerment of women. New York: Nova Science, in press.

[108]   Arokiasamy P, Pradhan J. Gender bias against female children in India. In: Manoranjan P, ed. Gender issues and empowerment of women. New York: Nova Science, in press.

[109]   Klasen S. Nutrition, health and mortality in sub-Saharan Africa: Is there a gender bias. J Dev Stud 1996; 32(6): 913-32.

[110]   Paci P, Murthi M. Economic transition and the position of women: A survey of the evidence. In: Bharati P, Pal M, eds. Gender disparity: Manifestation, causes and implication. New Delhi: Anmol Pub, 2006.

[111]   Dasgupta P. An inquiry into well-being and destitution. Oxford: Clarendon Press, 1995.

[112]   Kumar S, Nagar AL, Samanta S. Indexing the effectiveness of tax administration. Econ PolitWkly 2007; Dec: 104-10.

[113]   Rawls J. A theory of justice. Cambridge: Harvard Univ Press, 1971.

[114]   Patra N. State-wise pattern of gender bias in child health in India. Intl J Child Health Hum Dev2012; 5(3).

[115]   Sen AK. Demography and welfare economics. Empirica 1995; 22.

[116]   Sen AK. Social justice and distribution of income. In: AB Atkinson, F Bourguignon, eds. Handbook of income distribution. Elsevier, 2000.

[117]   Patra N. Credible neglect in *Incredible India*: Regional pattern of gender bias in child health in India.Intl Public Health J 2011; 3(3): 289-305.

[118]   UNDP. Human development report 1995: Gender and human development. United Nations Development Programme. Oxford Univ Press, 1995. (http: //hdr.undp.org/en/reports/global/hdr1995).

[119]   Patra N. A comment on infant mortality rate in India.Intl Public Health J 2012; 4(1): 25-31.

[120] Patra N. Inter-temporal pattern of gender bias in infant mortality in India: Evidence from NFHS and SRS data. Intl J Child Adolesc Health 2011; 4(1): 53-65.

[121] Reidpath D, Allotey P. Infant mortality rate as an indicator of population health. *J EpidemiolCommun Health* 2003; 57: 344–6.

[122] Pebley AR, Goldman N, Rodriguez G. Prenatal and delivery care and childhood immunization in Guatemala: Do family and community matter? Demography 1996; 33(2): 231-47.

[123] Padhi S. Infant and child survival in Orissa: An analysis with NFHS data. Econ PolitWkly 2001; Aug: 3316-26.

[124] Desai S, Alva S. Maternal education and child health: Is there a strong causal relationship? Demography 1998; 35(1): 71-81.

[125] Islam SMS, Islam MM. Influences of selected socio-economic and demographic factors on child immunization in a rural area of Bangladesh. Demography India 1996; 25(2): 275-83.

[126] Gage AJ, Sommerfelt E, Piani A. Household structure and childhood immunization in Niger and Nigeria. Demography 1997; 34(2): 295-309.

[127] Gauri V, Khaleghian P. Immunization in developing countries: Its political and organizational determinants. Policy Research Working Paper No. 2769. The World Bank, 2002.

[128] Steele F, Diamond I, Amin S. Immunization uptake in rural Bangladesh: A multilevel analysis. J Royal Statist Soc 1996; 159(2): 289-99.

[129] Panda PK. Female headship, poverty and child welfare: A study of rural Orissa. Econ PolitWkly 1997; Oct: WS73-82.

[130] Bose A. Health for all by 2000: Broken promises. Econ PolitWkly 2001; Mar: 905-7.

[131] [Gopalan C. Challenges to public health systems. Econ PolitWkly 1994; May: 1204-9.

[132] [ToI. Gender justice a myth. New Delhi: Times of India, 2011 Nov 10: 18.

[133] IIPS, Measure DHS+, ORC Macro. National family health survey (NFHS-2), 1998-99: India. Mumbai: Intl InstPopulatSci, 2000.

In: Child Health and Human Development Yearbook 2013   ISBN: 978-1-63117-939-6
Editor: Joav Merrick   © 2014 Nova Science Publishers, Inc.

Chapter 29

The effect of bibliotherapy on anxiety in children with cancer

Nicole M Schneider*, Mary Peterson, Kathleen A Gathercoal
and Elizabeth Hamilton
Graduate Department of Clinical Psychology, George Fox University, Newberg, Oregon,
United States of America

Abstract

Children who have cancer and undergo various treatment procedures tend to have higher levels of emotional distress than their peers. Although traditional therapy can be effective in decreasing such distress, bibliotherapy has been found to be a convenient, inexpensive, effective psychological intervention. This study examined how reading a disease-relevant story, embedded with literature-supported coping strategies, influenced a child's chronic illness-related distress. It was expected that children who read this book would experience a decrease in their perceived distress compared to their pre-intervention level distress. Twenty-one children ages 4 to 12 with various cancers, primarily hematological diagnoses, were recruited for this study and asked to rate their functioning across several domains utilizing the Child Outcome Rating Scale and a supplemental form targeting perceived physiological arousal. Participants were read an illustrated bibliotherapy intervention and subsequently asked to rate themselves utilizing the same scale both immediately after and several months later. Results indicate that perceptions of intrapersonal functioning improved and physiological arousal decreased immediately after the initial book reading. Significant improvements were found several months after the initial intervention when books were left with participants. This study demonstrates the value of a low-investment intervention.

Keywords: Psychology, pediatrics, oncology, bibliotherapy, anxiety

---

* Corresponding author: Nicole Schneider, PsyD, George Fox University, Graduate Department of Clinical Psychology. 422 N. Meridian St. V277, Newberg, OR 97132 United States. E-mail: nik.m.schneider@ gmail.com.

Introduction

Anxiety is the most common mental health problem in children, with 13% of children aged 9 to 17 in the United States experiencing it (1). Anxiety is paired with physiological arousal, including a more rapid heart rate and increased blood pressure in individuals experiencing such extreme stress (2). A child's constant worry may result in numerous somatic issues, including headaches, stomachaches, nausea, dizziness, and respiration (3). In up to half of those individuals who experience anxiety, co-occurring mental health problems also exist; usually the co-occurring problem is another anxiety disorder or a mood disorder, like depression (1).

Sub-clinical levels of anxiety are even more common and may occur in up to 25% of the general population of children. These symptoms may develop or become further exacerbated by stressful life events, which include a myriad of traumatic family situations or major life changes, like the death of a loved one, divorce of parents, birth of a sibling, or sudden or major illness or accident (3). While sub-clinical anxiety may later diminish, depending on a variety of factors and circumstances, it can also progress into clinically significant anxiety. As such, early intervention in sub-clinical levels of anxiety may prevent the development of future mental health problems.

Anxiety and cancer

While anxiety is quite common among children in the general population, its prevalence is particularly high in children who have serious health conditions and who are undergoing ongoing medical procedures, as in the case of cancer. Children with cancer may have trouble managing their stressors, especially those related to their medical care, which increases their overall anxiety (4). In one study examining this population, 27% of children who were recently diagnosed with acute lymphoblastic leukemia (ALL) in the month prior were found to be at risk for clinically significant anxiety (5).

The ALL study indicates that children with cancer experience a rate of anxiety that is twice as common as that in the general population. This is of concern because with anxiety often comes a decrease in quality of life; individuals who are anxious may be in a constant state of worry and even feel the physical burden of these emotions.

Predictors of increased stress and anxiety. There are several factors that have been demonstrated to be related to the level of anxiety that children with cancer experience. One predictor of emotional stress is the age at which a child is diagnosed with cancer, as it is inversely related to his or her level of anxiety; those diagnosed at a younger age tend to have more anxiety than those diagnosed at an older age (6). Presumably, this difference is due to a lack of development of cognitive skills that coping strategies hinge upon (7). Therefore, although cancer is unarguably traumatic for nearly any individual, it is even more so challenging for young children, which contributes to high levels of anxiety.

Another contributor to one's anxiety level is gender. In a comprehensive study of child survivors conducted in 2009, females were found to endorse anxiety symptoms one and a half times more often than males (8). While there are likely a number of contributing factors, many attribute this phenomenon to gender role socialization. For example, females' externalization of anxiety and worry tend to be reinforced more so than males, who are often socialized to "get over it" (9).

Anxiety levels are also related to pain levels. Anticipatory anxiety often co-occurs with pain, which is especially concerning since cancer medical procedures are often physically demanding. Bone-marrow biopsies, blood tests, and central line surgeries are all common cancer-related procedures that children are faced with experiencing during and following diagnosis (10). Not surprisingly, research has shown that children who have cancer are forced to employ coping strategies that are far beyond what a typical, healthy child would normally utilize (7).

Treatments for anxiety in children

Recently, research efforts have been devoted to studying symptoms of anxiety and emotional distress in children and discovering the most effective treatment methods. Treatment interventions for anxious children most often include traditional cognitive-behavioral therapy with a counselor or psychologist once per week over the course of several months (11). In working to diminishing anxiety, relaxation training is often utilized, in which individuals learn to be attuned to their breathing and their body's physical tension (12). Successful treatment occurs when patients are able to regulate their breathing and reduce muscle tension, which in turn reduces symptoms of anxiety, because stress and relaxation are mutually exclusive. Additionally, self-monitoring can be utilized, in which children rate how anxiety provoking a specific situation or event is, and how it affects them emotionally and physically (3). In such therapy sessions, the mental health professional focuses on helping the child recognize, understand, and learn appropriate coping skills to manage symptoms of anxiety.

Reducing anxiety in children with cancer

For children with cancer, there are a variety of attempts to manage treatment-related anxiety. Avoidant coping, which involves denying or evading the ongoing stressor, has been correlated with children's increased depression and anxiety (6). In contrast, acknowledging and working to emotionally cope with or adapt to the stressor is inversely related to anxiety (13). Further, encouraging self-statements by both parents and children has been associated with a more effective and less stressful adjustment to cancer with decreased levels of hopelessness (14).

Distraction is a coping strategy that is associated with less fear and distress when used during a medical procedure (15). When this strategy was encouraged with imagery and relaxation during physically demanding procedures, children reported having, on average, no additional fear after the intervention than they had originally. One notable change, however, was their perceived level of pain, which was *reduced* following the distraction, visualization, and relaxation tactics (16). Other effective strategies to lessen anxiety include helping children learn more about their illness and teaching them to be inquisitive about their disease (6).

An adjunctive method to reduce anxiety is bibliotherapy, in which books are utilized as a form of therapy. These books provide the individual with tools needed to better cope with their current life situation. Although not as effective as traditional psychotherapy, bibliotherapy has been found to be more effective than no therapy at all; giving non-cancer patients with mild to moderate anxiety psychoeducational literature about relaxation techniques and stress management diminished overall anxiety (17-18). Bibliotherapy interventions eliminated anxiety disorders in 15% of the sample children. In addition, this intervention can also be helpful in improving the problem-solving abilities of individuals (19).

Practically, bibliotherapy is far less expensive and much more accessible than traditional therapy, with an intervention book costing as little as $10. Psychotherapy, in contrast, is a far more financially-laden venture; a single counseling session by a mental health professional typically ranges from about $100 to $200 per 50-minute session and also requires one to navigate the logistics of scheduling an appropriate referral. Furthermore, psychotherapy is time-intensive, lasting several months at minimum, and labor-intensive, requiring the child's parents to schedule and attend sessions when their schedules are likely crowded with other medical appointments. Taken together, psychotherapy is quite costly when compared to bibliotherapy interventions (11). Although bibliotherapy may not be as effective as traditional psychotherapy, this economically and time efficient intervention holds a great deal of merit.

Bibliotherapy can be very helpful for children with cancer because it teaches individuals how to deal effectively with problems that are out of one's control and that cannot necessarily be eradicated (20). When bibliotherapy books have a character who the child can relate to, then children have a "powerful tool" to help them develop coping strategies (21; p. 19). Discussing the contents of the book is a crucial element of bibliotherapy, because the opportunity to generalize and apply the coping strategies allows the information to become an individualized intervention, thus increasing its effectiveness as a psychological tool (20). In addition, a bibliotherapy text can be read by a parent, allowing the natural parent-child relationship to further develop (22).

Not surprisingly, being diagnosed and subsequently receiving treatment for cancer presents a major, stressful change in both the life of the ill child and the life of his or her family. Though cancer treatment regimens vary depending on type and stage of cancer, among a myriad of other factors, the ensuing distress can last for months or even years. For children who are undergoing cancer treatments, therapeutic interventions can help them learn to cope with the psychological side effects of their disease.

Bibiotherapy is an accessible, relatively inexpensive, and yet still effective psychological tool for reducing anxiety. It is hypothesized that reading a children's book that describes what a character undergoes when he or she has cancer, along with coping strategies employed, will improve a child's subjective perception of functioning and decrease their perceived emotional distress.

Methods

Participants were English-speaking male and female children aged 4 to 12 years (M = 9.1, SD = 2.1) who had been diagnosed with cancer and undergoing or had recently completed treatment. Approximately 57% of participants were Caucasian (n = 12), 29% were Hispanic (n = 6), and 14% were African-American (n = 3). Fifty-seven percent were male (n = 12) and 43% were female (n = 9). Most participants had acute lymphoblatic leukemia (ALL) diagnoses (n = 14). Table 1 highlights the demographic distribution of the participants.

Table 1. Demographic data

	n	%
Gender		
Male	12	57.1
Female	9	49.2
Ethnicity		
Caucasian	12	57.1
African-American	3	14.3
Hispanic	6	28.6
Diagnosis*		
Acute Lymphoblastic Leukemia (ALL)	14	66.7
Other leukemia	1	4.8
Lymphoma	2	9.5
Neuroblastoma	1	4.8
Kidney cancer	1	4.8
Osteosarcoma	1	4.8
Hepatoblastoma	1	4.8
Unknown	1	4.8
Treatment Type**		
Chemotherapy	17	81.0
Radiation	2	9.5
Surgery	9	42.9
Oral medication only	1	4.8
Unknown	3	14.3
Treatment Clinic Type		
Inpatient	2	9.5
Outpatient	9	42.9
Both	7	33.3
Unknown	3	14.3
Primary Caregiver's Marital Status		
Married/Partnered	7	33.3
Divorced	3	14.3
Single/Widowed	7	33.3
Unknown	4	19.0

*Percentages do not add up to 100; one child had dual cancer diagnoses.
**Percentages do not add up to 100; many children received more than one treatment during their illness.

Procedure

As part of the informed consent process, patients and their caregivers were shown the intervention book, *Nikki's Day at Chemo*. The book was developed for this study and was embedded with coping strategies for a child diagnosed with cancer including the emotional implications of diagnosis and treatment. This bound book was written in English, illustrated with color pictures, and independently published. The intervention was provided in the patients' home by masters-level caseworkers who had been assigned to specific patients by the non-profit cancer foundation which provides psychosocial support to cancer patients and families.

Caseworkers provided participants (time 1) with a demographic questionnaire and a measure of general functioning, Child Outcome Rating Scale (CORS; 23). The CORS asks children to report their functioning across four domains: intrapersonal, family, school and global functioning. The CORS is designed as a 10-point visual analog scale with a frowning face on one end of the Likert-type scale and a smiling face on the other end of the scale. In addition to the standardized questions on the CORS, two symptom-specific items were included to assess physiological arousal.

The caseworker then read the book to the patient. Following the reading, the child was asked several questions about the book and its story line to gauge their comprehension level. Next, the child was asked how he or she would generalize or apply the coping strategies that were used by the character in the book in their own lives. For example, the book explained how Nikki used her imagination to "fly to the park" when she was nervous; in the intervention component of this protocol, the child was asked how he or she might use his or her imagination to feel better. Following the reading of the book and the discussion questions, which lasted approximately 15 minutes, the CORS and supplemental questions were repeated along with the participant's report of satisfaction with the book (time 2).

As an incentive to participate, patients were given a copy of *Nikki's Day at Chemo* after the caseworker visit was completed with the child's answers to his or her comprehension and coping strategy questions recorded inside. Caseworkers were paid for the home visit by the cancer foundation, which was reimbursed by the grant that supported this study.

Approximately one month after the initial visit patients' caregivers were contacted via the telephone number they provided on the initial questionnaire. Follow-up assessment packets were then mailed to patients' homes; the follow-up packets included a third and final administration of the CORS, a second satisfaction survey, a questionnaire regarding frequency of reading the book, and an updated demographic form to record any significant changes in treatment or disease status. Participants were asked the return the surveys as soon as possible.

Instruments

The Child Outcome Rating Scale (CORS) is a self-administered tool available in English (23). This measure is highly effective in measuring quality of life and self-esteem in children ages 6 to 12, as well as quantifying depression and anxiety as a whole. Its simplicity is likely to be appreciated by children, who are constantly undergoing extensive and draining procedures, as well as by their caregivers.

Results

This study examined whether a bibliotherapy intervention affected a child's subjective perception of functioning and level of emotional distress. It was hypothesized that reading a book describing coping strategies used by a child undergoing treatment for cancer would increase subjective perception of functioning as measured by the four domains (intrapersonal, family, school, and global) of the Child Outcome Rating Scale (CORS) as well as reduce perceived levels of physiological arousal.

Differences between Time 1 and Time 2

In order to compare participants' perception of functioning and emotional distress from immediately before and after the book reading ($n = 21$), a paired samples t-test was conducted. On the item targeting children's perceived ability to manage their nervousness, there was not a significant difference in the scores prior to the book reading ($M = 7.26$, $SD = 3.82$) and immediately after the book reading ($M = 7.82$, $SD = 3.17$); $t(20) = -0.93$, $p = 0.363$, but there was a small effect size (0.20). The results suggest that although statistical significance was not reached, the reading may lessen overall arousal; with a larger sample size, significance would have been reached. Other constructs tested yielded similar results; for example, paired-samples t-tests used to compare participants' intrapersonal functioning initially ($M = 8.08$, $SD = 2.41$) and following the book reading ($M = 8.72$, $SD = 1.65$); $t(20) = -1.1$, $p = 0.286$.

This data failed to show significance but yielded a small effect size (0.24). Table 2 shows the means for all outcome measures at T1 and T2. All other comparisons showed no effect (ES < 0.2).

Participants were also asked how *Nikki's Day at Chemo* compares to other books they have read, based on a 1 to 10 scale ($n = 21$). As a whole, participants indicated a general sentiment that they enjoyed the book, with higher scores indicating greater satisfaction ($M = 7.8$, $SD = 2.48$). All participants accurately answered basic comprehension questions following the initial book reading, suggesting that children sustained attention throughout. This comprehension check also served as a validity measure, ensuring that participants comprehended the material.

Table 2. Outcome measure means across time (T1 & T2)

	T1	T2
	Mean *(SD)*	**Mean** *(SD)*
Intrapersonal: How am I doing?	8.08 (2.41)	8.72 (1.65)
Family: How are things in my family?	8.13 (1.74)	8.47 (2.58)
School: How am I doing at school?	8.07 (2.58)	8.41 (2.07)
Global: How is everything going?	8.7 (1.72)	8.52 (2.14)
Physiological Arousal:		
Perceived ability to relax	7.86 (2.71)	8.31 (2.24)
Perceived ability to manage nervousness	7.26 (3.82)	7.82 (3.17)
Child's Satisfaction with Book	-	8.48 (2.32)

Table 3. Outcome measure means across time (T1 & T3)

	T1 Mean *(SD)*	T3 Mean *(SD)*
Intrapersonal: How am I doing?	8.47 (1.28)**	9.52 (0.68)**
Family: How are things in my family?	9.10 (1.06)	9.57 (0.78)
School: How am I doing at school?	9.32 (0.86)	9.93 (0.10)
Global: How is everything going?	8.82 (1.66)	9.93 (0.10)
Physiological Arousal:		
Perceived ability to relax	7.68 (3.00)	9.72 (0.44)
Perceived ability to manage nervousness	5.98 (5.19)	7.52 (3.85)
Child's Satisfaction with Book	-	8.95 (2.10)
Parent's Satisfaction with Book*	-	96 (8.94)
Frequency of Book Reading	-	1.40 (2.61)

*Parents rated the book on a 1 to 100 scale, with higher numbers indicating greater satisfaction.
**Significant differences ($p < .05$ for mean score comparison of intrapersonal functioning at T1 vs. T3). No other *t*-test comparisons yielded significant differences.

Differences between Time 1 and Time 3

Twenty-nine percent of participants responded to follow-up surveys, which were collected one to three months after the intervention. No significant patterns were found between participants who responded in time 3 compared to those who did not respond. Paired-samples *t*-tests were conducted to determine the change across the intrapersonal measure of the CORS from immediately before the initial book reading and from several months later ($n = 6$). With no reported differences in additional treatment or prognosis between T1 and T3, there was a significant improvement in scores reporting perception of intrapersonal functioning prior to the book reading ($M = 8.47$, $SD = 1.28$) and several months later ($M = 9.51$, $SD = 0.68$); $t(5) = -2.64$, $p = 0.046$. Table 3 presents the mean paired samples outcome measures at T1 and T3.

It is clear that children's sentiments about the book were relatively positive throughout the duration of this study. Using a scale ranging from 1 to 100, parents were asked to rate their perception of how much their child liked the book, with higher numbers indicating more satisfaction. Children ($n = 5$) appeared to be very satisfied with the book ($M = 94$, $SD = 13.4$). Parents ($n = 5$) appeared to have similar positive opinions about the book, as they were also asked to evaluate how much they liked it using the same 1 to 100 scale ($M = 96$, $SD = 8.94$).

Analysis of qualitative data

Post-intervention questions at Time 2 encouraged the child to apply the book character's coping strategies (e.g., talking to a trusted adult, using their imagination) to their own situation. Children were asked to identify someone they could turn to when they felt worried. When encouraged to think about how they might use their own imagination to feel better, the children responded with a range of adaptive coping strategies including "I could go to outer space to jump around freely and collect rocks," as well as go to "California" or to "the park, running, which I can't do right now." In the open-ended questions, several children expressed their desire to ask questions and share their feelings, just as the character in the book had done. One child told the caseworker "having you read this book to me makes me want to write my own story that everyone can read."

Parents generally agreed that the book was "appreciated" and "covers everything," with different individuals stating that "this is the first time I've seen a book like this where it explains everything so well" and it "captured everything a child needs to know or can feel in the book." Other parents noted that they "love the book" and that, along with their child, they "read it all the time." One of the parents further stated that reading the book has prompted her child to be more forward with asking his doctor questions, which has in turn allowed him to gain confidence to speak freely about his disease, with both peers at school and with the general public at a fundraising event.

Discussion

This study attempted to determine if a brief bibliotherapy intervention could affect a child's subjective perception of functioning and decrease his or her perceived emotional distress. Although a small pilot study, the findings supported the hypothesis that positive results that may emerge by providing children with a book that not only details a realistic portrayal of what one faces during a cancer experience, but also includes questions to activate coping strategies. Quantitative data suggested that the intervention might have improved the perception of intrapersonal functioning while decreasing physiological arousal on a self-report measure. For participants remaining in the study, the perception of improvement remained stable or increased during the three months following the intervention. Qualitatively, participants consistently recalled the specifics of the coping strategies employed in the book. Many children were able to custom-fit the strategies used by the main character to their own lives. During follow-up contact, qualitative responses indicated several children had continued to use the coping strategies that they learned from the book.

As previous literature on the subject suggests, bibliotherapy is an effective intervention, for reducing symptoms of anxiety and emotional distress (18). The study's positive results extend the literature by suggesting that bibliotherapy may also be an effective intervention for children who show sub-clinical levels of anxiety.

In recent decades, pediatric cancer survival rates have drastically improved. Compared to 50 years ago when a child's diagnosis was often synonymous with a death sentence, advances in treatments have vastly improved children's cancer prognoses. Statistics now show that approximately four out of five pediatric cancer patients survive at least five years past their diagnosis (24). Therefore, learning evidence-based strategies may continue to help patients when dealing with stress and anxiety throughout their lives, far beyond coping with their illness.

Aside from the positive outcome that children experienced, parents also appeared to benefit from the intervention. Many voiced their appreciation for this type of therapeutic tool aimed to help their children; several of them described positive effects that the book had on their children. Overall, participants' and parents' interest and enjoyment in the intervention highlight a demand for such products, yet a paucity of books targeted for children dealing with serious chronic illness exists.

Unlike other studies, this research focused on identifying and affecting a child's subjective perception of global functioning as well as reducing physiological arousal. This represents a unique contribution to the literature by looking at patients' perceptions across these domains, rather than using objective anxiety and biofeedback measures with a specific clinically diagnosed population. As sub-clinical anxiety is even more common than clinically significant anxiety, this is a relevant population for evidenced-based interventions (3).

Implications

This research demonstrates the effectiveness of a brief intervention that yields meaningful results in improving intrapersonal functioning as well as reducing physiological arousal. After participants had several months with the book, their improvements were even more evident, suggesting that the positive effects are likely to continue with increased exposure to the intervention. The bibliotherapy tool employed in this study is easy to use and portable, two qualities that are vital for patients and families with demanding and time-consuming medical treatment schedules. *Nikki's Day at Chemo* is further effective as it empowers both the parent and child to cope with cancer together. As a whole, this book represents a tool that is a low investment and has a high yield for an incredibly vulnerable population.

Limitations

This study has several limitations. With a greater participant pool, a randomized-control design could have been employed, allowing the participants to be parsed into two groups, one of which would be assigned *Nikki's Day at Chemo* and one of which would be assigned a non-cancer related control book of a similar length. This would have strengthened the validity of the study, as the change could then have been attributed to the specific intervention book, rather than reading in general. Another limitation was the varying times between participants' diagnoses; more stringent selection criteria would have been helpful so that, for example, newly diagnosed individuals could have been compared to their counterparts. Children who have dealt with their illness for several years compared to those who have recently been diagnosed undoubtedly have different levels of knowledge about their disease, treatment, and how to cope.

Directions for future research

Future research examining this specific book would be valuable. Based on qualitative responses from participants' parents, a future study identifying caregiver anxiety would be valuable, particularly in determining how a bibliotherapy tool like *Nikki's Day at Chemo* affects it. Finally, as the study was conducted in a single geographical region, it would be valuable to expand the study to include a wider, more diverse range of individuals in different geographical regions. As the bibliotherapy tool is currently written solely in English, a

Spanish translation would be valuable in order to expand eligibility criteria to include Spanish-speaking children in the United States.

Acknowledgments

This study was made possible by a generous grant from the Paul K. Richter Memorial Fund and the Evalyn E. C. Richter Memorial Fund. The study would also not have been possible without the participation of the Emmanuel Cancer Foundation in Scotch Plains, NJ or the children and their families who participated in this study.

References

[1]   Substance Abuse and Mental Health Services Administration 2009. Accessed 2010 April 18. URL: http://www.samhsa.gov/data/

[2]   Lang PJ, Davis M, Öhman A. Fear and anxiety: Animal models and human cognitive psychophysiology. J Affect Disord 2000; 61: 137-59.

[3]   Last CG. Help for worried kids. New York, NY: Guilford, 2006.

[4]   McCaffrey CN. Major stressors and their effects on the well-being of children with cancer. J Pediatr Nurs 2006; 21: 59-66.

[5]   Buchanan N, Maloney K, Tsang S, Stork LC, Neglia JP, Kadan-Lottick NS. Risk of depression, anxiety, and somatization one month after diagnosis in children with standard risk ALL on COG AALL0331. [Abstract] J Clin Oncol 2008; 26(15), np.

[6]   Frank NC, Blount RL, Brown RT. Attributions, coping, and adjustment in children with cancer. J Pediatr Psychol 1997; 22: 563-76.

[7]   Dcrevensky JL, Tsanos AP, Handman M. Children with cancer: An examination of their coping and adaptive behavior. J Psychosoc Oncol 1998; 16: 37-61.

[8]   Zeltzer LK, Recklitis C, Buchbinder D, Zebrack B, Casillas J, Tsao JC, et al. Psychological status in childhood cancer survivors: A report from the Childhood Cancer Survivor Study. J Clin Oncol 2009; 27: 2396-2404.

[9]   Stewart SH, Taylor S, Baker JM. Gender differences in dimensions of anxiety sensitivity. J Anxiety Disord 1997; 11: 179-200.

[10] Kuttner L, Bowman M, Teasdale M. Psychological treatment of distress, pain, and anxiety for young children with cancer. J Dev Behav Pediatr 1988; 9: 374-81.

[11] Kendall PC, Hudson JL, Gosch E, Flannery-Schroeder E, Suveg C. Cognitive-behavioral therapy for anxiety disordered youth: A randomized clinical trial evaluation child and family modalities. J Consult Clin Psychol 2008; 76: 282-297.

[12] Friedberg RD, McClure JM. Clinical practice of cognitive therapy with children and adolescents: The nuts and bolts. New York, NY: Guilford, 2002.

[13] Miller KS, Vannatta K, Compas BE, Vasey M, McGoron KD, Salley CG, et al. The role of coping and temperament in the adjustment of children with cancer. J Pediatr Psychol 2009; 34: 1135-43.

[14] Coletti DJ. Stressful medical procedures in the context of cancer: Patterns of parent and child coping strategies and psychological adaptation. Dissertation. Nashville, TN: Vanderbilt Univ, 1997.

[15] Windich-Biermeier A, Sjoberg I, Dale JC, Eshelman D, Guzzetta CE. Effects of distraction on pain, fear, and distress during venous port access and venipuncture in children and adolescents with cancer. J Pediatr Oncol Nurs 2007; 24: 8-19.

[16] Broome, ME, Lillis PP, McGahee TW, Bates T. The use of distraction and imagery with children during painful procedures. Eur J Cancer Care 2007; 3: 26-30.

[17]   Parslow R, Morgan AJ, Allen NB, Jorm AF, O'Donnell CP, Purcell R. Effectiveness of complementary and self-help treatments for anxiety in children and adolescents. Med J Aust 2008; 188: 355-9.

[18]   Rappee RM, Abbott MJ, Lyneham HJ. Bibliotherapy for children with anxiety disorders using written materials for parents: A randomized controlled trial. J Consult Clin Psychol 2006; 74: 436-44.

[19]   Forgan JW. Using bibliotherapy to teach problem solving. Interv Sch Clin 2002; 38: 75-82.

[20]   Rokke K. Bibliotherapy: A place for childrens' literature in dealing with cancer. J Pediatr Oncol Nurs 1993; 10: 57.

[21]   Nicholson JI, Pearson QM. Helping children cope with fears: Using children's literature in classroom guidance. Prof School Couns 2003; 7: 15-19.

[22]   Fosson A, Husband E. Bibliotherapy for hospitalized children. South Med J 1984; 77: 342-6.

[23]   Duncan BL, Miller SD, Sparks JA. The Child Outcome Rating Scale. Fort Lauderdale, FL: Authors, 2003.

[24]   Childhood cancer survivors: Healthy living. AICR Science Now 2010; 31: 1-2.

In: Child Health and Human Development Yearbook 2013   ISBN: 978-1-63117-939-6
Editor: Joav Merrick   © 2014 Nova Science Publishers, Inc.

Chapter 30

Association of parental involvement and the delay of sexual initiation in Grenadian adolescents

Cecilia Hegamin-Younger[1]*, Rohan Jeremiah[2], Christine Richards[1], Aaron Buzzard[1], Lynn Fakeye[1] and Cherise Adjodha[3]
[1]Department of Public Health and Preventive Medicine,
St George's University, Grenada, West Indies
[2]School of Public Health, University of Michigan, Ann Arbor, Michigan,
United States of America
[3]Global Health Collaborating Center, Grenada, West Indies

Abstract

The onset for sexual activity in Grenada is low. Approximately 74% of males have their first sexual encounter by the age of 12 and 55% of females by the age of 13 years. Outside of the health education course in school, the topic of reproductive health is not commonly addressed; putting adolescents at increased risk for teen pregnancies and transmission of sexually transmitted infections. A protective factor for the delay of sexual initiation is parental involvement. Using proxy measures of checking homework, knowing where the child is and understanding the child were used to examine the association of parental involvement and age of sexual initiation. The results provide evidence that parental involvement and the father-daughter relationship do delay sexual initiation for adolescent females. What is less understood are the factors that are associated with adolescent males' age of sexual initiation.

Keywords: Adolescence, sexuality, Grenada

---

* Corresponding author: Professor, Cecilia Hegamin-Younger, PhD, Department of Public Health and Preventive Medicine, St. George's University, Grenada, West Indies. E-mail: chyounger@me.com.

Introduction

Early sexual initiation during adolescence is a significant public health problem because of its associated risks with HIV/AIDS, sexually transmitted infections and teenage pregnancy. In the Caribbean the age of onset for sexual activity is relatively low (1). In addition to be being low, it is mostly forced or coerced initiation especially for young girls by adult men but also evident among young boys by their peers (2,3). This is of concern as adolescents comprise approximately 23% of the population (4). In developing countries, such as Grenada, with scarce resources, it is therefore important to address this problem as the consequences are costly, both socially and economically.

In Latin America and the Caribbean, between 1981 and 2005 there were a reported 1.7 million AIDS cases of which 38,000 cases were younger than age 15 years. In addition, between 1994 and 2005 the percentage of females living with AIDS increased from 6% to 31% (5). The adult prevalence rate from HIV in the Caribbean is only surpassed by that of sub-Saharan Africa with women and girls comprising 56% of the infected population (6). In Grenada in 2009 the estimated prevalence of persons living with HIV/AIDS was 0.57%6. However, according to the report, data on youth -- especially females -- was underrepresented because testing in this group remained a challenge.

In addition to these stark statistics, teenage pregnancies continue to be a burden in developing countries despite some progress being recorded in the Millennium Development Goals report of 2010 (7). Between 1990 and 2007 teenage pregnancy rates decreased from 65 to 52 births per 1000 women. During that same period, in Latin America and the Caribbean, the rates decreased from 91 to 74 (6). However, in Grenada, the rates increased from 23% to 32% of the total live births between 2003 and 2005 (5). These trends are worrisome as health systems in developing countries like Grenada are ill equipped to deal with the negative health outcomes. Consequently, it is imperative that health risk and protective factors among this population be understood so that interventions may be designed that will positively impact the Grenadian population.

Parental monitoring has been identified as a protective factor for delayed sexual initiation among adolescents (8,9). However, in the literature reviewed, no studies were found which examined this factor among Grenadian youth. Hence, this study was conducted to investigate the association between the health-compromising behaviors of adolescents, specifically sexual initiation, and parental involvement in the adolescents' daily lives.

This analysis provides a description of the risk behaviors of Grenadian adolescents and its associated indicators of parental connectedness. It is hoped that the results will be used to identify areas of focus for development of culturally appropriate interventions for delaying sexual initiation among Grenadian adolescents.

Methods

To examine the relationship between parental involvement and sexual initiation, a secondary data analysis was conducted using the 2008 Global School Based Student Health Survey (GSHS). The GSHS was developed by the World Health Organization (WHO) in collaboration with the United Nations Educational, Scientific and Cultural Organization

(UNESCO), the United Nations Children's Fund, and the Joint United Nations Program on HIV/AIDS to assess behavioral risk and protective factors in 10 fundamental areas (alcohol use, dietary behaviors, drug use, hygiene, mental health, physical activity, protective factors, sexual behaviors, tobacco use, violence and unintentional injury) across all countries served by the United Nations in order to develop priorities, establish programs, and advocate for resource allocation (10).

A two-stage cluster sample design was used to produce data representative of all students in Grenada. In the first stage, secondary schools were chosen with probability proportional to enrollment size in the first stage. The second stage selected individual classes randomly. All students enrolled in the selected classes were eligible to participate and were administered an 85-item survey. A total of 1,542 Grenadian students, ages 11-16 years, completed and returned the survey, yielding a 95% school response rate, 82% student response rate and 78% overall response rate (see table 1) (10).

For this study seven items were included in this analysis: 1) sexual intercourse activity, 2) age sexual intercourse was initiated, 3) number of partners, 4) closeness to parents, 5) student's perception of parents knowing where they are, 6) student's perception of understanding troubles and 7) student's perception of parent checking their homework. The last three measures were used as proxy measures of perceived parental involvement.

Data analysis

The demographic variables were summarized using frequencies and percentages. To assess the relationship between parental involvement and sexual intercourse, chi-square tests were conducted at a = 0.05 level of significance to determine associations. Chi-square test was used to see if there is a difference between the age of sexual intercourse initiation and parental involvement and closeness to parent(s). A correlation coefficient was used to assess relationships between age of initiation and number of sexual partners controlling for parental involvement. All analyses recognized a p-value < 0.05 as statistically significant. All outputs were generated via SPSS version 19.

Table 1. Demographic summary of secondary students (n=1,542)

	n (%)
Gender	
Female	843 (55.1)
Male	688 (44.9)
Abused by partner	164 (10.9)
Forced to have sex	
Female	39 (30.7)
Male	47 (18.3)
Had sex	390 (29.4)
Female	127 (33.1)
Male	257 (66.9)

Results

Of the responding secondary students, 55% were females and 29% of the students had engaged in sexual activity. Of the students engaging in sexual intercourse, 33% were females. There was a statistically significant difference in the distribution of age of sexual intercourse and gender (χ^2=42.14, p<.01). Overall, the majority of males (74.2%) had sex by age 12, whereas fewer than half (41.3%) of the females had sex prior to 12 years of age (see table 2). More females (43.6%) than males (16.1%) waited until they were 14 years or older. Proportionately, more males had multiple sex partners (see table 2). Whereas, the majority of females had fewer than two partners. The reported early initiation of sexual intercourse with males suggests that it plays a role in masculinity. The role of masculinity can be considered in two folds: one, a need to assert a young man's gender and sexual identities within an overtly patriarchal society that measures masculinity through very definite practices such as sexual intercourse with multiple partners. The second important aspect of masculinity among young boys is the presence of peer- pressure from other young men to be respected based on the ability to persuade young women to have sex with him. These constructs of masculinity are clear benchmarks of how a young teenage boys begin to define the initiation into adulthood (11).

There was a statistically significant difference between males and females number of sexual partners (χ^2= 17.97, p=.003). Even though more than 50% of the students (70.6% of females and 53.2% of males), irrespective of gender, have two or less sex partners, proportionately males had more sex partners (>2). The gendered differences among the reporting of sexual partners are grounded in cultural perceptions in how young men and women are allowed explore their sexualities. While it is widely perceived and accepted that young men measure their masculinity through multi-partnering, culturally if a young female attempts to do the same, she would have many negative labels such as being loose or considered a slut. There are greater social and cultural scrutiny for young women to control and hide their sexual expressions. Women with very limited sexual exposure and history are valued more when considering marriage (9,12,13).

To examine the connectedness of the adolescent with the parent, students reported their perception of feeling close to their mother and father, separately (see table 3 and 4). There is no clear trend that the connection with the mother with delayed sexual activity in both sexes. However, the perceived connection with the father suggests that the father-daughter relationship is an important factor in delaying the initiation of sexual activities.

To further understand the association of parental involvement a correlation analysis was conducted between the age of onset and the number of partners (see table 4). With the exception of rarely to never knowing where the child is (r=-.19, p=0.01), no significant relationships between age of onset and number of partners were found. There were significant correlations for females when the father was not perceived to be connected (r=-0.52, p<0.001), when the parent did not know what the child did (r=-0.51, p<0.001), and did not checking homework (r=-.48, p<0.001). The correlations suggest that when the parent was not perceived to be involved the earlier the age of initiation the more sex partners the female adolescent had.

Table 2. Summary of secondary students who initiated sexual activity (n=390)

	Males n (%)	Females n (%)
Age of 1st sexual intercourse[a]		
<=11 years	133 (53.6)	36 (28.6)
12	51 (20.6)	16 (12.7)
13	24 (9.7)	19 (15.1)
14	22 (8.9)	26 (20.6)
15	12 (4.8)	19 (15.1)
>=16	6 (2.4)	10 (7.9)
Number of sex partners[b]		
1	81 (31.9)	62 (49.2)
2	54 (21.3)	27 (21.4)
3	33 (13)	16 (12.7)
4	9 (3.5)	5 (4)
5	12 (4.7)	4 (3.2)
>=6	65 (25.6)	12 (9.5)

Note: a – χ^2 =42.14, p<.001.
b – χ^2 = 17.96, p=.003.

Table 3. Summary of the perception of closeness to parents

	Females		Males	
	Had sex	No sex	Had Sex	No Sex
No	66 (54.1)	236 (38.9)	112 (48.5)	118 (45.4)
Mother only	28 (23.0)	181 (29.9)	52 (22.5)	55 (21.2)
Father only	9 (7.4)	44 (7.3)	17 (7.4)	18 (6.9)
Mother & Father	19 (15.6)	145 (23.9)	50 (21.8)	69 (26.5)

**Table 4. Correlations of number of partners and age of initiation of sex:
By parental involvement**

Parental Involvement	Male	Female
Check homework		
Yes	-.16*	-.02
No	-.23	-.51**
Understands troubles		
Yes	-.20	-.32
No	-.13	-.48**
Know what child did		
Yes	-.15	0
No	-.19*	-.51**
Felt close to dad		
Yes	-.29	-.006
No	-.16	-.52**

Note: * indicates significance at the .05 level.
** Indicates significance at the .01 level.

Adolescent daughters were further analyzed to examine differences in adolescent females who had initiated sex and those who had not (see table 5). Overall, there was a statistical difference in parental involvement (χ^2=29.60, p<0.001). Parental involvement was summarized by the extent of involvement. Using the proxy measures, parental involvement was collapsed into very involved, in which all three measures were present, and not involved, in which none of the measures were present. In addition, the 2-measure combinations and 3-measure combinations were also included. The majority (62%) of the adolescent daughters who had sex reported no parental involvement, whereas only 38% of the adolescent daughters who did not have sex reported no involvement.

Of the combinations of proxy measures, there was a 7 percentage point difference in perception of daughters who perceived their parent(s) knew where they were and an almost 5 percentage point difference in daughters who perceived that their parent(s) knew where they were and checked their homework. This finding suggests that when a parent knows what their daughter is doing, they delay sexual initiation.

The relationship of the adolescent daughter with their parent or parents was also examined (see table 3). There was a statistically significant difference in the perceived closeness to the parent(s) and initiation of sex (χ^2=10.46, p=0.02). The majority (54%) of adolescents who have initiated sex did not perceive themselves to be close to either parent. In addition, there is 6-percentage point difference in the perception of being close to both parents (for adolescent males and females), further supporting the premise that parental relationship with adolescent daughters is important to the delay of sexual initiation.

Parental involvement was measured using three proxy measures. Students indicated their perception of their parents checking their homework, understanding them and knowing what they do. For each measure, there was a statistically significant difference in the students by gender. Overall, proportionately females who are sexually active indicated that they have minimal interaction with their parent(s) with respect to each proxy measure. This suggests that parental interaction and communication with female adolescents is integral to the delay of onset initiation of sexual activity. In contrast, there is no evidence of the association between parental involvement and delay of sexual initiation.

Table 5. Parental involvement

	Females		Males	
	Sex	**No sex**	**Sex**	**No sex**
Very involved	10 (8.3)	104 (17.3)	11 (4.9)	42 (15.8)
Understands & knows where they are	5 (4.1)	42 (7.0)	19 (8.4)	23 (8.7)
Checks homework and knows where they are	1 (0.8)	34 (5.7)	3 (1.3)	14 (5.3)
Checks homework and understands them	4 (3.3)	28 (4.7)	14 (6.2)	16 (6.0)
Knows where they are	10 (8.3)	94 (15.7)	22 (9.8)	29 (10.69)
Checks homework	7 (5.8)	31 (5.2)	25 (11.1)	17 (6.4)
Understands them	9 (7.4)	39 (6.5)	19 (8.4)	20 (7.5)
None	75 (62.0)	228 (38.0)	112 (49.8)	104 (39.2)

Conclusion

Promoting reproductive health involves a multi-sectorial approach. Not only is accurate factual information required, the community and family dynamics plays a role. Positive parenting expressed through attention paid to homework, understanding, and knowing where the student is, is essentially tied to a general increase of protective factors through exposure to a "stable home environment".

Father's play an important role in the emotional and social development of their daughters. There is evidence that supports the connectedness with the father figure is associated with the delay in sexual activity onset in females (14), thus challenging the belief that parenting does not involve emotional and social needs. The correlation between positive psychosocial development of girls and father-daughter relationships could be further analyzed. It is possible that it is not that the father-daughter relationship that is vital (i.e., positive parenting is not contingent upon the gender of the parent), but rather, when this relationship is problematic, girls then are vulnerable to early sexual activity. It is also possible that fathers abusing their daughters cause general instability that leads to the daughter's increased vulnerability to unsafe sex and early sexual activity. A negative relationship between a father and his daughter, and her early sexual initiation may very well be linked to child sexual abuse and incest issues, abandonment issues tied to her relationship with her mother and whether she has a positive, non-sexual affective relationship with others close to her (15,16). All of these concerns need to be further addressed.

An area of concern is the inequity of sexual activity between the genders. A limitation of the topic and methods is the potential for under-reporting of sexual activity of adolescent females and the over-reporting by male adolescents. Even with the possibility of opposite reporting biases, the results provide trends with respect to areas of concerns in Grenada. The results of this study suggest that boys have more sexual partners than girls in their age group. If so, with whom are they having sex with? This suggests that their sexual partners are older and/or younger. Early onset of male sexual activity may be linked to child sexual abuse (14). It is important to know who adolescent males are having sex with. While a personal self-image of masculinity may play a role, young boys may also be targets of sexual predators. More information is needed on as to who is encouraging boys to engage in sexual activity.

The same question can be asked of adolescent females, but for a different reason. Because females are reporting having sex less than males, the question becomes: why are women and girls more vulnerable and at risk of HIV in the 15 to 24 year age group? Females in this age group are four to six times more likely to become infected with HIV than males in the same group. Knowing the age of the sexual partners of adolescent females who are having sex under the age of 16 in also important. HIV studies suggest that they are sexual targets of older men, transactional sex, and child abuse (16-18).

Understanding the structural factors motivating early sexual initiation is important to develop preventive measures such as education, policy, policing and social services will be able to more effectively direct prevention efforts. From this analysis it is possible that structural factors such as the family dynamics, economic conditions, and domestic violence need to be further explored to properly address. Using this secondary analysis is the first step in identifying trends of adolescents in the Caribbean. Even though parental monitoring of adolescents is assessed with the delay of female adolescents initiation of sexual activity. A deepened understanding of the family dynamics needs to be explored.

References

[1]   World Bank. The World Bank Study on Caribbean Youth Development issues and policy directions. Washington, DC: The World Bank, 2003.

[2]   Le Franc E, Samms-Vaughan M, Hambleton I, Fox K, Brown D. Interpersonal violence in three Caribbean countries - Barbados, Jamaica and Trinidad and Tobago. Rev Panama Salud Publication 2008; 24(6): 409-21.

[3]   Inter-American Comission of Women. Study to enable the preparation of Pilot interventions to address intersections between HIV/AIDS and Violence Against Women in Barbados and Dominica. Washington, DC: Organisation of American States, 2009.

[4]   CARICOM Capacity Development Programme. National Census Report 2001, Grenada. Georgetown: Guyana, 2009.

[5]   Pan American Health Organization. Health in the Americas. Washington, DC: Pan American Health Organization, 2007.

[6]   UNAIDS. World AIDs Day Report 2011. Geneva: UNAIDS Joint United Nations Programme on HIV/AIDS, 2011.

[7]   United Nations. Millienum Development Goals Report 2010. Geneva: United Nations Department of Economic Development and Social Affairs, 2010. Accessed 2011 Sept 13. URL: http://www.un.org/millenniumgoals/pdf/MDG%20Report%202010%20En% 20r15%20-low%20res% 2020100615%20-.pdf

[8]   Deptula DP, Schoeny ME, Henry DB. How can parents make a difference? Longitudinal associations with adolescent sexual behavior. J Fam Psychol 2010; 24(6): 731-9.

[9]   Ohene SA, Ireland M, Blum R. The clustering of risk behaviors among Caribbean youth. Maternal Child Health J 2005; 9(1): 91–100.

[10]   Centers for Disease Control. School-based Student Health Survey (GSHS). Atlanta, Georgia. Accessed 2010 May 10. URL: http: //www.cdc.gov/gshs/countries/americas/grenada.htm

[11]   Plummer D, Simpson J. HIV and Caribbean Masculinities. New York: United Nations Educational, Scientific and Cultural Organization (UNESCO) Publication, 2007.

[12]   Eggleston E, Jackson J, Hardee K. Sexual attitudes and Behavior among young adolescents in Jamaica. Int Fam Plann Perspect 1999; 25(2): 78-84.

[13]   Singh S, Wulf D, Samara R, Cuca Y. Gender differences in the timing of first intercourse from 14 Countries. Int Fam Plann Perspect 2000; 26(1): 21-43.

[14]   Jones AD, Jemmott ET. Child sexual abuse in the Eastern Caribbean. Barbados: UNICEF Office for Barbados and the Easern Caribbean, 2010.

[15]   Finklehor D, Araji S. A Sourcebook on child sexual abuse. Thousand Oaks, CA: Sage, 1986.

[16]   Flemming J, Mullen P, Bammer G. A study of potential risk factors for sexual abuse in childhood. Elsevier Science 1996. Accessed 2009 Mar 30. URL: http://www. sciencedirect.com/science?_ob= ArticleURL&_udi=B6V7N-3T7F1F5-5&_user=10& _origUdi=B6V7N-3VWPMP7-7&_fmt=high&_ coverDate=01%2F31%2F1997&_ rdoc=1&_orig=article&_acct=C000050221&_version=1&_urlVersion=0&_userid=10&md5=cc4d04 05df872b1df63f2ec50d035f74.

[17]   Dunn LL. Situation of children in prostitution: A rapid assessment. Geneva: International Labour Organisation, 2001. Accessed 2009 Febr 04. URL: http://www-ilomirror.cornell.edu/public/english/ standards/ipec/simpoc/jamaica/ra/prostitution.pdf.

[18]   Barrow C. Adolescent girls, sexual culture, risk and HIV in Barbados. Paper for Salises 8th Annual Conference, March 26-28 2006. Accessed 2009 Mar 30. URL http://sta.uwi.edu/conferences/salises/ documents/Barrow%20%20C.pdf

In: Child Health and Human Development Yearbook 2013   ISBN: 978-1-63117-939-6
Editor: Joav Merrick   © 2014 Nova Science Publishers, Inc.

Chapter 31

Categorization activities performed by children with intellectual disability and typically developing children

Olga Megalakaki * *and Hanan Yazbek*

Université de Picardie, Faculté de Philosophie, Sciences Humaines et Sociales,
Chemin du Thil, Amiens, France

Abstract

The purpose of this study was to explore the use of categorization strategies and the mobilization of knowledge by children with intellectual disability, compared with typically developing children matched on mental or chronological age, with regard to three knowledge domains (animals, plants and artifacts). Method: To this end, we administered a match-to-sample task, where children had to make choices and justify them. Results and conclusion: Results revealed that children with intellectual disability performed similarly to typically developing children with regard to thematic categories, but had greater difficulty mobilizing and explicitly processing taxonomic categories. Concerning the type of knowledge were mobilized to justify the choices that were made, our results suggest that the deficits observed in individuals with intellectual disability vary according to the knowledge domain, as the participants in our study had greater difficulty with the animal and artifact domains than with plants.

Keywords: Categorization, animals, plants, artifacts, children with mental disability, typically developing children

* Corresponding author: Olga Megalakaki, Université de Picardie, Faculté de Philosophie, Sciences Humaines et Sociales, Équipe CRP-CPO EA 7273, Chemin du Thil, 80025 Amiens Cedex 1, France. E-mail: olga. megalakaki@u-picardie.fr.

Introduction

Research has shown that individuals with intellectual disability have lower performances than typically developing people of the same chronological or mental age. Moreover, the greater the complexity of the cognitive processing required to complete a task, the greater the difficulty encountered by people with intellectual disability. The results of different studies tally with the idea that knowledge is organized in memory in the same way, whether or not the person has a deficiency, but that people with intellectual disability have difficulty making effective use of their knowledge in tasks that require explicit processes. Furthermore, this deficit would appear to contribute to the emergence and maintenance of their difficulty in the course of development (1,2).

It has been observed that when a task requires automatic processing of the information, the performances of people with intellectual disability are equivalent to those of people without any such intellectual disability, whereas the former perform less well when the task needs controlled attentional processing, be it verbal or strategic (1-4).

Research on categorical organization looks at the structure or function of semantic memory, and how this differs across populations. Studies have shown that individuals with intellectual disability have difficulty exploiting the categorical links between stimuli, thereby preventing them from successfully performing recall and recognition tasks (5), developing metacognitive recall strategies (6) and understanding the semantic strategies that are proposed (7). The extent of this difficulty depends on the typicality of the material used (8,9). McFarland and Sandy (7) compared the performances of adolescents with intellectual disability with those of a group of chronological age-matched, intellectually average individuals on a task in which they had to memorize semantic information using three kinds of encoding (semantic, phonetic, no indication). Adolescents with intellectual disability performed similarly to the intellectually average participants in the phonetic and no indication conditions, but less well in the semantic condition. The authors concluded that semantic representations of concepts are less elaborated in people with intellectual disability. Similarly, the results reported by Glidden et al. (6) and Winters and Semchuk (5) illustrated the difficulty that people with intellectual disability have in effectively exploring semantic links and accessing information in immediate and delayed recall tasks. Results of studies by Winters and Hoats (8) highlighted equivalent semantic memory structures when items were relatively close to the prototype and difficulties for less frequent items. More recently, Hayes and Conway (9) noticed that, in short-term memorization, the ability to encoding and storage of exemplar characteristics (based on the retrieval and activation in memory of exemplars with the greatest overall similarity to the concept being categorized) were consistently less efficient in children with intellectual disability, whatever their mental age. By way of contrast, the ability to process prototypical categories, based on the proximity of the characteristics of the element being categorized to those of the categorization prototype, seem not to depend on intellectual efficiency. In short, people with intellectual disability possess categorical knowledge, but its elaboration may be impaired.

Other authors postulate that the differences observed between individuals with and without intellectual disability arise not from the organization of knowledge in memory but rather from the assessment procedures that are used, which require too many verbal and strategic skills. This position is defended by studies reporting better performances on tasks which do not directly draw on verbal or metacognitive skills (4,10-12). For example, Landau and Hage (10) found that children with intellectual disability performed similarly on picture sorting but less well on verbal tasks. The research by Sperber et al. (11) involving adolescents with or without intellectual disability highlighted differences in performances when participants had to verbalize semantic links between items. In a semantic priming task where the categorical relations were automatically activated, participants with intellectual disability performed similarly to their intellectually average counterparts. However, when the task required them to explicitly retrieve and use categorical knowledge to justify the categories they had produced, the adolescents with intellectual disability performed less well. According to these authors, differences in the performances of people with intellectual disability should be attributed not to the organization of knowledge in memory, but rather to difficulty mobilizing that knowledge. Gavornikova-Baligand and Deleau (13) and Gavornikova-Baligand (14) also highlighted a dissociation between the categorical organization of knowledge and its mobilization. The authors observed similar performances by participants with and without intellectual disability on a forced-choice categorization task requiring no intentional processing (pointing to items), but poorer performances by the former on a task that did require intentional processing (justification of associations and a sorting task).

The above-mentioned studies show that although people with intellectual disability have semantic information stored in memory, they also have a deficit in the way that information is accessed and processed. However, they tell us little about either the nature of this deficit or the areas of knowledge that are affected by it. The present study therefore set out to investigate the categorization strategies (15,16) that are used by children and the nature of the knowledge they mobilize in semantic memory for different knowledge domains, rather than the type of processing that is undertaken.

We chose to administer a categorization task because of the important role played by this cognitive activity in the organization of the conceptual world, and because of the opportunities it offers for manipulating the structural and functional characteristics of this organization. Research on conceptual development has shown that intellectually average children categorize information using several types of categories: perceptual (objects grouped together according to their appearance, shape/color), thematic (heterogeneous objects grouped together because they belong to a particular scene or event) and taxonomic (objects of the same kind grouped according to different types of shared properties, such as name, function, etc.). However, there are different theoretical conceptions concerning the development of these different categories. The first conception views the development of categories as a succession of hierarchical steps, with a shift from thematic to slot-filler (members of the same taxonomic category for example the foods eggs and cereal are part of the eating breakfast script) and taxonomic categories (17). According to the second theoretical conception, the acquisition of categories is neither hierarchical nor age-related. Thus, children are able to access all categories at a very early age (15), but favor different categories according to the nature of the task, individual characteristics and their own familiarity with the items in the experiment (15,16). According to Rosch (18), meanwhile, taxonomic categories are formed at a very early stage, on the basis of perceptual similarity and shared properties. Thus, basic-level categories are the ones that are learned most rapidly in the course of development.

These theoretical approaches refer to intellectually average children. However, we were interested in finding out which categorization strategies are implemented by children with intellectual disability and which types of knowledge they mobilize compared with typically developing children matched on mental or chronological age. To this end, we administered a forced-choice matching test in which children had to make a first choice and justify it, then make a second choice and again justify it. We elicited two choices in order to observe the children's cross-classification abilities. We systematically manipulated three ontological domains (animals, plants and artifacts) to underscore the distinction between living and nonliving things, which plays an important role in children's conceptual organization (19). Insofar as previous studies had shown that basic-level categories are the ones that are learned most rapidly (18), we focused on the superordinate level in our study.

We sought to answer two questions: How do children with intellectual disability categorize items? and Are they able to make effective use of categories in a task involving explicit recourse to them? We compared the performances of children with mild intellectual disability with those of typically developing children matched on mental or chronological age, in terms of 1) the types of choices they made (taxonomic or thematic) for the three ontological domains (animals, plants and artifacts), 2) their cross-classification abilities, and 3) the justifications they gave for these choices in relation to the three domains.

Methods

Our sample comprised 90 children, divided into three groups. A group of 30 children with mild intellectual disability (13 girls and 17 boys), but no organic intellectual disability was recruited from a special school in Amiens (in the north of France) and matched with typically developing children on mental and chronological age (13 girls and 17 boys) in each group, recruited from schools in Amiens. The participants with intellectual disability had a mean chronological age (CA) of 12.2 years (standard deviation (SD) = 2.3), a mean IQ of 62.4 (SD = 7.3) and a mental age (MA) of 6.2 (SD = 1.3). Their diagnosis of mild intellectual disability was based on French national criteria and those of the World Health Organization (WHO). The IQ and MA measures had been made of these children within the previous 12 months, based on the Wechsler Intelligence Scale for Children (WISC-IV) (20).

The 30 typically developing children matched on chronological age had a mean CA of 12.3 (SD = 0.9) and the 30 children matched on mental age had a mean CA of 5.11 (SD =1.3). Care was taken to ensure that they had no particular delay or advance. We deemed that their mental age was equivalent to their real age. The groups were established with the preliminary agreement, teachers, parents and children.

Material

We administered a match-to-sample task, contrasting a target item with a taxonomic associate, a thematic item and a perceptual item, namely a geometric figure that was the same color as the target item (see figure 1 for an example of the picture board and appendix 1 for the list of items). We used a geometric figure associated with the target item on the basis of color as our third item in order to make it easier to distinguish between the taxonomic and thematic items, and thus observe the children's cross-classification (taxonomic and thematic) abilities. The color (or predominant color) of the target item was copied using Paint software to fill in the geometric shape. Target items belonged either to the living or the nonliving world more specifically, to one of three ontological domains: animals, plants or artifacts. We used six items for each domain, basing our selection of taxonomic associates on a superordinate level.

We began constructing the experimental material by selecting items from two databases, looking for the most familiar items for 6-year-old children. We took identification and naming frequency into account for the BD2I database (21) and lexical frequency for MANULEX (22). The target items and their taxonomic associates in the animal domain were mammals (e.g., a dog and a giraffe). In the plant domain, they were flowers and trees (e.g., a daffodil and a tulip), and in the artifact domain, they were pieces of furniture (e.g., a bed and a bench). The thematic items were artifacts, places (e.g., a zoo and a circus) or natural things (a forest). We then tested the set of taxonomic and thematic associates we had chosen in order to make sure that the children would recognize them. In the pretest, each potential target was presented with either a taxonomic or a thematic associate, plus two items that were unrelated to the target. For each potential target, we therefore constructed eight boards (four with taxonomic associates and four with thematic associates) and the children (fifteen 5-6 year-olds and 15 children with intellectual disability of a different structure from the one we investigated in our experiment) had to say which item "went" with the target on each board. We then selected the associations that received the highest number of correct responses (approx. 75%). In order to determine the strength of association between targets and associates (taxonomic or thematic), we carried out an assessment task. Each target item was presented alongside three different taxonomic or thematic associates (those which had most often been recognized as associates by the children in the pretest). In random order, 30 first-year psychology students were asked to rate the strength of association of each pair on a 7-point scale ranging from 1 (no association at all) to 7 (very strong association). We retained those items that had been given equivalent ratings (4 to 6 points) as our taxonomic and thematic associates.

Figure 1. An example of the match-to-sample task.

A repeated-measures analysis of variance (ANOVA) was conducted (based on MANULEX lexical frequencies) to check the homogeneity of the target items and their taxonomic and thematic associates. This analysis failed to reveal any significant difference between the items. The resulting material consisted of 18 picture boards. The order of presentation of the target items was counterbalanced. The location of the taxonomic associates on the boards was also counterbalanced, resulting in the construction of six sets of 18 boards. For each version of the game, we used a separate form to record the items that were selected, together with their respective justifications.

Procedure

We conducted individual interviews lasting approximately 20 minutes. Interviews were recorded and transcribed, with the addition of the experimenter's notes. Children were tested in a quiet room at their school. One of the six versions, with its corresponding form for noting the choices, was selected at random. The experimenter asked the child to name the target item, then decide which of the other three pictures "went best" with the target item, emphasizing that there was no wrong answer. We deliberately used neutral instructions in order to avoid influencing the children's choices. The child was then asked to justify his or her choice: "Why did you put them together?" Once the first choice had been made, the experimenter asked the child to choose between the two remaining pictures and once more justify his or her choice.

Table 1. Data coding categories and criteria for attribution

Coding categories	Criteria for category attribution	Examples
Other	The child does not justify his or her choice, or the justification does not fit any of our coding categories.	*Because*
Perceptual	The justification refers to color, shape and/or physical attributes.	*They are the same color.* *They both have leaves.* *They both have paws.*
Spatiotemporal	Items are matched on the basis of a spatial and/or temporal link.	*The dog lives in the house.* *We can see horses and bears at the zoo.*
Functional	Items are linked by their functionality (what they are for).	*The bed goes with the little boy because the bed is for sleeping.*
Category membership	The child names the category to which the chosen items belong (animals, plants, artifacts).	*The dog goes with the giraffe because they are are both animals.*
Biological Properties	The items share the same biological property.	*The dog goes with the giraffe because they both eat.* *The daffodil goes with the tulip because they both grow.*

Coding criteria and data analysis

The children's first choices were coded according to whether the matches were taxonomic, thematic or perceptual. We coded the second choices in the form of response patterns, which simultaneously took both choices into account. There were therefore six possible patterns: Taxonomic-Thematic, Taxonomic-Perceptual, Thematic-Taxonomic, Thematic-Perceptual, Perceptual-Taxonomic and Perceptual-Thematic. We created a number of categories for coding the justifications (for coding categories, see Table 1). Our data were coded by two independent examiners and interrater agreement was 95%. All disagreements were discussed and resolved. For the statistical analysis, we conducted a repeated-measures ANOVA to compare the children's first choices and response patterns, and a chi-square analysis to compare their justifications.

Results

Type of first choice (taxonomic, thematic or perceptual)

For the first choice, when all three ontological domains were taken together, there was an interaction effect between type of choice and group, $F(4, 174) = 11.211$, $p < .05$. Overall, the typically developing children in the chronological age (CA) group made more taxonomic choices, $F(1, 87) = 26.757$, $p < .05$, and fewer perceptual choices, $F(1, 87) = 40.277$, $p < .05$, than the children in the other two groups. We did not observe any difference between the children with intellectual disability (IDC) and the typically developing children in the mental age (MA) group on taxonomic and perceptual choices. In general, the majority of choices made by the three populations were thematic and did not differ significantly (see figure 2). When ontological domains were considered separately, we found an interaction between type of first choice and group for each of the three domains (Animal: $F(4, 174) = 4.267$, $p < .05$, Plant: $F(4, 174) = 14.173$, $p < .05$, Artifacts: $F(4, 174) = 7.186$, $p < .05$). For all three domains, the children in the CA group made more taxonomic choices than the children in the other two groups, who did not differ significantly (Animal: $F(1, 87) = 10.776$, $p < .05$, Plant: $F(1, 87) = 32.159$, $p < .05$, Artifacts: $F(1, 87) = 11.361$, $p < .05$). All three groups made equivalent numbers of thematic choices for the animal and plant domains. For the artifact domain, however, the children in the CA group made more thematic choices than the children in the other two groups, $F(1, 87) = 6.898$, $p < .05$). The CA group also made fewer perceptual choices for the animal and artifact domains than the other two groups, who did not differ significantly (Animal: $F(1, 87) = 14.765$, $p < .05$, Artifacts: $F(1, 87) = 21.578$, $p < .05$). For the plant domain the MA group made more perceptual choices than the other two groups, who did not differ significantly ($F(1, 87) = 49.174$, $p < .05$) (see figure 3).

Type of second choice in relation to the first one

An analysis of results revealed an interaction between response pattern and group, $F(5, 435) = 9.09$, $p < .05$. Generally speaking, the Taxonomic-Thematic and Thematic-Taxonomic patterns, which showed that the children were capable of undertaking cross-classification for a given target, were less frequently observed in the IDC and MA groups, who produced more Perceptual-Thematic patterns than the CA group (see figure 4).

When ontological domain was taken into account, there was a triple interaction between domain, response pattern and group, $F(20, 870) = 3.06$, $p < .05$. For each of the three domains (animals, plants, artifacts), the Taxonomic-Thematic and Thematic-Taxonomic patterns were less frequent among the children in the IDC and MA groups, who tended to produce the Thematic-Perceptual and Perceptual-Thematic patterns, than among those in the CA group (see figure 4).

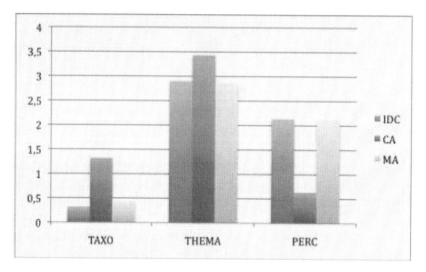

Figure 2. Mean number of Choice 1 matches made by children with intellectual disability (IDC) and children matched on mental age (MA) or chronological age (CA).

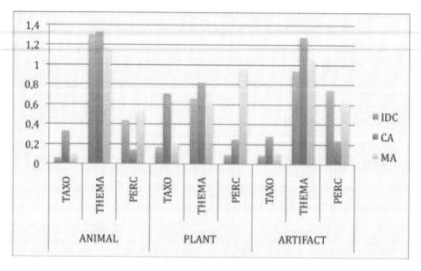

Figure 3. Mean number of Choice 1 matches made by children with intellectual disability (IDC) and children matched on mental age (MA) or chronological age (CA), according to ontological domain.

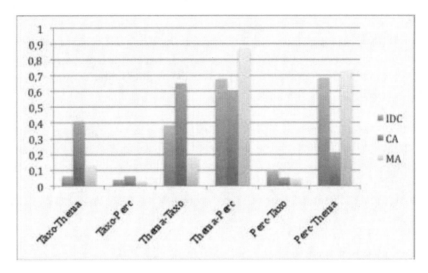

Figure 4. Mean number of patterns produced by children with intellectual disability (IDC) and children matched on mental age (MA) or chronological age (CA).

Nature of the justifications given by children for the three ontological domains

The children's justifications were analyzed in order to see whether there was any coherence between choices and justifications. For the taxonomic choices we consider the categories: "category membership" and "biological properties" as more advanced than others and showing the coherence between choices and justifications. To this end, we coded justifications given for taxonomic and thematic choices separately, according to each of our coding categories (see table 1 for a description of coding categories).

The justifications given for first and second choices were considered together (see table 2). We did not analyze the justifications for perceptual choices, as most of them concerned color.

We found a significant difference between the groups in the justifications they gave for taxonomic choices in the Animal domain, $X^2(8) = 123.189$; $p < .0001$. To justify their taxonomic choices, the children with intellectual disability made more frequent references to biological properties (IDC: 35%, CA: 8%, MA: 11.5%) and to the shared perceptual characteristics of the selected items (30%), whereas the two groups of typically developing children mainly cited category membership (CA: 78.4%, MA: 49.2%, IDC: 15%). All three groups alluded to spatiotemporal links (IDC: 16.6%, CA: 8% and MA: 27.5%). In justifications of thematic choices in the Animal domain, we again found significant differences between the groups, $X^2(4) = 50.502$; $p < .001$. Thematic choices were justified mainly by item functionality by the children with intellectual disability (IDC: 67.6%, CA: 35.7%, MA: 39.3%) and mainly by spatiotemporal links by the typically developing children (CA: 64.1%, MA: 58.9%, IDC: 29.4%).

The analysis of justifications of taxonomic choices for the Plant domain revealed a significant effect of group, $X^2(6) = 39.162$; $p < .001$. Children matched on mental age justified their taxonomic choices mainly by referring to category membership than the two other groups (who did not differ significantly) (CA: 90.8%, IDC: 80.6%, MA: 64.1%). Children in all three groups also cited biological properties (IDC: 14.7%, CA: 9.17%, MA: 9.7%). We did not find any significant differences between the groups for justifications of thematic choices in the Plant domain, $X^2(6) = 10.817$; ns. In all three groups, thematic choices were justified mainly by item functionality (approximately 84%).

For the Artifact domain, there was a significant different between the groups in their justifications for taxonomic choices, $X^2(8) = 108.571$; p < .0001. These were mainly justified by item functionality by the children with intellectual disability and children matched on mental age (55.3% and 58.8%, respectively) and by category membership by the children matched on chronological age (77.9%). For justifications of thematic choices, we also observed a significant difference between the groups, $X^2(4)= 46.28$; p < .001. The majority of children in the IDC and MA groups referred to item functionality (80% for both groups), whereas the children in the CA group justified their choices on the basis of either item functionality (60.4%) or spatiotemporal links (39.5%).

Table 2. Frequency and (percentage) of justifications given for taxonomic and thematic choices (Choices 1+2) by children with intellectual disability (IDC) and children matched on mental age (MA) or chronological age (CA) for each ontological domain (animals, plants, artifacts)

Categories	JUSTIFICATIONS of TAXONOMIC CHOICES (1+2)								
	IDC	CA	MA	IDC	CA	MA	IDC	CA	MA
	ANIMALS			PLANTS			ARTIFACTS		
Other	2 (5)	7 (5.6)	8 (11.5)	1 (1.1)	-	14 (15.2)	9 (13.8)	-	5 (7.3)
Perceptual	18 (30)	-	-	3 (3.4)	-	6 (6.5)	4 (6.1)	-	2 (2.9)
Spatiotemporal	10 (16.6)	10 (8)	19 (27.53)	-	-	-	7 (10.7)	9 (6.6)	6 (8.8)
Function	-	-	-	-	-	-	36 (55.3)	21 (15.4)	40 (58.8)
Category membership	9 (15)	98 (78.4)	34 (49.2)	71 (80.6)	99 (90.8)	59 (64.1)	9 (13.8)	106 (77.9)	15 (22)
Biological property	21 (35)	10 (8)	8 (11.5)	13 (14.7)	10 (9.17)	13 (9.7)	-	-	-
TOTAL	60/ 360*	125/ 360	69/ 360	88/ 360	109/360	92/ 360	65/3 60	136/ 360	68/ 360
JUSTIFICATIONS of THEMATIC CHOICES (1+2)									
Other	5 (2.8)	-	3 (1.7)	8 (5.4)	3 (1.59)	9 (6.1)	4 (2.5)	-	10 (6.1)
Spatiotemporal	51 (29.4)	111 (64.1)	99 (58.9)	4 (2.7)	10 (5.3)	10 (6.8)	27 (16.8)	66 (39.5)	21 (12.9)
Function	117 (67.6)	62 (35.8)	66 (39.2)	126 (85.1)	169 (89.8)	122 (83.5)	129 (80.6)	101 (60.4)	131 (80.8)
Biological property	-	-	-	10 (6.7)	6 (3.1)	5 (3.4)	-	-	-
TOTAL	173/ 360	173/ 360	168/ 360	148/ 360	188/ 360	146/ 360	160/ 360	167/ 360	162/ 360

* 6 animals x 30 children x 2 choices = 360.

Discussion

The aim of this research was to study categorization strategies and mobilization of knowledge in relation to three ontological domains (animals, plants, artifacts), by analyzing the types of matching choices (taxonomic and thematic) and their justifications given by children with intellectual disability, comparing the latter with typically developing children matched on mental or chronological age.

The results for first choices showed that children with intellectual disability performed similarly to both groups of typically developing children for thematic choices (the predominant choice). The IDC and MA groups performed similarly, but less well, than the CA group for taxonomic choices, making more perceptual choices instead.

An analysis of the response patterns that simultaneously took both the first and second choices into account showed that all the children were capable of undertaking cross-classification for a given target as all of them were able to make two choices, albeit in different proportions. However, if we consider the patterns taxonomic/thematic and thematic/taxonomic, as the most developed, we observe that the IDC group performed similarly to the MA group but less well than the CA group. The patterns thematic/perceptual and perceptual/thematic are the most present in the IDC group and in the MA group.

The analysis of justifications for taxonomic and thematic choices revealed differences between the three groups of children. The CA group cited category membership to justify their taxonomic choices for the animal and artifact domains more often than the other two groups. However, there were no differences between the IDC and CA groups in their justifications of taxonomic choices for the plant domain, with both groups mainly citing category membership. The IDC group tended to use item functionality to justify their thematic choices for the animal and artifact domains, whereas the typically developing children also mentioned spatiotemporal links. In the case of the plant domain, all the children justified their thematic choices by referring to item functionality.

In line with previous studies, we observed lower performances by children with intellectual disability when they were required to explicitly retrieve and use categorical knowledge to justify the taxonomic choices they had made (10,13). This suggests that they had greater difficulty extracting the conceptual invariants needed to mobilize the categories. If we assume that taxonomic categories are abstractions from the perceived world and are based on interpretive representations of relations between objects, mobilizing high-level cognitive processes, our results suggest that children with intellectual disability have difficulty mobilizing these categories, which require a higher level of abstraction and conceptualization than thematic categories. Thus, the present results corroborate previous findings showing that people with intellectual disability have difficulty processing semantic information (7) or perform less well when tasks are explicit or controlled (1,3,11,14).

The higher number of taxonomic choices made by the CA group and their use of category membership to justify these choices showed that they had fully mastered these categories and found it easy to mobilize them in a task involving explicit recourse to them.

The fact that the children matched on mental age were able to make taxonomic choices shows that these categories are available even to young children and thus supports the pluralist theory of categorical development for typically developing children (15,16). The preference for thematic choices displayed by all three groups has already been reported in studies with typically developing children and has been attributed either to individual preferences or to task characteristics (16, 23) and strength of association (24).

Our analysis of justifications yielded additional information about the nature of the differences we had observed. Results showed that there was often no coherence between choices and justifications, especially in the case of taxonomic choices. Like other authors (25) we noticed that a choice classified as "taxonomic" could be justified "thematically", by referring to spatiotemporal links between the chosen items (e.g., "we see horses and bears at the zoo"). In this case, we can conclude that the choice was not a genuine taxonomic one. Similarly, a "thematic" choice could be justified by citing the item's biological properties (e.g., "the flower goes with the watering can because it needs water to grow"). This lack of coherence between choices and justifications shows that, in the absence of justifications, we cannot know the true nature of a choice. It is therefore difficult to identify the basis on which children categorize and, consequently, to draw inferences about the underlying mobilization of their knowledge. Furthermore, according to Tulving's model of semantic memory (26), the organization of knowledge relies on abstract semantic links between the concepts, and the quality of these links depends directly on the quality of the processing.

Thus, the analysis of justifications of taxonomic choices yielded more specific information concerning the verbalization of the semantic links between the items and highlighted differences between the justifications given by the three groups, though more so for the animal and artifact domains than for plants. For the latter, the responses of the children with intellectual disability were similar to those of the typically developing children matched on chronological age. For the Animal domain, the IDC group relied more on observable biological properties or physical attributes to justify matching ("the dog and the giraffe both eat" or "the mouse goes with the rabbit because they both grow", or "they both have paws"), whereas the typically developing children mentioned category membership ("the dog goes goes with the giraffe because they are both animals"). It may be that children with intellectual disability more readily mobilize information based on visible properties and find it harder to make the abstractions needed to mobilize taxonomic categories, as defined by Nelson (17). This would make memory retrieval more costly and could partly explain the difficulties they encounter in tasks requiring the explicit processing of information. For their part, typically developing children can more readily mobilize overall concepts, by performing the abstractions needed to include several exemplars within the same category. This interpretation would appear to support previous results showing that the differences observed between people with intellectual disability and intellectually average individuals concern the way in which knowledge is organized in memory (5-9). Similarly, for Artifacts, the analysis of justifications showed that the CA group mainly cited category membership to justify their taxonomic choices, whereas the IDC and MA groups justified all their choices thematically, whether they were taxonomic or thematic, citing item functionality. These results are in line with those reported by other authors for typically developing young children, showing that artifacts are viewed in terms of their functional characteristics and living things in terms of their biological properties (27). We also noticed differences between the populations in their justifications of thematic choices for the animal domain. The IDC group referred more often to the functionality of the items they had chosen, explaining the purpose of each object, whereas both groups of typically developing children took a more general view, basing their justifications on spatiotemporal links.

For Plants, there were fewer differences in the justifications given by the three populations for taxonomic and thematic choices. Children with intellectual disability and children matched on chronological age provided similar justifications for their taxonomic choices, mainly citing the items' category membership ("the daisy and the lily-of-the-valley are plants"). In the same way, all the children tended to justify their thematic choices by referring to item functionality. Accordingly, our results suggest that semantic links in the Plant domain were mobilized in a similar way by both children with intellectual disability and typically developing children. In this particular instance, the need for verbal skills and explicit processing proved less of a hindrance to the mobilization of information. These results contradict previous findings suggesting that poor verbal and strategic skills can, in themselves, explain deficits observed in people with intellectual disability (4,11,12,14). Thus, our observations suggest that the deficit varies according to the knowledge domain being studied. This is an interesting finding, especially as we know that it is difficult to acquire the Plant domain because of it particular status (perceptual markers for attributing biological mechanisms, such as movement, breathing, etc., are not directly accessible) (28).

Conclusion

On the basis of previous studies showing that people with or without intellectual disability perform similarly on tasks calling for automatic retrieval processes, it has been inferred that knowledge is organized in a relatively similar way in both populations. The difficulties displayed by children with intellectual disability have thus been attributed to attentional processes governing access to knowledge and the way in which this knowledge is then mobilized (8,12). Our results support this interpretation and go one step further, by showing that these differences vary according to category (taxonomic or thematic) and knowledge domain. Our study recorded equivalent performances by children with intellectual disability and typically developing children matched on mental or chronological age on the mobilization and processing of thematic categories. Insofar as this type of conceptual organization is based on contextual information that is readily available in the environment, our results suggest that the knowledge subtending thematic classification is mobilized in a similar way by both populations. Throughout the experiment, however, the children with intellectual disability had greater difficulty justifying their taxonomic choices, revealing a deficit in mobilizing and explicitly processing taxonomic categories, which reflect the organization of semantic information in memory. In line with previous findings (5-9), this result suggests that people with intellectual disability have difficulty implementing efficient information processing strategies. Our results show that the extent of this deficit depends on the knowledge domain being probed, as the participants in our study had greater difficulty with the animal and artifact domains than with plants. For animals, children with intellectual disability more readily mobilized shared biological properties and physical attributes, whereas the typically developing children cited category membership more often. However we have to mention the limitations of our study as we have not control the verbal ability of the participants. Nonetheless, we believe that the introduction of categorization activities in different knowledge domains would allow for more tailored interventions, drawing on recipients' potential in order to help them to construct more abstract knowledge which could then be transferred to other domains and other situations. This is the goal we are currently pursuing, through the design of categorization activities intended to promote the learning of a certain number of concepts and help children with intellectual disability realize their full potential.

Appendix. List of items in the match-to-sample task

	Target items	**Taxonomic**	**Thematic**	**Perceptual**
ANIMALS	Brown dog	Giraffe	Kennel	Brown circle
	White horse	Bear	Saddle	White lozenge
	Orange lion	Cow	Circus	Orange parallelogram
	Gray rabbit	Mouse	Cage	Gray square
	Brown monkey	Cat	Zoo	Brown trapezoid
	Gray elephant	Pig	Forest	Gray triangle
PLANTS*	White and orange daisy	Houseplant	Vase	Orange parallelogram
	Daffodil	Tulip	Garden spade	Yellow square
	Pink rosebush	Poppy	Watering can	Pink square
	Cherry tree	Lemon tree	Basket	Red triangle
	Target items	Taxonomic	Thematic	Perceptual
	Appletree	Fir tree	Ladder	Red trapezoid
	Banana palm	Oak	Rake	Yellow lozenge
ARTIFACTS	Yellow bed	Bench	Boy	Yellow parallelogram
	Green bookcase	Armchair	Book	Green circle
	Brown desk	Sideboard	Notebook	Brown triangle
	Gray table	Shelf	Plate	Gray square
	Blue wardrobe	Stool	Coat hanger	Blue trapezoid
	Pink sofa	Chair	Cushion	Pink lozenge

* The fruit trees were shown bearing fruit.

References

[1]   Vicari S, Bellucci S, Carlesimo GA. Implicit and explicit memory: A functional dissociation in persons with Down's syndrome. Neuropsychologia 2000; 38: 240–51.

[2]   Atwell JA, Conners FA, Merrill EC. Implicit and explicit learning in young adults with mental retardation. Am J Ment Retard 2003: 108, 56–68.

[3]   Ellis NR, Woodley-Zanthos P, Dulaney CL. Memory for spatial location in children, adults, and mentally retarded persons. Am J Ment Retard 1989: 93: 521-7.

[4]   Bebko JM, Luhaorg H. The development of strategy use and metacognitive processing in mental retardation: Some sources of difficulty. In: Burack JA, Hodapp RM, Zigler E, eds. Handbook of mental retardation and development Cambridge: Cambridge University Press, 1998: 382–407.

[5]   Winters JJ, Semchuk MT. Retrieval from long-term store as a function of mental age and intelligence. Am J Ment Deficiency 1986; 90: 440-8.

[6]   Glidden LM, Bilsky LH, Mar HH, Judd TP, Warner DA. Semantic processing can facilitate free recall in mildly retarded adolescents. J Exp Child Psychol 1983; 36: 510-32.

[7]   McFarland CE, Sandy JT. Automatic and conscious processing in retarded and nonretarded adolescents. J Exp Child Psychol 1982; 33: 20-38.

[8]   Winters JJ, Hoats DL. Comparison of verbal typicality judgments of mentally retarded and nonretarded persons. Am J Ment Deficiency 1986; 90: 335-41.

[9]   Hayes BK, Conway RN. Concept acquisition in children with mild intellectual disability: Factors affecting the abstraction of prototypical information. J Intellect Dev Disabil 2000; 25: 217-34.

[10]   Landau BL, Hage JW. The effect of verbal cues on concept acquisition and retention in normal and educable mentally retarded children. Child Dev 1974; 45: 643-50.

[11]   Sperber RD, Ragain RD, McCauley C. Reassessment of category knowledge in retarded individuals. Am J Ment Deficiency 1976; 81: 227-34.

[12]   Sperber RD, McCauley C. Semantic processing efficiency in the mentally retarded. In: Brooks P, Sperber R, McCauley C, eds. Learning and cognition in the mentally retarded, Hillsdale, NJ: Erlbaum, 1984: 141–63.

[13]   Gavornikova-Baligand Z, Deleau M. La catégorisation chez les adultes déficients intellectuels: Déficit de structuration ou de mobilisation? Revue Francophone de la Déficience Intellectuelle 2004; 15 : 5-21. [French]

[14]   Gavornikova-Baligand, Z. Catégories implicites, catégories explicites et déficience intellectuelle. Enfance 2005; 57: 253-60. [French]

[15]   Bauer PJ, Mandler JM. Taxonomies and triads: Conceptual organization in one-to two-year-olds. Cogn Psychol 1989; 21: 156-84.

[16]   Kalénine S, Garnier C, Bouisson K, Bonthoux F. Le développement de la catégorisation: L'impact différencié de deux types d'apprentissage en fonction des catégories d'objets, naturels ou fabriqués. Psychologie et Éducation 2007; 1: 33-45. [French]

[17]   Nelson K. Making sense: The acquisition of shared meaning. New York: Academic Press, 1985.

[18]   Rosch E. Principles of categorization. In: Rosch E, Lloyd BB, eds. Cognition and categorization. Hillsdale, NJ, Erlbaum, 1978: 21-48.

[19]   Gelman SA, Opfer JE. Development of the animate-inanimate distinction. In: Goswami U, ed. Handbook of childhood cognitive development. Malden, MA: Blackwell, 2002: 151-66.

[20]   Wechsler D. Wechsler Intelligence Scale for Children (WISC IV). Paris: ECPA, 2005.

[21]   Cannard C, Bonthoux F, Blaye A, Scheuner N, Schreiber AC, Trinquart J. BD2I: Normes sur l'identification de 274 images d'objets et leur mise en relation chez l'enfant français de 3 à 8 ans. L'Année Psychologique 2006; 106: 375-96. [French]

[22]   Lété B, Sprenger-Charolles L, Colé P. Manulex: A grade-level lexical database from French elementary-school readers. Behav Res Methods Instruments Computers 2004; 36: 166-76.

[23]   Megalakaki O, Yasbek H, Fouquet N. Activités de catégorisation chez les enfants déficients intellectuels légers et les enfants tout-venant appariés par âge mental. Neuropsychiatrie de l'Enfance et de l'Adolescence 2010; 58: 317-26. [French]

[24]   Scheuner N, Bonthoux F, Cannard C, Blaye A. The role of associative strength and conceptual relations in matching tasks in 4- and 6-year-old children. Int J Psychol 2004; 39: 290-304.

[25]   Lucariello,J, Kyratzis A, Nelson K. Taxonomic knowledge: What kind and when? Child Dev 1992; 63: 978–98.

[26]   Tulving, E. Episodic and semantic memory. In: Tulving E, Donaldson W, eds. Organization of memory. New York: Academic Press, 1972: 381-403.

[27]   Grief ML, Kemler Nelson DG, Keil FC, Gutierrez F. What do children want to know about animals and artifacts? Psychol Sci 2006; 17: 455-9.

[28]   Inagaki K, Hatano G. Young children's recognition of commonalities between animals and plants. Child Dev 1996; 67: 2823–40.

Section four – Acknowledgments

In: Child Health and Human Development Yearbook 2013   ISBN: 978-1-63117-939-6
Editor: Joav Merrick   © 2014 Nova Science Publishers, Inc.

Chapter 32

About the editor

Joav Merrick, MD, MMedSci, DMSc, is professor of pediatrics, child health and human development affiliated with Kentucky Children's Hospital, University of Kentucky, Lexington, United States and the Division of Pediatrics, Hadassah Hebrew University Medical Center, Mt Scopus Campus, Jerusalem, Israel, the medical director of the Health Services, Division for Intellectual and Developmental Disabilities, Ministry of Social Affairs and Social Services, Jerusalem, the founder and director of the National Institute of Child Health and Human Development in Israel. Numerous publications in the field of pediatrics, child health and human development, rehabilitation, intellectual disability, disability, health, welfare, abuse, advocacy, quality of life and prevention. Received the Peter Sabroe Child Award for outstanding work on behalf of Danish Children in 1985 and the International LEGO-Prize ("The Children's Nobel Prize") for an extraordinary contribution towards improvement in child welfare and well-being in 1987.

Contact:
Office of the Medical Director, Health Services, Division for Intellectual and Developmental Disabilities, Ministry of Social Affairs and Social Services, POB 1290, IL-91012 Jerusalem,Israel.
E-mail: jmerrick@zahav.net.il

In: Child Health and Human Development Yearbook 2013   ISBN: 978-1-63117-939-6
Editor: Joav Merrick   © 2014 Nova Science Publishers, Inc.

Chapter 33

About the National Institute of Child Health and Human Development in Israel

The National Institute of Child Health and Human Development (NICHD) in Israel was established in 1998 as a virtual institute under the auspicies of the Medical Director, Ministry of Social Affairs and Social Services in order to function as the research arm for the Office of the Medical Director. In 1998 the National Council for Child Health and Pediatrics, Ministry of Health and in 1999 the Director General and Deputy Director General of the Ministry of Health endorsed the establishment of the NICHD.

Mission

The mission of a National Institute for Child Health and Human Development in Israel is to provide an academic focal point for the scholarly interdisciplinary study of child life, health, public health, welfare, disability, rehabilitation, intellectual disability and related aspects of human development. This mission includes research, teaching, clinical work, information and public service activities in the field of child health and human development.

Service and academic activities

Over the years many activities became focused in the south of Israel due to collaboration with various professionals at the Faculty of Health Sciences (FOHS) at the Ben Gurion University of the Negev (BGU). Since 2000 an affiliation with the Zusman Child Development Center at the Pediatric Division of Soroka University Medical Center has resulted in collaboration around the establishment of the Down Syndrome Clinic at that center. In 2002 a full course on "Disability" was established at the Recanati School for Allied Professions in the Community, FOHS, BGU and in 2005 collaboration was started with the Primary Care Unit of the faculty and disability became part of the master of public health course on "Children and society". In the academic year 2005-2006 a one semester course on "Aging with disability" was started as part of the master of science program in gerontology in our collaboration with the Center for Multidisciplinary Research in Aging. In 2010 collaborations with the Division of Pediatrics, Hadassah Medical Center, Hebrew University, Jerusalem, Israel.

Research activities

The affiliated staff have over the years published work from projects and research activities in this national and international collaboration. In the year 2000 the International Journal of Adolescent Medicine and Health and in 2005 the International Journal on Disability and Human development of De Gruyter Publishing House (Berlin and New York), in the year 2003 the TSW-Child Health and Human Development and in 2006 the TSW-Holistic Health and Medicine of the Scientific World Journal (New York and Kirkkonummi, Finland), all peer-reviewed international journals were affiliated with the National Institute of Child Health and Human Development. From 2008 also the International Journal of Child Health and Human Development (Nova Science, New York), the International Journal of Child and Adolescent Health (Nova Science) and the Journal of Pain Management (Nova Science) affiliated and from 2009 the International Public Health Journal (Nova Science) and Journal of Alternative Medicine Research (Nova Science).

National collaborations

Nationally the NICHD works in collaboration with the Faculty of Health Sciences, Ben Gurion University of the Negev; Department of Physical Therapy, Sackler School of Medicine, Tel Aviv University; Autism Center, Assaf HaRofeh Medical Center; National Rett and PKU Centers at Chaim Sheba Medical Center, Tel HaShomer; Department of Physiotherapy, Haifa University; Department of Education, Bar Ilan University, Ramat Gan, Faculty of Social Sciences and Health Sciences; College of Judea and Samaria in Ariel and in 2011 affiliation with Center for Pediatric Chronic Diseases and Center for Down Syndrome, Department of Pediatrics, Hadassah-Hebrew University Medical Center, Mount Scopus Campus, Jerusalem.

International collaborations

Internationally with the Department of Disability and Human Development, College of Applied Health Sciences, University of Illinois at Chicago; Strong Center for Developmental Disabilities, Golisano Children's Hospital at Strong, University of Rochester School of Medicine and Dentistry, New York; Centre on Intellectual Disabilities, University of Albany, New York; Centre for Chronic Disease Prevention and Control, Health Canada, Ottawa; Chandler Medical Center and Children's Hospital, Kentucky Children's Hospital, Section of Adolescent Medicine, University of Kentucky, Lexington; Chronic Disease Prevention and

Control Research Center, Baylor College of Medicine, Houston, Texas; Division of Neuroscience, Department of Psychiatry, Columbia University, New York; Institute for the Study of Disadvantage and Disability, Atlanta; Center for Autism and Related Disorders, Department Psychiatry, Children's Hospital Boston, Boston; Department of Paediatrics, Child Health and Adolescent Medicine, Children's Hospital at Westmead, Westmead, Australia; International Centre for the Study of Occupational and Mental Health, Düsseldorf, Germany; Centre for Advanced Studies in Nursing, Department of General Practice and Primary Care, University of Aberdeen, Aberdeen, United Kingdom; Quality of Life Research Center, Copenhagen, Denmark; Nordic School of Public Health, Gottenburg, Sweden, Scandinavian Institute of Quality of Working Life, Oslo, Norway; Centre for Quality of Life of the Hong Kong Institute of Asia-Pacific Studies and School of Social Work, Chinese University, Hong Kong.

Targets

Our focus is on research, international collaborations, clinical work, teaching and policy in health, disability and human development and to establish the NICHD as a permanent institute at one of the residential care centers for persons with intellectual disability in Israel in order to conduct model research and together with the four university schools of public health/medicine in Israel establish a national master and doctoral program in disability and human development at the institute to secure the next generation of professionals working in this often non-prestigious/low-status field of work.

Contact
Joav Merrick, MD, DMSc
Professor of Pediatrics, Child Health and Human Development
Medical Director, Health Services, Division for Intellectual and Developmental Disabilities, Ministry of Social Affairs and Social Services, POB 1260, IL-91012 Jerusalem, Israel.
E-mail: jmerrick@inter.net.il

In: Child Health and Human Development Yearbook 2013   ISBN: 978-1-63117-939-6
Editor: Joav Merrick   © 2014 Nova Science Publishers, Inc.

Chapter 34

About the book series "Pediatrics, child and adolescent health"

Pediatrics, child and adolescent health is a book series with publications from a multidisciplinary group of researchers, practitioners and clinicians for an international professional forum interested in the broad spectrum of pediatric medicine, child health, adolescent health and human development.

- Merrick J, ed. Child and adolescent health yearbook 2011. New York: Nova Science, 2012.
- Merrick J, ed. Child and adolescent health yearbook 2012. New York: Nova Science, 2012.
- Roach RR, Greydanus DE, Patel DR, Homnick DN, Merrick J, eds. Tropical pediatrics: A public health concern of international proportions. New York: Nova Science, 2012.
- Merrick J, ed. Child health and human development yearbook 2011. New York: Nova Science, 2012.
- Merrick J, ed. Child health and human development yearbook 2012. New York: Nova Science, 2012.
- Shek DTL, Sun RCF, Merrick J, eds. Developmental issues in Chinese adolescents. New York: Nova Science, 2012.
- Shek DTL, Sun RCF, Merrick J, eds. Positive youth development: Theory, research and application. New York: Nova Science, 2012.
- Zachor DA, Merrick J, eds. Understanding autism spectrum disorder: Current research aspects. New York: Nova Science, 2012.
- Ma HK, Shek DTL, Merrick J, eds. Positive youth development: A new school curriculum to tackle adolescent developmental issues. New York: Nova Science, 2012.
- Wood D, Reiss JG, Ferris ME, Edwards LR, Merrick J, eds. Transition from pediatric to adult medical care. New York: Nova Science, 2012.

CONTACT
Professor Joav Merrick, MD, MMedSci, DMSc
Medical Director, Medical Services
Division for Intellectual and Developmental Disabilities
Ministry of Social Affairs and Social Services
POBox 1260, IL-91012 Jerusalem, Israel
E-mail: jmerrick@zahav.net.il

Index

A

abstraction, 443, 447
abuse, 56, 57, 76, 77, 132, 156, 163, 168, 176, 261, 451
academic growth, 310
academic performance, 10, 97, 98, 105, 144
academic success, 120
access, xii, 70, 122, 165, 179, 194, 199, 211, 239, 249, 281, 320, 323, 325, 328, 350, 354, 371, 406, 407, 421, 435, 445
accessibility, 186, 260
accommodation, 349, 350
accounting, 196, 276
acid, 225, 226
acquaintance, 254
acute lymphoblastic leukemia, 412
AD, 162, 325, 430
adaptation, 40, 49, 52, 263, 295, 421
Addiction Severity Index (ASI), 150
ADHD, 165, 181
adjustment, vii, 16, 30, 44, 47, 69, 71, 76, 77, 78, 98, 105, 146, 150, 157, 160, 162, 167, 194, 413, 421
Administration for Children and Families, 271
administrative support, 263
adolescent adjustment, 80
adolescent behavior, 114, 116, 132
Adolescent Behavior Questionnaire, 112, 118, 122, 128
adolescent boys, 180
adolescent development, xi, 40, 53, 69, 70, 71, 72, 77, 78, 79, 80, 81, 94, 96, 187, 194, 271, 457
adolescent female, 423, 428, 429
adolescent problem behavior, 37, 53, 81, 93, 97, 182, 186, 196
adult learning, 271
adult literacy, 202, 204, 208

adulthood, 23, 37, 52, 108, 111, 123, 152, 187, 196, 295, 426
adults, 16, 77, 96, 111, 123, 133, 166, 182, 195, 200, 286, 287, 291, 292, 295, 296, 302, 344, 349, 446
advancement, 121, 321
adverse conditions, 31, 34, 45, 101
adverse effects, 56, 79, 146
advertisements, 336
advocacy, 451
affective disorder, 146
affirming, 309
Africa, 320, 325, 344, 351
African-American, 71, 80, 337, 340, 341, 415
agencies, 36, 164, 179
aggregation, 372
aggression, 52, 55, 59, 60, 61, 62, 64, 65, 70, 132, 135, 138, 139, 140, 252, 291, 292, 293
aggressive behavior, 36, 51, 64, 65, 112, 122, 291
aggressiveness, 133
agonist, 302
agriculture, 229, 250
AIDS, 80, 424
alcohol abuse, 147, 157, 160, 162, 166
alcohol consumption, 105, 161
alcohol dependence, 146
alcohol problems, 148
alcohol use, 146, 161, 425
alcoholism, xiii
Algeria, 221, 222, 226, 227, 228
algorithm, 271
allele, 274
alters, 261
altruistic acts, 112, 122
altruistic behavior, 108, 120
AME, 325
American Psychiatric Association, 167
American Psychological Association, 316
amino, 227

amino acid(s), 227
amniocentesis, 406
analysis factor, 200
analytical framework, 200, 214, 219, 231, 407
anatomy, 261
anemia, 228, 274, 275, 276, 283
anger, 60, 287
ANOVA, 43, 102, 332, 438, 439
anthropologists, 235
anthropology, 288
antisocial behavior, 51, 53, 71, 80, 109, 110, 112, 114, 116, 122, 123, 128
anxiety, 70, 80, 146, 147, 148, 149, 150, 152, 155, 156, 157, 159, 160, 162, 166, 167, 175, 177, 256, 285, 292, 312, 411, 412, 413, 414, 416, 419, 420, 421, 422
anxiety disorder, 146, 148, 150, 156, 157, 159, 160, 162, 166, 167, 412, 414, 421, 422
apathy, 242, 369
aplastic anemia, 276
applied psychology, 252
appointments, 414
appraisals, 77
apraxia, 297, 298, 299, 303
arithmetic, 360
arousal, 411, 417
arsenic, 227
articulation, 289
ASI, 150, 151, 152, 154, 155, 158, 159
Asia, 37, 92, 164, 354, 355, 405, 406, 407, 455
Asian countries, 26
asphyxia, 276
assault, 65, 74, 137
assertiveness, 6, 85, 94
assessment, xi, 8, 27, 80, 84, 85, 97, 107, 108, 109, 113, 146, 151, 162, 163, 182, 227, 228, 257, 264, 266, 269, 295, 307, 308, 314, 316, 416, 430, 434, 437
assessment procedures, 434
assessment techniques, 182
assessment tools, 85, 146
assets, xi, 26
asthma, 339
asymmetry, 354
atmosphere, 6, 10, 28, 29, 30, 34, 42, 44, 63, 64, 86, 88, 97, 100, 137, 141
attachment, 315, 316
attitudes, 12, 16, 29, 31, 34, 35, 45, 60, 63, 64, 65, 91, 100, 186, 192, 195, 196, 254, 294, 322, 325, 336, 355, 430
attribution, 438
audit, 135, 142
authority, 60, 65, 132, 281

autism, 271, 307, 308, 309, 310, 312, 314, 315, 316, 317, 457
autonomy, 204, 211, 214, 216, 218, 219, 250, 357, 369, 408
autosomal recessive, 277
aversion, 252, 360, 365
avoidance, 56, 132
awareness, 32, 85, 94, 106, 120, 204, 210, 211, 216, 217, 244, 248, 276, 283, 294, 329, 367, 370, 371

B

bad behavior, 108
Bangladesh, 325, 367, 405, 406, 409
Barbados, 430, 431
bargaining, 320
barriers, 116, 269, 286, 289, 294, 325, 355
base, 142, 313, 316
basic education, 70, 211, 239, 354
basic needs, 70, 141
BD, 405, 406, 407
behavior therapy, 180
behavioral disorders, 144, 296
behavioral manifestations, 315
behavioral problems, 260, 261, 271
benchmarks, 426
beneficial effect, 192
benefits, 25, 29, 43, 83, 88, 95, 97, 101, 104, 122, 227, 277, 288, 324, 345, 354, 371
beverages, 223, 226, 328, 347
BI, 98, 102, 103, 104
bias, 35, 85, 93, 104, 105, 219, 336, 353, 355, 356, 357, 358, 359, 362, 363, 364, 365, 366, 368, 369, 370, 371, 405, 406, 407, 408, 409
biofeedback, 420
biotin, 227
bipolar disorder, 160
birth rate, 233
birth weight, 275, 276, 338
births, 205, 206, 211, 215, 239, 241, 273, 275, 276, 277, 278, 280, 281, 282, 321, 338, 366, 424
Black students, 330
blood, xii, 111, 274, 276, 277, 412, 413
blood pressure, 412
blood supply, 274
blood vessels, 274
blueprint, 106
BMI, 221, 223, 224, 325
body weight, 223
bonding, 31, 34, 36, 45, 71, 73, 101, 105, 188, 191, 288, 292
bonds, 222
boredom, 16

brain, 260, 261, 271, 274, 296, 307, 314, 315
brain functions, 315
brain structure, 315
Brazil, 322, 325, 349, 351
breakdown, 146, 147, 162, 232, 233, 239
breast milk, 339, 341, 342
breastfeeding, 201, 202, 213, 214, 216, 229, 232, 244, 246, 248, 249, 250, 337, 338, 339, 340, 341, 342, 353, 358, 359, 360, 361, 362, 365, 368, 372
breathing, 298, 299, 300, 302, 303, 413, 445
breeding, 277
brothers, 292, 294, 354
bullying, 56, 57
burn, 343, 344, 345, 346, 347, 348, 349, 350, 351
businesses, 7, 9

C

calcium, 221, 226, 227
calibration, 168, 363
calorie, 328
cancer, 411, 412, 413, 414, 415, 416, 417, 419, 420, 421, 422
cannabis, 74
capacity building, 281
carbohydrate, 221, 224, 225, 227
caregivers, 292, 343, 345, 346, 347, 349, 350, 416
Caribbean, 67, 132, 143, 424, 430
Caribbean countries, 430
carotenoids, 227
cascades, 144
case studies, 26, 288
case study, ix, 3, 4, 13, 285, 287, 288, 291, 292, 293, 294, 295, 297, 298, 299, 302, 407
cash, 111, 222
casinos, 96, 161
catalyst, 230
categorization, 59, 66, 133, 135, 140, 433, 434, 435, 443, 445, 447
category a, 438
Caucasians, 340
causal relationship, 165, 172, 409
CDC, xii, 261, 270, 338
Census, 70, 79, 105, 240, 356, 405, 430
challenges, 6, 52, 96, 269, 273, 282, 290, 292, 295, 308, 311, 312, 317
character traits, 84
Chicago, 224, 454
chicken, 334, 335
child abuse, 271, 429
child bearing, 239
child development, 70, 79, 260, 297
child maltreatment, 261, 270, 271

child mortality, 219, 320, 321, 322, 323, 325, 358, 359, 405, 406, 407
child protection, 37
child rearing, 239
childhood, 111, 117, 118, 120, 123, 128, 195, 215, 216, 252, 257, 260, 261, 271, 275, 277, 283, 289, 298, 316, 320, 322, 324, 327, 328, 330, 338, 339, 342, 344, 351, 359, 360, 361, 362, 363, 365, 367, 368, 369, 406, 407, 408, 409, 421, 430, 447
childhood cancer, 421
childhood disorders, 195
childrearing, 211
China, xi, 3, 22, 25, 39, 55, 57, 58, 67, 69, 83, 131, 144, 145, 167, 169, 175, 182, 185, 189, 192, 193, 226, 228, 405
cholesterol, 224, 225, 227
choline, 227
chromium, 227
chronic illness, 411, 420
circus, 437
cities, 146, 165, 256, 322, 323
civil society, 371
clarity, 17, 18, 110
classes, 27, 41, 44, 60, 86, 92, 97, 104, 236, 241, 248, 262, 290, 355, 425
classification, 78, 295, 359, 436, 440, 443, 445
classroom, vii, 7, 28, 29, 30, 34, 42, 44, 49, 55, 56, 57, 58, 59, 60, 62, 63, 64, 65, 66, 67, 72, 86, 100, 118, 128, 131, 132, 133, 134, 135, 136, 137, 138, 140, 141, 142, 143, 144, 172, 422
classroom management, 66, 132, 144
classroom settings, 56, 66, 72, 131, 132, 172
cleft lip, 276
cleft palate, 276
clients, 84, 150, 159, 163
climate, 6
clinical diagnosis, 147
clinical judgment, 151, 313
clinical psychology, 113
clothing, 223
clustering, 430
clusters, 85, 236
CNS, 182
coding, 59, 133, 135, 438, 439, 441
cognition, 117, 447
cognitive abilities, 289
cognitive ability, 286
cognitive activity, 435
cognitive development, 22, 447
cognitive dysfunction, 261
cognitive function, 162
cognitive impairment, 148
cognitive process, 260, 434, 443

cognitive processing, 260, 434
cognitive skills, 412
cognitive therapy, 421
cognitive-behavioral therapy, 413
coherence, 441, 444
coke, 334
collaboration, 163, 165, 223, 424, 453, 454
college students, 170, 182
colleges, 324
color, 416, 435, 436, 438, 441
combined effect, 127
commercials, 336
communication, 6, 7, 9, 11, 12, 62, 64, 65, 74, 77, 94, 96, 135, 139, 140, 188, 193, 195, 260, 281, 285, 286, 287, 288, 289, 290, 294, 296, 297, 308, 313, 315, 335, 370, 428
communication skills, 7, 11, 12, 94
communities, xii, 26, 36, 145, 170, 246, 252, 255, 256, 273, 274, 277, 281, 283, 324, 341, 349, 350, 351, 355, 356
community, 22, 32, 38, 46, 50, 51, 53, 101, 120, 127, 147, 148, 160, 161, 164, 165, 199, 200, 201, 202, 204, 205, 207, 208, 212, 213, 215, 217, 230, 232, 235, 238, 244, 274, 275, 277, 281, 286, 289, 293, 323, 344, 350, 372, 407, 409, 429
community service, 289
comorbidity, viii, 145, 146, 147, 148, 157, 158, 159, 160, 161, 163, 166, 168, 171
compassion, 32, 46, 101
compensation, 262
competitiveness, 7
complexity, 252, 308, 319, 320, 323, 434
complications, 299
composition, 355, 400, 405, 408
comprehension, 257, 266, 269, 416, 417
Comprehensive Social Security Assistance, 70, 72, 73, 173, 178
compulsive behavior, 170
compulsory education, 120
computer, 182, 293, 299
computing, 304
conception, 65, 132, 133, 201, 231, 435
conceptual model, 91
conceptualization, 117, 443
conduct disorder, 165, 293
conference, 92, 263, 270
confidentiality, 35, 41, 58, 72, 87, 134, 172, 187, 193
configuration, 74, 188
conflict, 71, 74, 85, 94, 109, 111, 123, 144, 257
conflict resolution, 85, 94
conformity, 132, 141
confrontation, 63
congruence, 19, 21

consciousness, 142
consensus, 59, 78, 135, 140, 171
consent, 4, 58, 72, 76, 111, 112, 122, 134, 172, 187, 223, 254, 262, 276, 288, 345
Constitution, 325, 354, 355
construct validity, 17, 19, 21, 109
construction, 5, 85, 275, 372, 438
consumption, 78, 185, 186, 187, 189, 192, 193, 195, 204, 328, 330, 331, 336
contraceptives, 233, 234, 235, 239, 241, 249
control group, 92, 180, 251, 253, 254, 315
controversial, 8, 260
convenience sampling, 18, 21, 142
convention, 10
convergence, 234, 257, 370
conversations, 292
cooking, 204, 208, 343, 347, 348, 349, 350
cooperation, 120, 144, 282
coordination, 370
coping strategies, 159, 180, 411, 412, 413, 414, 416, 417, 418, 419, 421
copper, 227
coronary heart disease, 407
correlation analysis, 29, 43, 426
correlation coefficient, 88, 216, 363, 364, 366, 368, 425
cost, 27, 120, 211, 239, 244, 313, 342, 356
cough, 74, 76, 233, 243, 244, 353, 358, 359, 360, 361, 362, 365, 368, 372
coughing, 76
counseling, 58, 59, 113, 135, 142, 146, 162, 163, 164, 274, 276, 282, 283, 308, 414
covering, 341
CPI, 98, 191
creative thinking, 314
creativity, 252, 308
criminal behavior, 146
criminal justice system, 262
criminality, 296
crises, 274
critical thinking, 288
cross-cultural comparison, 21
CRP, 433
Cuba, 222
cues, 447
cultivation, 120
cultural beliefs, 106
cultural norms, 356
cultural tradition, 276, 355
cultural values, 66, 257
culture, xi, 40, 96, 116, 122, 132, 143, 186, 192, 193, 296, 404, 405, 431
cumulative percentage, 88

curricula, 39

curriculum, 4, 13, 27, 28, 29, 30, 31, 34, 35, 41, 43, 44, 45, 49, 85, 91, 100, 118, 128, 253, 261, 263, 268, 269, 270, 457

curriculum development, 118, 128

CV, 203

Czech Republic, 351

D

data analysis, 67, 144, 358

data collection, 28, 41, 58, 66, 72, 87, 97, 112, 133, 134, 142, 143, 148, 149, 172, 175, 187, 358

data set, 41, 112

database, 437, 447

death rate, 361

deaths, 199, 201, 205, 206, 207, 208, 209, 211, 214, 215, 216, 217, 218, 256, 273, 275, 276, 277, 278, 281, 282, 338, 344

debts, 152

decay, 85

deciliter, xii

decision makers, 4

deductive reasoning, 121

deficiency, 147, 166, 225, 226, 228, 275, 283, 296, 434

deficit, 63, 165, 181, 293, 294, 297, 316, 434, 435, 445

delinquency, 26, 67, 71, 80, 142, 179, 180

delinquent behavior, 27, 36, 56, 66, 71, 86

demographic change, 407

demographic characteristics, 18, 151, 153, 159

demographic data, 149, 358

demographic factors, 121, 172, 180, 241, 246, 358, 359, 366, 367, 368, 369, 409

demography, 405

Denmark, 455

Department of Education, 454

dependent variable, 29, 30, 43, 76, 77, 151, 175, 176, 200, 241, 246, 300, 330, 361, 366, 369

depression, 16, 52, 53, 70, 80, 146, 147, 149, 152, 160, 161, 166, 175, 177, 181, 195, 290, 291, 296, 412, 413, 416, 421

depressive symptoms, 70, 80, 147, 159, 161, 166

deprivation, 368

depth, 10, 104, 252, 285, 288, 358

despair, 20

detection, 163, 169, 178, 186, 260, 275, 276

developed countries, 321

developing brain, 315

developing countries, 219, 320, 321, 323, 325, 344, 406, 407, 409, 424

developing nations, 322

developmental change, 193

developmental disorder, 271, 316

developmental milestones, viii, 259, 260, 261, 262, 264, 265, 266, 267, 268, 269, 270, 311, 312

developmental psychology, 315

developmental theories, 115

deviation, 235

DHS, 322, 406, 409

diagnostic criteria, 148, 170

diagnostic markers, 298

dialogues, 254, 289

diarrhea, 233, 243, 244, 276, 322

diet, 328, 331, 334, 335

dietary habits, 214, 336

dietary intake, 223, 335

dieting, 330, 333

differential treatment, 406

diffusion, 52, 235

dignity, 108, 257

direct observation, 26, 143, 285, 288

disability, 260, 286, 287, 288, 289, 290, 291, 292, 293, 294, 295, 296, 351, 433, 434, 435, 436, 437, 439, 440, 441, 442, 443, 444, 445, 447, 451, 453, 455

disclosure, 171

discomfort, 111

discrimination, 206, 219, 229, 244, 248, 250, 293, 302, 354, 355, 356, 371, 407, 408

diseases, 241, 244, 248, 295, 320, 323, 324, 338, 342, 350, 351, 356

disorder, 146, 147, 148, 150, 151, 152, 155, 156, 157, 158, 159, 160, 161, 162, 163, 165, 168, 181, 182, 286, 298, 299, 308, 311, 313, 314, 315, 316, 317, 457

dissociation, 104, 435, 446

distress, 56, 107, 111, 114, 115, 116, 117, 119, 120, 124, 125, 126, 127, 129, 149, 152, 159, 160, 162, 164, 170, 257, 411, 413, 414, 421

distribution, 177, 206, 218, 235, 274, 407, 408, 415, 426

distribution of income, 408

District of Columbia, xii

diversification, 255

diversity, 283, 355

dizziness, 412

doctors, 281, 337, 338

domestic chores, 244

domestic violence, 354, 429

dominance, 148

dosage, 40, 49

draft, 250

drawing, 60, 61, 65, 137, 138, 256, 265, 312, 445

dream, 290

drinking water, 202, 204, 226, 354
drug abuse, 26, 51, 156, 286
drugs, 98, 275
DSM-IV-TR, 167
dysthymic disorder, 160

E

early adolescents, viii, 15, 16, 17, 21, 81, 169, 170, 185, 193, 195
earnings, 204, 208, 210, 211, 372
East Asia, 96
eating disorders, 150
echoing, 78
economic development, 218, 219, 229, 231, 239, 240, 250, 275, 320, 355, 357, 365, 404
economic disadvantage, 69, 70, 71, 77, 78, 80, 106
economic growth, 96, 356
economic power, 354
economic status, 73, 78, 149, 152, 159, 169, 172, 173, 175, 176, 178, 179, 181, 248, 274
economic well-being, 71
economics, 196
ECPA, 447
ecstasy, 74
editors, 37, 51, 79, 80, 181, 182, 194, 195
educated women, 211, 229, 239
educational attainment, 149, 229, 234, 249
educational background, 125
educational opportunities, 355
educational programs, 308
educational psychology, 143
educational quality, 93
educational research, 296
educational settings, 58
educators, 26, 37, 67, 179, 261, 262, 269, 308
EEG, 315
Egypt, 322, 408
elaboration, 371, 434
electricity, 204, 346, 347, 359, 370
electroencephalography, 315
elementary school, 57, 67, 142, 143, 253
eligibility criteria, 262, 421
e-mail, 339
emotion, 117, 194, 293, 296
emotion regulation, 194
emotional disorder, 253
emotional distress, 128, 165, 411, 413, 414, 417, 419
emotional experience, 256, 309, 310, 315
emotional intelligence, 5, 11
emotional problems, 285
emotional state, 8, 251

empathy, 107, 108, 109, 110, 111, 114, 115, 116, 117, 119, 120, 121, 123, 124, 125, 126, 127, 129, 252, 310, 314
empirical studies, 26, 108, 171, 328
employment, 57, 96, 150, 151, 195, 239, 240, 241, 244, 354, 355, 357, 370, 405
employment opportunities, 96, 355, 357, 370
employment status, 241, 244
empowerment, 195, 199, 202, 204, 205, 208, 209, 210, 211, 214, 215, 216, 217, 218, 353, 355, 356, 357, 359, 367, 369, 370, 408
encoding, 434
encouragement, 5, 127, 328, 337
endangered, 405
endowments, 70
enemies, 6
energy, viii, 56, 221, 222, 223, 224, 225, 227, 349
enforcement, 371
enhanced service, 164
enrollment, 425
environment, 9, 35, 161, 202, 204, 222, 253, 256, 258, 261, 263, 269, 290, 297, 310, 322, 328, 330, 333, 334, 335, 336, 344, 365, 370, 429, 445
environmental conditions, 349
environmental factors, 230, 320
epidemiologic, 166
epidemiology, 282, 351
epilepsy, 346
equality, 323, 355
equipment, 275
equity, 319, 320, 321, 325, 355, 360, 365, 372
ethical standards, 8
ethics, 8, 9, 94, 108
ethnic groups, 320, 323, 325
ethnicity, 80, 323, 336, 339
etiology, 164, 168, 315
Europe, 342, 404
European Union, 227
event-related potential, 315
everyday life, 9, 18, 120
evidence, 67, 79, 95, 105, 109, 142, 144, 161, 164, 186, 193, 250, 271, 308, 313, 321, 325, 335, 353, 358, 359, 360, 361, 369, 406, 408, 419, 423, 428, 429
evidence-based program, 271
examinations, 84, 222, 230
exclusion, 321, 323, 335
executive function, 121
executive functioning, 121
exercise, 213, 243, 246, 303, 328, 363
exile, 222
Existence Subscale of the PIL (EPIL), 17
experimental design, 259, 271

expertise, 256, 313

explicit memory, 446

exploitation, 371

exposure, 76, 186, 187, 189, 190, 192, 193, 194, 196, 204, 208, 209, 210, 211, 261, 329, 333, 335, 336, 367, 368, 369, 370, 420, 426, 429

externalities, 407

externalizing behavior, 56, 78, 193

extraversion, 117, 129

extreme poverty, 323

F

facial expression, 62

facilitators, 49

factor analysis, 88, 93, 122, 334

FAI, 188, 195

fairness, 372

faith, 10

Family Assessment Instrument, 74, 188, 195

family conflict, 96

family environment, 173

family factors, 78, 173, 185, 187

family functioning, 69, 71, 72, 75, 80, 106, 185, 186, 187, 188, 189, 191, 192, 193, 195, 308, 315

family income, 78, 181

family life, 170, 233

family members, 73, 74, 152, 154, 175, 177, 188, 289, 292, 293

family planning, 230, 232, 406

family system, 204, 230, 233, 235

family therapy, 51, 163, 180, 307

family violence, 146

famine, 405

fantasy, 107, 114, 115, 116, 117, 121, 124, 126

fast food, 334, 335

fat, 221, 224, 227, 328, 330, 331, 334, 336

fat intake, 221, 224

fatty acids, 227

fear, 17, 126, 252, 281, 285, 287, 289, 291, 292, 294, 312, 413, 421, 422

feelings, 6, 8, 10, 11, 35, 71, 75, 108, 109, 111, 141, 147, 161, 175, 177, 252, 285, 286, 288, 289, 292, 293, 294, 310, 313, 419

fertility, 229, 230, 231, 232, 233, 234, 239, 240, 249, 277, 278, 356, 357, 405, 407

fertility rate, 234, 239, 240

fetus, 230

fever, 233, 243, 244, 353, 358, 359, 360, 361, 362, 365, 368, 372

fiber, 225, 227

fidelity, 40, 49, 51, 52, 93

films, 189, 190

financial, 10, 72, 73, 79, 146, 147, 159, 160, 161, 163, 165, 173, 188, 189, 191, 192, 294, 354

financial condition, 72

financial resources, 165

financial support, 294

Finland, 454

first aid, 294

flame, 300, 303

flight, 312

flowers, 437

fluid, 142

focus groups, 13, 23, 52, 53, 67, 86, 93, 144, 182, 196

folate, 227

food, 111, 200, 221, 222, 223, 227, 327, 328, 329, 330, 331, 332, 333, 334, 335, 336, 343, 347, 348, 349, 350, 354, 356, 407, 408

food industry, 336

food intake, 221, 223, 328, 330, 331, 334

food products, 329

force, 6, 10, 108, 125, 240, 292, 357

formation, 16, 17, 22, 70

formula, 341, 359, 360, 363, 365

foul language, 60, 61, 64, 65, 74, 76, 138, 139

fragile site, 295

France, 433, 436

free recall, 446

freedom, 17, 21, 141

friendship, 105, 294

fruits, 331, 336

functionalism, 37

funding, 13, 26, 29, 42

fundraising, 419

future orientation, 70

G

gambling, viii, 57, 96, 98, 145, 146, 147, 148, 149, 150, 151, 152, 154, 156, 157, 158, 159, 160, 161, 162, 163, 164, 165, 166, 167, 168

gel, 347

gender differences, 79, 115, 119, 123, 126, 180, 406

gender equality, 354, 360

gender gap, 353, 357, 358, 359, 360, 361, 362, 363, 364, 365, 366, 369, 370

gender inequality, 354, 355, 365, 367, 368, 407

gender role, 118, 128, 413

general education, 4, 5, 7, 9

General Health Questionnaire, 182

general knowledge, 294

generalizability, 21, 92, 171, 270

generalized anxiety disorder, 147, 162

genetic defect, 276

genetic disorders, 276, 291
genetic endowment, 407
genetic factors, 201, 231, 277
genetics, 161, 283, 286, 328
genitals, 190
Georgia, 259, 262, 430
Germany, 223, 455
gerontology, 454
gestation, 276, 338
gestures, 264, 292, 309, 310, 311, 312
Giraffe, 446
GNP, 357, 370
God, 288
goiter, 226, 228
good behavior, 75
governance, 170
governments, 351
governor, 317
grades, 27, 29, 30, 34, 35, 58, 181, 252, 330
grading, 84
granola, 331, 334
grass, 281
Greece, 251, 252, 253, 257
Grenada, 423, 424, 425, 429, 430
growth, 6, 9, 37, 50, 81, 93, 96, 104, 121, 196, 228,
    244, 260, 274, 275, 276, 287, 315, 356, 357, 370,
    371, 407
Guatemala, 324, 409
guidance, 58, 133, 151, 252, 264, 269, 300, 422
guidelines, 163, 187, 241, 252, 265, 298, 316, 329
guilt, 108, 118, 175, 177
Gulf Coast, xii
Guyana, 430

H

happiness, 99, 120, 122
harmful effects, 163
harmony, 74, 188, 193
HE, 296
head injury, 298
health care, xii, 163, 211, 241, 249, 272, 274, 275,
    276, 281, 320, 323, 324, 350, 354, 355, 356, 358,
    366, 367, 370, 372, 406, 407, 408
health care costs, xii, 163
health care programs, 324
health condition, 365, 412
health education, 343, 348, 349, 350, 351, 423
health information, 344, 358
health practitioners, 186
health problems, 337, 340, 344, 412
health risks, 120
health services, 162, 275, 320, 323, 325

health status, 231, 320, 355, 364, 365
heart disease, 276
heart rate, 412
height, 223, 224, 275, 340, 362
helping behavior, 128
helplessness, 147, 159, 175, 177
hemoglobin, 273, 274, 275, 276, 277, 282, 283
hemoglobinopathies, viii, 273, 274, 275, 276, 277,
    278, 279, 281, 282, 283
hemoglobinopathy, 274
hemolytic anemia, 274, 276
heroin, 74
heterosis, 283
high school, xii, xiii, 16, 18, 57, 67, 110, 116, 119,
    121, 127, 170, 182, 330, 336
higher education, 248
higher-order thinking, 94
Hispanics, 340
history, 96, 241, 256, 262, 275, 277, 288, 295, 302,
    349, 358, 405, 426
HIV, 51, 276, 323, 344, 424, 425, 429, 430, 431
HIV/AIDS, 344, 424, 425, 430
homes, 154, 222, 347, 349, 350, 416
homework, 56, 60, 61, 62, 64, 65, 66, 133, 137, 138,
    139, 140, 186, 266, 423, 425, 426, 427, 428, 429
homogeneity, 438
honesty, 6, 8
hopelessness, 16, 22, 71, 147, 413
horses, 438, 444
host, 222, 226, 227
hostility, 56, 65, 70, 132, 139, 149, 152, 160, 181
hotel, 9
House, 53, 321, 454
household income, 78, 202, 367, 370
housing, 149, 262, 320, 322
human, xi, 6, 16, 84, 91, 94, 120, 230, 257, 275, 289,
    291, 293, 294, 314, 338, 341, 354, 355, 368, 371,
    404, 405, 408, 421, 451, 453, 455, 457
human capital, 120, 371
human development, 355, 368, 408, 451, 453, 455,
    457
Human Development Report, 355
human existence, 16
human milk, 338, 341
human motivation, 16
human nature, 16
human resources, 275
human right, 354
human values, 6
Hungary, 67, 144
husband, 204, 210, 322, 372
hygiene, 202, 210, 211, 249, 323, 425
hyperactivity, 165, 181

hypothesis, 48, 126, 147, 161, 202, 218, 232, 248, 316, 320, 321, 356, 367, 419

hypothetical situations, 5, 108

I

ICC, 113

ID, 13, 22, 36, 51, 79, 92, 98, 102, 103, 165, 181, 183, 194, 286

ideal, 142, 236, 241, 288

identification, 78, 93, 182, 196, 259, 260, 262, 264, 268, 270, 271, 437, 447

identity, 16, 69, 70, 71, 73, 74, 76, 77, 78, 85, 94, 104, 121, 179, 188, 191, 192, 193, 293

idiopathic, 298

imagery, 413, 421

image(s), 79, 254, 447

imagination, 308, 416, 418

imitation, 141, 298, 299, 308

immigration, 169, 172, 175, 176, 179, 181

immune system, 320

immunity, 322, 325

immunization, 201, 202, 204, 229, 232, 233, 241, 242, 244, 246, 247, 248, 249, 276, 406, 409

improvements, 3, 200, 218, 263, 319, 324, 411, 420

impulsive, 8, 147, 161

impulsiveness, 168

impulsivity, 147

in transition, 296, 405

inbreeding, 277

incidence, 202, 232, 274, 342, 356

income, 70, 71, 79, 149, 151, 152, 153, 158, 159, 173, 239, 250, 262, 269, 347, 348, 349, 350, 355, 367, 370, 408

income distribution, 408

indecisiveness, 159

independence, 189, 191, 222

independent variable, 29, 30, 43, 76, 77, 175, 209, 214, 216

indirect effect, 80, 246, 248

individual character, 435

individual characteristics, 435

individual differences, 120, 308

individual perception, 21

individual students, 144

individuals, 36, 50, 104, 146, 148, 159, 160, 161, 162, 164, 168, 171, 186, 192, 202, 204, 227, 287, 289, 290, 293, 307, 324, 330, 336, 412, 413, 414, 419, 420, 433, 434, 444, 447

industrialization, 235, 239

industry, 96, 370

inequality, 319, 320, 322, 323, 324, 354, 360, 365, 368, 404, 406, 408

inequity, 230, 319, 320, 323, 429

infancy, 201, 275, 286, 315, 316

infant care, 204, 211

infant feeding practices, 202, 232

infant mortality, 199, 200, 201, 202, 203, 204, 205, 206, 211, 212, 213, 214, 215, 216, 217, 218, 273, 274, 275, 276, 277, 278, 281, 282, 319, 320, 338, 342, 365, 407, 408, 409

infants, 202, 260, 271, 274, 308, 315, 316, 337, 338, 340, 341, 365

infection, 274, 276

inferences, 444

information processing, 121, 445

informed consent, 42, 149, 223, 262, 288, 345, 416

infrastructure, 204, 205, 208, 209, 210, 218

ingredients, 78, 223, 328

initiation, 36, 423, 424, 425, 426, 427, 428, 429, 430

injuries, 343, 344, 345, 346, 347, 348, 349, 350, 351

injury, 201, 271, 276, 344, 345, 348, 349, 350, 351, 425

injury prevention, 350

insane, 291

insecurity, 294

institutions, 85, 164, 343, 344, 345

instructional activities, 34

integration, 80, 252, 270, 315, 316

integrity, 6, 8, 51, 94, 194

intellectual disabilities, 292, 295

Intellectual Disability, ix, 433

intelligence, 8, 287, 293, 316, 446

interaction effect, 439

intercourse, 190, 425, 426, 430

internal consistency, 19, 21, 107, 109, 110, 112, 113, 115, 149, 167, 189

internal validity, 92, 265

internalizing, 78

International Labour Organisation, 430

internship, 10

interpersonal communication, 9, 10, 11, 85, 94

interpersonal conflict, 94

interpersonal relations, 63, 132, 151, 160

interpersonal relationships, 63, 132

interpersonal skills, 8, 86

intervention strategies, 178, 179, 180, 344

intonation, 297, 298, 299, 300, 303

invariants, 443

invasion of privacy, 140

investment, 356, 411, 420

iodine, 221, 226, 227, 228

Ireland, 430

IRI, 111, 112, 114, 123, 125

iron, 225, 226, 227, 275

irritability, 177

Islam, 409
Islamabad, 290
isolation, 293, 310, 322
Israel, ii, x, xi, 297, 451, 453, 455, 458
issues, 16, 17, 22, 52, 70, 71, 78, 93, 94, 106, 115,
    121, 144, 163, 168, 233, 262, 298, 321, 323, 370,
    408, 412, 429, 430, 457

J

Jamaica, 430
Japan, 226, 228
jaundice, 274, 276
joints, 302
junior high school, 110
justification, 435, 438

K

kidneys, 274
kindergarten, 36, 299
kindergartens, 299
kinship, 250, 408
Korea, 166, 405

L

labeling, 66, 164
labour force, 239, 355, 357
language development, 286
language skills, 292
lateral sclerosis, 22
Latin America, 424
laws, xii, 108
LDCs, 325
lead, 4, 6, 7, 40, 121, 159, 208, 226, 260, 274, 275,
    287, 294, 298, 309, 310, 311, 312, 324, 338, 339,
    341
leadership, 4, 5, 6, 7, 8, 9, 10, 11, 83, 86, 94
leadership style, 6, 10
learners, 264, 269, 289
learning, 5, 6, 7, 8, 9, 10, 34, 38, 44, 49, 56, 57, 58,
    59, 63, 64, 65, 66, 84, 86, 94, 96, 100, 128, 131,
    132, 133, 134, 136, 137, 139, 140, 141, 142, 143,
    144, 244, 252, 256, 257, 260, 264, 286, 287, 295,
    296, 298, 299, 308, 313, 366, 369, 370, 419, 446
learning disabilities, 295, 299
learning efficiency, 8
learning environment, 49, 136, 143, 144
learning outcomes, 84
learning process, 8, 49, 56
learning skills, 287

legs, 111
leisure, 286
lending, 108
lens, 141, 142
leukemia, 415
level of education, 125, 152, 208, 229, 248, 250
liberalization, 165
liberty, 355
LIFE, 98, 102, 103, 151, 152, 155, 167
life changes, 412
life course, 80
life cycle, 407
life satisfaction, 15, 16, 17, 19, 71, 97, 98, 102, 104
Life Satisfaction Scale, 103
lifetime, 146, 147, 148, 151, 152, 153, 154, 155, 157,
    158, 159, 160, 161, 162
light, 34, 50, 133, 193, 223, 256
Likert scale, 18, 30, 31, 32, 44, 45, 46, 47, 74, 75,
    149, 188, 189
lipids, 225
liquids, 350
literacy, 193, 208, 209, 211, 215, 240, 260, 262, 271,
    272, 320, 353, 354, 356, 357, 370
liver, 339
liver disease, 339
living conditions, 323, 365
local youth, 96, 167
logistics, 414
loneliness, 159, 294
longevity, 355
longitudinal study, 67, 70, 72, 78, 80, 106, 117, 118,
    128, 144, 171, 172, 180, 187
love, 6, 74, 141, 188, 287, 294, 312, 419
LSD, 333
lying, 300, 303

M

macroeconomics, 404
macronutrients, 222, 224, 227
magazines, 11, 189, 190
magnesium, 227
magnitude, 359, 366, 368
Mainland China, 72, 73, 170, 172, 173, 175, 187,
    191
major decisions, 204, 208, 210
major depressive disorder, 147, 157, 160, 166
majority, 48, 101, 186, 240, 320, 337, 338, 341, 350,
    366, 426, 428, 439, 442
malaria, 276
malnutrition, 227, 276, 353, 358, 359, 361, 362, 366,
    368, 369
maltreatment, 261, 271

mammals, 437

man, 285, 288, 293, 426

management, 8, 9, 51, 58, 66, 67, 84, 94, 134, 143, 144, 168, 196, 248, 256, 275, 276, 290, 296, 414

manganese, 227

MANOVA, 123

manpower, 143

marginalization, 70

marijuana, 148

marital conflict, 146

marital status, 73, 149, 151, 159, 173, 188, 269

marketing, 196, 328

marriage, 99, 173, 274, 277, 282, 370, 426

married women, 204, 208, 210, 211, 214, 233, 234, 235

marrow, 413

masculinity, 426, 429

mass, 186, 204, 208, 209, 210, 223, 324, 367, 368, 369

mass media, 186, 204, 209, 210, 367, 368, 369

materialism, 126, 128

materials, viii, 4, 5, 16, 57, 78, 81, 84, 139, 140, 185, 186, 187, 189, 190, 191, 192, 193, 195, 261, 263, 264, 265, 266, 267, 269, 270, 422

maternal control, 75

mathematics, 256, 287

matrix, 19, 20, 89, 209, 211

matter, 9, 64, 70, 252, 405, 409

MB, 67, 117, 144, 166, 167

measles, 241, 276, 366

measurement(s), 16, 72, 116, 118, 172, 221, 222, 223, 300, 302, 315, 366, 369

media, 9, 179, 187, 193, 194, 195, 208, 211, 261, 328, 329, 330, 333, 335, 336, 359, 367, 370

median, 20, 70, 122, 321, 368

medical, xii, 150, 165, 166, 201, 202, 203, 216, 217, 218, 222, 229, 232, 233, 241, 243, 244, 246, 248, 249, 250, 257, 269, 270, 271, 275, 281, 288, 321, 338, 343, 345, 348, 353, 357, 358, 360, 361, 362, 365, 372, 412, 413, 414, 420, 421, 451, 457

medical care, 201, 202, 203, 218, 229, 232, 233, 241, 243, 244, 246, 248, 249, 250, 275, 321, 348, 412, 457

medical science, 288

medication, 163, 204, 244, 415

medicine, 76, 222, 455, 457

Mediterranean, 351

melody, 298

membership, 438, 441, 442, 443, 444, 445

memory, 85, 434, 435, 444, 445, 447

memory retrieval, 444

meningitis, 276

mental age, 293, 434, 436, 439, 440, 441, 442, 443, 446

mental disorder, 146, 164, 166, 167

mental health, 8, 52, 70, 71, 79, 80, 94, 145, 146, 148, 161, 162, 164, 167, 168, 195, 261, 270, 271, 315, 316, 320, 412, 413, 414, 425

mental retardation, 286, 287, 288, 295, 296, 310, 446

mentally retarded adolescents, 296

messages, 300, 328, 350

meta-analysis, 51, 93, 271

metacognitive skills, 435

methodology, 205, 285, 288, 321, 337

micronutrients, 221, 222, 225

Microsoft, 264

Microsoft Word, 264

middle class, 236

migration, 167, 323

Ministry of Education, 258

Minneapolis, 166, 257

minorities, 359

miscarriages, 275

mission, 453

misuse, 150, 179

mobile phone, 60, 65, 113, 137

models, 10, 26, 37, 71, 84, 205, 213, 233, 246, 261, 298, 313, 315, 359, 361, 369, 407, 421

modernisation, 231, 357

modernity, 235

modernization, 186, 229, 232, 233, 235, 240, 246, 248, 249, 250

modifications, 109, 110, 115, 164, 263, 264, 268, 269

modules, 150

molybdenum, 227

mood disorder, 146, 147, 148, 150, 155, 157, 160, 161, 167, 168, 412

Moon, 13, 92

moral behavior, 108, 118

moral development, 108, 109, 117, 118

moral identity, 16, 22

moral judgment, 117, 118

moral reasoning, 108, 109, 111, 115, 116, 117, 118, 119, 120, 121, 123, 128

morale, 94, 289

morality, 9, 16, 22, 63, 94, 96

morbidity, 158, 210, 274, 275, 277, 281, 282, 322, 344, 354, 355

Morocco, 222, 406

mortality, viii, 199, 200, 202, 205, 213, 214, 215, 216, 217, 218, 219, 256, 274, 275, 276, 277, 278, 281, 282, 283, 319, 321, 322, 323, 324, 325, 338, 344, 351, 353, 354, 356, 357, 358, 359, 361, 362, 365, 368, 369, 405, 406, 407, 408, 409 mortality rate, 199, 205, 275, 276, 323, 338, 351, 354, 409

mother tongue, 58, 134

motivation, 21, 35, 49, 65, 66, 84, 117, 118, 126, 128, 129, 136, 260, 294, 307

motor control, 260, 298, 303

motor skills, 260, 300

motor system, 315

MR, 80, 286

multidimensional, 51, 126

multiple factors, 328

multiple regression, 48, 87, 91, 92, 158, 174, 176, 215

multiple regression analyses, 87, 91, 158

multiple regression analysis, 48, 92, 174, 176, 215

multivariate analysis, 75, 76, 123, 211, 229

muscles, 298, 302

music, 60, 61, 65, 138

mutuality, 74, 188, 193

N

naming, 437

narratives, 133, 140

National Academy of Sciences, 314

National Health and Nutrition Examination Survey, 328

National Research Council, 314

National Survey, 36

nausea, 412

needy, 109, 111, 122, 323

negative affectivity, 166

negative consequences, 146

negative emotions, 8, 141

negative influences, 96

negative outcomes, 50

negative relation, 119, 127, 429

neglect, 261, 271, 356, 408

negotiation, 288

Nelson Mandela, 6

nerve, 314

nervous system, 313

nervousness, 417, 418

Netherlands, 67, 80, 144

neurobiology, 161, 316

neurophysiology, 261

neutral, 267, 397, 438

New Zealand, 165

next generation, 455

niacin, 227

nickel, 227

nicotine, 146, 150, 155, 157, 160, 161, 167

Nigeria, 323, 325, 409

NMR, 274, 276

Nobel Prize, 451

normal children, 290, 292

normal distribution, 224

normative acts, 112

North Africa, 354, 355

Norway, 455

nuclear family, 235

nurses, 256, 338

nursing, 256, 281, 337, 340, 341

nursing home, 256

nutrient(s), viii, 221, 222, 223, 224

nutrition, 202, 211, 214, 216, 227, 228, 275, 319, 320, 323, 328, 329, 330, 331, 332, 334, 335, 336, 341, 354, 361, 365, 371, 406, 407, 408

nutritional deficiencies, 276

nutritional status, 356, 406

O

Obama, 294

obedience, 64, 65, 66, 132, 141

obesity, 327, 330, 336, 338, 339, 341, 342

obstacles, 308, 355

obstruction, 274, 311

occupational therapy, 308, 312

OCD, 299

offenders, 51

oil, 346

Oklahoma, 261

one dimension, 40, 92

operations, 199, 200

opportunities, xii, 12, 70, 77, 86, 87, 88, 89, 248, 294, 311, 312, 354, 355, 356, 407, 435

opportunity costs, 229, 250

organize, 298, 312

organs, 274

outpatients, 150, 166

overlap, 324

overweight, 327, 328, 330, 336

ownership, 354

P

P.A.T.H.S., vii, xi, 12, 13, 21, 23, 25, 26, 27, 33, 34, 36, 37, 39, 40, 41, 51, 52, 53, 66, 67, 79, 81, 84, 85, 93, 95, 96, 97, 104, 106, 142, 144, 180, 181, 182, 183, 186, 187, 194, 196

Pacific, 93, 164, 455

pain, 252, 413, 421

pairing, 270, 330

Pakistan, 285, 290, 405, 406, 407

Panama, 430
panic disorder, 148, 162
pantothenic acid, 227
parallel, 333
parental care, 406
parental consent, 74, 134
parental control, 72, 77, 78, 79, 193
parental involvement, 423, 424, 425, 426, 427, 428
parenthood, 276
parenting, 52, 69, 70, 75, 77, 78, 80, 121, 186, 188, 195, 262, 429
parenting styles, 195
parity, 355, 368
pathologist, 299
pathways, 80, 314, 325, 370
PCA, 205, 211, 363, 365
peace, 285, 294
pediatrician, 261, 267, 271
peer relationship, 128, 141, 293, 314
penalties, 407
perfusion, 274
perinatal, 275, 278, 281
permission, 60, 65, 136, 282, 290, 372
personal achievements, 211
personal communication, 226
personal development, 5, 6, 7, 9, 10, 11, 28, 42, 86, 87, 88, 89, 94, 101
personal history, 262
personal identity, 6, 10, 94
personal qualities, 7, 86
personal relations, 16
personal relationship, 16
personal values, 120
personality, 11, 17, 94, 128, 165, 171, 186, 287, 288, 290, 291, 292, 293
personality characteristics, 186
personality disorder, 165, 287, 291, 292
personality factors, 171
personality research, 17
personality traits, 94, 291
person-oriented approach, 52
Philadelphia, xii, 295
phobia, 156
phobic anxiety, 149, 152, 160
phonemes, 299
phosphorus, 226, 227
physical abuse, 261
physical activity, 328, 425
physical aggression, 56, 64, 65, 132, 139, 140
physical characteristics, 224
physical education, 143
physical health, 170, 261
physical resemblance, 264

physical therapy, 308
physicians, 260
Physiological, 417, 418
physiological arousal, 411, 412, 416, 417, 419, 420
piano, 293, 300
pilot study, 18, 106, 339, 419
pitch, 297, 298, 299, 300, 301, 302, 303
placenta, 276
plants, 433, 436, 437, 438, 440, 442, 443, 444, 445, 447
platform, 9, 164, 293
play activity, 312
playing, 57, 60, 61, 64, 65, 66, 135, 137, 138, 139, 140, 141, 186, 254, 293, 300, 311, 335, 349
pleasure, 6, 147, 160, 182, 289, 313
PM, 67, 128, 182, 195, 196, 250, 405
pneumonia, 276
polarity, 312
policy, 26, 38, 162, 179, 195, 303, 320, 321, 323, 338, 344, 355, 365, 366, 369, 370, 371, 429, 430, 455
policy makers, 26, 179, 320, 371
policymakers, xii
polio, 204, 241
politeness, 137, 141
politics, 324
population, xii, 40, 96, 105, 109, 146, 167, 168, 181, 186, 193, 194, 201, 202, 203, 232, 236, 238, 239, 240, 263, 269, 283, 287, 296, 313, 315, 317, 319, 320, 323, 324, 325, 354, 360, 365, 368, 405, 409, 412, 420, 424
population group, 324
positive attitudes, 40
positive correlation, 107, 114, 115, 116, 117
positive externalities, 354
positive feedback, 104
positive relationship, 43, 116, 120, 211, 367
positive youth development approach, 12, 26
posttraumatic stress, 147
potassium, 221, 225, 227
potato, 331
potential benefits, 105
poverty, 69, 70, 71, 72, 75, 77, 78, 79, 80, 81, 199, 203, 204, 209, 211, 212, 214, 216, 217, 218, 239, 240, 276, 278, 281, 294, 351, 354, 356, 357, 407, 409
poverty line, 70, 72, 204, 209, 211, 212, 240
PRC, 3, 15, 25, 39, 55, 69, 83, 95, 107, 119, 131, 145, 169, 185
predators, 429
predictive validity, 51, 167
predictor variables, 229, 241, 327, 335, 359

pregnancy, 192, 202, 203, 208, 214, 216, 239, 275, 283, 286, 367, 368, 370, 424
prejudice, 355
prematurity, 276
preparation, 35, 36, 42, 51, 66, 79, 143, 181, 194, 223, 350, 430
preparedness, 34
preschool, 295
presentation skills, 8
President, 6, 294
prestige, 211, 239, 320
prevalence rate, 146, 147, 162, 170, 424
prevention, xi, xii, 22, 37, 38, 40, 41, 51, 52, 91, 93, 106, 163, 176, 178, 179, 180, 228, 249, 261, 271, 281, 343, 344, 347, 348, 350, 351, 429, 451
primary school, 56, 67, 143, 170, 222, 227, 348
principles, 106, 108, 141, 298, 312, 315, 317, 360, 372
private sector, 281
probability, 168, 176, 178, 200, 202, 204, 229, 425
probe, 259, 262, 265, 268
problem behavior(s), 55, 56, 57, 58, 59, 60, 61, 62, 63, 64, 65, 66, 67, 69, 71, 74, 75, 78, 81, 98, 106, 133, 134, 135, 136, 137, 138, 139, 140, 141, 142, 143, 144, 173, 179, 180, 181, 186, 192, 293
problem solving, 286, 422
problem-solving, 260, 414
professional development, 29
professional growth, 28
professionals, xi, 26, 113, 117, 149, 162, 163, 337, 338, 341, 342, 453, 455
profit, 416
prognosis, 418
program outcomes, 40, 41, 49, 51, 93
program staff, 35
programming, 298, 324, 336
project, vii, xi, 5, 8, 25, 26, 27, 29, 34, 36, 37, 41, 49, 67, 96, 106, 144, 149, 165, 167, 186, 296, 316, 405
proliferation, 187, 193
promax rotation, 88
pronunciation, 300, 302
proposition, 200
prosocial acts, 127
prosocial behavior, viii, 16, 17, 19, 107, 108, 109, 114, 116, 117, 118, 119, 120, 121, 123, 124, 125, 126, 127, 128, 129
prosocial development, 109, 116, 120, 127
prosperity, 357, 370
protection, 201, 232, 354, 371
protective factors, 67, 78, 144, 193, 424, 425, 429
prototype, 434
PST, 149, 155

psychiatric disorders, 145, 146, 147, 148, 150, 151, 152, 153, 154, 155, 156, 157, 158, 159, 160, 161, 162, 163, 164, 165, 166, 168, 182, 295
psychiatric morbidity, 71, 165
psychiatry, xii
psychological distress, 149, 152, 160, 161, 162
psychological well-being, 15, 16, 17, 19, 22, 23, 71, 80, 106, 170, 182, 192, 195
psychologist, 413
psychology, 9, 79, 117, 118, 128, 195, 256, 258, 437
psychometric approach, 22
psychometric properties, 15, 17, 21, 83, 84, 85, 88, 91, 98, 107, 109, 111, 123, 167, 182
psychopathology, 16, 23, 146, 160
psychosocial development, 16, 67, 144, 429
psychosocial dysfunction, 152
psychosocial factors, 22
psychosocial functioning, 146, 157, 160
psychosocial support, 416
psychotherapy, 163, 296, 316, 414
psychoticism, 149, 152, 160
public awareness, 164, 179
public health, xii, 38, 211, 273, 282, 320, 321, 337, 342, 344, 354, 360, 362, 370, 372, 409, 424, 453, 455, 457
public schools, 328
public service, 453
Puerto Rico, xii
pumps, 337, 340, 341, 342
punishment, 132, 141
P-value, 224

Q

qualitative research, 4, 57, 58, 133, 134, 142, 144, 296
quality control, 276
quality of life, 17, 98, 230, 275, 355, 412, 416, 451
quartile, 205
Queensland, 257, 296
questionnaire, 18, 22, 35, 42, 72, 73, 74, 83, 84, 87, 97, 109, 110, 111, 119, 123, 149, 167, 170, 172, 173, 174, 182, 187, 253, 316, 345, 416

R

race, 329, 333, 336, 339, 354
Radiation, 415
radio, 351, 371
rate of change, 50
rating scale, 166
RE, 36, 73, 188, 190, 191

reactions, 52, 132, 257, 313, 331
reactivity, 128
reading, 5, 57, 60, 61, 65, 107, 110, 111, 113, 115, 117, 123, 261, 264, 287, 298, 299, 329, 411, 414, 416, 417, 418, 419, 420
reading skills, 287
realism, 264, 269
reality, 4, 171, 256, 288, 371
reasoning, viii, 23, 107, 108, 109, 110, 111, 113, 114, 115, 116, 117, 119, 121, 123, 124, 125, 126, 127, 327, 328, 330, 332, 334, 336
recall, 171, 227, 289, 434
recalling, 288, 291
recidivism, 261
reciprocity, 108, 314, 315
recognition, 8, 73, 77, 141, 188, 191, 262, 434, 447
recommendations, 10, 110, 162, 227, 264, 338, 339, 341, 351
reconstruction, 356
recovery, 159, 356
recovery process, 159
recreation, 151
recreational, 186, 196
reflexes, 298
reform, 4
refugee camps, 222, 226, 227, 228
refugees, 221, 222, 227
regression, 25, 29, 30, 33, 35, 39, 43, 48, 49, 83, 91, 119, 125, 126, 151, 157, 158, 174, 175, 176, 178, 229, 233, 246, 332, 333, 345, 349, 359, 361, 366, 367, 368, 372
regression analysis, 43, 125, 174, 176, 246, 332
regression model, 175, 229, 233, 333, 367, 368
regulations, 56, 60
rehabilitation, 289, 290, 291, 293, 351, 451, 453
rejection, 120, 287
relationship quality, 94
relatives, 151, 164, 204, 210, 244, 277, 292, 372
relaxation, 413, 414
relevance, 17, 49, 57, 85, 107, 109, 110, 113, 115, 117, 150, 263, 321
reliability, 8, 17, 18, 19, 21, 43, 50, 59, 85, 88, 91, 93, 98, 107, 109, 110, 113, 115, 117, 122, 135, 142, 149, 150, 167, 188, 264, 265, 267, 316
relief, 354
religion, 275, 354, 359, 367, 371
religiosity, 16
religious beliefs, 257
rent, 262
replication, viii, 35, 117, 166, 185, 193, 194, 196
representativeness, 66, 113, 115, 142
reproductive age, 234
reputation, 8

requirements, 75
research facilities, 282
researchers, xii, 21, 26, 40, 49, 71, 78, 84, 113, 117, 122, 132, 135, 142, 147, 164, 170, 171, 176, 179, 180, 252, 256, 285, 288, 320, 328, 339, 366, 367, 457
resentment, 211, 239
resilience, 6, 10, 11, 26, 28, 29, 31, 34, 42, 45, 71, 73, 85, 94, 101, 167, 186, 188, 191, 271
resistance, 168, 312
resolution, 94
resource allocation, 425
resources, 178, 211, 218, 239, 249, 260, 271, 281, 344, 356, 369, 407
respiration, 412
response, 59, 60, 86, 91, 92, 111, 116, 121, 123, 135, 141, 151, 181, 188, 194, 218, 246, 257, 260, 264, 265, 267, 314, 323, 332, 337, 339, 359, 425, 439, 440, 443
responsiveness, 40
restrictions, 292
retardation, 274, 275, 286, 287, 295, 296, 356, 407, 446
retirement, 17, 21
revenue, 96
RH, 67, 79, 143, 166, 336
rhythm, 298, 311
riboflavin, 227
rights, 354, 355
risk factors, 147, 151, 260, 271, 343, 344, 345, 348, 349, 351, 430
risks, 36, 349, 424
risk-taking, 192
role conflict, 35
role-playing, 263
root(s), 281, 371
routines, 286
rules, 56, 66, 122, 133
rural areas, 230, 236, 248, 253, 255, 256, 281, 366, 370, 371
rural population, 275

S

safety, 70, 261, 286
sample design, 425
sanitation level, 322
saturation, 226
savings, 293
scarce resources, 424
scarcity, 281
schizophrenia, 146, 147, 150, 156, 157, 161, 167
scholarship, 6, 10

school adjustment, 97, 98, 102, 104, 106, 195
school community, 252
school failure, 26, 71
schooling, 204
science, 5, 52, 92, 256, 288, 430, 454
scope, 40, 359, 372
secondary data, 13, 52, 93, 325, 358, 424
secondary education, 67, 143, 248, 346
secondary school education, 96
secondary school students, 12, 40, 56, 57, 58, 69, 71, 110, 112, 131, 134, 140, 142, 178
secondary schools, 26, 66, 72, 96, 97, 112, 121, 142, 144, 169, 172, 180, 425
secondary students, vii, 34, 57, 95, 425, 426, 427
security, 120
sedentary lifestyle, 329, 330, 336
selenium, 227
self-assessment, 5
self-awareness, 8, 34, 46, 86, 101, 121, 313
self-concept, 94, 186
self-confidence, 16, 32, 46, 101
self-control, 66, 179
self-discipline, 66
self-efficacy, 71, 74, 188, 191
self-employed, 248
self-esteem, 16, 70, 71, 80, 94, 108, 182, 416
self-image, 429
self-interest, 108
self-monitoring, 413
self-reflection, 8, 86
self-report data, 70, 165, 193
self-sufficiency, 222
self-understanding, 9, 10, 11, 12, 85, 94
self-worth, 120, 141
semantic information, 434, 435, 443, 445
semantic memory, 434, 435, 444, 447
semantic priming, 435
Senate, 321
sensations, 313
sensitivity, 149, 152, 155, 160, 256, 287, 421
sensory systems, 314
sepsis, 276
services, 40, 84, 149, 162, 164, 165, 166, 175, 177, 202, 211, 212, 218, 272, 275, 320, 322, 324, 366
SES, 71, 78
sex, 71, 98, 103, 104, 112, 186, 192, 194, 195, 196, 219, 223, 233, 241, 246, 248, 275, 354, 355, 356, 357, 359, 367, 405, 407, 408, 425, 426, 427, 428, 429
sex differences, 112
sex ratio, 355, 357, 405, 407
sexual abuse, 429, 430
sexual activities, 426

sexual activity, 423, 424, 426, 427, 428, 429, 430
sexual behavior, 26, 71, 80, 186, 192, 194, 196, 425, 430
sexual desire, 192
sexual harassment, 192
sexual health, 195
sexual intercourse, 51, 74, 76, 193, 195, 425, 426, 427
sexuality, 192, 194, 195, 196, 423
sexually transmitted diseases, 276
sexually transmitted infections, 423, 424
shame, 293
shape, 50, 120, 330, 435, 437, 438
shock, 252
showing, 4, 6, 66, 79, 91, 133, 146, 159, 160, 170, 174, 179, 250, 265, 269, 310, 312, 441, 443, 444, 445
sibling, 122, 292, 412
siblings, 289, 290, 291, 292, 406
sickle cell, 273, 274, 277, 278, 282, 283
sickle cell anemia, 283
side effects, 414
SIDS, 338
signals, 297
signs, xiii, 148, 175, 186, 271, 281, 286
silicon, 227
Singapore, 92, 146, 166
skilled workers, 248
skills training, 11
sleep apnea, 339
small communities, 256
smoking, 98, 160, 161, 168
smoothness, 56
SMS, 409
social activities, 289
social behavio(u)r, 121, 287, 371
social capital, 121
social competence, 6, 10, 11, 29, 31, 34, 46, 71, 73, 85, 94, 101, 120, 167, 188, 191, 293
social consequences, xii, 168
social context, 193, 256
social costs, xii
social desirability, 35, 112, 117, 193
social development, 128, 219, 239, 249, 287, 429
social environment, 118, 120, 128, 129, 202, 204
social group, 238
social hierarchy, 367
social impairment, 287
social inequalities, 321, 325
social influence, 116, 127, 357
social influences, 127, 357
social information processing, 36
social interactions, 120, 291, 293, 294

social network, 186
social norms, 96
social organization, 257
social phobia, 181
social psychology, 128
social reality, 142
social relations, 170, 179, 285
social relationships, 170, 179
social roles, 133
social rules, 286
social security, 99, 122, 189
social services, 429
social situations, 127
social skills, 142, 144, 286, 287, 293, 312
social skills training, 142, 144
social support, 167, 180
social welfare, 84
social workers, 28, 41, 49, 84, 96, 98, 104, 110, 149, 157, 162, 163, 289
socialization, 127, 192, 193, 260, 413
society, xi, 7, 9, 10, 11, 32, 46, 96, 101, 109, 120, 121, 146, 159, 175, 179, 211, 235, 239, 256, 286, 288, 290, 291, 292, 293, 294, 322, 324, 351, 355, 356, 405, 426, 454
socioeconomic background, 192
socioeconomic status, 70, 71, 78, 323
sociology, 288
sodium, 227
software, 300, 345, 436
solution, 17, 18
somatization, 149, 152, 160, 421
South Africa, 71, 80
South Asia, 219
SP, 74, 98, 103, 188, 191, 195
Spain, viii, 67, 144, 221, 222, 223, 224, 225, 226, 228
spatial location, 446
special education, 63
speculation, 269
speech, 286, 289, 292, 293, 297, 298, 299, 300, 303, 308
speech sounds, 298
spending, 177, 241
spirituality, 6, 10, 72, 74, 85, 94, 188, 191
spleen, 274
splenomegaly, 274
split-half reliability, 17
Squared Multiple Correlations (SMC), 19
Sri Lanka, 325
SS, 195, 278, 279, 280, 303, 408
SSA, 70, 72, 173, 178
stability, 16, 19, 91, 168, 170, 171, 172, 174, 176, 178, 179, 266

stabilization, 299, 302
stakeholders, 27, 49, 85, 142
standard deviation, 33, 47, 223, 224, 225, 226, 260, 368, 436
standard error, 115
standard of living, 208, 210, 211, 217, 218, 239, 354, 356, 359, 367, 368, 370
statistics, 19, 20, 29, 43, 73, 74, 78, 173, 338, 424
stigma, 52, 70, 78, 80, 288
stigmatized, 70
stimulation, 260
stock, 277
storage, 434
stoves, 349
strategy use, 446
stress, 8, 23, 49, 56, 67, 70, 71, 78, 80, 96, 156, 165, 167, 192, 261, 271, 275, 298, 354, 412, 413, 414, 419
stressful events, 6
stressful life events, 167, 171, 412
stressors, 412, 421
structural equation modeling, 50, 92
structuralism, 37
structure, 15, 17, 18, 19, 21, 22, 84, 87, 88, 96, 186, 219, 229, 232, 233, 235, 238, 239, 241, 242, 246, 248, 249, 250, 261, 298, 356, 408, 409, 434, 437
structuring, 261
student achievement, 93
student development, 64
style, 70
subgroups, 40, 50, 188, 276
subjective experience, 27, 92
sub-Saharan Africa, 325, 408, 424
substance abuse, 22, 27, 36, 53, 66, 71, 75, 80, 86, 147, 161, 163, 164, 166, 167, 168, 179, 195
Substance Abuse and Mental Health Services Administration, 421
substance use, 36, 146, 147, 148, 150, 156, 157, 160, 161, 166, 167, 168, 180, 192, 193
substitutes, 341
succession, 435
sudden infant death syndrome, 338
suicidal ideation, 16
suicide, 17, 20, 292
sulfate, 227
Sun, ii, iii, vii, viii, 13, 23, 37, 51, 52, 53, 55, 67, 92, 93, 106, 131, 132, 143, 144, 182, 196, 457
supervision, 148, 195, 286, 358
supervisor, 351
Supreme Court, 371
surface area, 346
surveillance, 260, 271, 342

survival, 141, 201, 202, 203, 218, 219, 231, 277, 278, 319, 322, 323, 324, 325, 338, 354, 356, 357, 361, 365, 405, 406, 407, 409, 419
survival rate, 419
survivors, 344, 412, 421, 422
sustainability, 38
sustainable development, 283
Sweden, 455
Switzerland, 67, 144, 406
symbolism, 310
symmetry, 360
sympathy, 65, 109, 111, 120, 126, 127, 129, 289
symptoms, 70, 80, 147, 148, 149, 151, 152, 157, 160, 162, 163, 170, 181, 281, 314, 412, 413, 419
syndrome, 56, 147, 164, 166, 168, 273, 274, 275, 276, 277, 282, 286, 446
synthesis, 168, 272
syphilis, 276

T

tactics, 94, 413
Taiwan, 67, 109, 144, 150, 170, 182, 193
target, 180, 261, 274, 313, 338, 436, 437, 438, 440, 443
Task Force, 195, 261, 328, 342
teacher performance, 85, 87
teachers, vii, 11, 28, 31, 34, 35, 41, 45, 49, 55, 56, 57, 58, 59, 60, 61, 63, 64, 65, 66, 67, 88, 96, 98, 101, 104, 110, 111, 112, 131, 132, 133, 134, 135, 136, 137, 140, 141, 142, 143, 179, 252, 263, 436
teacher-student relationship, 84, 132, 141
teaching effectiveness, 93
teaching evaluation, 93
teaching experience, 30, 58, 59, 135
team members, 7, 9, 11
teams, 7, 9, 58, 127
techniques, 50, 59, 84, 92, 135, 180, 227, 253, 276, 297, 298, 299, 302, 307, 312, 313, 414
technology, 132, 182, 257, 270, 275, 356
teens, vii, xii, 1, 128, 161
teeth, 289
telephone, 182, 416
television viewing, 327, 330, 331, 332, 333, 334, 336
temperament, 260, 421
tenants, 346
tension(s), 52, 126, 252, 298, 413
territorial, 222, 277
territory, 70, 71
terrorism, 294
tertiary education, 96
tertiary sector, 248
test data, 97, 104
test scores, 287
testing, 84, 109, 110, 113, 300, 424
test-retest reliability, 109, 110, 111, 112, 113, 115, 117, 123
tetanus, 201, 241, 276, 281
Tetanus, 219
textbook, 9, 62, 64, 66, 139, 140, 141
Thailand, 322
thalassemia, 273, 274, 275, 276, 277, 278, 282
theatre, 251, 371
theoretical approaches, 435
theoretical support, 30, 34
therapeutic interventions, 414
therapist, 300, 303, 311, 312, 313, 314
therapy, 180, 258, 300, 303, 307, 308, 311, 312, 411, 413, 414, 421
thiamin, 225, 227
Third World, 355, 407
thoughts, 75, 160, 171, 180, 252, 288, 289, 310, 330, 408
threats, 92
threshold level, 240
tobacco, 74, 148, 157, 160, 161, 168, 425
tobacco smoking, 160, 168
tones, 300
tourism, 96
toys, 222, 310
trachea, 298
traditions, 355
training, 7, 11, 13, 23, 28, 37, 42, 49, 51, 52, 53, 58, 59, 96, 135, 144, 148, 163, 164, 165, 182, 263, 265, 266, 267, 269, 275, 281, 312, 316, 338, 358, 405, 406, 413
traits, 4, 5, 6, 117, 129, 235, 286
trajectory, 261, 275
transferrin, 226
transformations, 314
transition period, 16
translation, 113, 115, 117, 421
transmission, 423
transport, 281
traumatic brain injury, 303
treatment methods, 413
trial, 7, 26, 27, 37, 51, 105, 106, 180, 261, 271, 315, 421, 422
triangulation, 35, 49
Trinidad, 430
Trinidad and Tobago, 430
tuberculosis, 241
Turkey, 67, 144
twist, 63

U

umbilical cord, 210
UN, 325, 355
underlying mechanisms, 231
UNDP, 408
UNESCO, 425, 430
UNHCR, 227
uniform, 248, 358
unique features, 33
United Kingdom, 16, 56, 57, 132, 455
United Nations, 70, 79, 211, 222, 227, 322, 325, 355, 408, 424, 430
United Nations Development Programme, 408
United Nations High Commissioner for Refugees, 227
United States, xi, xii, xiii, 37, 55, 67, 80, 131, 132, 144, 168, 195, 259, 261, 307, 327, 337, 338, 341, 342, 411, 412, 421, 423, 451
universality, 252, 254, 257
universities, 4, 7, 26, 84, 96
university education, 4, 11, 222
urban, 80, 204, 211, 230, 234, 235, 236, 239, 241, 244, 246, 248, 249, 250, 251, 253, 255, 256, 275, 281, 322, 323, 325, 359, 366, 368, 369, 371
urban areas, 211, 236, 239, 248, 256, 281, 325, 366, 368, 369, 371
urbanisation, 239, 356, 357
urbanization, 235, 239, 240, 323
US Department of Health and Human Services, 271
USA, 67, 223, 224

V

vaccinations, 204, 207, 208, 214, 216
vaccine, 204, 241, 281
Valencia, 221, 223
validation, 17, 22, 80, 106, 109, 110, 117, 122, 128, 142, 195
valuation, 365
vanadium, 227
vandalism, 56
variations, viii, xi, 36, 199, 200, 202, 205, 215, 231, 274, 320, 323, 357, 405
varimax rotation, 18, 19, 334
vegetables, 331, 336
velocity, 298
venipuncture, 421
versatility, 300
Vice President, 3, 25, 39, 69, 83, 145, 169, 185
victimisation, 354
victims, 274

video games, 186
videos, 186, 189, 190
violence, xii, 144, 262, 291, 425, 430
viscosity, 274
visualization, 264, 269, 413
vitamin A, 227
vitamin B1, 227
vitamin B12, 227
vitamin B6, 227
vitamin C, 227, 325
Vitamin C, 225
vitamin D, 221, 225, 227
vitamin E, 225, 227
vitamin K, 227
vitamins, 228
volatility, 252
volunteer work, 122
volunteerism, 17, 23
vulnerability, 323, 406, 429
vulnerable people, 274, 281

W

wages, 281, 356
war, 294, 323, 343, 345
Washington, 36, 167, 227, 257, 271, 295, 296, 316, 430
watches, 289, 294, 371
water, 202, 224, 225, 227, 320, 323, 338, 347, 444
wealth, 70, 236, 241, 248, 320, 354, 359, 367, 368, 370
wear, 265
web, 195, 271
web sites, 195
webpages, 138
websites, 189, 329
Wechsler Intelligence Scale, 436, 447
welfare, 70, 230, 269, 325, 351, 355, 370, 408, 409, 451, 453
welfare economics, 408
welfare state, 325
well-being, 19, 21, 71, 120, 128, 209, 320, 371, 404, 408, 421, 451
West Africa, 228
West Indies, 423
Western countries, 40
WHO, 241, 316, 320, 325, 351, 407
witchcraft, 281
withdrawal, 57, 177
WMD, 37
Wofoo Foundation Scholarship, 6, 9, 12
word frequency, 301
work environment, 354

workers, xi, 27, 28, 33, 35, 42, 113, 167, 202, 205
workforce, 248
working women, 244, 250
workload, 84
workplace, 10
World Bank, 409, 430
World Health Organisation, 351
World Health Organization (WHO), 168, 226, 228, 325, 338, 342, 351, 424, 436
World War I, 323
worldwide, 274, 293, 315, 328, 338
worry, 412, 413
wrestling, 286
wrists, 302

Y

yield, 84, 85, 201, 232, 420
young adults, 23, 151, 192, 194, 195, 292, 293, 296, 446
young people, xi, 11, 96, 110, 111, 112, 113, 115, 116, 117, 120, 121, 123, 132, 141, 181, 186, 187, 192, 193, 342
young women, 426
youth studies, 71, 95, 96, 105, 106

Z

Zimbabwe, ix, 343, 344, 345, 349, 350, 351
zinc, 227, 325